MASSACHUSETTS DEPARTMENT OF AGRICULTURE
Dr. Arthur W. Gilbert
Commissioner

BIRDS OF MASSACHUSETTS

AND OTHER NEW ENGLAND STATES

BY

EDWARD HOWE FORBUSH

PART I. WATER BIRDS, MARSH BIRDS AND SHORE BIRDS

Illustrated with Colored Plates from Drawings by
LOUIS AGASSIZ FUERTES

AND

Figures and Cuts from Drawings and Photographs by
THE AUTHOR AND OTHERS

ISSUED BY AUTHORITY OF THE LEGISLATURE
1925

COMMONWEALTH OF MASSACHUSETTS, DEPARTMENT OF AGRICULTURE

THE economic value of birds to the people of the Commonwealth has been long considered important. This Commonwealth has recognized its importance by devoting a special division of the Department of Agriculture to the study of birds and their relations to the activities of its people. But Massachusetts citizens value birds, not merely for their usefulness in destroying insect pests or in bringing profits or affording sport — we also regard them highly for their esthetic value and the joy they bring into our lives. There is therefore every reason for the State to interest itself in their study and protection.

The Commonwealth of Massachusetts is fortunate in having the services of one of the country's foremost authorities in economic ornithology, Edward Howe Forbush. Mr. Forbush is known to a wide public through his able and authoritative writings, and his many articles in magazines and newspapers. Two books, Useful Birds and Their Protection, and Game Birds, Wild-Fowl and Shore Birds, both written by him and published by the State, have proven very popular and valuable. The former has run through three editions, the latter through two editions, and both are now out of print.

Mr. Forbush inaugurated a new epoch in bird study when he began to issue on behalf of the State his monthly bulletins. These summarized the reports he received every month from numerous correspondents in this and other New England states, as well as Canada and along the North Atlantic seaboard, and gave new knowledge of the effect of storms, cold waves and the like on the distribution and movements of birds. More recently hitherto unknown facts revealed by bird-banding have been reported in these bulletins.

The ripe fruits of his life work in the field of ornithology are now being incorporated in The Birds of Massachusetts. This is the first complete and comprehensive work on the birds of this State. It marks notable advances in our knowledge of the local distribution of species and handles the recondite subject of molts and plumages.

There is reason to believe that this work when completed in the three volumes with colored plates by Fuertes, the foremost ornithological artist in this country, will constitute a notable contribution to the literature of ornithology, and will afford a valuable source of reference to all students of birds as well as bird lovers.

ARTHUR W. GILBERT,
Commissioner.

PREFACE

THE Commonwealth of Massachusetts never has issued any publication containing full descriptions and colored plates of the birds recorded within its boundaries. In 1839 a report was made to the Great and General Court of Massachusetts by Rev. William B. O. Peabody, which contained a list of the birds of Massachusetts with annotations on two hundred and eighty-six species. In 1864 the Massachusetts State Board of Agriculture published, in connection with the eleventh annual report of its Secretary for the year 1863, an annotated list of two hundred and eighty-seven species, prepared by Mr. Edward A. Samuels. The Commonwealth also assisted Mr. Samuels in publishing the Birds of New England (1870) by purchasing and distributing a considerable number of copies of the work.

In 1907 the first edition of Useful Birds and Their Protection containing brief descriptions of a part of the birds of the State was issued by the Massachusetts State Board of Agriculture. In 1912 the first edition of A History of the Game Birds, Wildfowl and Shore Birds of Massachusetts and Adjacent States was issued by the same agency of the Commonwealth. Both of these works, however, were chiefly economic and treated only a part of the birds of the Commonwealth, stressing their utility and the means of conserving them.

Many papers on the birds of Massachusetts have been published within the last fifty years, notably the Birds of Massachusetts, by Messrs. Reginald Heber Howe Jr., and Glover M. Allen, but most of them are mere local lists with annotations, and not one of them contains adequate descriptions or colored plates of the species. The demand for such information as plates and descriptions alone can furnish has grown insistent with the years. Not only do people of rural communities seek such knowledge; the great and increasing army of bird students also requires it.

Birds may be ranked among the noblest forms of life. Experience has shown that without special protection at the hands of man many species are likely to become extinct. Some of those that are hunted as game now need special care. Licenses to hunt certain birds within the borders of the Commonwealth are issued to citizens annually, and the number of such hunters now approximates one hundred thousand. Probably most of these hunters would be unable to recognize all the birds that they are privileged to shoot under their licenses, to say nothing of the large number of species that are protected by law. Many people who hunt birds desire such information concerning them as it is purposed to include in the present volume. The book is intended, therefore, to fill a long-felt want.

The objects of the work are: (1) to interest the general public of Massachusetts and New England in birds and their rational conservation, (2) to provide our citizens with a means of identifying birds in the field or in the hand, (3) to furnish such other information regarding birds as the people desire and need. Long experience as State Ornithologist in answering their questions has perhaps qualified the author in some degree for the latter service.

The author is under great obligation to Mr. John A. Farley for editing the volume and for constant assistance and advice; to Messrs. Samuel Henshaw and Outram Bangs for the privilege of examining specimens in the Museum of Comparative Zoölogy at Harvard College; to Mr. James Peters at the Museum for assistance there, and to Drs. Harry C. Oberholser and C. W. Richmond for extending similar privileges at the National Museum at Washington; also to Dr. Wilfred H. Osgood, of the Field Museum, Chicago, and Drs. Frank M. Chapman and Jonathan Dwight, of the American Museum, New York, all of whom have freely offered the privileges of the collections under their charge. Mr. W. Sprague Brooks, of the Boston Society of Natural History, also granted the privilege of examining his collection, as did Messrs. Frederic H. Kennard and A. Cleveland Bent. Mr. Kennard also furnished many notes, including the field notes of the late Mr. F. B. McKechnie, and Mr. Bent has been extremely kind and helpful in many ways. Col. John E. Thayer tendered the use of his great collection of North American birds and their nests and eggs. Dr. B. H. Warren of Pennsylvania contributed many notes and much useful information, including weights of many game-birds. Mr. W. L. McAtee sent proof sheets of his "Local Names of Migratory Game Birds." The following persons from various New England states have given valuable aid in various ways: Messrs. Arthur H. Norton of Maine; Karl A. Pember and George L. Kirk of Vermont; Herbert Parker, Aaron C. Bagg, Winthrop Packard, Albert A. Cross, Charles L. Whittle, Laurence B. Fletcher, Joseph A. Hagar and F. H. Scott of Massachusetts; Harry S. Hathaway of Rhode Island; C. W. Vibert, Wilbur Smith, Aretas A. Saunders, Lester W. Smith and E. W. Schmidt of Connecticut. Dr. Arthur A. Allen of Cornell University has contributed photographs and notes.

Mr. Arthur Stubbs and many others have submitted field notes or migration data, and about 400 correspondents, many of them official observers in ornithology for the Massachusetts Department of Agriculture, have contributed notes on the migrations and habits of birds. The author is greatly indebted to Mr. Louis Agassiz Fuertes, the artist, who has illustrated this volume, for cordial coöperation and assistance and the use of field notes in respect to the colors of the soft parts of water birds. The J. Horace McFarland Co. and D. Appleton and Co. have kindly furnished some electrotypes and permitted their use.

Permission to quote from the Practical Handbook of British Birds should be acknowledged. Ornithologists everywhere are indebted to Messrs. H. F. and G. Witherby, who have produced this excellent handbook which contains much original work by specialists. Acknowledgment should also be given to the following persons and publishing firms for authority to quote from or refer to the publications set against their names: Dr. Joseph Grinnell, The Game Birds of California; Mr. Ralph Hoffmann, A Guide to the Birds of New England and Eastern New York; Dr. Charles W. Townsend, Audubon's Labrador and other publications; The Marshall Jones Co., Dr. Townsend's Beach Grass; Dr. Frank M. Chapman, Camps and Cruises of an Ornithologist, and Bird-Lore; L. C. Page and Co., Key to North American Birds; Dr. Glover M. Allen and Mr. Reginald Heber Howe Jr., The Birds of Massachusetts; Mr. Howe and Mr. Edward Sturtevant, The Birds of Rhode Island; The University Society, Birds of America. The Editor of The Nation and The Athenæum gives permission to quote from an article by Mr. J. B. Massingham.

Mr. J. H. Fleming, of Toronto, has placed the author under great obligation by revising the geographical distribution of the species.

It remains to acknowledge the services of those who have given advice and information on technical subjects: Dr. Witmer Stone, of the Academy of Natural Sciences, Philadelphia, and Drs. H. C. Oberholser and T. S. Palmer, of the Biological Survey, have been especially kind in this regard.

From the inception of the undertaking, the members of the Department of Agriculture have consistently supported the project. Dr. Arthur W. Gilbert, Commissioner of Agriculture, has strongly advocated the necessary appropriations before legislative committees, and has given the author that constant and cordial support without which the publication would have been impossible.

CONTENTS

CONTENTS xiii

LIST OF ILLUSTRATIONS

PLATES

xv

FIGURES

CUTS IN THE TEXT

INTRODUCTION

WHEN the task of preparing a work on the birds of Massachusetts was undertaken, the fact became apparent at once that practically all the birds of New England must be included. There are very few species recorded in New England which have not been taken in Massachusetts and these few are mere accidental visitors. A glance at the map of New England shows that Massachusetts lies directly across the region and is contiguous to every other state except Maine, the southwestern boundary of which is only about fifteen miles from the northeastern border of Massachusetts. Migratory birds passing through New England in their northward and southward flights naturally go through or over Massachusetts and many of them remain for a time within her borders. The long outreaching arm of Cape Cod extends farther out to sea than any other of the outlying coasts of these states. Many water-birds cross it or land upon it, and seabirds from far-away islands and waters are likely to be blown there by hurricanes. Many shore-birds, which in their autumnal migrations reach South America largely by sea, are deflected and driven on the Massachusetts coast by such storms.

The so-called West Indian hurricanes that occasionally move northward near the Atlantic coast of the United States are so violent as to carry birds many hundreds of miles. If one of these gales occurs at a time when birds are migrating over waters lying in its course, it is likely to be followed by the appearance along our coast of birds rarely seen there.

The following notes regarding the relation of West Indian hurricanes to irruptions of birds from the south were prepared for this volume by Mr. James Mackaye:

"Southern storms coming up the Atlantic coast from the Gulf region are of the usual revolving type, but are divided into two classes: (1) storms which are part of the general west-east drift of cyclonic areas, and (2) West Indian hurricanes which are unique in movement and usually in violence. These last originate normally eastward of the Gulf of Mexico, moving at first from east to west, and then as a rule recurve in a wide sweep and pass out in a northeasterly direction over the Atlantic. Their tracks are sometimes far at sea, sometimes close to the coast, and sometimes partly over the land.

"Prof. E. B. Garriott, in his monograph on 'West Indian Hurricanes' (Bulletin H of the Weather Bureau) lists 95 such hurricanes between the years 1878 and 1900 inclusive, distributed throughout the year as follows:

MONTH	NUMBER	
May	1	
June	3	
July	3	
August	25	
September	25	
October	32	
November	3	
December	3	Total 95

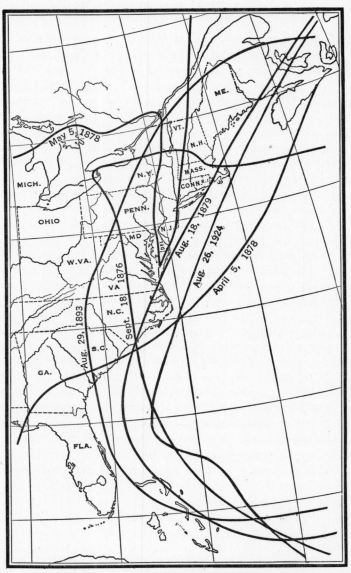

Map showing courses of six storm centers connected with incursions of southern birds into New England. Dates indicate time of nearest approach of centers to Massachusetts.

Of these storms 76 recurred in the manner described, making an average of three or four hurricanes a year (mostly in late summer or autumn) traveling along or near the Atlantic coast.

"Examination of the records of southern birds * to be found in this volume discloses five fairly definite incursions into New England or vicinity since the organization of the Weather Bureau. These were in 1876, 1878, 1879, 1893 and 1924.

"The map shows the paths of the storms most closely connected with these five sudden invasions, and the table shows the correlation (in time) between the several storms and the corresponding incursions. It will be observed that, with the exception of the invasion of the Glossy Ibis in May, 1878, all were probably due to West Indian hurricanes. That particular spring irruption was doubtless caused either by the storm of April 5, which closely resembled a West Indian hurricane in its characteristics, or by the abnormally moving storm of May 5, combined with the south winds which prevailed all along the coast for some days previous to that date — most likely to the latter.

"The extraordinary flight of Killdeers in November, 1888, referred to on page 467, was closely connected with the most violent of the three November hurricanes recorded by Garriott, and the only one which, on account of its severity, he singles out for special description as an example of the violent action and stress of such storms. He says: 'On the morning of the 27th of November the center was just off the New England coast; on the afternoon of the same day it had passed into Maine,' [1] and 'on the afternoon of . . . November 28 . . . several flocks of Killdeer were seen . . . on the extreme point of Cape Elizabeth, Maine. . . . On the following day . . . hundreds of the Plovers were to be seen along the shores of the Cape.' [2]

"During this storm, which caused losses of millions of dollars, a barometric pressure below 29 inches was recorded, and a wind velocity of 84 miles an hour.

"The only (two) definite records of the very rare Man-o-war-bird contained in this volume were unmistakably associated with severe storms. In October, 1876, a normally moving storm coming from the west-southwest developed high winds along the coast, and snow fell as far south as North Carolina. On the 15th the storm center reached Nova Scotia and the Halifax Man-o-war-bird † was taken on the 16th. On October 14, 1893, the center of a West Indian hurricane passed over Buffalo, N. Y., the nearest point of its passage to Massachusetts, and the New Bedford Man-o-war-bird † was taken October 17th.

"That the severity of a storm is an important factor in bringing birds from the South is indicated by many facts cited elsewhere in this volume,[3] and also by the fact that the hurricanes of September, 1876 and August, 1879 and 1893, which presumably brought the irruptions of those years, are among the limited number cited by Garriott as 'important,'

---

* By southern birds are meant such as breed in the South.
[1] Garriott, E. B.: "West Indian Hurricanes," Bulletin H, Weather Bureau, 1900, p. 41.
[2] Brown, Nathan Clifford: Auk. Vol. VI, 1889, p. 69.
† See p. 172.
[3] See pages 127, 131, 132, 144, 171, 172.

from their severity and destructive effects on life and property. The April storm of 1878 was not classed by Garriott as a hurricane, and the August hurricane of 1924 occurred much later than his publication. That both were violent, however, the latter notably so, is well attested by the records. The incursion of the Glossy Ibis in 1850 * and the accompanying great storm are not included in this summary because they occurred before the establishment of the Weather Bureau."

RELATION BETWEEN STORMS AND INCURSIONS OF SOUTHERN BIRDS INTO NEW ENGLAND AND VICINITY SINCE 1876.

DATE OF ARRIVAL OF STORM CENTER AT POINT NEAREST TO MASSACHUSETTS	DATE, PLACE AND SPECIES OF FIRST BIRD RECORDED IN INCURSION	SPECIES OF SOUTHERN BIRDS RECORDED DURING INCURSION
Sept. 18, 1876	Sept. 20, 1876 Granby, Conn. Sooty Tern[1]	Sooty Tern
April 5, 1878 or † May 5, 1878	May 4, 1878 Eastham Glossy Ibis	Glossy Ibis
Aug. 18, 1879	Aug. 19, 1879 Sandwich, Woods Hole Black Skimmer	Black Skimmer
† Aug. 29, 1893	Aug. 28, 1893 Oneida Lake, N. Y. Black-capped Petrel	Black-capped Petrel Black Skimmer
Aug. 26, 1924	Aug. 26, 1924 Nantucket Black Skimmer	Black Skimmer Sooty Tern Oyster-catcher

The exact manner in which these great disturbances bring southern birds to our shores must be largely a matter of conjecture, but from the known facts regarding the progress of the storms some assumptions may be made.

These hurricanes, moving north as they do, naturally carry with them any birds flying in their path. It may be assumed theoretically that the influence of such great disturbances on southern sea-birds is exerted in the following manner: The wind revolves around the storm center in a direction opposite to the course of the hands of a watch held in a horizontal position. The effect of this revolving gale is felt at a great distance from

* See pages 310, 311.

[1] Sage, Bishop & Bliss: Birds of Connecticut, 1913, p. 24.

† In comparing these dates with those adjoining in column 2 it should be borne in mind that at any given latitude the high winds caused by northward moving storms begin to blow before the arrival of the storm centers at that latitude.

the center, and the wind velocity is said to reach at times over 100 miles an hour at sea. Probably no bird can long face a gale blowing 60 to 70 miles an hour. As the storm center at sea usually moves first toward the Atlantic coast north of the Caribbean sea, birds flying over waters that lie south of the center but at some distance from it and under the full influence of the gale would be carried first eastward out to sea, then northward and finally as the storm center moved north along the coast would be driven in from the southeast, east or northeast upon the shore, provided they lived to reach it. Others nearer the storm center might be carried more than once around it before reaching land. Birds migrating at or near the center of the disturbance probably would be caught in the tremendous upward draught there, and might be carried to great heights. Only birds of powerful flight would be likely to withstand the storm, and small land birds driven to sea by one of these hurricanes probably would never see land again. Sea-birds caught near the surface by hurricanes are sometimes crumpled up and driven into the sea. In many cases birds cast ashore during these storms are completely exhausted, and in some cases many die of exhaustion after they reach the shore. Such storms probably account for most of the accidental occurrences of sea-birds on the coasts of Massachusetts.

Northward movements of storm-driven southern birds should not be confused with migratory flights of birds that move north commonly in summer from their nesting places. Birds have a tendency to wander after the nesting season, and although the general trend of migration then is southward, many birds are prone to move first in various directions. It is at this season that certain birds are most likely to appear north of their breeding-grounds. Some of the herons apparently regularly do this. For example: Little Blue Herons and Egrets in small numbers go far north of their breeding places after their nesting time. Black-crowned Night Herons also show a tendency to movement in that direction and specimens have been taken three or four hundred miles north of their known breeding place. The map (page xxiv) and the data given with it show in part the movements of banded and identified birds from a Night Heronry in Barnstable.

Massachusetts is diversified in physical features which range from the sandy shores and dunes of Cape Cod, Essex and Ipswich to the fertile fields of the Connecticut Valley, and from the rocky coast of the North Shore to the high forested hills of Berkshire County in its extreme western area. Its natural features provide suitable feeding places and (in many cases) breeding-grounds for birds that can live in any part of New England. Birds that rarely breed north of southern Connecticut sometimes come up the Connecticut Valley into Massachusetts; birds that breed in northern Maine pass through Massachusetts in migration or come here in winter. Most of the water birds and shore birds breed outside of New England. As the present volume deals only with such birds, we are now concerned chiefly with their haunts while in migration, namely: the water, swamp, marsh and shore areas. Therefore the life zones of New England birds will not be treated here, but will be given in the introduction to the second volume.

New England is blessed with a very extensive shore line. Including her island coasts and all the various indentations in her shores, the coast line measures about 2,372 miles.

MAP SHOWING PLACES WHERE BLACK–CROWNED NIGHT HERONS WERE RECOVERED.*

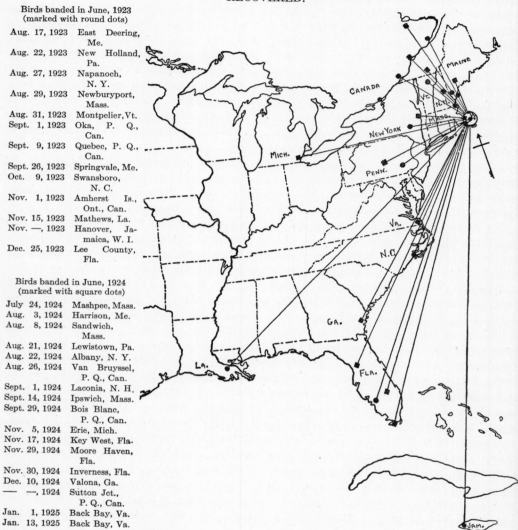

Birds banded in June, 1923
(marked with round dots)

Aug. 17, 1923	East Deering, Me.
Aug. 22, 1923	New Holland, Pa.
Aug. 27, 1923	Napanoch, N. Y.
Aug. 29, 1923	Newburyport, Mass.
Aug. 31, 1923	Montpelier, Vt.
Sept. 1, 1923	Oka, P. Q., Can.
Sept. 9, 1923	Quebec, P. Q., Can.
Sept. 26, 1923	Springvale, Me.
Oct. 9, 1923	Swansboro, N. C.
Nov. 1, 1923	Amherst Is., Ont., Can.
Nov. 15, 1923	Mathews, La.
Nov. —, 1923	Hanover, Jamaica, W. I.
Dec. 25, 1923	Lee County, Fla.

Birds banded in June, 1924
(marked with square dots)

July 24, 1924	Mashpee, Mass.
Aug. 3, 1924	Harrison, Me.
Aug. 8, 1924	Sandwich, Mass.
Aug. 21, 1924	Lewistown, Pa.
Aug. 22, 1924	Albany, N. Y.
Aug. 26, 1924	Van Bruyssel, P. Q., Can.
Sept. 1, 1924	Laconia, N. H.
Sept. 14, 1924	Ipswich, Mass.
Sept. 29, 1924	Bois Blanc, P. Q., Can.
Nov. 5, 1924	Erie, Mich.
Nov. 17, 1924	Key West, Fla.
Nov. 29, 1924	Moore Haven, Fla.
Nov. 30, 1924	Inverness, Fla.
Dec. 10, 1924	Valona, Ga.
— —, 1924	Sutton Jct., P. Q., Can.
Jan. 1, 1925	Back Bay, Va.
Jan. 13, 1925	Back Bay, Va.

The birds were banded as nestlings at Barnstable, Massachusetts, in 1923 and 1924, by members of the Northeastern Bird Banding Association. The location of the heronry is in the center of the circle at the right.

* The *recovery* of a banded bird means the taking of the bird at some locality other than that at which it was banded.

New England is a well watered country. A late atlas maps 4,926 streams and 3,967 lakes and ponds. In addition to these there are very many small streams, "pond holes," "sloughs," and pools that do not appear on any map of the region. Also in spring, when water-fowl are migrating northward, the water surface is often much augmented by the flooding of swamps, river meadows and low fields, and there are thousands of rain-water or snow-water pools in low spots in pastures and fields which may attract wild-fowl. In late summer, the season of drought, the lowering waters uncover flats and bars in lakes and rivers and thus expose feeding-grounds for shore birds. Along the coasts of New England there are many extensive salt-marshes and flats which are bared daily by the recession of the tides. There are also many pools and tidal streams in these marshes and on these flats which contain at times an abundant food supply for both marsh and aquatic birds. In the lower river valleys much marshland borders the streams, and both on the coastal plain and in the interior former shallow lakes and ponds have, in the course of time, filled with growing and decaying vegetation, and now form wooded swamps or sedgy marshes attractive to marsh birds. Nature therefore has provided bountifully for her feathered children of the shores, waters and marshes, and if New England has not now an adequate supply of water-birds in their seasons it is the fault of the inhabitants, who, with their neighbors to the north and south, have reduced the numbers of these fowls and driven them away by wanton and continuous persecution and slaughter. We have only to turn to the records left us by some of the chroniclers of early exploration and settlement in Massachusetts to learn of the myriads of swans, geese, brants, ducks, shore birds and marsh birds that once flocked in their seasons along our coasts. Undoubtedly the principal inland waters also teemed with them, and though our modern civilization will never see such sights again, there has been considerable increase under recent protective laws, and conservation methods may, in time, greatly multiply the numbers of these birds.

The coastline of New England and the larger river valleys running north and south are great highways for the migrations of water birds. Many birds in their northward flight pass along the coast on the way to their boreal breeding-grounds. Some, like the Brant, follow the shore to the Gulf of St. Lawrence and then strike across the country to Hudson Bay and so on to the Arctic regions. Others fly along the coast only until they reach the rivers of Maine and then turn northward up the river valleys and through the lake regions. Still others veer to the north near where the Connecticut shore bends eastward and so pass up the valley of the Hudson or that of the Connecticut. Lake Champlain, a part of the Hudson River route, lies largely in Vermont and is responsible for bringing many water birds into that state; but the Connecticut Valley is the principal inland highway of bird migration lying within the New England states. Passing as it does through western Massachusetts, it is of particular interest to the Massachusetts ornithologist. The river from source to mouth runs 360 miles to the sea, traversing the entire length of two states, between which it forms the boundary, and crossing two more, thus becomes the chief waterway of New England.[1]   The general direction of its flow is slightly west of south.   The valley is bounded by many landmarks; high hills on either hand serve to mark the way, with the winding, shining river ever in view.   The Merrimack River in New Hampshire and the Androscoggin, Kennebec, Penobscot, St. Croix, St. John and Allegash in Maine together with the Maine lakes offer other routes by which water birds may reach the Canadian provinces.

It is unfortunate for those who delight in field study of birds that many people living in the interior know so little about the water birds.   These birds are not so common or accessible inland as land birds, and constant persecution has made them shy, but on most of the larger lakes and rivers as well as on smaller bodies of water some of them may be found in their seasons, and there are now a considerable number of lakes or reservoirs which are public reservations where shooting is not allowed.   In such places water birds soon become comparatively unsuspicious and may be rather closely approached.   On most large bodies of water in retired situations, some of these birds may be watched with binoculars or a telescope during the seasons of migration.

Thus far this introduction has dealt with New England as a country fitted for the sojourn of water birds, and both the usual and extraordinary conditions which favor their occurrence here.   It now remains to give some explanation of the plan of the book itself.

The technical names of birds used in this volume are mainly those of the Third Edition of the Check-List of North American Birds issued by the American Ornithologists' Union and the various supplements thereto published later in The Auk.   The synonyms given in the vernacular under the heading "Other Names" are chiefly such as are used in New England.

In the descriptions the forms used by the eminent American ornithologists, Baird, Coues and Ridgway, have been largely followed.   Technical verbiage has been omitted, however, as far as possible, in order that the ordinary reader may be able to understand the terms used without reference to the dictionary.   A few terms, such as "primaries" and "secondaries" have been used as a matter of convenience.   These are explained by cuts appended to the Introduction (see pages xxix and xxx).   The descriptions are abridged to save space.   Most of them have been compared with many specimens and prepared in such a way as to allow for a certain amount of individual variation.   It has been impossible in the limited space allowed to describe all fixed and transitory stages of plumage, or to give complete descriptions in all cases, but it is hoped that those given will be sufficient, in connection with the illustrations, to enable the novice to identify most species.   In certain cases, especially where young birds of different species or individuals of different races closely resemble one another, the services of an expert ornithologist will be required to distinguish them.   This is unavoidable.

The measurements of birds were obtained from all convenient available sources, in-

---

[1] Bagg, A. C.: The Connecticut Valley — a Highway for Bird Migration.   Auk, Vol. XL, 1923, pp. 256–275.

cluding a large number of specimens, with the intention of approximating in most cases maximum and minimum measurements of each species.

The term "nuptial plumage" as used in this volume denotes a plumage worn during the mating season, but partially molted later in the breeding season, as in most ducks, cormorants and a few species of terns. In most adult ducks the full winter and spring plumage and the nuptial plumage are the same in most cases, while the eclipse plumage is assumed in summer. Male eiders in high plumage have a peculiar development of two outer tertials or inner secondaries, the end of the vane being much expanded and its shape changed. Probably this is found only during the nuptial season. This plumage is depicted on plate 17, while only the winter plumage is described, as that is the dress usually seen in New England. No specimens with the perfected tertials were available for description. The term "breeding plumage" indicates a plumage worn during the entire breeding season (including breeding and upbringing of young), as in most terns, gulls and many other birds. Some terns, however, have a full black cap in the nuptial season, a part of which is lost during the breeding season. In such cases the full black cap indicates nuptial plumage.

The colors of the soft parts of birds (bills, eyes, ceres, feet, etc.) are very variable. These colors may vary according to sex, and change from time to time with age and season. Some tints change immediately after death. The descriptions recorded by ornithologists differ widely regarding these colors. Some of these descriptions were taken from living birds in various stages, others from dead birds, and many from dried skins in which the colors of soft parts rarely approximate those of the living birds. Correct descriptions of these colors and their variations would require study of the living birds for a long series of years. The author has been guided in his statements regarding these colors by his own observations and notes, by the notes of collectors and ornithological artists, especially those of Mr. L. A. Fuertes, who makes the colored drawings for the work, and by the descriptions of the most eminent and trustworthy ornithologists; but information from all these sources is still inadequate. It was impossible to supply fully the demand for information about the molts of birds. Comparatively few people have made a study of this subject, and such knowledge as we have has come largely from examinations of dried skins of birds in museums. Unfortunately in American museums there are not enough specimens showing molt to enable one to complete the study, and there is so much individual variation in the matter of dates when molting begins or ends and the ages at which the young arrive at full maturity, that the facts are rather obscure and difficult to ascertain. Authorities differ more or less in statements regarding these matters. The trapping and banding of birds, a comparatively new method of research in ornithology, provides a great opportunity for the study of molts by repeated examinations of the same individuals among living wild birds.

To assist the student, some of the most striking or readily discernible colors or markings of each species have been treated briefly in this volume under the head of "Field Marks."

In studying birds afield a knowledge of the notes and calls of the different species is as useful as an acquaintance with field marks. Syllables supposed to represent the more common vocal utterances of birds have been assembled in this volume under the heading of "Voice." Such transcriptions of birds' utterances leave much to be desired, and in most cases owe something to the imagination of the persons recording them, as different listeners often record the same notes in dissimilar words or syllables; but when properly rendered vocally they will resemble in a greater or less degree the actual calls or cries of the birds, and may serve, together with the field marks, to fix both the identity of the bird and the sound of its notes in the mind of the observer. Usually it is impossible to record more than a few of the commonly heard calls of each species. There are many low or soft notes that rarely are heard by human ears.

As hereinbefore stated, most of the birds described in this volume do not breed in New England; therefore the record of their breeding is in most cases brief and perfunctory. It has not been possible to ascertain the period of incubation of some or to procure certain other data in regard to them.

No measurements of eggs were taken, but their dimensions are those given by standard authorities and collectors. These measurements are not given always in uniform order, but are transcribed in each case in the original form.

The ranges are based upon those given in the Check-List of the American Ornithologists' Union (Third Edition, 1910), but are modified by later information which brings them more nearly up to date, and are corrected to conform to changes in names and boundaries in Canadian territory — northern or northeastern Manitoba, for example, now is substituted in most cases for central Keewatin. Our knowledge of the geographic distribution of birds is very far from complete. Birds are great wanderers, and stragglers may appear at times at points very far from their regular habitats. The ranges as now recorded in unsettled regions are dependent not so much on the actual distribution of birds as on the distribution or wanderings of ornithologists. Our practical knowledge of the occurrence of birds in Arctic regions is derived from the explorations of very few persons, and we know little of the distribution of water-birds in northern Canada and much of South America. Doubtless the ranges of many species will be far better known in future years.

Information regarding the season during which each species may be found in Massachusetts was obtained in part from published records but mainly from notes furnished by a considerable number of observers. The dates are so arranged as to show as far as possible the seasons when the species may be reasonably expected here; extreme dates and seasons when the species is rare are given in parentheses. The seasons in most cases will correspond more or less closely (according to distance) with the seasons of the same species in the other New England states.

Under "Haunts and Habits" is given as much of the biography of each bird, particularly during its sojourn with us, as space allows, including some items in respect to food and migrations.

Under "Economic Status" there is transcribed, as is required by the Act authorizing the preparation of the work, some account of the utility of orders, families and species. Where little is known of the economic status of the species, reference usually is made to the page on which the economic status of the family is given.

In connection with the distribution of birds, a number of comparative terms are used to describe the numerical status of a bird in different regions or localities. These terms graduate from "accidental" to "very abundant" in the following order: (1) Accidental, (2) Casual, (3) Occasional, (4) Very rare, (5) Rare, (6) Uncommon, (7) Not uncommon, (8) Common, (9) Very common, (10) Abundant, (11) Very abundant. "Accidental" and "casual" have similar meanings according to the dictionary, but as used in this volume they describe different degrees of rarity.

Here the word "accidental" denotes a purely fortuitous occurrence, when the bird appears far outside the ordinary range of the species, while the word "casual" denotes a less rare appearance, occurring usually in migration outside of the regular migration route.

Many descriptive terms used in this work are explained by the cuts that follow. A glossary of terms together with a bibliography and an index of all three parts will be appended to the last volume.

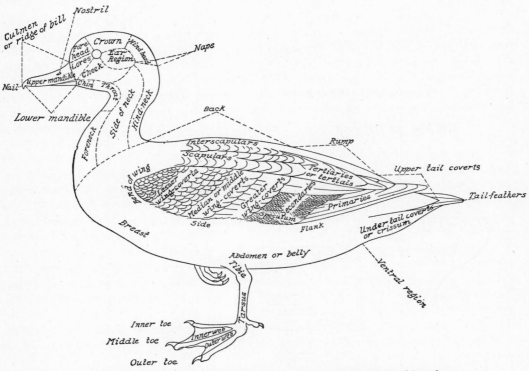

Topography of a duck showing terms used in describing birds in this volume.

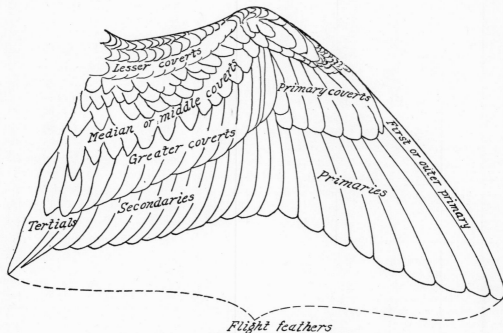

Topography of outer or upper surface of spread wing of a shore bird.

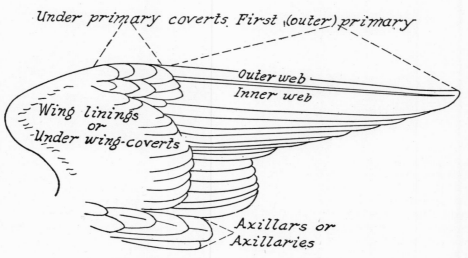

Topography of inner or under surface of wing.

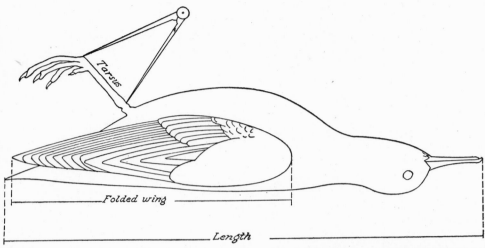

Method of measuring length, folded wing and tarsus. The bird should be extended full length upon the back, without stretching, upon the ruler or steel tape. The wing measurement may be taken by pressing the wing flat upon a ruler, or by measuring along the outer surface of wing with a steel tape measure. The spread is taken by spreading the wings to full extent upon a flat surface, placing a mark at the tip of each wing and then measuring the distance. For reasons readily seen in practice this measurement is not very reliable.

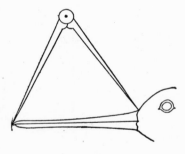

Bill

Method of measuring the bill from its tip to the feathers of the forehead. This is the length of the bill (the chord of the culmen or ridge). All bills of specimens treated in this volume are so measured unless it is otherwise stated under the measurements of a species. Some ornithologists measure bills with a tape carried along the culmen or ridge. In birds with hooked bills this method considerably increases the measurement.

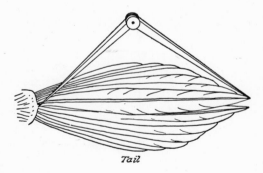

Tail

Method of measuring the tail. One point of the dividers is placed between the roots of the two middle tail feathers and pressed to the skin, while the other touches the tip of the longest tail feather.

BIRDS OF MASSACHUSETTS

CLASS AVES BIRDS

Birds as a class have a close affinity to reptiles from which they are believed to have developed. Birds are distinguished from all other animals by their feathers which are modified scales.

The Class *Aves* has been divided into toothed and toothless birds, all of the former being long extinct and known to us only by their fossilized remains. Some so-called modern birds have toothed bills, but no real teeth.

SUB–CLASS CARINATÆ: KEEL–BREASTED, TOOTHLESS BIRDS

The birds of today are divided into two sub-classes: *Ratitæ*, or raft-breasted, toothless birds, which includes flightless species like the Ostrich which have no keel to the breast bone, and *Carinatæ*, or keel-breasted toothless birds, which have a thin keel-like projection in the middle of the breast bone, to which the powerful breast muscles which help to move the wings are attached.

No species of the sub-class *Ratitæ* are native to North America; all North American species belong to the *Carinatæ*.

According to the classification adopted by the American Ornithologists' Union, the *Carinatæ* are divided into the following sixteen Orders: *Pygopodes* (Diving Birds), *Longipennes* (Long-winged swimmers), *Tubinares* (Tube-nosed swimmers), *Steganopodes* (Totipalmate swimmers), *Anseres* (Lamellirostral swimmers), *Odontoglossæ* (Lamellirostral waders), *Herodiones* (Herons, Storks, Ibises, etc.), *Paludicolæ* (Cranes, Rails, etc.), *Limicolæ* (Shore Birds), *Gallinæ* (Gallinaceous Birds), *Columbæ* (Pigeons and Doves), *Raptores* (Birds of Prey), *Psittaci* (Parrots, Macaws, Paroquets, etc.), *Coccyges* (Cuckoos, etc.), *Pici* (Woodpeckers, Wrynecks, etc.), *Macrochires* (Goatsuckers, Swifts, etc.) and *Passeres* (Perching Birds). This last great order includes over half of all known birds. All these orders with the exception of *Odontoglossæ* and *Psittaci* are represented among the birds of Massachusetts.

1

ORDER PYGOPODES. DIVING BIRDS.

Number of species in North America 32; in Massachusetts 11.

Birds of this order are formed especially for diving and swimming under water. Their bony framework is long and extends backward, enclosing the internal organs in such a way that they are protected from extreme pressure of water at great depths. The name of the order is derived from two Greek words signifying that the feet are attached to the hind parts. The legs are placed so far back and so buried in the body (in most species of this order) that the birds, when walking on land, are obliged to stand nearly erect. Most of them sit in this posture, squatting on the feet and tarsi, or else lie down, resting on the breast. Locomotion on land is ordinarily slow and difficult, but most species can move rapidly for a short distance when obliged to reach water. The toes are either webbed or lobed; the tarsi more or less flattened. The wings are comparatively short, never reaching, when folded, to the end of the tail (which is either very short and of many feathers or merely rudimentary), and are used at times, with or without the feet, in progression beneath the surface. This under-water wing action may be employed either habitually or only occasionally to assist a bird in escaping from its enemies or in pursuing its speedy prey. The food of these birds consists largely of fish and other aquatic animal life, supplemented to some extent in many cases by aquatic vegetation. The Pygopodes, owing to their shortness of wing, find it difficult or even impossible to rise from a level land-surface; when once in the air, however, most of them fly rapidly. The bill is hard and various in shape, but it is never widened laterally like that of ducks and geese, and is never lamellated. The plumage is dense, and when in good condition waterproof.

The order is divided into two suborders. The first (*Colymbi*) includes grebes (*Colymbidæ*) having a rudimentary tail; the second (*Cepphi*) comprises loons (*Gaviidæ*) and auks, murres and puffins (*Alcidæ*), with tail short but fully developed.

SUBORDER COLYMBI. GREBES.

Number of species in North America 6; in Massachusetts 3.

FAMILY **COLYMBIDÆ**. GREBES.

Number of species in North America 6; in Massachusetts 3.

Modern systems of biologic classification present first the lowest and simplest forms. In the present work, following the system of classification adopted by the American Ornithologists' Union, the grebes come first, as among North American birds they seem to rank nearest to the reptiles from which birds sprang. Grebes can stand nearly erect upon their feet, but when stranded on land and pursued there by an enemy, both old and young progress more or less on all fours like a turtle or a lizard. In swimming under water they sometimes use both wings and feet.

PLATE 1

PLATE 1

HORNED GREBE
Page 8
Winter Plumage
Adult in Breeding Plumage

HOLBŒLL'S GREBE
Page 4
Adult in Breeding Plumage
Winter Plumage

PIED–BILLED GREBE
Page 11
Adult in Breeding Plumage

All one-fourth natural size.

Louis Agassiz Fuertes

The characters of the family are the same as those of the suborder. Among them are the following: Body depressed or flat; bill usually compressed, sharp-pointed, of variable length, either longer or shorter than head, ridge either nearly straight, a little concave or quite convex toward tip; eyes far forward, with a narrow stretch of bare skin extending from each eye to the base of the upper mandible; head usually adorned with crests or ruffs in the breeding season; neck long and slender; plumage compact, rather hair-like above, silky below; when well dressed, waterproof, so that a grebe in good condition never gets wet to the skin; wings short and concave with *eleven* developed primaries; bastard quills and greater wing-coverts comparatively long; tail rudimentary, without quills and practically useless; legs so enclosed by the skin of the trunk that only the tarsi move freely; feet especially adapted for swimming but different from those of other lobe-footed birds; toes flattened and further widened by broad lobes, and connected in varying degrees by basal webs; hind-toe elevated, lobed and free; nails broad, flat and arranged on the toe somewhat like human nails. The whole foot forms a compound paddle which spreads on the back stroke and closes on the forward stroke. A vigorous grebe when held in the hand can work these paddles so fast that they seem a mere haze, like a hummingbird's wings in motion.

FOOT OF A GREBE

Many birds have air-cells in various parts of their bodies which communicate with their lungs. The ability to fill these air-cells as well as the lungs and to empty them at will may account in part for the manner in which grebes and other Pygopodes are able to sink quietly below the surface without diving, or to float partly submerged. Their power to compress the feathers and thus to expel the air from beneath them may also assist in this manœuver — in which perhaps the feet may sometimes play a part. In flight the feet extend well out behind the tail, the place of which they seem to take in steering. Grebes are among the most aquatic of birds. They may be distinguished from ducks by the narrow sharp-pointed bill, narrow head and neck, tailless aspect and lobed feet.

A peculiar characteristic of this family is the habit of eating feathers. Kearton writes that his boatman on the Norfolk Broads, a capable and veracious observer, told him that the young of the Great Crested Grebe (*Podiceps cristatus*) secure themselves on the back of the parent by seizing some of her feathers in their bills. This boatman (Alfred Nudd) once found a grebe chick with three feathers plucked from its parent's back and swallowed to the very base of their shafts. Kearton suggests that possibly thus the habit of feather-eating is formed and continued. Commonly when the stomach of a grebe is opened, many feathers are found.[1]

Dr. Alexander Wetmore in his "Food and Economic Relations of North American Grebes" describes the feathery mass which most grebes' stomachs contain and which consists of feathers, some of which are dislodged when preening and then devoured. He

---

[1] Kearton, Richard: Our Rarer British Breeding Birds, 1899, p. 36.

says: "It may be suggested that the feathers act as a strainer to prevent the passage of fish-bones or large fragments of chitin into the intestine until they have been reduced to a proper size and condition by the process of digestion." [1]

ECONOMIC STATUS. Feeding as they do mainly on the smaller forms of aquatic life, animal and vegetable, grebes have but slight economic importance. "The results obtained by stomach examinations show that they do not depend wholly or even chiefly on fish. On the contrary they eat a large number of crawfishes, which often severely damage crops, and they consume numbers of aquatic insects, which devour small fishes and the food of such fishes." [2] Dr. Wetmore in his Bulletin No. 1196 (already cited) also holds that the suspicion that grebes are seriously detrimental to certain valuable fishes is without actual foundation in fact. Speaking of the large Western and Holbœll's Grebes he says: "But on the whole they cannot be considered actually injurious, as the kinds [of fish] eaten are in most cases of little or no value to man."

Colýmbus hólbœlli (REINHARDT). Holbœll's Grebe.

Other name: RED-NECKED GREBE.

Plate 1.

DESCRIPTION. — Bill straight, tapering, long and rather slender. *Adults in breeding plumage (sexes alike)*: Sometimes seen in spring in Massachusetts. Crests short and ruffs not prominent; forehead, top of head and back of neck, greenish-black; back brownish-black with slight grayish or buffy edgings to many feathers; wing-coverts and primaries chocolate-brown, latter with black shafts; secondaries mainly white with black shafts mostly, and brownish tips; some if not all specimens have lesser upper wing-coverts more or less white (see small figure in plate 1); linings of wings and axillars whitish; a broad well-defined patch of bright silvery-ash on chin, upper throat and sides of head, whitening along upper and posterior edges; lower throat and front and sides of neck deep brownish-red, which pales as it extends to breast; below glossy white, shaded with silvery-ash, each feather with dark shaft-line and terminal spot, producing a dappled appearance; sides mostly blackish; lower part of base of upper mandible and most of lower, yellowish (specimens taken in middle October had upper mandible greenish-black, lower greenish-yellow); tarsi and feet black on outer side, dull greenish-yellow sometimes mottled with bluish on inner side; "legs and feet black" (W. L. Dawson); most of lower mandible orange-yellow changing to greenish-yellow on lower edge of upper mandible; iris always bright yellow (E. W. Nelson); iris carmine (Coues). (The difference in color of iris, thus recorded by these and other authorities, probably is due to age or season; colors of eye, bill and feet vary.) *Adults in fall and winter plumage* (as seen from October to April in Massachusetts): Some individuals show change to breeding plumage in late February or early March; crests not noticeable; red of neck replaced by brownish-ash or dusky; chin, throat, and cheeks pale grayish, sharply defined against dusky neck; an upright whitish spot or bar on either side of back of head; below mainly silvery-white; bill mostly yellowish or greenish-yellowish, ridge and tip more or less dusky; some if not all specimens with large patch of white on upper fore wing, mainly on lesser upper wing-coverts, extending from shoulder to middle forearm; secondaries chiefly white as in breeding plumage. *Young in first winter plumage:* Closely resemble winter adult but colors duller and not so pure; chin and throat whiter but usually mottled dusky; crown browner; neck sometimes reddish, and sharply defined pattern of head so con-

---

[1] United States Department of Agriculture, Department Bulletin No. 1196, 1924, p. 4.

[2] McAtee, W. L., and Beal, F. E. L.: United States Department of Agriculture, Farmers' Bulletin No. 497, 1912, p. 19.

spicuous in adults much obscured; iris dark brown, brownish-yellow or yellow; outside of tarsi and feet blackish, inside more or less yellow. *Downy young:* Considerable variation but generally black above, fading later to blackish-brown or seal-brown; white below when first hatched; head and neck broadly striped black and white.

MEASUREMENTS. — Length 18.00 to 20.75 in.; spread 30.00 to 32.00; folded wing 7.00 to 8.00; bill 1.64 to 2.40; tarsus 1.90 to 2.50. Female smaller than male.

MOLTS. — Young birds acquire in September first real (juvenal) plumage which retains signs of youth on head and neck, both of which show stripes of black and white, while neck is more or less reddish; stripes disappear during fall, but often reddish tint on neck retained through winter and until first nuptial plumage is acquired (A. C. Bent); Mr. Bent, who has studied the plumages of Holbœll's Grebe, believes immature birds become "indistinguishable from adults" at first postnuptial molt, when bird is one year old, but is not positive that another year is not required to complete change; the various changes of color in plumage, eyes, feet and bill seem to indicate that more than one year may be required for this species to reach full maturity — in some cases at least; adults have partial prenuptial molt in early spring, "involving mainly head and neck," and full postnuptial molt in autumn.

FIELD MARKS. — Size less than Black Duck, much larger than other Massachusetts grebes, but much smaller than loons; carries head horizontally like a loon; in winter resembles Red-throated Loon, but is smaller and has no white spots on back; neck thinner than that of any loon; *white wing-patch* (which distinguishes it from loons) shows plainly in flight or when wing is flapped, but often is covered by body-feathers when wing is closed; colors in winter similar to those of the smaller Horned Grebe, but cheeks not so shining white; also adults have whitish upright spot toward back of head nearly surrounded by gray, which can be seen at close range (see plate 1).

VOICE. — Love-notes in Manitoba begin with series of loon-like wailing cries, loud and piercing at first, running off into series of short, plaintive, vibrating wails — *Ah-ooo, ah-ooo, ah-ooo, ah-ah-ah-ah;* sometimes end in a staccato chattering trill — *whaaa, whaaa, whaaa, whaaa, whaaa, whaaa, chitter-r-r-r-r-r* (A. C. Bent); loud trumpetings suggest cries of loon (Mrs. Lizzie T. Burt); coarse, prolonged, nasal *quonk* suggests braying of donkey (P. M. Silloway); an explosive *kup;* an exceedingly harsh note not unlike voice of angry crow but much louder; calls given more slowly, *car, car,* three or four times, sometimes lengthened to *caar,* and again broken or quavering, like *c-a-a-r* or *c-a-a-ar* (William Brewster); note suggested by the syllables *wit'-tah* not loud but rather high, the first part higher than the second (Robert J. Sim); spring call, *naar-ah-haah-hah! naar-ah-haar-hah! naar-ah-haar-hah!* (Miss Elizabeth Dickens).

BREEDING. — In watery marsh or marshy lake. *Nest:* Built of marsh-grass, reeds, rushes, etc., usually among reeds or water brush, sometimes on muskrat house, sometimes floating, but attached to surrounding vegetation. *Eggs:* Generally 3 to 5, sometimes more, up to 8; size varying greatly, 2.10 to 2.35 by 1.25 to 1.45 in.; ovate to narrow elongate; whitish, bluish- or greenish-white to buff, but almost always stained and dirty. *Dates:* Throughout breeding range eggs found chiefly in June, and nearly all that month. *Incubation:* Period 22 or 23 days, when hatched in incubators (A. C. Bent). One brood yearly.

RANGE. — North America and eastern Asia. Breeds from northeastern Siberia, northwestern Alaska, northern Mackenzie, Ungava (northern Quebec), and Hudson Strait south to northern Washington, North Dakota, southwestern Minnesota and southwestern New Brunswick; winters mainly on Atlantic and Pacific coasts from Maine, southern Ontario, southern Wisconsin and southern British Columbia south to southern California, southern Colorado, Ohio Valley, North Carolina and casually Georgia and Tennessee; in Asia south to Japan; recorded in winter from Pribilof and Aleutian Islands and winters along coast of northern Pacific from Alaska to Washington.

DISTRIBUTION IN NEW ENGLAND. — Fall and spring migrant, coast and interior, and regular winter resident coastwise; casual in winter in interior and generally rare to casual in spring and autumn on larger ponds, lakes and rivers.

SEASON IN MASSACHUSETTS. — September 10 to May 25.

HAUNTS AND HABITS.   A bright clear day in January, a gentle breeze, a river mouth where the rippling flood flows into the sparkling sea, a lazy swell washing gently on the bar where a herd of mottled seals is basking in the sun, Old-squaws and Golden-eyes in small parties — such a scene at Ipswich is a fit setting for the great Grebe that winters on our coasts.   Here we find the bird, nearly always shy and wary, resting low in the water, its head held horizontally much like that of a loon, alert, diving "like a flash" and ready for any eventuality.   Sometimes, loon-like, it floats with its head held under water while spying below for its prey.   First we see it, then it has vanished!   For nearly a minute we search the face of the waters in vain, when suddenly it reappears, but at a greater distance.   Now as we hold the glass on it, it disappears again so quickly that we can hardly tell how it went.   Like all grebes Holbœll's often dives with a sudden forward spring, but it can let itself down into the water backward either slowly or swiftly.   Several observers have reported that this species when diving remains under water about fifty-five seconds.   Sometimes when alarmed it exposes only enough of its head to enable it to see, while keeping its body below the surface.   It can do this for long periods, swimming so slowly and gently as to escape observation.

In Massachusetts Holbœll's Grebe is usually the least common of the grebes, and stays mostly in wide waters where it can keep more than a gunshot from shore, but where no shooting is allowed, it becomes tame and unsuspicious.   It may be seen off either rocky cliffs or sandy shores, and often is most common off isolated isles like Block Island or headlands like Nahant, where it sometimes gathers in numbers.   Occasionally it is seen far out at sea.   Sometimes in spring or autumn one or two individuals, or even a small flock, may be met with in some of the larger fresh-water ponds, lakes or rivers of New England; but otherwise the species is rather seldom seen in the interior of southern New England, except when severe cold waves freeze up the Great Lakes or other large lakes of States or Provinces to the westward in which, in ordinary seasons, many of the birds pass the winter.   Such lakes are most often frozen over in February, when the winter temperature of the water reaches the minimum.   Then these wintering grebes must either remain to be frozen in or must climb out upon the ice where they lie helpless, as they cannot rise from the slippery surface; or they must attempt to escape by flight from the fast-freezing lakes.   In trying to reach the sea with wings unaccustomed to long flights, some become fatigued and fall or alight on the snow or ice in New England, eastern New York and New Jersey.   Probably at such times individuals have fallen helpless in all the inland counties of Massachusetts, and doubtless many are never found and perish of starvation and cold.   Many reach the sea but in a weakened condition.   Miss Elizabeth Dickens, of Block Island, Rhode Island, informs me that in some seasons hundreds of these birds die along the shores of that island.   During severe storms some are driven in from the sea and die miserably in extreme cold weather when they find no open water in the ponds.

Dr. Warren tells of an instance in Pennsylvania where an individual of this species dashed through the glass into a greenhouse.[1]   It doubtless mistook the glass for water as

---

[1] Warren, B. H.: Birds of Pennsylvania, 1890, p. 3.

wearied Canada Geese, similarly deceived in a fog and storm, have been known to alight on the wet roof of a large shed covered with gray roofing felt.

Often when swimming in shallow water beneath the surface, Holbœll's Grebe uses only its feet, striking out with both at once and moving very rapidly ; but in clear, deep water where there are no obstructions, a frightened bird has been seen to use its wings vigorously and to dart about so swiftly that the eye could barely follow its movements.[1] In ordinary swimming on the surface the lobed feet strike downward and outward much as a canoeman paddles. When the bird is really alarmed, it seldom flies, but dives at once.

This species stands well on its feet and can walk or run for short distances with the tarsi at an angle of about 45 degrees. Mr. Robert J. Sim had a captive specimen that slept on its breast with its head on its back and its feet entirely concealed under its wings.[2] Mr. J. A. Farley has seen birds of this species apparently dozing on the water with head drawn in on the chest.

Holbœll's Grebe is most common along New England coasts and on the larger inland waters in migration in October and November and again in late March and early April. My only summer record for this species in New England is that of a lone bird at Isle au Haut, Maine, July 1, 1919, recorded by Dr. Chandler Foot. Possibly this bird was a cripple. In migration Holbœll's Grebe assembles in flocks, and now and then numbers appear where food is plentiful along our shores ; but usually in Massachusetts waters the species is rather solitary. In migratory flights along the coast it flies commonly not far above the water with head and neck extended and feet stretched out behind.

Mr. Wilbur F. Smith of South Norwalk, Connecticut, wrote to me March 27, 1916, that he had observed Holbœll's Grebes fishing near an anchored boat on which a fisherman lived. The birds had become so fearless that they sometimes approached within a few feet of the boat. They fished all day, were fishing at ten P.M. when the fisherman retired, and were still fishing at daylight when he awoke. The fish taken, Mr. Smith says, were mainly little flounders found at the bottom, although one bird was seen with a large smelt. Mr. Smith noted that when a bird had swallowed a particularly large fish, it put its head on its back and went to sleep. This suggests that they feed day or night until satisfied, and then sleep. Herring Gulls bothered them repeatedly by attempting to snatch the fish from their bills, but the grebes by diving seemed usually to foil their tormentors. When feeding in salt water this fast swimmer overtakes the swiftest small fish. Occasionally it catches a fish too large to hold readily and swallow quickly, which wriggles away from the beak-hold. Then the eager bird dives "like a flash" and seizes its prey again. Sometimes it carries such a fish to shallow water where it strikes, pounds and slaps it about until the victim succumbs. Then the active bird throws its own head up and backward until it seems to strike the back and so works the fish down its widely distended throat. The food of this bird on salt water seems to consist largely of fish and

---

[1] Cahn, Alvin R.: Auk, Vol. XXIX, 1912, p. 440. (See also Department Bulletin No. 8, Massachusetts Department of Agriculture, 1922, pp. 9–10.)

[2] Wilson Bulletin, Vol. XVI (old series), 1904, p. 71.

crustaceans. Mr. Bent says that it can live in lakes where there are no fish. He asserts that in Manitoba it lives largely on crayfish, amblystomæ and aquatic insects, and that it takes tadpoles, aquatic worms, small crustaceans, mollusks and vegetable substances.[1] It also takes earthworms and beetles.

ECONOMIC STATUS. See page 4.

Columbus aurítus LINNÆUS. Horned Grebe.

Other names: DIPPER; HELL-DIVER; DEVIL DIVER.

Plate 1.

DESCRIPTION. — Bill straight and tapering. *Adults in nuptial plumage (sexes alike):* Occasionally seen in late April or May in Massachusetts. Forehead, crown, chin and very full handsome ruff on sides of head below eyes glossy greenish-black; brownish-yellow stripe over eye, widening and deepening in color toward end of long crest and darkening to chestnut between eye and bill; above generally brownish-black, each feather pale edged; primaries light chocolate-brown with pale brown inner webs and white bases, shafts black except at base; secondaries mainly white, "inner ones black with white tips and innermost white with black bases"; under surface of wing, except terminal half of primaries, largely white; neck (except dark stripe at back) and sides of body rich "chestnut," "reddish-brown," "brownish-red" or "purplish vinaceous-red," mixed with dusky on flanks; elsewhere below silky white; iris, carmine with fine white inner ring (sometimes even scarlet with irregular yellow ring, A. C. Bent); bill black, tipped yellow; feet dusky on outer edges, the rest yellow or yellowish. *Adults in fall and winter plumage* (as commonly seen in Massachusetts). Similar but grayer; no noticeable ruffs or crests and no bright colors, but crown blackish and sides of head white; some specimens have rufous markings behind eyes; black of cheeks and red of neck replaced largely by silky white, lightly washed with ashy-gray on front and sides of neck and lower belly; some specimens have a second white wing-patch on upper fore wing, including more or less of lesser upper wing-coverts from shoulder to elbow, and extending slightly down on tertials, this white space often mottled with dusky. *Young in first winter plumage:* Similar but cheeks sometimes not so pure white and probably always without rufous markings behind eyes; bill smaller and lighter colored, usually dusky on ridge but elsewhere tinged olive, yellowish, orange, or sometimes bluish-white; outer sides of legs and bottoms of feet dusky, inner sides of legs and upper sides of feet much lighter, pearly-gray, greenish or yellowish. *Downy young:* Dusky, almost black above, striped and spotted grayish-white; white stripe on hind head and white V on forehead extending down on sides of neck; sides of head, neck and throat white, sometimes tinged with salmon-buff, spotted and streaked dusky; sides dusky; below white.

MEASUREMENTS. — Length about 12.50 to 15.25 in.; spread about 24.00; folded wing 5.40 to 6.00; bill about .90; tarsus 1.60 to 1.75.

MOLTS. — First or juvenal plumage following natal down not unlike first winter plumage, but shows some dusky stripes and spots on head and throat; first winter plumage shows some of these markings and in spring of second year after prenuptial molt adult plumage is assumed; adults molt partially in late March, April and May and completely in autumn.

FIELD MARKS. — Size of Green-winged Teal but head and bill smaller; in nuptial plumage we have no grebe like it; in autumn adults may show some signs of breeding plumage on throat; in winter plumage its *pure white fore neck, cheeks and underparts* (white extending up from throat to nape), *absence of brown in* its plumage, its *straighter, slenderer bill,* and *its conspicuous large white wing-patch* (which

---

[1] The fullest life history of Holbœll's Grebe has been written by Arthur Cleveland Bent in his "Life Histories of North American Diving Birds," Smithsonian Institution, United States National Museum, Bulletin No. 107, 1919. All North American diving birds are more exhaustively treated in this excellent bulletin than in any other work.

always shows when wing is spread) distinguish it from the Pied-billed Grebe; *small* size and short bill distinguish it from Holbœll's Grebe.

VOICE. — Love-calls a wonderful combination of weird, loud, striking cries, a series of croaking and chattering notes followed by several prolonged, piercing shrieks (A. C. Bent); a curious far-sounding note of complaint, *keogh, keogh,* with a nasal twang or more sharply *keark, keark* or *yark, yark* (W. L. Dawson); in large companies there is a perpetual conversational undertone (Lynds Jones).

BREEDING. — In rushy borders of ponds or sloughs or on their shores; singly or in small colonies. *Nest:* Wet rotten reeds, flags or other rubbish and mud, often partly or wholly afloat but anchored to growing vegetation, sometimes on a tussock or on wet foreshore. *Eggs:* 3 to 5 and up, rarely 10; indistinguishable from those of Pied-billed Grebe. *Dates:* April 6 to August 12 in various parts of North America (A. C. Bent). *Incubation:* Period unknown. So far as known only one brood reared in a season; wide variation in egg-dates may indicate two broods occasionally.

RANGE. — Northern parts of Northern Hemisphere. Breeds from near Arctic coast to northern United States, Maine, Minnesota, southern Wisconsin, and northern Nebraska; also in Iceland, northern continental Europe and Siberia; recorded in summer in Massachusetts, Connecticut, Michigan and Indiana; in the East, winters mainly from Maine and New York to Florida and Louisiana and on west coast from southern Alaska to southern California and southward; most interior winter records are from region of Great Lakes; also winters in central and southern Europe, northern Africa and Azores, and on coasts of China and Japan to Tropic of Cancer; casual in Greenland and in Bermuda and Commander Islands.

DISTRIBUTION IN NEW ENGLAND. — Common fall and spring migrant and common winter visitant coastwise, especially common during mild winters; irregular, sometimes common, in migration in interior waters; breeds casually in northeastern Maine; may have bred in Massachusetts and Connecticut.

SEASON IN MASSACHUSETTS. — (September 14) October 1 to May 28 (July 6).

HAUNTS AND HABITS. In its full nuptial plumage the Horned Grebe is a handsome bird. In sunshine its ruffed and crested head and rich, deeply colored neck and flanks glow resplendent. Even in the modest dark and white plumage of winter in which it is usually seen in New England, with its pure, satiny white breast, it is delicately handsome, and it seems as if aware of its distinction. Its head is carried proudly and when at ease it rides the water lightly and gracefully. Even in the finest plumage, however, it seems like a freak, with its fluffy tufted head and handsome fore parts, its rather ordinary-looking, plain back and its lack of any appreciable tail to balance its frontal beauties. Like all grebes the bird seems somehow to have been left unfinished; yet it is admirably adapted to its mode of life.

It may be found in winter almost anywhere along the New England coast, is more common than Holbœll's Grebe, and sometimes in migration is abundant locally not only on the coast but also in the interior. Occasionally severe easterly storms drive large flocks into the ponds of interior Massachusetts. This bird is not generally so wary as the preceding species and frequents narrower streams and smaller ponds. Mr. H. K. Job once found a pair in Connecticut in a little brook from which they seemed unable to rise.[1]

Ornithologists have repeatedly asserted that grebes cannot rise in the air if once stranded on the ground. Nevertheless, Mr. Charles H. Rogers says that Mr. Walter

---

[1] Job, Herbert K.: The Sport of Bird Study, 1908, p. 272.

Granger and himself, while at Long Beach, Long Island, New York, saw a Horned Grebe on the shore, which, on their approach, scuttled away from the water, rose against the wind and circled about, flying several hundred yards before alighting.[1]   This incident of course cannot be considered proof that any other species ever flew under such conditions, but if one can do so another may.   The flight of this Grebe is strong and often direct and long-continued.   In rising from the water it splashes along on the surface for a long distance before it can gain sufficient impetus to launch itself into the air.   In flight it appears much like a loon except for its small size, the greater rapidity of its wing strokes and its conspicuous white wing-patches.   On the surface it swims with alternate strokes of its lobed paddles and dives quickly and gracefully with closed wings.   When observing this species diving in a tank, I have never seen one open or use its wings under water, but Mr. C. W. Vibert, of South Windsor, Connecticut, who kept one alive for a time, says that it often used the slightly raised wings while swimming under water. Mr. C. A. Clark told me on November 9, 1917, that he with a friend watched two Horned Grebes diving on Walden Pond in the Lynn woods.   The watchers took up their positions on a hill above the water where by looking down from this eminence they got a very clear view of the pond below.   There were in the pond many small fishes that looked like minnows, which the grebes pursued and some of which they caught.   With a glass the manœuvers of the birds could be seen plainly.   Mr. Clark says that the wings were held partly open and now and then a quick stroke was given with them.   In catching the elusive fish the birds frequently darted their heads to the right or left as their prey dodged and doubled in flight.   Several other observers have reported the use of the wings by this grebe for propulsion under water.[2]

Dr. Langdon illustrates the precocity of the young of this species by the assertion that when fully developed chicks which he removed prematurely from the eggs were placed in the water, they immediately swam and attempted to dive.[3]

No bird is more at home on the water than this grebe.   It often sleeps there with its head on its back and its bill turned to the right and buried under its scapulars.   Like the loon it turns on its side or back to preen the feathers of its breast.   It is driven from coast waters in winter only by severe storms when a few, stranded on ice or snow, are found occasionally in the interior.

On the Atlantic coast it passes in numbers; and in October and November and again in March and April its greatest flights occur, usually a mile or two off shore.   When migrating in the interior it oftens follows the course of a river, swimming with the current very early in the morning or just before dark.   At times it flies at a considerable height.

Various authorities have given notes on the food of this species which is known to consist largely of small fish, crustaceans, tadpoles, lizards, leeches, beetles, grasshoppers, locusts, many aquatic insects, a few snails and spiders and some vegetal food.   The best

---

[1] Auk, Vol. XXXV, 1918, p. 218.
[2] Department Bulletin No. 8, Massachusetts Department of Agriculture, 1922, pp. 10–12.
[3] Dawson, William Leon: Birds of Ohio, Vol. II, 1903, p. 631.

account of its food that I have seen is that given by Mr. W. L. McAtee in Farmers' Bulletin No. 497, U. S. Department of Agriculture. He found an average of 66 per cent. of feathers in the contents of the stomachs examined and suggests that feathers are fed to the young. They are finely ground in the gizzard and are believed to be digested and assimilated. It has been suggested that they are eaten as an aid to digestion, but one would suppose them to be more likely a hindrance.

The food of the Horned Grebe, exclusive of feathers, is thus listed by Mr. McAtee in an analysis of the food contents of 57 stomachs: Beetles, chiefly aquatic, 23.3 per cent.; other insects nearly 12 per cent.; fish 27.8 per cent.; crawfish 20.7 per cent.; other crustaceans 13.8 per cent., with a little other animal matter, and a small quantity of vegetal food in two stomachs.[1]

ECONOMIC STATUS. Evidently these grebes were feeding not only on fish but on the enemies of both fish and crops, and the evidence seems to indicate that they do more good than harm.

Podilýmbus pódiceps (LINNÆUS). Pied-billed Grebe.

Other names: DABCHICK; WATER-WITCH; DIPPER; DIDAPPER; HELL-DIVER; LITTLE DIVER.

Plate 1.

DESCRIPTION. — Bill very stout, its ridge much downcurved. *Adults in nuptial plumage (sexes alike):* Crown, back of head and back of neck grayish-black, with slightly lighter feather-edgings; sides of head and neck brownish-gray; a conspicuous, long, broad, black throat-patch, the black extending upward at base of lower mandible; rest of upper plumage dark brown or brownish-black, edges of feathers barely lighter; primaries and secondaries chocolate-brown, latter often with some whitish or white, mostly on inner webs; below silvery-ash, closely mottled dusky; mottling most apparent on sides; lower belly mostly dusky; bill "light, dull bluish or bluish-white," dusky on ridge and sometimes at tip, almost encircled near middle by a black band which includes nostrils; iris brown and white; eyelids white; "feet greenish-black outside, leaden-gray inside" (Coues). *Adults in winter plumage:* Similar but more brownish generally; feathers of back with paler edges; top of head and nape dusky brown; throat white *without black throat-patch,* though some adults have traces in autumn; neck beneath, breast and sides with more or less light russet-brown mottled dusky, darker behind; lower belly grayish; other under plumage silky-white, often almost unspotted, but sometimes much spotted with dusky; bill dusky-yellowish, no black band. Many immature birds retain on head and throat until into October black and white markings suggestive of the nestling plumage. *Downy young:* Mainly black with four whitish stripes on back of neck and back; white throat and fore neck striped and spotted with black; crown black more or less variegated with bright brown, with two pairs of longitudinal white stripes meeting or closely approaching on forehead; sides of body more or less washed with dusky; other under plumage grayish-white.

DOWNY YOUNG PIED-BILLED GREBE.

About ½ natural size.

MEASUREMENTS. — Vary greatly. Length about 12.00 to 15.00 in.; spread about 22.00 to 24.50; folded wing 4.50 to 5.25; bill about .85; tarsus about 1.50.

---

[1] McAtee, W. L., and Beal, F. E. L.: United States Department of Agriculture, Farmers' Bulletin No. 497, 1912, p. 19.

MOLTS. — Young bird is nearly full-grown before down disappears entirely to be replaced by juvenal plumage; many young birds retain black and white striped head until late in October; others change by that time into winter plumage; black throat of adult and black band on bill appear just before breeding season. It seems probable that full adult plumage is "acquired during the first year" (A. C. Bent); adults molt completely in autumn and partially in spring.

FIELD MARKS. — Smaller than a teal; unmistakable in nuptial plumage because of black throat and pied bill; in late autumn or winter, when these marks are wanting, may be known from Horned Grebe by thick hen-like bill with curved upper mandible, general brownish tinge of fore neck and breast where other bird is white and absence of shining white cheeks which distinguish Horned Grebe; also no large conspicuous white wing-patches (but a line of white often shows on tips of secondaries when wing is spread and there is some white under wing).

VOICE. — "*A loud sonorous cow-cow-cow-cow-cow-cow-cow-cow-cow-uh cow-uh.* The notes vary in number and are sometimes followed by wailing *cows* or *uhs;* these love notes of male are sometimes joined by those of female *cuk-cuk-cuk* followed by a slower *ugh, ugh, ugh*" (F. M. Chapman); *pr-r-r-r-tow-tow-tow-tow* (E. E. Thompson); "an odd bubbling giggle *keggy, keggy, keggy, keggy, keggy, keggy, keggy,* etc. rendered very rapidly; also a single excited *aou*" (W. L. Dawson); *cuck-cuck-cuck-cuck, kow, kow, kow, kow,* suggesting notes of a cuckoo; a loud *wah'-hoo, wah'-hoo, wah'-hoo, wah'-hoo,* suggesting the note of a loon; a low alarm *toot, toot, toot,* (Ralph Hoffmann); alarm note *keck, keck;* call to the young, *cup, cup* (A. A. Allen).

BREEDING. — In cattail swamps, marshes, ponds and sloughs. *Nest:* A heap of reeds partially decayed, or flags bent or matted down with perhaps some coarse sedgy grasses; usually in water from one to three feet deep, in a lagoon, grassy pond or cattail marsh; among reeds, flags or water brush; most of the nest-material below the surface; a shallow depression contains the eggs. *Eggs:* 3 to 10, usually 5 to 7; about 1.70 by .95 in.; generally "elliptical," ovate, smooth-shelled; dull bluish-white or pale olive-white, usually stained by contact with wet nest-material to a dirty brown. *Dates:* April 23 to June 28, Massachusetts; May 15 to August 8, New York and New Jersey. *Incubation:* Period 23 to 24 days; both sexes incubate. Not positively known that more than one brood is raised in a season.

RANGE. — North and South America generally, in suitable places, but very local. Breeds from British Columbia, Great Slave Lake, Saskatchewan, northeastern Manitoba, Ontario, Quebec and New Brunswick south to Chile and Argentina; winters south from New York and New Jersey (occasionally), Vancouver Island, Washington, Arizona, Texas, Mississippi and Potomac Valley southward; recorded casually from Cape Horn and Bermuda.

DISTRIBUTION IN NEW ENGLAND. — Summer resident, breeding locally in suitable localities throughout most of New England; common autumnal migrant, less common in spring; casual in winter in mild seasons in southern New England.

SEASON IN MASSACHUSETTS. — March 1 to December 12; reported also in January and February.

HAUNTS AND HABITS. When autumn comes, when the leaves have turned to crimson and gold, when white frost lies on the meadows at sunrise, when noisy jays and busy squirrels are gathering their winter stores, then, on the winding reaches of some sluggish river where the pickerel-weed and arrow-plant grow and where wild rice and cattail flags wave in the breeze, we may find the "Water-witches." If undisturbed and at ease, they ride almost as lightly and buoyantly upon the water as an Indian canoe or an autumn leaf wafted along the surface. When apprehensive they sink slowly down, swimming with only the head or head and neck above water; but when really alarmed they go under so quickly that one can hardly see how they vanish. Often after such a disappearance

Photograph by Dr. Frank N. Wilson

Fig. 1. — Pied-billed Grebe on Nest

Fig. 2. — Nest and Eggs of Loon

The pale appearance of the eggs is caused by reflection of light from their glossy
surface

the eager hunter searches in vain, for the scared bird swims under water until it reaches the water-plants on the margin and there rests with only its bill and perhaps also its eyes above the surface, so deftly concealed that its hiding place is rarely discovered. My friend, the late Charles E. Bailey, who was extremely handy with a gun and as sharp-eyed as a lynx, asserted that one of these birds committed suicide when it saw him aiming, as he felt sure that it never came up. Its apparent descent to the lower regions so quickly as often to escape a charge of shot, and its occasional total and complete disappearance have given it the euphonious appellation of "Hell-diver." There is evidence to the effect that when wounded it sometimes seeks a hiding place at the bottom and dies there either clinging to or entangled in pond weeds or other aquatic vegetation.[1]

In the old days of flintlock guns the bird dived at the flash in the pan and eluded the shot. Even now in these days of smokeless powder, if low in the water and at a goodly distance, it may escape the gunner, as its body lies mostly under water, and the head and neck offer a small and instantly vanishing mark. The wild-fowler should not shoot it as it is likely to act as an involuntary decoy to flying ducks which see in its presence a sign that the coast is clear and descend without suspicion. Blunderers and ignoramuses with guns there be, however, who pursue this harmless bird which is of little value as food. If successful, they either throw their victim away or keep it only long enough to display as a trophy of marksmanship.

In the breeding season the Pied-billed Grebe is shy and secretive, keeping generally well out of sight, but its presence may be detected by the sonorous notes which it often utters during the mating time. At this season it frequents cattail swamps, large marshes and stagnant, reed-bordered ponds where the nest is built. When the water is deep enough, the nest floats, attached to stems of reeds, flags or bushes. It is large, measuring from 12 to 15 inches in diameter, and sometimes the material used would almost fill a bushel basket. Usually it is built high enough to keep the eggs above water, but they are rarely dry. A small colony of the species consisting of several nests and their occupants often occupies a small pond or marsh.

When the mother bird leaves her eggs, if time allows, she covers them with some of the "muck and truck" from the nest, although Mr. A. M. Collette, who watched the species in Kansas, found that some of them used fresh grasses to cover the eggs. This grebe is so shy and secretive in the breeding season that it covers and leaves the nest at the first alarm; but Mr. Collette[2] and several other naturalists by using great care have ascertained that the species, like other grebes, if undisturbed, remains on the nest attending to the duties of incubation most of the time, night or day. This seems to dispose of the old notion that this grebe incubates only at night and, covering the eggs in the morning, leaves them all day to be incubated by the heat of the sun and the fermentation of the decaying nest-material. It may, however, so leave them for brief periods. Apparently its eggs will withstand long neglect, for Mr. W. L. Dawson records that, having col-

---

[1] Department Bulletin No. 8, Massachusetts Department of Agriculture, 1922, p. 40.
[2] Transactions Kansas Academy of Science, Vol. XIII, 1891–92, pp. 49–50.

lected some eggs of this species and taken them home, he was somewhat disconcerted two days later when the disimprisoned young ones "cheeped" lustily, "forty hours from the nest." [1]

Mr. Griffing Bancroft tells how quickly the parent is able to cover the nest and disappear when disturbed. On June 9, 1920, he happened by good fortune to surprise one of these birds on her nest. He says that when approached the bird slipped off, but while doing so covered the eggs completely in about two seconds by three quick pecks at the nesting material. As the bird half rose on the nest, the eggs could be plainly seen; when she dived beneath the surface, they were quite covered. [2] When the eggs have been thus concealed, the nest appears as a mere heap of trash such as may be found anywhere in a marsh. Mr. George Atkinson tells of a similar habit of this bird in the Canadian Northwest. He says that in 1906 the Dabchick was conspicuous on any pond of any size between Portage LaPrairie and Edmonton. He reports that he did not find the species covering the eggs with rubbish and leaving them during the day, but that he regularly disturbed the birds sitting on the nests. When flushed, they were seen to "flap a considerable quantity of the decayed reed foundation over the eggs as though to hide them." [3]

Mr. C. H. Pease sent me some notes on the nesting of this species in 1913 at Canaan, Connecticut, which have since been published by Mr. A. C. Bent in his Life Histories of North American Diving Birds. The nest was completed and contained one egg when he found it on May 22. An egg was laid daily until May 28 when the eighth and last was deposited. The first two young birds hatched at 9.15 A.M. June 21. On June 22 only one young bird remained in the nest. On July 3 the young appeared to be "half grown."

The young can take to the water immediately after they are hatched and do so if disturbed. In any case they do not remain long in the nest. They swim and dive readily as soon as they strike the water but cannot stay very long beneath the surface. Dr. A. A. Allen says that he watched some that extended the wings at nearly right angles in swimming and diving. [4]

This species like other grebes often carries the tiny young upon its back. In the face of danger the young are covered by the mother's wings while she swims away buoyantly. If she dives, she usually carries the young under water with her and emerges with them still concealed as it were in her pockets. Often the little ones ride about on the back of the mother sometimes entirely hidden beneath the scapulars or wing-coverts, or with only their little heads peeping out. At such times, if the mother dives, the young often remain floating on the water; and even when held under the wings, if the parent bird becomes frightened, the chicks sometimes come to the surface, perhaps because the mother uses her wings in swimming under water to hasten her flight. But she has been observed, when closely pursued, to push the young from her back and, evidently at a signal from her, "each baby took a portion of the mother's tail in its bill and all disap-

[1] The Birds of Ohio, Vol. II, 1903, p. 634.   [2] Condor, Vol. XXII, 1920, p. 206.
[3] Macoun, John and James: Catalogue of Canadian Birds, 1909, p. 8.   [4] Bird-Lore, Vol. XVI, 1914, p. 246.

peared under the water, coming up some distance away with the babies still clinging to mother's tail." [1] (Loons are said to have a similar habit.) Dr. A. A. Allen tells of seeing a young grebe plunge from the back of one parent and swim to the other.

Ordinarily in shoal-water diving the species seems to make little or no use of its wings, but while under the surface it has been seen to use them. Audubon records that two grebes of this species, which were caught in a net, were placed in a large tub where they swam around the sides like puffins, using their feet and wings "in accordance," and staying a long time under water. He says again that this species "during submersion" employs its wings, as he had an opportunity of observing while some that he was pursuing passed under the boat. Chester A. Reed says of the habit, "In my boyhood I frequently cornered these birds in a creek or small cove, so that in order to escape it was necessary for them to swim under the boat. At these times we could plainly see their mode of progression. They flapped their wings in much the same way as in flying, and this in addition to their feet is what gives them their great speed. On one of these occasions, as the grebe was going under the boat, my companion in his excitement leaped overboard, clothes and all. By some accident he happened to catch the bird by the neck." [2] I have many reports from trustworthy observers who have seen this species using both wings and feet under water and a few have observed the use of the wings alone. Probably the use of both wings and feet explains the great speed which grebes sometimes are able to attain under water, and possibly all grebes use both wings and feet in deep diving, in pursuing their swift and elusive prey or in escaping from some of their larger enemies.

The Pied-billed Grebe though swift and graceful in the water is quite awkward on land. It can walk or run slowly while standing on its feet with the body inclined forward at an angle, but if much hurried it throws itself forward on its belly, and scrambles along with both wings and feet as if it were swimming. It lives largely and sleeps often on the water, but Audubon asserts that he has seen the species resting at evening on beds of reeds such as are found in some of its favorite haunts. If severely or mortally wounded and not pursued, it seeks the shore, if possible, where it rests on its breast. Probably all waterfowl instinctively turn to the shore in such a case. While it is true that the plumage of grebes and other water birds is impervious to water when they are in good health and able to keep the feathers well dressed, it seems to lose its water-proof character when the bird is ill or wounded. I once saw such a bird kept in a tank. The feathers became water-soaked and draggled, and the bird though taken from the tank soon died.

The southward migration of the species begins during September in New England. The earliest arrival reported at Block Island, Rhode Island, was September 16. By November 15, most of the "Pied-bills" have left New England for the South; but during the exceedingly mild winter of 1920–21 the species was reported a few times in Massachusetts, Rhode Island and Connecticut, and also on Long Island. As the Pied-billed Grebe is mainly a fresh-water bird and frequents chiefly still or sluggish waters, it commonly moves southward when such waters freeze and remains in the South until

---

[1] Peck, Grace H.: Bird-Lore, Vol. XXI, 1919, p. 110.   [2] American Ornithology, Vol. I, 1901, p. 149.

March when the ice breaks up on the lakes and rivers of southern New England. It then returns, and in April its cuckoo-like notes may be heard in the ponds and marshes where it breeds. It is supposed to migrate at night, and it would seem that its small wings could not make very long flights, but it has been seen at daybreak coming to shore over wide bays and estuaries.

The food of this grebe consists of small fish and other small forms of animal life, as frogs, tadpoles, snails, crustaceans, leeches and aquatic insects, together with vegetal matter such as seeds and other parts of water-plants. Audubon says that he found in the gizzard a quantity of hair and a feather-like substance which he found was the down of certain plants such as thistles with the seeds remaining undigested and attached. Like all grebes they eat feathers, balls of which are usually found in their stomachs, but the nutritive value of these to the grebe is unknown.

ECONOMIC STATUS. See page 4.

SUBORDER CEPPHI. LOONS AND AUKS.

Number of species in North America 26 ; in Massachusetts 8.

FAMILY GAVIIDÆ. LOONS.

Number of species in North America 5 ; in Massachusetts 2.

Loons are larger than grebes. They have stout, strong, straight, narrow, tapering, sharp-pointed and sharp-edged bills with which they strike and hold their finny prey. Unlike grebes the head is fully feathered to the beak with no crests or ruffs. The plumage is often more or less velvety about the head and neck, but hard and glossy elsewhere. The front toes are connected by a web extending to their tips, and the tail though very short is not downy like that of a grebe, but is equipped with stiff quills. Loons are especially noted for their diving powers, the long distances that they travel under water and their great speed beneath the surface where like grebes they use either feet or wings, or both, for propulsion. Like grebes and anhingas they can alter their specific gravity quickly and swim with the body wholly or partly under water, with only head and neck exposed. In plumage the sexes are alike. Immature birds and winter adults are similar to each other, but are usually much duller in color than summer adults. The voice is loud and resonant.

FOOT OF LOON

ECONOMIC STATUS. No thorough all-the-year-round study of the food of loons has been made. Therefore their economic status remains undetermined. They feed mainly on aquatic animal and vegetal life and probably play their part as regulators of subsurface life in lakes where they breed.

"The possibility that the Loon may render a service to conservers of game fishes, by holding in check in some degree the destroyers of fish-eggs, such as suckers and horned-

PLATE 2

PLATE 2

LOON

Page 17

ADULT IN WINTER PLUMAGE

ADULT IN BREEDING PLUMAGE

RED-THROATED LOON

Page 28

WINTER PLUMAGE

ADULT IN BREEDING PLUMAGE

All one-sixth natural size.

pouts, or in destroying the fishes affected with contagious gill-fungus and other diseases, has never been given consideration.   There is, however, an element of probability in this, for, by the law of survival of the fittest, the physically inferior individuals, whether inherently weaker or the victims of disease, are the ones that habitually fall prey to their enemies.   Unquestionably it is the weaker specimens of the species eaten that constitute the greater part of the Loon's diet.   On the other hand some, as the suckers, are very destructive to the finest game-species, eating large quantities of their eggs, while themselves of little value as food or game.   Weed and Dearborn say that 'the fish they consume are generally worthless.'   As a matter of fact very little has been made known of the economic status of the Loon, but this little is considerably in its favor. Aquatic insects large enough to attract the attention of the Loon are predaceous, and in some instances have proved to be factors of sufficient importance to demand active measures for their suppression in fish ponds " (Arthur H. Norton).

Gávia ímmer (BRÜNNICH). Loon.

Other names: GREAT NORTHERN DIVER; BIG LOON.

Plate 2.

DESCRIPTION. — *Adults in breeding plumage (sexes alike)*: Head and neck rich, glossy, velvety greenish-black with some lustrous purplish reflections; a transverse patch of sharply-defined white streaks on throat; a larger similar patch lower down on either side of neck, sometimes meeting behind; sides of breast striped black and white; upper plumage, sides and flanks black, thickly marked, except on flight-feathers, upper tail-coverts and tail with sharply-defined spots of pure white; each contour-feather with two spots, those on back and scapulars square or rectangular, others oval; below, including axillars and wing linings, white; dusky band around lower belly; bill shining black; iris red; legs black or blackish on outer side, light bluish-gray inside; feet black or blackish below, light bluish-gray above.* *Adults in winter plumage:* Generally dark brown or blackish above, with no light feather-edgings; feathers of back and scapulars square-tipped with a faint suggestion of white spots of nuptial plumage; chin, throat and other under parts mainly white; bill and feet much lighter than in summer, lower mandible and part of upper "ivory colored" (M. Bedford); iris reddish-brown; apparently some fully adult birds, perhaps very old, do not assume the winter plumage.   *Young in first winter plumage:* Similar, but birds of first year have smaller bill than adult; bill light horn color in autumn, dark on ridge, darker in spring, but never black; iris brown; feet much like those of winter adult; top of head and back of neck sooty; feathers of throat and breast sometimes pure white but often finely mottled dusky; feathers of back rounded instead of square-tipped; above blackish-brown with broad light gray feather-edgings, particularly those of fore-back.   *Downy young:* Brownish-black, fading as bird grows older; central part of belly white, tinged on sides with grayish.

MEASUREMENTS. — Length 28.00 to 36.00 in.; spread about 52.00 to 58.25; folded wing 12.40 to 16.00; tail 2.60 to 4.00; bill 2.70 to 3.90; tarsus 3.00 to 3.90.

MOLTS. — Juvenal plumage is partly molted in winter; first winter plumage is worn through summer and for nearly a year without much modification, light edgings above bleaching to white or wearing away and throat becoming whiter toward spring; autumnal (postnuptial) molt is complete and followed early in the fall by second winter plumage, which is similar to first winter plumage except that dark crown is

---

* Some fully adult loons in high breeding plumage may have tarsi and feet entirely black, as some authorities assert, but among many loons examined I have found only one so colored.

more clearly defined, throat pure white, and feathers of back, which still have broad light edgings, more *nearly square-tipped:* this plumage is worn for only a short time by some individuals which begin to show signs of molt into second nuptial plumage in November or December by growth of a few jet-black feathers with white spots on back, wings, rump and flanks; usually this molt is not much in evidence until February; from then on prenuptial molt advances to head and neck and by April or May second nuptial plumage is complete; this is similar to adult nuptial plumage but duller, more dingy, and often with more or less white in chin and throat; some specimens in this plumage have sexual organs somewhat enlarged, indicating that they probably breed when about 2 years old; bill now black and never again as light as in young; at next postnuptial molt bird becomes fully adult, when a little over 2 years old; adult winter plumage assumed during this third fall is worn for a short time only; third-year postnuptial molt probably is complete and begins sometimes by the last of August, but sometimes not until October; the prenuptial molt (also complete) may begin in November or later and may not be completed until spring.

NOTE. — As an example of complete spring molt of the Loon, the following is of interest: On March 12, 1921, I picked up at Nantucket a very large and heavy dead Loon apparently in its second winter plumage. There were no signs of breeding plumage except some dark feathers in the upper wing-coverts which were spotted with white. The flight-feathers had been molted recently. The primaries were so short that the white under wing-coverts projected beyond their tips; secondaries also were very short. Evidently this bird if alive would have been unable to fly.

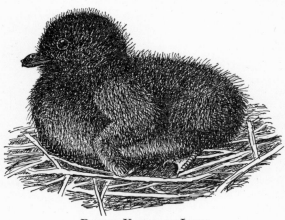

DOWNY YOUNG OF LOON
About ½ natural size.

FIELD MARKS. — Size of small goose; black and white adult unmistakable in summer; in winter resembles Red-throated Loon but larger and feathers of back *margined* with grayish where the "Red-throat" is *spotted* with light gray *or whitish;* bill stouter, heavier and usually straighter than that of Red-throat's which is more slender and often seems a little upturned.

VOICE. — Loud resonant calls; at night-fall or before storm *A-ooo'-oo* or as often written *O'-Ō-ōōh;* common laughing call *hōo, hŏŏ, hŏŏ, hŏŏ, hŏŏ,* uttered in peculiar vibrating tremolo (E. H. Eaton); *o-ha-ha-ha-ho!* (Robert J. Sim); four calls (1) a short cooing note, (2) a long drawn-out note known to guides as the night call, (3) the laughing call, (4) the storm call, a peculiar and weird performance (W. L. Underwood); the "silly song," *Oh-a-le' cleo'-pee'-a-rit, cleo'-pee'-a-rit, cleo'-per'-wer-wer!* a soft mellow pleasing *Ō láir* in rather a disconsolate tone (Robert J. Sim).

BREEDING. — Usually about shores of inland lakes; sometimes near sea. *Nest:* In shallow water or on shore of some lake or pond or on island in pond near or just above high water mark; a mere hollow in sand with a few blades of grass and sticks surrounding it; a bed of moss and weeds built on rocky ground; a mass of reeds and other vegetation on edge of marsh; a depression in top of old muskrat house or grassy tussock; sometimes lined with material from bog and bits of grass or turf; sometimes shadowed by bushes or undergrowth, often open and unconcealed; practically a trough-like depression in which sitting bird faces the water. *Eggs:* 2; about 3.50 by 2.25 in.; elongated, pointed; varying from olive-green to dark olive-brown, spotted with dark brown and blackish and occasionally with lighter spots of drab. *Dates:* June 2 to August 10, Maine and New Hampshire. *Incubation:* Period close to 29 days (O. W. Knight); 29 days (Burns). One brood yearly.

RANGE. — Northern part of Northern Hemisphere, chiefly North America. Breeds in America from Arctic coasts and islands south to western Washington, northeastern California, northern Iowa, northeastern Indiana, northern Ohio (formerly), northeastern Illinois, Pennsylvania (casually), northern New York, Connecticut (casually) and Massachusetts (rarely); recorded in summer (not breeding) in southern California, Mississippi, North Carolina, South Carolina, New Jersey, New York and Massachusetts; also from Outer Hebrides, Shetlands and coast of Norway; winters mainly in United States and in western Europe; in United States from Great Lakes and Maine (Nova Scotia casually) to Florida and Gulf coast and from British Columbia to Lower California; in Europe from British Isles south to Azores, Madeira, Mediterranean and Black Sea.

DISTRIBUTION IN NEW ENGLAND. — Summer resident in northern New England; resident on Maine and New Hampshire coast; rare in summer in southern parts of Maine, New Hampshire and Vermont and very rare at that season in Massachusetts, Rhode Island and Connecticut; not uncommon fall and spring migrant generally; abundant migrant along New England coast where more or less common all winter; less common transient in interior.

SEASON IN MASSACHUSETTS. — September 1 to June 11; casual in summer; breeds very rarely and locally. Young loons with their parents are reported now and then in summer on our coast. Recent reports are of a pair of half-grown flappers with parents seen by Winthrop Packard, July 27, 1921, in Buzzards Bay off the Falmouth shore; and two young with parents reported by Harry V. Long, June 21, 1922, at Cohasset.

HAUNTS AND HABITS. The Loon is a wonderful, powerful, living mechanism fashioned for riding the stormy seas. See him as he mounts high above the waves, neck and legs fully extended "fore and aft," and bill a trifle raised which gives to his whole form a slight upward bend, his wings beating powerfully and moving as steadily as the walking-beam of a side-wheel steamship. He is driving straight ahead into the teeth of the gale and making greater headway than the laboring steamer that steers a parallel course. Now he slants downward, and striking just beyond the top of a towering wave shoots down its inclined surface and rises again on the coming crest. Here, midway of the wide bay where the seas are running high and wildly tossing their white tops, with a wintry gale whipping the spray from them in smoky gusts, the Loon rests at ease, head to the wind and sea like a ship at anchor. The tossing and the tumult disturb him not, as he rides, light as a birch canoe, turning up his white breast now and then on one side as he reaches unconcernedly backward to preen his feathers. His neck narrows at the water-line into a beautifully modeled cutwater. His broad paddles push his white breast to the tops of the great waves, where it parts the foam as he surmounts the crests and glides easily down into the gulfs beyond. The freezing spray that loads the fishing fleet with tons of ice seems never to cling to his tough and glossy plumage; or if it does, he washes it off among the fleeing fishes away down in the warmer currents near the bottom of the bay.

Often toward nightfall I have heard his wild storm-call far out to windward against the black pall of an approaching tempest like the howl of a lone wolf coming down the wind; and have seen his white breast rise on a wave against the black sky to vanish again like the arm of a swimmer lost in the stormy sea. Sailors, hearing the call, say that the loons are trying to blow up an "easterly." At times his cries seem wailing and sad as if he were bemoaning his exile from his forest lake. Such is the Loon in his winter home off our coast; for there he lives and braves the inclemency of the season. Of all the wild creatures that persist in New England, the Loon seems best to typify the stark wildness of primeval nature.

No doubt the bird once bred in most of the ponds in the northern tier of states. Now its breeding places in the United States are comparatively few. Fifty years ago it nested about many ponds in Massachusetts. Now I know of none where a breeding pair may be surely found. Rarely we hear of young Loons raised in our state, but in the nesting season most of our inland waters know the birds no more. They were "shot out" at a great expenditure of powder and lead or driven out by continual persecution. They died hard; but they are gone, perhaps never to return.

In the breeding season Loons love the solitude of northern lakes where shores are shaded by fir and spruce and where the still pure water seldom mirrors a human face. Islands in quiet lakes are the favorite breeding-grounds of this species, and there in June or July the young are hatched. These take to the water soon after they leave the eggs. They swim readily, using their feet alternately or both together, and soon learn to dive well and to remain for some time under water.

During his courtship the male frequently rushes about on the water, actually running almost upright upon the surface, with open bill and closed wings. He sometimes assumes a similar position and makes the same rushes when the young are threatened by his greatest enemy, man.[1]

There seems to be a belief among some ornithologists that Loons rarely if ever use their wings in swimming under water. They have been seen to swim in tanks and in shallow weedy waters with their wings closed, but one who has witnessed the speed with which Loons travel long distances beneath the surface in deep and unobstructed waters will find it hard to believe that such rapid progress can be made by the use of the feet alone. A submerged Loon which I followed in a boat propelled by two rowers in the shallows of the Banana River, Florida, and which apparently could not use its wings to get up speed because of the shallowness of the water and the weedy growth on the bottom, was so slow that the boat kept pace with it, and its progress was easily watched. A Loon in deep water where it could use both wings and feet has been known to outspeed an ordinary motor-boat. Loons are hardy deep divers and are said to have been taken in fish-nets 60 feet below the surface. Professor Collett, as quoted by Mr. Bent, says that a Yellow-billed Loon was taken on a hook laid at a depth of almost 15 fathoms (90 feet). Ordinarily it is impossible to observe a Loon in deep water, but occasionally under favorable conditions for observation they have been seen to use the wings. Dr. Coues had an excellent opportunity to watch some Pacific Loons (*Gavia pacifica*) at the Bay of San Pedro on the coast of southern California in 1865 where, as they had been little hunted, he had no difficulty in securing all the specimens that he desired. He says that they were tamer than any other waterfowl that he had ever seen. They came up to the wharves and

---

[1] For detailed account of nesting and some other habits of Loon see article by Robert J. Sim, Bird-Lore, Vol. XXV, 1923, pp. 167–175.

played about as unconcernedly as domestic ducks. They swam constantly all about vessels in the harbor and as the water was exceedingly clear their under-water activities could be plainly seen. Coues says "I could follow their course under water; see them shoot with marvelous swiftness through the limpid element, as urged by powerful strokes of the webbed feet and beats of the half-opened wings, they flew rather than swam." He saw them catch fish and even noted the bubbles of air clinging like sparkling jewels to their plumage.[1] Dr. Coues gives the impression that these Loons habitually used both wings and feet in their swift under-water flight. These birds evidently were not frightened or hurried in the least by any human agency, as Dr. Coues says elsewhere that from the stern of a steamer anchored in the quiet and transparent water of the harbor of San Pedro, southern California, he once watched the movements of some Loons which were playing about the vessel without alarm of any kind. As they swam and dived he traced them under water. They appeared to swim in every direction, using wings and feet, and actually flew through the water, as in aërial flight. They seemed to change course by their feet, and propel by means of the wings.[2]

Dr. T. S. Palmer, of the United States Biological Survey, tells me that his observations on this species confirm those of Dr. Coues regarding use of wings, but in his case the birds were frightened as they were pursued by people in boats. Mr. C. Wm. Beebe, who has had exceptional opportunities to observe Loons in tanks, wrote to Dr. C. W. Townsend that Grebes and Loons use their wings in times of emergency to turn quickly or "to get up a burst of speed." If they use them for this purpose in the confined space of a tank, how much more must they use them when speed and quick turning are necessary in diving in very deep water or while pursuing their prey or escaping from their enemies. Mr. William Brewster told Dr. Townsend that Loons in diving under boats to avoid being hemmed in, or in hurrying from their nests, use their wings as well as their feet, and Mr. F. H. Allen says that young Loons use both wings and feet in diving.[3] Mr. A. C. Bent writes: "When wishing to indulge in an unusual burst of speed it uses both feet and wings with marvelous effect, but ordinarily I believe that the wings are not used."

I have reports from twenty-four naturalists who have seen Loons use their wings alone or both wings and feet under water at varying speeds and for different purposes.

Holbœll asserted that the Loon had been observed to remain under water for eight minutes but this hardly seems probable.

Although the Loon is graceful and swift on or in the water, it is at a disadvantage on land. It has been asserted that it cannot under any circumstances rise in the air from the land nor from the water unless aided by a head wind, and that it must have more room than can be furnished by a small pool, and even then it seems obliged to flutter and run spatteringly along the surface for some distance to get impetus enough to rise in the air. When the young are well grown, the family, often joined by some neighboring adults,

---

[1] Coues, Elliott: Birds of the Northwest, 1874, p. 723.   [2] Coues, Elliott: Forest and Stream, Vol. I, 1873, p. 149.
[3] Townsend, C. W.: Auk, Vol. XXVI, 1909, p. 235.

frolic for a brief time on the water and then fall into line side by side, and, lifting their wings simultaneously, run an apparent foot race over the surface with "incredible speed" for a quarter of a mile, and turning race back to the starting-point. They repeat this over and over again. During these races the wings are held out and about half opened. At the end of the performance the male, female and neighbors leave for other fishing grounds and the young scatter to find food. This play evidently tends to train the muscles of the young birds and to fit them for flight. Such races are rather rarely seen along our coast.

The ordinary, steady, level flight of the Loon is familiar to all who know the bird, but under favorable conditions it can soar or circle with set wings. Mr. Robert J. Sim, who has spent much time watching Loons on their breeding-grounds, says that in flight their feet are carried well back of the tail and well spread, with the outer toe of each foot highest. As seen from behind, the position of the feet may be shown thus.

Often a Loon will sleep on the water by rolling on its side, tucking its bill under its scapulars, stowing one foot under the feathers of the flank and automatically paddling with the other. On our coasts Loons rarely are seen on land unless wounded, but Audubon satisfied himself that on their breeding-grounds they spend the night on shore. I once saw at nightfall a pair resting on the beach of an isolated island in British Columbia. Mr. Bent says that "when it is safe to do so they often come ashore to sleep" and that he has several times surprised a single bird well up on a beach "where it had been spending the night or had gone ashore to dry and sand its plumage." The attempts of such a bird to regain the water were more rapid than graceful, as it often fell on its breast as it scrambled down the beach, humping its back, darting its head and neck about and straining every muscle to make speed, with rather surprising success. It is quite generally asserted that Loons cannot walk well on land. In fact the name Loon is understood to be derived from the old English word "lumme," a lummox, an awkward person. Though ungraceful on land by reason of its hidebound legs and the peculiar position of its feet, the Loon can make remarkable speed for short distances when racing toward water. It uses its wings in place of fore legs and so flaps and scrambles along. I have seen Loons on land go off into the water "like a flash" and Dr. Nelson mentions a case in which he was unable to overtake an unwounded Black-throated Loon on land.[1]

Mr. Aaron C. Bagg, who pursued a Loon on the beach, says that its locomotion was accomplished partly by the feet and partly by the wings, which were not flapped as in flight but used like a pair of crutches. Sometimes the bill also was used "like a pick" to keep the balance.

When the ice begins to break up in the spring, the migration of the Loons begins. They follow close to melting ice, and late in April begin to appear in the Maine lakes. All through this month small flights of Loons pass from time to time up the New England coast; but the great migration to the Arctic regions comes from about the 15th to the 30th of May and sometimes a few migrants are moving until after June 1st. Usually they

[1] Nelson, E. W.: Report upon the Natural History Collections Made in Alaska between the Years 1877 and 1881, 1887, p. 37.

fly with the bill closed, but sometimes on warm days a bird may be seen with its bill wide open as if for air. The great days of the loon-flight are usually warm with southwesterly winds. Then the birds fly low and fast. Morning and night they come. Passing Long Island they go to the southward of Narragansett Bay and come up Buzzards Bay, crossing Cape Cod near the Canal and so on into Cape Cod Bay where they lay a course for the Bay of Fundy. Another flight keeps well out to sea and goes north outside Cape Cod, passing eastward of Truro and Provincetown, bound apparently for Nova Scotia, Newfoundland and Baffin Bay. Their low flight on a southwest wind is very noticeable. When the wind comes from another quarter, they are likely to fly very high and so attract less notice.

A strong, swift, submarine diver, the Loon glides or flies at will far down the depths where it pursues its prey. Often little fish are swallowed under water. Mr. J. A. Mackenzie watched a Loon take 6 minnows out of a school before coming to the surface.[1] The Loon brings the larger and stronger fish to the surface and mauls them there. If such a fish escapes, the bird dives in pursuit and soon overtakes its prey.

Along the shores of the Atlantic the Loon is believed to feed chiefly on fish. It feeds to some extent on crabs and mollusks, and also on frogs, leeches, aquatic insects and water plants. Dr. P. L. Hatch says that Loons can do without fish and frogs when supplied with aquatic vegetation, and both Audubon and Dr. B. H. Warren note that they found such food in Loons' stomachs. Mr. E. O. Grant writes that he dissected a Loon in Maine that had only "grass or weeds" in its stomach.

It is difficult to see how a Loon manages to swallow a flounder "as wide as a man's hand," but they catch and eat such fish. Mr. George H. Mackay on April 18, 1890, on West Island, Sakonnet Point, Rhode Island, saw a Loon preparing to swallow a flounder. The fish, he says, was about 5 inches in diameter. The Loon dropped it on the water, pecked it and bit it. When the fish escaped the bird dived after it and thus kept at it for fully five minutes; then stretching up his head with the bill pointing toward the sky, swallowed it. Mr. Mackay says he could hardly have believed this possible had he not seen it.

Mr. Sydney Chase, of Nantucket, writes that on May 3, 1922, he watched a Loon, perhaps 100 yards off shore. The bird went down and stayed under as a rule about 40 seconds, but once was under water about a minute and came up with a flounder that Mr. Chase asserts must have been at least four inches across, and possibly six. The bird took the fish by the head with his bill and kept biting it, evidently trying to crush and kill it, and he finally succeeded by shutting his bill together on its head. Then he easily swallowed the fish head foremost, took a little water in his mouth, rinsed it, shook his head and dived again.

I have watched Loons to see how they could so reduce flounders as to swallow them. On March 11, 1922, in Nantucket Harbor, I saw a Loon swallow two within half an hour. One of them appeared to be rather more than four inches in diameter. Both fish seemed

---

[1] *Recreation*, Vol. VIII, 1898, p. 283.

to be dead when brought to the surface as they did not struggle. It would be interesting to know how the bird killed them under water. The Loon worked a long time with the flounder in its bill, apparently crushing it, possibly to contract it; finally the fish was swallowed with apparent ease. As it went down the Loon's gullet, it seemed to be reduced in width at least one-third. Whether this was done by crushing the fish with the bill and rolling it against the breast or was accomplished in the process of swallowing, I could not determine. Fishermen say that the Loon "rolls the fish up."

Crabs are bitten and broken in preparation for eating and their legs are often discarded. At low tide the Loon sometimes will feed on tide flats in shallow water like a goose by merely dipping its head and neck under water.

I find no very convincing evidence that Loons kill and eat other birds. Roderick Macfarlane says that an Eskimo of his party saw a Pacific Eider struck and killed on the wing by a Yellow-billed Loon.[1] Dr. Townsend in his excellent history of the birds of Essex County tells of a Loon that chased a flock of young mergansers, the Loon swimming under water while the mergansers flapped along on the surface until they gained the shore while the "disappointed Loon" swam about outside.[2]

The late George O. Welch claimed to have the best of evidence that Loons killed and ate birds up to the size of a duck, but I have not seen any published notes from him on the subject.

A writer in Forest and Stream contributes the following: "The loons, or some of them, seem to be very hostile to ducks. I have witnessed some encounters between them. In one case, when a duck and her family were sailing quietly along, I saw them make a mad rush, the old one calling loudly, when suddenly out of the water rose a large loon and attacked them with great fury, churning the water into foam with his wings in the pursuit. He seemed to me to secure one of the young ducks, with which he disappeared under the water. At another time I witnessed a contest between a loon and an old duck — the latter defending her young apparently. In each of these cases the loon was concealed under the water, and rose suddenly from it to the attack."[3] H. J. LaDue records the attack of a Loon on a Coot.[4] Evermann and Clark assert that a "good observer" at Lake Maxinkuckee states that he saw a Loon chase, capture and devour a "helldiver."[5]

ECONOMIC STATUS. See page 16.

NOTE. Dr. Louis B. Bishop describes a supposed new race of the loon, to which he gives the name of Lesser Black-billed Loon, *Gavia immer elasson*. If this form is recognized by ornithologists, the Loon will necessarily become *Gavia immer immer*. A male of the proposed race taken at Concord, Massachusetts (without date) was found in the collection of William Brewster. The only subspecific differ-

[1] Mair, Charles: Through the Mackenzie Basin, 1908, p. 295.
[2] Townsend, C. W.: Memoirs of the Nuttall Ornithological Club, No. III, The Birds of Essex County, Massachusetts, 1905, p. 80.
[3] Forest and Stream, Vol. LIII, 1899, pp. 84, 85.
[4] Bird-Lore, Vol. XXI, 1919, p. 358.
[5] Evermann, Barton Warren, and Clark, Howard Walton: Lake Maxinkuckee. A Physical and Biological Survey, State of Indiana. Department of Conservation, Publication No. 7, Vol. I, 1920, p. 492.

ence discovered by Dr. Bishop is that of size, the new race being the smaller. Dr. Bishop's careful measurements, together with the range of this race as far as known, are given in The Auk, Vol. 38, 1921, pages 364 to 370. Some of the comparative measurements given by him in millimeters and here reduced to inches follow:

G. immer

	FOLDED WING	TAIL	EXPOSED CULMEN	DEPTH OF BILL AT BASE	TARSUS	OUTER TOE WITH NAIL
Largest male	16.00	4.00	3.71	1.15	3.82	5.75
Smallest female . . .	13.75	3.23	2.95	.88	3.22	4.45

G. elasson

	FOLDED WING	TAIL	EXPOSED CULMEN	DEPTH OF BILL AT BASE	TARSUS	OUTER TOE WITH NAIL
Largest male	14.64	3.40	3.35	.99	3.59	4.77
Smallest female . . .	13.12	2.78	2.69	.83	3.05	4.20

Length and Spread

	LENGTH		SPREAD	
	Immer	Elasson	Immer	Elasson
Largest	34.12	30.98	58.25	54.00
Smallest	32.00	28.18	54.37	50.81

NOTE. **Gavia árctica** (LINNÆUS). **Black-throated Loon.**

Mr. A. C. Bent in his Life History of North American Diving Birds (Bulletin No. 107, Smithsonian Institution, United States National Museum), says that he has no reason for including the life history of the European Black-throated Loon in that work.

This bird has been reported or recorded several times in New England and also in other parts of eastern North America, but Mr. F. Seymour Hersey (Auk, Vol. XXXIV, 1917, p. 283) shows that all available specimens now extant must be referred either to the Pacific Loon or to the common Loon — except three casual Alaskan specimens of *arctica*, supposed to be of an Asiatic form. Apparently there is no authentic specimen of *Gavia arctica* to be found in North America. Therefore the Pacific Loon, which is a loon with a *black throat*, but not *the* Black-throated Loon, appears to be the only "black-throated loon" that has any status as a bird of New England.

Apparently those authors (of which unfortunately I am one) and collectors who have assigned *Gavia arctica* to a place among the birds of New England have been either mistaken in the identity of the specimens or have unquestioningly followed the lead of others. Such a mistake is not to be wondered at, as the two forms closely resemble each other and probably intergrade. It is possible that *arctica* may yet be found here, but thus far there is no authentic record.

Gavia pacífica (Lawrence). Pacific Loon.

DESCRIPTION. — Smaller than Loon; like Black-throated Loon but smaller; paler gray on hind-head and neck; also white streaks on sides of neck less prominent (because of gray background instead of black as in Black-throated Loon); bill shorter, and smaller. *Adults in breeding plumage (sexes alike)*: Chin, throat and front of neck black or purplish-black, shading gradually through bronzy-greenish reflections on sides of head into *"very pale smoky grayish"* (sometimes nearly white) on top of head and back of head and neck, much darker on forehead, growing lighter behind, separated on sides of neck from black on fore neck by a series of white streaks *on a dark gray background;* a crescentic bar of short white streaks across throat; sides of lower neck and upper breast streaked narrowly black and white (in some individuals shorter streaks which nearly meet in front); upper surface of body glossy greenish-black or bluish-black, each feather of scapulars and of sides of upper back with two white angular spots near tip — one on each web (in some cases coalesced); these spots arranged in cross rows, largest on scapulars; wing-coverts black and (except primary coverts and feathers on edge of wing) dotted with small ovate white spots; flight-feathers black, their inner webs and under side of tail glossy grayish-brown; tail brownish-black above; sides and flanks glossy black; a blackish line across vent; rest of under plumage white except a part of under tail-coverts which are blackish-brown tipped white and ax-illars which are streaked centrally blackish. *Adults in winter plumage:* Whole top of head and back of neck to near base, dark brown tinged grayish; rest of upper plumage slightly glossy blackish-brown sometimes margined darker (in certain individuals some scapulars with pair each of small, sub-terminal, whitish spots); wing-coverts brown; flight-feathers with glossy brownish-black outer webs and tips, dark brown shafts, pale brown inner webs; tail-feathers black, white-tipped; below white; under tail-coverts as in summer; white on sides of head extending from base of lower mandible back under eye to sides of nape, slightly mottled where white and grayish-brown meet; usually a narrow line of brown across upper throat; feathers on sides of breast next to dark brown of upper plumage have brown shaft-streaks; flanks dark brown; feathers next to under plumage have outer webs mostly white; a narrow (usually incomplete) dark brown line across vent; *axillars* white, sometimes with dark brown shafts and terminal shaft-streaks; under wing-coverts white, posterior ones with pale brown central streaks. *Young in first winter and succeeding summer plumage:* A mixture of feathers of juvenal plumage and adult winter plumage; feathers of back show both blackish (adult) and ashy-edged (juvenal) feathers; neck-stripes may begin to show. *Young in juvenal plumage:* Top of head and back of neck like adult winter but more brown, less gray; rest of upper plumage dark brown, feathers with broad, ashy-gray margins, giving bird a scaled appearance, most conspicuous on upper back and scapulars, less so on hinder plumage; sides of neck next white of throat more finely mottled brown than in adults, mottling sometimes extending across neck and on throat; prominent brown line across vent; posterior under tail-coverts dark brown with narrow white tips; wing-feathers and primary coverts as adult but all wing-coverts tipped grayish-brown or ashy; gray tips of upper plumage and white tips of tail wear off considerably by January; "iris brown; bill bluish, culmen dusky; feet blackish on outer and livid-blue on inner surface" (Allan Brooks). *Downy young:* Seal-brown on back, lightening on sides, head and neck; breast and belly paler, becoming light drab and gradually paling when second down is assumed.

MEASUREMENTS. — Length about 24.00 in.; spread 40.00 or less; folded wing 11.00 to 12.25; tail 2.05 to 2.40; length of bill 1.90 to 2.35; height of bill at nostrils .50 or less; tarsus about 2.50.

MOLTS. — From early winter into summer the young seem to be molting more or less, gradually assuming winter plumage of adult but apparently not getting full adult winter plumage until second winter, after a complete autumnal molt (some may require another year); adults have a complete prenuptial and a complete postnuptial molt.

FIELD MARKS. — In breeding plumage *light* gray or whitish top of head and hind neck distinguish this species from Loon, and black throat from Red-throated Loon; indistinguishable in winter from any Loon, in field, but much smaller than *Gavia immer*.

VOICE. — "A peculiar harsh cry *kok, kok, kok*" (J. Murdoch); a loud, weird, prolonged shrill scream (R. Macfarlane).

BREEDING. — About deep water lakes; also swamps and sloughs in Arctic tundra; near water on Barren Grounds or in wooded regions of interior. *Nest:* Sometimes merely bare ground; sometimes a small heap of vegetation close to water. *Eggs:* 1 or 2; in size between those of common Loon and those of Red-throated Loon; "usually elliptical ovate"; greenish-olive to dark umber with blackish blotches or spots. *Dates:* June 8 to July 23, Alaska and Northwest Territory. *Incubation:* Period probably about 28 days; probably by both sexes.

RANGE. — North America and Pacific coast of Asia. Breeds from Bering Sea, northwestern Alaska, Banks Island and Melville Peninsula south to central British Columbia, southern Mackenzie, northeastern Manitoba and southeastern Hudson Bay (mouth of James Bay); also in northeastern Siberia and probably from Aleutian and Near islands along Pacific coast of Asia to Japan; winters mainly along Pacific coast south to southern Lower California; casual in Guadaloupe Island, Arizona, New Mexico, Iowa, New York and New Hampshire.

DISTRIBUTION IN NEW ENGLAND. — One record. *New Hampshire:* Specimen (unsexed, full spring plumage) shot in May, 1910, at Hampton Beach by S. A. Shaw and now in mounted collection of Boston Society of Natural History.

HAUNTS AND HABITS. Probably the Pacific Loon is the only Black-throated Loon that has been taken in New England. We have but one authentic record of its occurrence which can be substantiated by a specimen. It is quite possible, however, that other individuals of this race may appear here, as the bird is known to breed, casually at least, near James Bay. In winter plumage it is only by a careful examination of the specimen in hand that this species (though smaller) can be distinguished from the Loon. It frequents the same waters as the Loon. Nothing is recorded of its habits in New England. In general they seem to be similar to those of the common Loon.

The bird subsists largely on fish and takes some frogs. It breeds mostly about fresh water lakes and goes to salt water largely in winter.

NOTE. European systematists now separate the Black-throated Loon into four forms: one (*Colymbus arcticus arcticus*) in Europe and eastern Asia; another (*C. a. suschkini*) in Western Siberia; the third (*C. a. virdigularis*) in Eastern Siberia; and the fourth (*C. a. pacificus*), the Pacific Loon, which is the form most likely to occur in New England.

Gavia stelláta (Pontoppidan). Red-throated Loon.

Other names: RED-THROATED DIVER; CAPE DRAKE; CAPE RACE; CAPE RACER; SCAPEGRACE; LITTLE LOON; SPRAT LOON; PEGGING AWL LOON; PEPPER-SHINNED LOON; TUTCHMUNK.

Plate 2.

DESCRIPTION. — Bill varies much in size and shape but usually slender, concave at nostrils and gently convex at tip. *Adults in breeding plumage (sexes alike)*: Crown, nape, back of neck and sides of lower neck glossy greenish-black, three latter streaked narrowly white; white streaks extend so as to nearly meet in front of breast; fore neck with long triangular patch of bright chestnut; rest of head and neck clear, bluish-gray; prevailing color elsewhere above, also sides under wings, brownish-black; all with greenish gloss and thickly marked with *small oval white spots;* primaries blackish, paler on inner webs; below (including lining of wings) white; axillars with narrow dusky shaft-streaks; tail narrowly tipped white; bill blackish, a little lighter at tip; iris red; feet colored like those of the common Loon. *Adults and immature in winter plumage:* Similar to common Loon, but crown and back of neck bluish-gray, feathers of former bordered whitish; upper plumage marked with small oval spots of white, and throat pure white. *Young in first winter plumage:* Birds of the first year similar to winter adults but have V-shaped white spots on back; throat more or less grayish or mottled; bill bluish-white, darker on ridge; iris brown. *Downy Young:* Dark brown above, shading into drab below.

MEASUREMENTS. — Length 24 to 27 in.; spread about 44.00; folded wing 10.00 to 11.50; tail 1.73 to 2.06; bill 2.00 to 2.25; tarsus about 2.75.

NOTE. This bird varies much in size, shape and markings. Some summer adults have very few spots on back; some first year birds have many diamond-shaped or V-shaped markings and are more spotted than adults.

MOLTS. — In juvenal plumage head and neck are mottled with "mouse gray" and dirty white; upper parts dusky, mottled on back with light grayish spots or V-shaped marks; a partial postjuvenal molt apparently takes place in late winter and early spring which gives head and neck more resemblance to that of adult, but throat-patch is lighter and duller and much restricted; at first postnuptial molt in second autumn bird assumes adult winter plumage, and with second prenuptial molt in spring of third season it takes on adult nuptial plumage; adults apparently have a complete prenuptial molt and a complete postnuptial molt.

FIELD MARKS. — Smaller than Loon; seen here rarely in May in full nuptial plumage which is unmistakable; in autumn or winter, at close range, with a good glass, distinguishing white spots may be seen on upper plumage where the Loon has only light edgings; toward spring some examples of Common Loon may show scattering white spots, but surest distinction is rather slender bill often slightly upturned (or concave at nostrils) which can be noted at longer range than spots; however, bill varies in size and shape and often the two species are indistinguishable at a distance unless close together.

VOICE. — The bird seems rather silent with us in winter but more vocal toward spring and very noisy on its breeding grounds. Russians have named it Gegara from its note, a harsh *gr-r-ga gr-r, gr-r ga, gr-r, ga* (E. W. Nelson); a goose-like honking cry, also a variety of weird loud cries similar to those of common Loon (A. C. Bent); ordinary call note *ak ak* (H. Seebohm).

BREEDING. — About (or in) lakes or ponds, sometimes in small shallow pools. *Nest:* Like the Loon, it sometimes makes no nest other than a mere hollow in sand or mud on some island. Sometimes a nest is built of vegetation, lined with straws and even a few feathers, always near water, sometimes in it where shallow. *Eggs:* 2; variable in size, about 3.00 by 1.75 in.; vary from bister or sepia in darkest eggs to deep olive-buff; some nearly spotless but usually well spotted with very dark shades of brown and underlying spots of various shades of drab. *Dates:* May 10 to July 15, various parts of range; May 30 to July 5, Labrador and Hudson Bay (A. C. Bent). *Incubation:* Period 24 to 28 days (Faber); both sexes incubate (Yarrell).

RANGE. — Northern part of Northern Hemisphere. Breeds in North America from northern Alaska, Banks Island, Melville Island, Ellesmere Island, Grant Land and northern Greenland south to Commander Islands, western Aleutian Islands, Glacier Bay, Queen Charlotte and other British Columbia islands, southern Mackenzie, northern Manitoba, south-central Quebec, New Brunswick and Newfoundland; winters in North America principally along Pacific and Atlantic coasts, in Aleutian Islands and southern British Columbia to southern California, and from Maine and Great Lakes to Florida; recorded casually in interior in eastern North America as far south as Missouri; a few birds summer locally in northern United States; breeds also in northern Europe and Asia and winters south to Mediterranean and southern China.

DISTRIBUTION IN NEW ENGLAND. — Migrant and winter resident, coastwise mainly; rare in interior; occasionally reported in summer in Maine but "does not breed" (O. W. Knight).

SEASON IN MASSACHUSETTS. — As in New England, winter resident coastwise; common transient visitor in autumn; less common in late winter and spring; August 27 to May 30 (July 2).

HAUNTS AND HABITS. The Red-throated Loon commonly appears in considerable numbers on our coast in late September or October but is rarely recorded in ponds or streams of the interior. Some individuals of this species winter along the New England coast. In spring the larger number either go north through the interior or else pass far out to sea as the species is much less common here in spring than in autumn. Like the common Loon it begins moving northward along our coast in March and some are still passing in May. In habits and appearance the bird is much like the common Loon while with us but it differs in one respect; it can rise readily and fly from even a small pool, springing into the air with little difficulty, even without the aid of a breeze; although like the Loon if frozen out of a pond in winter, it seems unable to rise from the ice and thus is captured or starved. Like the Loon, also, it uses its wings under water when necessary to increase its speed.

Dr. George Suckley noted carefully the subsurface motions of one of this species which was attempting to escape out of a lagoon to the open water of the Straits of Fuca by swimming through a narrow outlet. Although slightly wounded it moved so fast that he was obliged to run as rapidly as possible to keep up with it. As the water was clear and shallow, he was able to watch its motions. The neck was fully extended, and the bird used the wings as in flying in addition to the ordinary motions of the feet. "Indeed," he wrote, "the bird was flying through water instead of air." [1]

Mr. A. C. Bent gives the following interesting account of these Loons in the autumnal migration:

"The migration along the New England coast is mainly in October accompanying the main flight of the scoters. After leaving the fresh-water lakes of their summer homes they resort to the seacoast for migration and seem to prefer to spend the fall and winter on salt water. When traveling they fly at a great height and in a direct course along the shore, a mile or two out from land; they usually fly singly, although often several are in sight at one time, widely scattered. There is, however, some sociability among them, most noticeable on foggy days, when they manage to keep in touch with

[1] Suckley, George, and Cooper, James Graham: The Natural History of Washington Territory and Oregon, 1860, p. 280.

each other by frequent interchange of call notes, as if helping each other to maintain the same general line of flight. They are even somewhat gregarious at times, gathering in small parties on the water to rest and calling to their passing companions; these gatherings are sometimes quite noisy, and are well known to gunners as 'Loon caucuses.'" [1]

This species while with us seems to feed mainly on fish. Its food so far as known is similar to that of the common Loon, but Mr. Bent says that it takes fish-spawn also.

ECONOMIC STATUS. See page 16.

FAMILY **ALCIDÆ**. AUKS, MURRES AND PUFFINS.

Number of species in North America 21 ; in Massachusetts 6.

Birds of this family, like other *Pygopodes*, have the legs attached to the rear end of the body, but seem to stand a little higher in the scale of evolution than the grebes and loons. They are not so highly specialized for swimming with the hind limbs, which are not provided with an extension or apophysis of the tibia beyond the knee-joint, such as in loons and grebes appears to add muscular power to the legs. The feet are webbed and three-toed (hind toe wanting). Birds of this family habitually use their wings in swimming under water. All species stand or sit more or less upright, and most of them walk badly owing to the posterior position of the legs. Most of them in sitting or walking rest more or less on the tarsi, but some can stand upright on their toes. The tail is perfect, of 12 to 16 feathers (18 rarely). The bill varies much — from a shape somewhat similar to those of loons or grebes, as in murres, to curious forms with ridges, furrows and deciduous horny protuberances, as in puffins. Head completely feathered; nostrils feathered or naked. All species are altricial, as the young ordinarily remain on land, and are fed by the parents until quite well grown or able to fly. All members of the family are normally marine, though they sometimes reach the interior in migration when their favorite northern salt waters are covered with ice.

The family reaches its highest development in the North Pacific, where the greatest numbers of genera and species are found. A few species are still abundant in parts of the North Atlantic. The family is divided into four subfamilies according to feathering of nostrils, shape and structure of bill, and other characters.

ECONOMIC STATUS. No exhaustive investigation of the food of auks, murres and puffins has been made. They have little economic importance on the coast of New England.

SUBFAMILY **FRATERCULINÆ**. PUFFINS.

Number of species in North America 3 ; in Massachusetts 1.

This group with one exception is confined to North Pacific and Polar waters; nostrils a mere slit, naked and remote from feathers; bill large, flattened, much higher than wide

---

[1] Bent, A. C.: Life Histories of North American Diving Birds, Smithsonian Institution, United States National Museum, Bulletin No. 107, 1919, p. 79.

PLATE 3

PLATE 3

BLACK GUILLEMOT
Page 35
Young in First
Winter Plumage

Adult in
Breeding Plumage

PUFFIN
Page 31
Adult in Breeding Plumage

Adult in Winter Plumage

RAZOR–BILLED AUK
Page 43
Adult in Winter Plumage

BRÜNNICH'S MURRE
Page 40
Adult in Winter Plumage

DOVEKIE
Page 46
Winter Plumage

All one-fourth natural size.

and supplied in breeding season with a number of deciduous plates, which increase its size, but which drop off later; rosette at angle of mouth; inner claw enlarged and considerably curved.

Fratércula árctica arctica (LINNÆUS). Puffin.

Other names: SEA-PARROT; PAROQUET.

Plate 3.

DESCRIPTION. — Tail of 16 feathers; a grotesque bill nearly as long as head and about as high as long, much compressed laterally and ornamented with highly-colored, deciduous, horny plates. *Adults in nuptial plumage (sexes alike)*: Crown grayish-black or brownish-black, usually separated by a narrow, gray, cervical line from glossy black of other upper plumage; chin, throat, face and sides of head mainly light ashy, nearly white before eye; color sharply defined against dark crown and neck; dark ashy patch on each side of throat; above from head backward, brownish-black to clear black, continuous with a broad band of same color around neck under throat; below from neck white; under surface of wings pearly-gray; upright, conical, bluish, horny appendage on upper eyelid, horizontal one on lower; naked edges of eyelids vermilion; iris light grayish-blue or "bluish-black" (C. W. Townsend); base of bill and first ridge dull yellowish, next section grayish-blue, end section vermilion; tip of lower mandible and two terminal grooves often dull yellowish; rosette at angle of mouth orange; mouth and tongue light yellow; feet red. *Adults in winter plumage:* Similar; face dusky or blackish; cheeks and throat dark gray; no bright colors nor appendages on eyelids; rosette shrunken and pale; highly colored, *deciduous parts of bill have been shed leaving it smaller, darker and more contracted at base*, but still more or less red toward tip; feet orange or yellow. *Young in first winter plumage:* Much like winter adult, but bill less developed, smaller, weaker, more pointed; above glossy brownish-black; below white; iris hazel; feet pale olive. *Downy young:* Above dark sooty "brown with drab shadings"; color varies in intensity in different specimens; middle of belly white, sometimes tinged light gray or yellowish; bill much smaller in proportion than in adult, not so convex.

MEASUREMENTS. — Length 11.50 to 13.50 in.; spread 21.00 to 24.00; folded wing 6.50 to 7.50; tail 2.25 to 2.87; bill 1.60 to 1.90; arc of ridge about 2.10; tarsus 1.00 to 1.50. Female averages smaller than male.

MOLTS. — Apparently young birds retain first winter plumage through the next spring and later molt into winter plumage indistinguishable from that of adult. Adults have either a limited or complete prenuptial molt in spring and a partial or complete postnuptial molt in autumn.

FIELD MARKS. — Adults at close range are unmistakable; in autumn a young puffin with undeveloped bill might be mistaken at a distance for a Razor-billed Auk or even a Brünnich's Murre; the puffin is smaller than either, floats high on water and presents a "chunky" appearance.

VOICE. — A low purring note, *purr -la-la-la* (C. W. Townsend); deep-throated mirthless laughter (J. M. Boraston); a long, deep, slowly rising *awe* (E. Selous); "a hoarse grunt or groan" (F. M. Chapman).

BREEDING. — Usually on sea-islands and in colonies. *Nest:* Usually a burrow in soil, sometimes under rock or in crevice. *Eggs:* 1, sometimes 2; average about 2.50 by 1.75 in.; rounded ovate; granular; dull white, occasionally marked with indistinct spots, dots and scratches of pale purplish, sometimes with splashes of pale yellowish-brown or concealed chocolate; usually stained with earth. *Dates:* June 6 to July 27, Gulf of St. Lawrence and Maine. *Incubation:* Period 1 month (T. M. Brewer); 36 days (in incubator); both sexes incubate. One brood yearly.

RANGE. — Coasts and islands of North Atlantic. Breeds in North America from southern Greenland (casually northern Greenland) and Ungava Bay south to Nova Scotia, Bay of Fundy and eastern Maine, and in Europe from Norway and British Isles south to Portugal; winters south to Massachusetts and casually to Long Island, and Delaware River, Pennsylvania, and in Europe south to coast of Morocco and casually to Azores; accidental at Ottawa (one record); recorded by Audubon from the Savannah River.

DISTRIBUTION IN NEW ENGLAND. — Breeds off coast of Maine at Machias Seal Island and summers regularly (a few) at Matinicus Rock which is the most southerly breeding-station in the United States; "though regularly present in summer, there is a question whether the birds now breed there at all or do so irregularly" (Arthur H. Norton); said to have laid eggs on Eastern Egg Rock in 1908; resident eastward from Machias Seal Island; uncommon winter resident off entire Maine coast; rare winter visitor off Massachusetts coast mainly north of Cape Cod; accidental or casual in winter off Rhode Island coast.

SEASON IN MASSACHUSETTS. — October 16 to March 19, Essex County (C. W. Townsend); Puffin found drowned in Eugene Haines' fish-trap, Sandwich, Cape Cod Bay, June 5, 1924; reported by Benjamin S. Harrison.

HAUNTS AND HABITS. "Way down east" on Machias Seal Island, off the easternmost part of the Maine coast, lies the nearest real refuge and breeding-place of the Puffin to the United States. Here where the sea dashes heavily against jagged rocks, and the wind blows the white spray high and far, the Puffin now makes its last stand near our shores.

The serio-comic appearance of the little feathered clown is laughable. The bright and handsome colors of its nuptial array are forgotten in contemplation of its peculiar and amazing appearance. Its bright little eyes seem spectacled, while its parrot-like bill like a great, highly-colored Roman nose is masked by an outer coating which is mostly shed at the end of the breeding season. The bird stands erect like a little soldier, its red splay feet slightly straddled and planted firmly on the rock, resting not on its tail and tarsi, but standing up high and clear. Add to its ludicrous clownish appearance a voice of deep, sepulchral tones "full of the deepest feeling" and capable of harsh croakings, and we have a character in feathers — a solemnly comical Mr. Punch among birds.

On the wing the Puffin buzzes about as if upon important business. It tumbles out of its hole, flies down and into the sea, flies around under water, flies out again, and here it comes back to the rocks, its great "red nose" pointing the way, its little "sabre-like" wings beating the air like a threshing-machine and its red feet spread out behind. When it comes up from the depths to find that it is being overtaken by a steamboat, it is very likely to "lose its head" and show the most comical kind of apprehension and indecision. It dips its head under water as if to dive, then raises it and tries to fly, gives this up and finally dives through a wave, comes flying out on the other side and dives again until finally it has blundered and floundered out of the way. When under water it seems to use its wings mainly for progression and its feet chiefly for steering, as it does when flying in the air.

A live Puffin in captivity is rarely seen. One such was brought, about February 1, 1922, to the Department of Agriculture, State House, Boston, from Kingston by Mr. Harold Cooke, who several days previously caught the bird about 10 P.M. in his garage during a gale. How and when the Puffin entered the garage was a mystery. Although a wild seafowl the bird seemed at home from the beginning, and apparently knew that it was among friends. It accepted food (fish, clams and *spaghetti*) readily, and allowed petting. It ran across the floor, and stood quite upright when food was held out to it. It was sent to the Boston Zoölogical Park and was kept for some time where it had access to a pool of water. The Superintendent, Mr. George F. Morse, Jr., informed me that in swimming under water the bird used its wings for propulsion, extending them quite fully to the carpal joint but holding the primaries parallel with the body. The Puffin's wings are so small that it appears to have difficulty in rising from the water, except in a breeze; but they move so fast that it can fly with great rapidity once in the air. On the surface it swims well.

Mr. Harrison F. Lewis kindly sends me the following notes on the erratic behavior of the Puffin on its breeding-grounds:

"Owing to its grotesque appearance, the Puffin is a most amusing and interesting bird to watch. At Perroquet Island, near Bradore, Canadian Labrador, I found that if I sat nearly motionless, even though fully exposed to view, Puffins at a little distance soon acted as if quite unconscious of my presence. This was during the period July 10–14, 1921, when incubation was going on. Every few minutes an incubating bird pattered out of its burrow, often apparently for no purpose but to relax its cramped muscles, obtain a breath of fresh air, and view the surroundings. After issuing from the burrow the bird usually stood up very straight, stretched itself, and fluttered its wings for a moment. One could readily imagine it yawning and complaining of the tiresomeness of incubation.

"If I walked slowly toward a Puffin perched on a rock, the bird often alternated for a considerable time between the desire to escape by flight and the desire to avoid the exertion required to get under way. It looked at the advancing human being, apparently decided that it had better depart, crouched for a spring into the air, then, at the last instant seemed to find the necessary effort too great, and relaxed to watch the intruder again. As the source of trouble continued to advance, its fears temporarily gained the ascendency over its indolence, and the performance was repeated. After several repetitions of this behavior the bird finally pitched forward into headlong, clumsy flight.

"Considerable numbers of Puffins were almost always resting on the water near Perroquet Island. I found that if I approached these slowly and quietly, by gently sculling a small rowboat, their curiosity impelled them to swim slowly toward me. When within twelve or fifteen feet of the boat, however, they were likely to be seized with fear and fly hurriedly away."

It is extremely unfortunate, to say the least, that this remarkable bird should now be in some danger of extirpation on American shores. The thousands of these birds that once bred along the coast from the Maine islands to near the Arctic Circle are largely gone — the victims of the fishermen and eggers of the United States and Canada. Let us hope that our Canadian neighbors will find some means to save the remnant of these swarming hosts, for their presence adds something to the joy of living. Puffins are now rare winter visitors to the coast of southern New England. Indeed we have no record from the Connecticut coast, and the birds are seen in Massachusetts chiefly in hard winters and mainly along the rocky shores of our northeastern county of Essex where a few are met with occasionally near Cape Ann. They are seldom seen here on shore and probably never in their nuptial plumage which they molt in August and September. At this time also they shed their primaries like many species of ducks and are unable to fly, so that if overtaken by a severe storm far at sea they are said to perish by thousands. During the autumnal molt the birds shed the coating of the bill in nine pieces, and with it go the bright colors of the nuptial season. When the wing quills have grown again, the birds migrate southward but normally keep far from land.

Dr. Charles W. Townsend in Bulletin No. 107 of the Smithsonian Institution describes the courtship of this bird as follows :

"I have watched groups of these birds off the southern coast of Labrador during the courtship season. They swim together in closely crowded ranks, rarely diving, for their thoughts are not on food. At frequent intervals individuals rise up in the water and flap their wings as if from nervousness. Again two males fight vigorously, flapping their wings meanwhile and making the water foam about them. Again two, possibly a pair, hold each other by the bills and move their heads and necks like billing doves. Now several are seen to throw their heads back with a jerk until the bill points up, and this is repeated a number of times. Edmund Selous (1905), who has watched this action near at hand in the puffins of the Shetlands, says the bill is opened wide but no sound is uttered. The brilliant lining of the mouth is therefore the result of sexual selection and it evidently forms a part of the courtship display." [1]

The Puffin usually nests in colonies. A famous one is that on Perroquet Island, visited by many ornithologists since Audubon (1840) whose description is vivid. The burrows are dug in a steep slope or bank of some island and carried inward, downward and upward for an arm's length or more. In some cases the burrow curves so that the nest is close beneath the entrance hole. The nest consists of a little dead grass with sometimes a few feathers. In reaching into a nest I have found gloves very useful, as the Puffin often is at home and will bite and scratch like a cat or as much like one as a bird can. Its claws and beak are sharp and strong.

Dr. Townsend says that the work of burrowing falls chiefly to the male, and that at times he is so intent on it that he allows himself to be caught in the hand. The claws, especially the inner, are strong, curved and sharp and thus especially adapted for digging. Dr. Townsend informs us that the young are able at the age of four or five weeks to follow their mothers to sea.

Puffins are very hardy birds and do not commonly migrate very far south of their breeding range. They appear during the latter half of October off the coast of Massachusetts in very small numbers and are believed to go northward in March. Migration dates, however, are almost wholly lacking.

Puffins feed largely on small fish and other forms of marine life. Doubtless also the

---

[1] Bent, A. C.: Smithsonian Institution, United States National Museum, Bulletin No. 107, 1919, p. 90.

powerful bill enables them to crush small crustaceans and mollusks as do the Tufted Puffins on the Pacific coast.

ECONOMIC STATUS. See page 30.

NOTE. Audubon figures and describes a Tufted Puffin (*Lunda cirrhata* (Pallas)) shot, he says, in the winter of 1831–32 by a fisherman-gunner at the mouth of the Kennebec River in Maine. No other bird of the species was seen. The skin of this bird is said to have been deposited in the Museum of Comparative Zoölogy at Harvard College. As the only specimen there that is accredited to Audubon is labeled as taken on the Pacific coast, the Audubon record for Maine may be questionable.[1] This species was recorded also by Verrill in New Brunswick. There is no record of its capture in Massachusetts. Kumlien says (Polar Expedition, 1877–78): "Off the North Labrador coast I noticed on several occasions a small auk (?) intermediate in size between *Mergulus alle* and *Uria grylle*, with much the same pattern of coloration as the former, but with tufts or plumes of white feathers on the head. I saw some with single young, and at one time killed three at a single discharge; but the ship was under such headway that the sailor stationed in the waist could not reach them with his pole and net. The bird is entirely unknown to me, but I suspect it will be found to be one of the small auks hitherto supposed to belong only to the North Pacific." [2]

Dr. J. A. Allen also reports the probable occurrence of one of the auklets on Cape Cod.[3] The bird was described to him by an intelligent and trustworthy gunner and fisherman. Dr. Allen believed it to be "apparently" a Crested Auklet (*Æthia cristatella*).

If such Pacific coast species have really been known to appear on the Atlantic coast of the Continent, there is a bare possibility that some of these Alcidæ may occur sometimes on the coast of Massachusetts. The Tufted Puffin is easily identified by its great bill and the long, streaming, yellowish tufts on each side of the head.

SUBFAMILY **ÆTHIINÆ**. AUKLETS, MURRELETS AND GUILLEMOTS.

Number of species in North America 14 ; in Massachusetts 1.

Nostrils naked or incompletely covered by feathers ; bill with or without deciduous appendages ; with or without crests ; inner claw not specialized.

Cépphus grýlle (LINNÆUS). Black Guillemot.

Other names: WHITE-WINGED GUILLEMOT; WHITE GUILLEMOT; SEA PIGEON.

Plate 3.

DESCRIPTION. — Bill straight, sharp-pointed; wings rather short; *first primary longest;* tail of 12 feathers. *Adults in breeding plumage (sexes alike):* Sooty-black with slight greenish reflections (darker on back); wings and tail black; lesser upper wing-coverts, terminal half of greater upper wing-coverts, axillars and under wing-coverts white; in some specimens narrow band of black in white wing-patch; iris brown or black; bill and claws black; mouth and feet carmine, vermilion or coral-red; in July wings begin to fade and in August wings and tail become gray, white upper wing-coverts become soiled and plumage loses its green gloss; as molt proceeds, bird becomes more or less marbled with black and white, back retaining much black. *Adults in winter plumage:* Wings and tail black; wing-patch as in summer white; head and neck, rump and under plumage mainly white; back, hind neck and top

---

[1] Ornithological Biography, Vol. III, 1835, p. 364.
[2] Kumlien, Ludwig: Bulletin of the United States National Museum, No. 15, 1879, p. 103.
[3] Auk, Vol. II, 1885, p. 388.

of head blackish-dusky and white, varying in individuals; some old birds may retain black plumage through winter. *Young in first winter plumage:* Similar to winter adults but less white and more dusky, particularly on head; white wing-patches much obscured and broken by black tips of feathers. *Young in juvenal plumage (acquired usually in August):* Sooty-black above, white below, heavily mottled on sides with dusky, less so on breast and belly and finely spotted on throat (A. C. Bent). *Downy young:* Sooty-black above, somewhat paler or grayish below.

DOWNY YOUNG BLACK GUILLEMOT
About ½ natural size.

MEASUREMENTS. — Length 12.00 to 14.00 in.; spread about 23.00; folded wing 6.00 to 7.30; tail about 2.00; bill about 1.30; tarsus 1.25. Male averages slightly larger than female.

MOLTS. — Juvenal plumage is soon replaced by first winter plumage, which change is completed in October or later; in spring young birds molt either wholly or partly into black and white plumage of adult; spring molt includes all but wings and tail and is much prolonged or varies greatly in date; some birds appear in full summer plumage by February 1; others are still in practically full winter plumage in May, and some are still molting as late as June 18 (birds in both summer and winter plumage may be seen before March 1 off coast of Massachusetts); they assume adult winter plumage in second autumn (A. C. Bent).

FIELD MARKS. — Slightly smaller than Green-winged Teal. The White-winged Scoter is the only New England bird that at all resembles this species in summer; but white wing-patches of Guillemot are farther forward, much larger and more conspicuous when the bird floats on the water; also Guillemot is much smaller than Scoter and has smaller, narrower and more pointed bill; nothing like it in our waters when in its "white" winter plumage.

VOICE. — "A faint, shrill, piping whistle. When disturbed on nest, a hissing note" (A. C. Bent); a hoarse, whining whistle (A. J. Parker).

BREEDING. — On sea-islands or shore-cliffs. *Nest:* In crevice, rift or fissure in cliff or sea-ledge, or space under some rock, or among large loose rocks, often so far back under rock as to be inaccessible. *Eggs:* Laid on bare ground, rock, pebbles or gravel. Usually 2, rarely 1; about 2.25 to 2.50 by 1.50 to 1.60 in.; nearly elliptical; white, bluish-white, greenish-white or creamy, sometimes covered with small spots of various shades of brown and lilac; more often with fewer small spots and with large spots grouped about larger end. *Dates:* June 12 to July 16, Maine (A. C. Bent). *Incubation:* Period about 21 days (A. C. Bent). One brood yearly.

RANGE. — Coasts and islands of northeastern North America and northwestern Europe. Breeds from Maine to southern Greenland and Ungava (northern Quebec); winters from Cumberland Sound south to Cape Cod and casually to New Jersey and Pennsylvania; in Europe breeds from Iceland east to Scandinavia and White Sea and south to northern Scotland; in winter south to northern France.

DISTRIBUTION IN NEW ENGLAND. — Common winter resident coastwise in Maine and occasionally seen in open ponds and rivers; a not uncommon summer resident and breeder on Maine islands from Eastern Egg Rock eastward; rather uncommon winter visitant coastwise in New Hampshire; very rare and irregular in winter coastwise in Rhode Island; recorded once in Connecticut.

SEASON IN MASSACHUSETTS. — August 28 to April 23; rather common winter visitant as far south as Massachusetts Bay; usually most common in January and February; reported casually in July at Nahant.

HAUNTS AND HABITS. The sinuous coast of Maine is a little over 1,300 miles in length, so many are the islands and so irregular and deeply indented are the rock-ribbed shores.* The deep bays, coves and inlets offer some of the finest harbors in the land, and off shore lie scores of little rocky islands and dozens of low sandy islets, many of which are in summer the nurseries of sea-birds. Some of these sea-girt islands, some forested more or less with spruce and fir, are frequented by the handsome, little Black Guillemot. Their rocky formation and the loose blocks of stone and boulders piled upon them afford ideal nesting sites for a bird that seeks a secure place to hide its eggs.

There, above ordinary high-water mark, the "Sea Pigeon" makes its home, well back under some great stone; or it inhabits the rifts of bare ledges far out at sea. The little domicile requires no furnishing, as the bird is a primitive cave dweller, its roof the sheltering rock, overlooking the heaving sea. Here in their little caves the downy young are fed, and from their rocky fastnesses they go out into a world of water and of sky. Often during cruises along the Maine coast I have watched the Guillemots flying back and forth between their great storehouse, the sea, and their little caves in the rocks.

Now and then you may see the male in his courtship pursuing the female. He is an ardent lover, but she is coy. She dives and he pursues her. She comes to the surface and he is close at her heels. She swims away and he follows, running and splashing along the water. She flies and he chases after, until finally she seems to accept his attentions as if to be rid of his importunities. The mating over, they hunt for a suitable cavity as remote and inaccessible to their enemies as possible. They are gregarious and often may be seen in groups sitting on the rocks close to the sea. Normally in many parts of their range they nested in large colonies, but along the coasts of the Maritime Canadian Provinces their eggs have been taken for food so constantly throughout the season that the numbers of the species are few compared with its former abundance. In Maine where many island colonies are protected by wardens of the National Association of Audubon Societies, the Guillemots have a better chance for undisturbed nesting; and as they frequently find crevices where their eggs and young are inaccessible, their numbers have not been so reduced as have those of other species whose nesting places are more conspicuous.

In flight this species progresses swiftly, usually close to the water, its white wing-patches flashing in the sunlight and its bright red feet extended behind. On the water it rides as buoyantly as a Wood Duck. When approached by a boat, it has a trick of lowering the head quickly and repeatedly as if about to go under, but it is more likely to fly than to dive. In rising from the water, which it does easily, it aids itself by striking the surface with its feet. In diving and swimming under water it uses its wings more than its feet and seems to fly rapidly under water.

In New England the Black Guillemot may be looked for in winter (and even in summer) on rock-bound coasts. It leaves its breeding-places when the young are able to care for themselves. Many of this species winter slightly south of their summer range. It commonly drifts southward along the Maine coast from September until late Decem-

---

* The United States Geological Survey gives the tidal shore-line of the mainland as 558 miles and of the islands, 761 miles, a total of 1,319 miles. (Bulletin No. 689: United States Geological Survey, p. 220.)

ber.   Early in March it turns northward, and its numbers in New England waters begin to decrease.

Small fishes, little mussels and other small shellfish, crustaceans, marine worms and insects seem to form the principal food of the species, but Selous asserts that he has seen it eating seaweed.[1]

ECONOMIC STATUS.   See page 30.

SUBFAMILY **ALCINÆ**.   AUKS AND MURRES.

Number of species in North America 3; in Massachusetts 3.

Nostrils linear, densely feathered, quite covered by feathers; bill long with no appendages ; no crests ; these birds are the largest of the family and are abundant in the North Atlantic.

HEAD OF MURRE   HEAD OF BRÜNNICH'S MURRE
Both ½ natural size.

Úria troílle troille (LINNÆUS).   **Murre.**

Other names: COMMON MURRE; FOOLISH GUILLEMOT.

DESCRIPTION. — Bill long and rather slender; tail of 12 feathers. *Adults in breeding plumage* (*sexes alike*): Head and neck rich, dark brown (sometimes olive-brown), in some cases a little grayer on crown; other upper plumage dark sooty-brown; most feathers of back and rump with slightly lighter edges; secondaries narrowly but sharply tipped white; sides and flanks mainly white, streaked lightly or heavily dusky-brown; below from throat or lower fore neck pure white; lining of wings white, varied with dusky-brown; bill black; inside of mouth yellow; iris dark brown; feet dark or blackish; some individuals have narrow white ring around eye with white line extending back from it above ear region (this variation is responsible for the form *ringvia*, recognized as a species by Ridgway). *Adults in winter plumage:* Similar, but white of under plumage extends to bill, up sides of head to mouth, and up sides of neck, leaving only narrow band of dark brown on back of neck; also a white stripe extends upward and forward from white of neck on either side of upper hind head, separated from white of throat by a dark stripe running back from eye; bill and feet lighter or more brownish than in breeding plumage. *Young in first winter plumage:* Smaller; very similar, but with less white (or no white) on sides of head and slight mottling or washing of dusky on throat and fore neck; bill smaller and "like the feet in part light colored." *Downy young:* Grayish-brown above, almost black on head and neck which are variegated with long, whitish or buffy filaments; throat often mottled white; below whitish.

[1] Selous, Edmund: The Bird Watcher in the Shetlands, 1905, p. 203.

MEASUREMENTS. — Length about 17.00 in.; spread about 30.00; folded wing 7.75 to 8.30; tail about 2.25; bill 1.60 to 2.45; tarsus 1.35 to 1.60. Female averages smaller than male.

MOLTS. — Juvenal plumage not much different in color from that of downy young; by October 1 replaced by first winter plumage; partial molt in spring followed by plumage closely resembling breeding dress of adult; in next autumn immature bird molts again, and takes on adult winter plumage; this is soon molted and some birds appear in spring plumage in December; adults have a complete molt in autumn (July or August to November) and a complete molt November to April.

FIELD MARKS. — Size larger than teal; in any plumage may be distinguished from Razor-billed Auk (in field) and Brünnich's Murre (in hand) by its longer, more slender bill, and from winter loons by its much smaller size, white cross-line on wing and unspotted and very dark back; bills of young birds are shorter and more slender than those of adults; hence confusion may arise between the young of both murres, also Razor-bills and Puffins, all of which are difficult to distinguish in the field.

VOICE. — Adults — *Arr-r-r-r — orr-r-r-r — errr-r-r-r;* young — *Irrr-r-r-idd — Irrr-r-r-idd* (Gatke); "a soft, purring sound suggested by its name" (A. C. Bent).

BREEDING. — In colonies on sea-islands. *Nest:* None; egg laid on shelf of rocky cliff, or on earth or rock. *Eggs:* 1; 3.00 to 3.50 by 2.00 in.; "ovate pyriform" to "elliptical ovate"; light green, light blue, creamy or whitish or other light, varying shades variously washed, spotted and otherwise marked with shades, lines and scrawls of brown, lilac, olive, lavender, etc., and often clouded or washed with two or three colors. *Dates:* May 20 to July 25, Gulf of St. Lawrence (A. C. Bent). *Incubation:* Period about 28 to 30 days. One brood yearly.

RANGE. — Coasts and islands of North Atlantic and northeastward in Arctic to Spitzbergen. Breeds in North America from southern Greenland and southern Ungava (central Quebec) south to Magdalen Islands and Newfoundland (formerly to Nova Scotia); winters south to Maine; casual in Massachusetts; breeds in Europe south to coast of Portugal, and winters south to Mediterranean and west coast of Morocco; recorded from Canary Islands.

DISTRIBUTION IN NEW ENGLAND. — Casual in winter off coast; doubtless formerly more common; doubtless, also, less rare than supposed; "was years ago a regular breeder off Cape Sable Island and at Gannet Rock in the Gulf of Maine" (Arthur H. Norton); only four positive Massachusetts specimens (all in collection of Boston Society of Natural History):[1] Bird in full breeding plumage taken June 26, 1913, at Penikese Island by Dr. Stanley Cobb; male taken May 18, 1921, at Essex by A. B. Fuller; bird taken March 29, 1922, at Brant Rock, Marshfield; male sent to me by Rev. Smith O. Dexter from Westport Point (where it was taken April 7, 1923) and transferred to Boston Society of Natural History. There is also in the Society's collection a specimen labeled merely "Massachusetts" and recorded by Dr. G. M. Allen.[2] Captain Donald B. MacMillan reports taking a Murre in the winter of 1920 in Provincetown Harbor, but the specimen was not preserved.

HAUNTS AND HABITS. The Murre which formerly bred in countless numbers on the coast and islands of the North Atlantic has been reduced to an insignificant remnant of its former hosts by the insane policy of slaughter and plunder which has possessed many people in the United States and some of their Canadian neighbors ever since the settlement of the country.

Samuels (1867) intimated that the Murre was rather common in his day on our coast, but evidently he failed to separate it from the next species.[3]

---

[1] Brooks, W. Sprague: Auk, Vol. XLI, 1924, p. 163.

[2] Occasional Papers of the Boston Society of Natural History, VII. Fauna of New England, II. List of the Aves. Boston, June, 1909, p. 6.

[3] Samuels, Edward A.: Birds of New England, 1870, p. 570.

Knight records a single specimen taken in Maine and placed in the collection of the Portland Society of Natural History and notes that the species is said to have nested formerly on Grand Menan.[1]

Occasionally the Murre is reported on the Massachusetts coast in winter, but probably most of these cases are referable to Brünnich's Murre. I have never knowingly seen the bird alive. For the best, fullest and most recent life-history of the species the reader is referred to Bulletin No. 107, Smithsonian Institution, United States National Museum, Life Histories of North American Diving Birds, by Mr. Arthur Cleveland Bent, a work for which all ornithologists owe the author a debt of gratitude.

ECONOMIC STATUS. See page 30.

Uria lómvia lomvia (LINNÆUS). Brünnich's Murre.

Other name: THICK-BILLED GUILLEMOT.

Plate 3.

DESCRIPTION. — Bill short, wide and deep, upper outline of upper mandible curved throughout, its cutting edges dilated and denuded toward base where those of Murre are feathered; this bare space flesh-colored in life; tail of 12 feathers. *Adults in breeding plumage (sexes alike):* Similar to Murre, but crown and nape darker, contrasting with lighter and browner sides of head; form more robust; "legs light colored" (Lord Lilford). *Adults in winter plumage:* Similar; upper parts dusky or sooty, more or less glossy; sides of head brownish to .50 inch below eye; sooty of neck nearly meets at point in front, almost forming a collar and nearly enclosing white of throat; tips of secondaries white as in summer; below pure white; linings of wings mainly white. *Young in first winter plumage:* Fully 2 inches shorter than adult and much less in other measurements; bill smaller, thinner and generally weaker; similar to winter adult but often lighter on back, and somewhat spotted or washed with dusky on throat. *Downy young:* Blackish above, varying individually to various shades of brown, shading off to brownish-gray on throat and sides; many long whitish or pale buff filaments on head and neck; breast and belly mainly white or whitish but less white below than in preceding species.

MEASUREMENTS. — Length 18.00 to 19.75 in.; spread 24.50 to 32.00; folded wing 7.45 to 8.80; tail about 2.25; bill about 1.40; tarsus 1.40 to 1.55.

MOLTS. — Plumage and plumage changes of this species are very similar to those of the Murre.

FIELD MARKS. — Size of a small duck; practically indistinguishable from Common Murre in field; barely distinguishable from it (if seen close to) only by the thicker, shorter, stouter bill, darker head and light flesh-colored stripe on mandible near gape; from the Razor-billed Auk, in field, by its smaller, more slender bill; from loons or grebes by its plain black back and the white line on the wing; when murres of either species are rising or alighting on the water their bodies seem to flatten; if viewed from behind when on wing, the white feathers of flanks and white under tail-coverts overlap on to the black back and tail respectively so that white shows behind wings on both sides of rump and tail; when the birds are seen flying *en profile* the white wing linings show and might be mistaken at a distance for a white wing patch.

VOICE. — Young birds — shrill emphatic cries like *"beat it, beat it"*; adults — a soft purring note and a loud croaking (A. C. Bent); a hoarse, guttural note; another like the bleating of a sheep (Turner).

BREEDING. — On sea-islands in colonies. *Nest:* None; egg laid on bare ledge of rocky cliff. *Eggs:* 1, perhaps rarely 2; great variety of colors and markings (a few spotless) but most of them indistinguishable either in size or color from those of preceding species. *Dates:* Those given by Mr. Bent from Green-

---

[1] Knight, Ora W.: Birds of Maine, 1908, p. 34.

land, Labrador and the Gulf of St. Lawrence run from June 5 to July 18. *Incubation:* Period about 28 days (A. C. Bent); both sexes incubate. One brood yearly.

RANGE. — Coasts and islands of North Atlantic and Arctic. Breeds in North America from northern Greenland and coasts and islands of Arctic Ocean south to Gulf of St. Lawrence; stated by Manly Hardy (in Vol. II, of the Osprey for 1897, p. 26) to have bred "over 50 years ago" [about 1847 Ed.] on a Maine island; in Europe breeds on Arctic islands and in Asia along parts of Siberian coasts; winters from edge of ice in southern Greenland south off Atlantic coast to Delaware, more rarely to South Carolina; more or less common occasionally in region of Great Lakes; rarely south of Great Britain and North Sea.

DISTRIBUTION IN NEW ENGLAND. — Common winter visitant along Maine coast and accidental inland; irregular winter visitor coastwise (but sometimes locally abundant) in the other sea-coast states; casual or accidental in most of interior but has been common transient at times on Lake Champlain, Vermont.

SEASON IN MASSACHUSETTS. — October 27 to May 1.

HAUNTS AND HABITS. Along the bleak, desolate, rocky and inhospitable shores of the North Atlantic and Arctic oceans, from the Gulf of St. Lawrence to northern Greenland, Brünnich's Murre in migration or in summer is one of the commonest of the waterfowl. It bred formerly in countless thousands on the coasts and islands of Newfoundland and Labrador, but now it is found in such immense numbers only in its far northern retreats where the white man rarely goes.

Mr. A. C. Bent gives an account by Mr. Elmer Ekblaw of a rookery of these birds on Saunders Island where he says there are literally millions; that the noise they make is appalling, and that when they leave the island cliffs at the sound of a gun, the rush of wings sounds like a passing tornado.

The egg of a Murre is more or less flattened on the sides and pointed at the small end so that when it is disturbed or displaced, it tends to roll in a circle and stay on the ledge where it lies. When the birds are suddenly alarmed, many eggs are displaced, nevertheless, by the owners themselves and pushed off the rock and into the sea. A Murre does not sit upon its single egg like most birds, but stands erect over it like a penguin and pokes it into place with the bill.

Murres can dive at the flash of a gun and are difficult to kill at long range. They use their wings for under-water swimming at which they are as expert as a loon. The following notes from Mr. and Mrs. Richard B. Harding show at least one method employed by an individual of this species in swimming under water. Three birds were observed February 27, 1921, from Cunningham's Bridge, Cohasset, Massachusetts, swimming in a tidal stream. Mrs. Harding says:

"The circumstances were quite unusual. Mr. Harding and I observed the birds from a bridge some twelve feet above the water which was clear, so we could plainly see the actions of the nearest bird. The birds were now diving at intervals, and averaged 30–35 seconds under water; one was diving close to the bridge from which we could distinctly see it under water, swimming with powerful strokes of the wings, held as in cut, *Position under water* primaries parallel and most of the power in the wing-butts. It dived in the ordinary feeble fluttering manner of the murre using both wings and feet, but once under water it seemed to drag the feet and use the wings or, to be more exact, wing-butts, entirely. In this connection it is interesting to note *why* it was diving. The current was bearing it towards the bridge somewhat faster than the bird could swim *on* the surface. By swimming *under* the surface it could gain on the current, thereby indicating more speed under than on the surface. The bird was neither frightened nor feeding.

"The wings were used on the descent and on the level under water, but on rising to the surface were held rigid in the position above indicated."

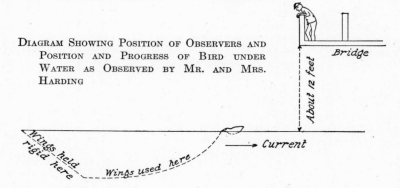

DIAGRAM SHOWING POSITION OF OBSERVERS AND POSITION AND PROGRESS OF BIRD UNDER WATER AS OBSERVED BY MR. AND MRS. HARDING

"The cut shows clearly the position of the observer while observing the bird's actions under water. Depth of water 8 to 10 feet."

Usually not many birds of this species arrive until late November off the Massachusetts coast where they seem most numerous usually in January and February. Commonly they remain well offshore but sometimes, particularly during severe easterly storms, they come into open estuaries. Captain Donald B. MacMillan tells me that at such times the exhausted birds while asleep have been killed with oars by boys in Provincetown Harbor. They frequent waters off both rocky and sandy shores. In New England they are found most commonly on the Maine coast and on the northernmost shores of Massachusetts. By March they are again moving northward, and in May and June they reach the farthest northern points at which they are known to breed. In some winters a few of these birds are found scattered about the interior as far or farther south than the Great Lakes. Such a dispersal to the interior is believed to be caused in some cases by storms; but Mr. J. H. Fleming gives good reasons for the belief that sometimes the Murres are driven out of Hudson Bay by the freezing of the surface, and so fly southward seeking open water, many of them becoming exhausted and coming to earth in their fruitless search. There have been record flights in the late fall on the lower lakes (Erie and Ontario) when most of the birds die, seemingly of starvation.

Brünnich's Murre feeds on small fishes, crustaceans and other marine food, as do all Murres. Its food has never been carefully studied.

ECONOMIC STATUS. See page 30.

Álca tórda Linnæus. **Razor-billed Auk.**

Other names: TINKER; ICE-BIRD; SEA CROW. PLATE 3.

DESCRIPTION. — Bill much compressed laterally; knife-like upper mandible hooked and cross-grooved; tail of 12 feathers. *Adults in breeding plumage (sexes alike):* Head and upper neck all around and other upper plumage generally dark brown or slaty-black, brown on sides of head and neck, much darker on top of head, deepening to slaty-black on other upper plumage; glossy on back; a sunken white line from base of upper mandible to upper eyelid; secondaries narrowly and sharply tipped white; below, including under wing-coverts and axillars, white; bill slaty or black, white band crossing both mandibles near middle; inside of mouth yellow; iris dark brown or bluish; feet black. *Adults in winter plumage:* Similar but white below reaches bill and sides of neck; conspicuous white line before eye now obliterated, but white line across bill remains. *Young in first winter plumage:* Similar to winter adult but smaller, duller and paler; much more white or gray about head and neck; bill very much smaller, more pointed and lacking grooves and white cross-line of adult bill. *Downy young:* Variable; sooty or blackish-brown; lighter or more brown on rump; overlaid with rufous on crown; paler or much lighter, often whitish, on head, neck and below. More or less of the downy filaments above are paler at tips giving chick a lighter appearance than would be given by the down alone.

MEASUREMENTS. — Length 16.00 to 18.50 in.; spread 25.00 to 27.00; folded wing 7.75 to 8.50; tail about 3.50; bill 1.25 to 1.30; tarsus 1.25 to 1.40.

MOLTS. — The natal down is changed in a few weeks for juvenal plumage, and very soon winter dress is assumed, so that young bird is in first winter dress in late September or early October; after a partial prenuptial molt in spring the head takes on a nuptial plumage similar to that of adult, but youth of bird can be determined by smaller and more pointed bill which lacks grooves so prominent on that of adult; date of this prenuptial molt varies; there is a complete postnuptial molt beginning in August after which young bird assumes adult winter plumage; adults have a partial prenuptial molt of body feathers in winter or spring (date varying greatly) and complete postnuptial molt in autumn.

FIELD MARKS. — Adults in winter plumage (as we see them) may be distinguished from Brünnich's Murre by stouter build, larger head, longer tail and (especially) compressed, hooked bill; sometimes when seen on water at a little distance, white line across bill seems to cut off its end, and head appears like that of a pig; shortened neck contracts the white on its side into a more or less narrow band extending up nearly to nape, and bird appears as a dark pig-headed bird crossed by two white marks; white on sides of neck extends up much farther toward nape than in Murre; Mr. Bent tells us that Dr. C. W. Townsend remarks that when "Razor-bills" fly away, they show white on either side of a black median line (murres show this also), while the Puffin under such circumstances shows a solid black back; the "Razor-bill" often (but not always) carries its comparatively long tail upright when resting or swimming on the water; the Murre sometimes does this, but tail is shorter than that of Razor-bill.

VOICE. — Hoarse, guttural notes or low croaking sounds (A. C. Bent); notes in courtship like syllables *odd arr* and *hur-ray* (F. O. Morris).

BREEDING. — On sea islands; in colonies. *Nest:* None; eggs laid on ledge of rock or in fissure in cliff, resting on bare rock or small stones, in plain sight or partially concealed. *Eggs:* 1 (rarely 2 are found together); 3.00 by scant 2.00 in. (Coues); elliptical-ovate or elongate-ovate, never really pear-shaped; shell coarse, thick, tough and lustreless; sometimes resemble some Murres' eggs in color (though never green) but not in shape; color varies from bluish- or greenish-white or pinkish-buff to dull yellow or yellowish; markings vary from small spots to blotches and scrawls of darker shades of brown. *Dates:* May 24 to July 25, Gulf of St. Lawrence. *Incubation:* Period about 30 days (in incubator); by both sexes (A. C. Bent).

RANGE. — Coasts and islands of North Atlantic and Arctic oceans. Breeds in America from Greenland south to Newfoundland and New Brunswick, formerly occasionally to Maine, and in Europe from Iceland south to British Isles and Channel Islands and east to coast of Norway and Lapland; winters from southern Labrador south to Ontario, Long Island, and rarely or casually to Virginia and North Carolina, and in Europe south from British Isles to Azores and Canary Islands and east to Mediterranean and Adriatic seas; recorded in interior of America west to Lake Ontario.

DISTRIBUTION IN NEW ENGLAND. — Common winter visitant coastwise in Maine; not uncommon in some winters on coasts of New Hampshire and Massachusetts; less common on those of Rhode Island and Connecticut; sometimes abundant locally off outlying points on any of these coasts except Connecticut.

SEASON IN MASSACHUSETTS. — Not uncommon irregular winter visitant coastwise; October 27 to April 15 (May 12).

HAUNTS AND HABITS. After a long easterly winter storm, in clearing weather when the dark blue wintry seas are stirred by the gusts of a brisk northwester, we may find the hardy "Razor-bill" riding at ease off the storm-beaten ledges of the North Shore. It swims lightly, swiftly and easily with head sometimes raised but commonly drawn in and often the tail is cocked jauntily upward. It flies with the head held close to the body and level with it and does not stretch its neck forward like a loon, cormorant or murre but, like murres, it tips from side to side in flight, showing its breast and back alternately. Like auks, murres and guillemots in general it employs its wings in under-water flight, raising them as it dives and using them either partly closed like fins or not quite as fully opened as in flight. It is an expert diver going down to great depths and swimming for long distances under water.

On March 12, 1922, on the beach at Nantucket I surprised a "Razor-bill" apparently asleep on some seaweed close to the water. In my attempt to catch the bird it menaced me with open bill, flapping wings and strident cries, but before I could seize it, it plunged into the water and swam and dived, opening its wings to nearly full length when under water and moving them backward and forward. The bird moved fast, but the wings were not flapped so rapidly as when used in the air. I could not see the feet; apparently

Forward Stroke *Back Stroke*

they were hidden by the tail. I saw the same bird or another go off from the beach in the same way later in the day. The wing motion was absolutely unlike that observed in Brünnich's Murre by Mr. and Mrs. Harding (page 41) or that observed in the Razor-bill by several authorities.

Selous asserts that the wings are "raised from and brought downwards again towards the sides in the same position in which they repose against them when closed." [1] This is a very different motion from the one that I observed, for in that case the wings were not brought near the body (see cut).

Yarrell gives an interesting account by Mr. Theodore Walker of how the mother bird inducts her offspring into the mysteries of swimming and diving. Sometimes if it proves obstinate, the mother takes it by the back of the neck and flies down with it to the sea. In teaching it to dive, she seizes it by the neck and dives with it. Up it comes again, only to get another dousing until finally it dives to escape its mother, and "so endeth the first lesson."

---

[1] Selous, Edmund: Bird Watching, 1901, p. 151.

Mr. Harrison Lewis sends me the following notes on this species: "Razor-billed Auks are still quite numerous on some parts of the Canadian Labrador coast, near Cape Whittle. In this region they breed upon islands, where their eggs are deposited in crevices in the solid rock, or under protecting boulders, so that they are usually difficult to reach. Where many birds are incubating together, however, some eggs are almost always in easily accessible situations.

"During the period of incubation, those Auks which are not sitting upon the eggs often stand in groups on rocks from which they can obtain a good view of the surroundings. Upon the approach of an intruder these birds fly away and alight upon the water. Probably, in doing so, they give warning to their incubating mates, for the latter usually scramble hurriedly out from their rocky homes and fly away to join the others. Occasionally, however, an incubating Razor-bill will remain on its egg, in some secure situation, despite the approach of a man to the nearest possible point. In such cases the bird usually faces its unwelcome visitor and opens its mouth very wide.

"Razor-billed Auks possess much curiosity, and the occupants of a boat passing near them can readily entice them to fly by within a few yards by cheering and waving their hands."

"Razor-bills" are staunch and hardy sea-birds and although many of them in autumn follow the last flights of the scoters down the New England coast, they commonly keep well offshore, even in midwinter. Probably they are far more common off our coasts in winter than the number reported by landsmen would lead us to believe. During the winter of 1921–22 many were cast up dead or dying on the south shore of Nantucket. Most of these birds had become soaked with crude oil floating on the sea. Sometimes large numbers perish in another way. Mr. Edward Babson, writing on December 28, 1920, from Gloucester, stated that many Razor-bills had been caught offshore in gill-nets by the local gill-netting steamers, as many as two bushels of the birds being taken on one occasion from the nets where they had become entangled and drowned while diving for food.

This is another of the birds that formerly were abundant from Maine to Labrador and which man's rapacity has reduced in all this territory to a mere remnant of its former numbers. Its habit of nesting in rifts and holes and hiding its eggs in the crevices of inaccessible cliffs has saved it thus far to posterity.

The Razor-billed Auk moves southward to Massachusetts mainly in November and December and is most common off our coasts in December, January and February. In March and April it moves north again to its breeding grounds, migrating mainly at a considerable distance from our shores.

This bird feeds often in the ocean, many miles from land, and its food consists largely of small fish, crustaceans and other marine organisms which it gets from the waters or the bottom of the sea.

ECONOMIC STATUS. See page 30.

SUBFAMILY **ALLINÆ**. DOVEKIES.

Number of species in North America 1 ; in Massachusetts 1.

This subfamily includes but one genus characterized by nostrils rounded, incompletely feathered ; bill without appendages, small, short, obtuse ; size small ; no crests ; tail normally of 12 feathers.

Álle alle (LINNÆUS). **Dovekie.**

Other names: LITTLE AUK ; PINE-KNOT ; KNOTTY ; ICE-BIRD ; LITTLE ICE-BIRD.

Plate 3.

DESCRIPTION. — *Adults in breeding plumage (sexes alike)*: Head, neck and all upper plumage glossy bluish-black, except sides of head, throat and front of neck which shade into sooty-brown ; scapulars narrowly edged white, forming white streaks ; secondaries sharply and narrowly tipped white, forming a narrow white bar on wing ; below from neck pure white ; some long feathers on upper flanks streaked black ; linings of wings dusky, varied in some cases with whitish ; bill black ; inside of mouth light yellow ; iris brown ; feet flesh-colored with black webs. *Adults in winter plumage*: Similar, but white of under plumage extends to bill and nearly or quite around nape. *Young in first winter plumage*: Similar to adult but upper plumage duller and browner ; some dusky mottling on sides of head and neck and across breast ; bill smaller ; feet dusky-greenish. *Young in juvenal plumage*: Strangely resembles nuptial plumage of adult. *Downy young*: Uniformly sooty-slate, paler or more grayish below (Ridgway).

MEASUREMENTS. — Length 7.25 to 9.15 in. ; spread 13.86 to 15.50 ; folded wing 4.50 to 5.25 ; tail 1.50 to 1.75 ; bill about .50 ; tarsus .75 to .85. Female smaller than male.

MOLTS. — Before end of September young bird undergoes a molt of body plumage which is succeeded by first winter plumage ; at first prenuptial molt in spring young bird takes on a dress indistinguishable from adult ; adults have partial prenuptial molt early in spring and complete postnuptial molt in August and September (A. C. Bent).

FIELD MARKS. — Its extremely small size, together with its black back and white breast, distinguish this, the smallest winter sea-fowl on this coast.

VOICE. — Harsh squeak uttered sometimes just as it dives ; note at nest a pretty chirrup or pipe *try* and *eye* (F. O. Morris) ; also likened to syllables *al-le* (A. C. Bent).

BREEDING. — On sea-cliffs or steep slopes covered with loose rocks. *Nest*: Crevice among rocks or rubble or horizontal cleft in cliff, sometimes lined with pebbles or bits of grass. *Eggs*: 1, rarely 2 ; 1.60 to 1.85 by 1.10 to 1.25 in. (Coues) ; pale greenish-blue, usually unmarked, but occasionally indistinctly streaked with yellowish-brown at larger end (H. Seebohm). *Dates*: Earliest eggs at Etah, north Greenland, last week in June ; laying at its height first week of July. *Incubation*: Period 24 days (Hantzsch) ; shared by both parents (H. Seebohm). One brood yearly ; young begin hatching about middle of July (W. Elmer Ekblaw).

RANGE. — Coasts, islands and offshore waters of North Atlantic and Arctic. Breeds in northern Greenland, Ellesmere Island, Baffin Island and on other Arctic coasts and islands, also in northern Iceland, Spitzbergen, Novaya Zemlya and east to Franz Josef Land ; winters from southern Greenland south to New York, New Jersey, Virginia and casually South Carolina and from North Sea and British Isles south along coasts of Europe to Azores, Canary and Madeira Islands.

DISTRIBUTION IN NEW ENGLAND. — Rather irregular winter visitant coastwise ; at various times either rare, uncommon or abundant according to weather conditions ; rare winter visitant on Rhode Island coast ; very rare in Connecticut coastal waters ; casual inland in all New England states (one taken May 31, 1910, in summer plumage at Bennington, Vt. Dr. L. H. Ross *in litt.*) : Mr. Arthur H. Norton notes (Auk, Vol. XXVIII, 1911, p. 481) a pair in mixed nuptial and winter plumage that he saw

July 15, 1911, about 6 miles from Machias Seal Island, off the Maine coast, and adds on the authority of Capt. Merton Thomas, late keeper of Matinicus Rock light, that a Dovekie was seen frequently in the summer of 1910 near the Rock.

SEASON IN MASSACHUSETTS. — (September 20) November 4 to May 1 (June 3).

HAUNTS AND HABITS. In January, 1878, during a great freeze in the north I was on a steamer off the Virginia capes, bound for Florida. We were far offshore as the captain was making a good offing in passing Hatteras, for a great easterly storm was brewing which soon burst in full force and smashed our steering-gear, so that we lay for four hours in the trough of a mighty sea, exposed to the full fury of the cyclone. Before the storm broke, hundreds of dovekies could be seen scattered on the heaving seas. This was the first time that I had seen the little things alive, and their activities impressed themselves upon my memory. As the steamer's bow approached, some of the birds dipped forward and with partly opened wings flew diagonally downward into the depths. Others pattered along on the surface, some flying from wave-crest to wave-crest and "skittering" over or through their tops; while still others fluttered into the air and flew along for a short distance, only to alight again or to dip below the surface. All was excitement in their little companies as they fled from the great black, smoking monster, as it rushed furiously on. The impression made on my youthful mind by the sight of these little birds at home far out on that wild sea in the face of a coming storm has never been effaced.

The Dovekie is reported to dive with open wings and to use the wings alone for progressing beneath the surface; but I have seen it dive with wings closed, slightly lifted or widely spread, apparently as the exigency of the moment required.

Mrs. Lidian E. Bridge writes that while standing on a high rock overlooking the sea at Rockport, she saw two Dovekies swimming under water and using both wings and feet. As they met she says, they uttered "an absurd little screech, short and sharp."

The fishermen call Dovekies "Pine Knots" or "Knotties" to indicate their extreme hardiness, for they are indeed as "tough as a pine knot." They are rarely numerous near shore, but offshore they fly in small flocks with quick wing-beats close to the waves, or else rest on the sea.

Probably the Dovekie is abundant during every winter on the fishing banks off the New England coast. The winter of 1920–21 was remarkably mild; nevertheless, on the coasts of Massachusetts and Rhode Island numbers of Dovekies were found dead or disabled, their feathers soaked with crude petroleum, discharged upon the water by some steamship or oil barge. A few uninjured birds also were seen along our shores. In the winter of 1919–20, which was very severe, the "ice-birds" were abundant off the coast of Virginia.

Dovekies seem to be able to weather an ordinary gale, but now and then a protracted storm rising to hurricane force exhausts them and drives many ashore and even into the interior, where some alight in streams or in ponds if these are open. If the ponds are covered with ice, the birds finally fall spent on the snow, ice or frozen ground, from which it is believed they never rise again, since many have been picked up dead under such circumstances.

Captain Donald B. MacMillan states that sometimes in winter at Provincetown large numbers of Dovekies are driven on the coast or into the harbor and beaten to death by the sea and washed to the beach where the skunks feed on them.

Mr. J. A. Farley tells me that he found a Dovekie on Plymouth Beach which had fallen on pebbly ground and, being unable to rise in the air, had worn away its webs in its attempts to walk until its toes resembled those of a sandpiper, the entire web having been destroyed.

The greatest inland flight of this species of which we have any recollection was in November, 1871. Brewster gives the date as November 15.[1] This occurred during a very violent easterly gale accompanied by torrential rain. Probably on that occasion the Dovekies appeared in every county in Massachusetts. They were not only scattered over eastern Massachusetts and Worcester County but reached the Connecticut valley and were reported from Belchertown ponds ("winter of 1872"), near Amherst.[2] Since then the species has been seen or taken casually west to Hampden, Hampshire and Franklin counties, but I can find no record for Berkshire County.

This little auk is a "God-send" to the Eskimo on its return home to the Arctic regions at the advent of spring. The Eskimos welcome its arrival with joy as we welcome the return of the bluebird, for its coming means to them not only the recurrence of the vernal season but often the transition from starvation to plenty. Captain Donald B. MacMillan, who has seen, several times, the return of the birds after the dark winter in the North, graphically describes the scene as follows: "But what is that great, pulsating, musical note which seems to fill all space? Now loud and clear, now diminishing to a low hum, the sound proclaims the arrival of the true representative of the bird-life of the Arctic, the most interesting and most valuable of all, the bird which means so much to the Smith Sound native — the dovekie or little auk (*Alle alle*). The long dark winter has at last passed away. The larder open to all is empty. The sun is mounting higher into the heavens day by day. Now and then a seal is seen sunning himself at his hole. The Eskimos are living from hand to mouth. And then that glad cry, relieving all anxiety for the future, bringing joy to every heart, '*Ark-pood-e-ark-suit! Ark-pood-e-ark-suit!*' (Little auks! Little auks!)." [3]

Thus the Eskimos hail these — the first small birds of spring. They come in clouds, like the driving snow, and fill the air with the uproar of their wings. The Eskimos kill them by thousands. The children, expert in stone throwing, knock down many. Some are eaten raw. An Eskimo boy will pick up the quivering body of one of these little birds, tear open its breast and eat the warm and bleeding creature right out of its skin, leaving little else than skin and feathers.

---

[1] Brewster, William: Memoirs of the Nuttall Ornithological Club, No. IV. Birds of the Cambridge Region of Massachusetts, 1906, p. 90.

[2] Clark, Herbert L.: Birds of Amherst and Hampshire County, Massachusetts, 1887, p. 45.

[3] MacMillan, Donald B.: Four Years in the White North, 1918, pp. 105–106.

I have heard Capt. MacMillan describe the common method of catching Dovekies. An Eskimo woman ascends the steep and rocky slope where the Dovekies have their nests, sits in a hole among the rocks and sweeps with a long-handled dip-net, catching birds as they fly past, as a child catches butterflies. Sometimes as a flock passes, she will get several birds at one sweep with her 15-inch net. Thousands of these birds are *cached* in the frozen ground to be used in winter for food, and many of the skins are made into birdskin shirts. The eggs also are useful as food, and the children squeeze into the crevices and holes in rocky hillsides to collect them. All this has no noticeable permanent effect on the great abundance of this bird, and as it nests in the far north where the destructive white man is a rarity, its future seems secure. The Dovekie has many enemies besides man. The Arctic fox seeks its nest and no doubt sometimes catches it there. The Glaucous Gull, the Raven and the Gyrfalcon take their share. The white whale catches it on the sea and no doubt it has other submarine enemies, among them seals and large fish.[1]

Probably Dovekies begin to leave their northernmost breeding grounds in late July and early August, but many never go much farther south than the edge of the ice pack and some remain in southern Greenland. Occasionally a few appear on the New England coast in September, but they are seen rarely in abundance along the Massachusetts coast until the latter part of November. They migrate at sea, move southward slowly, and seldom appear in great numbers near shore unless driven in by severe storms. They begin to move northward in February, and the migration is at its height in March. In these two months they begin to appear in numbers at their homes beyond the Arctic circle, but they do not reach northern Greenland until about May 15.

Mr. A. C. Bent quotes Mr. W. Elmer Ekblaw to the effect that the food of young Dovekies consists largely of so-called "shrimps," numerous in Arctic waters, and so-called "blackberries" or little black "arthropods," abundant there also. Many crustaceans, small fish and bits of seaweed have been found in their stomachs. They are said to store quantities of crustaceans in their mouths and gullets when feeding their young, as the swallow fills for the same purpose its capacious maw with insects. The Dovekie is brought forth on the earth but gets its sustenance from the sea, that great fecund mother of varied and multitudinous life.

ECONOMIC STATUS. See page 30.

ORDER LONGIPENNES. LONG-WINGED SWIMMERS.

Number of species in North America 47 ; in Massachusetts 28.

This order of swimmers includes Skuas and Jaegers, Gulls, Terns and Skimmers. All have long, pointed wings reaching when closed beyond the base or even beyond the end of the tail, which normally has twelve feathers; all have open lateral nostrils, small, free hind toe and webbed front toes.

[1] Ekblaw, W. Elmer: Quoted in Life Histories of North American Diving Birds by A. C. Bent, 1919, p. 219, Bulletin No. 107, Smithsonian Institution, United States National Museum.

FAMILY **STERCORARIIDÆ**. SKUAS AND JAEGERS.

Number of species in North America 4 ; in Massachusetts 4.

This family includes long-winged swimmers with hooked bill, upper mandible saddled with a large sheath or so-called false cere, and nostrils opening beneath its edges — a character common to no other water-birds. The hook at the end of the bill appears as a separate part of its covering. There is a peculiar dark phase of each species, and one genus has the middle tail feathers much elongated. All birds of this family are virtually sea-hawks, with powerful wings, strongly hooked beaks and stout, curved claws. They are the most predatory of all sea-birds, the "robbers of the sea." They subsist largely by killing birds and small mammals, eating eggs, or robbing weaker birds of their food.

ECONOMIC STATUS. These birds seem to be of little economic importance.

Catharácta skúa (BRÜNNICH). Skua.

Other names: GREAT SKUA; SEA-HEN; SEA-HAWK.

Plate 4.

DESCRIPTION. — Large, powerful, robust; wings moderately long; primaries very broad, and rounded at tips; tail short, broad and nearly even or a trifle rounded at tip; feathers on sides of nape elongated and rigid with long disconnected fibrillæ; bill stout and heavy, shorter than middle toe without claw; tarsus shorter than middle toe and claw. *Adults (sexes alike and apparently no differences in seasonal plumages except such as are due to wearing and fading)*: Above blackish-brown, more or less varied with small spots and markings of whitish; each dark feather with spot of rusty toward end, which (in some specimens at least) fades into whitish along shaft; crown and upper fore part of head with little whitish or rusty; axillars and under wing-coverts grayish-brown slightly tinged cinnamon; wings and tail blackish; shafts yellowish-white except toward tips; quill-feathers of wings and tail white toward base, white on tail concealed by coverts, but appearing on outer primaries as conspicuous white spot or patch, largest on under side but conspicuous on upper side; some specimens with rusty spots on sides and flanks; bill and claws blackish; cere grayer; iris dark brown; feet dull black. In dark phase this species is quite uniformly blackish with white wing-patch very conspicuous. *Young in first winter plumage:* Similar to adults but often smaller; bill more slender; cere poorly developed; feathers of neck shorter and more rounded; wings shorter and rounded; colors similar to adult but more rufous, duller, more blended, with few if any white spots; rusty spots duller, numerous and large especially on edge of fore wing and smaller upper wing-coverts; quill-feathers of wing and tail dull brownish-black, shafts yellowish-white, darker toward ends; white patch on wing largely covered from above but plainly visible from below; bill, tarsi and feet more brownish, feet sometimes varied with yellowish or whitish. *Downy young:* Buffy-gray or ruddy-gray; darker and sometimes ruddier above than below.

MEASUREMENTS. — Length about 20.00 to 22.00 in.; folded wing 15.75 to 16.25; tail about 6.00; tarsus 2.60 to 2.75; bill (chord) 2.10, (along ridge) 2.23.

MOLTS. — Young birds may become as adults at first postnuptial molt when a little over a year old, but perhaps not for a year or two later (A. C. Bent); adults have a complete postnuptial molt (July to December); probably they have a partial prenuptial molt in spring.

FIELD MARKS. — Large size, near that of Herring Gull; robust shape; dark brown or blackish color; blackish legs and feet; white patch on primaries conspicuous in flight; *short, slightly-uptilted tail;* jaegers also show some white on wing and in dark plumage might be mistaken for Skuas; but their

PLATE 4

PLATE 4

LONG–TAILED JAEGER
Page 58
Adult

PARASITIC JAEGER
Page 55
Light Phase

Dark Phase

POMARINE-JAEGER
Page 52
Adult

SKUA
Page 50

All one-eighth natural size.

Louis Agassiz Fuertes

wings in flight are long, angular, bent at carpal joint and sharp-pointed, resembling those of a falcon, while those of Skua are broader and rounded at tips and held fully spread like those of soaring Red-tailed Hawk or eagle; all jaegers, except very young, show elongated middle tail-feathers; Skua has none and tail of young often appears slightly forked.

VOICE. — Usually silent in our waters. Its cry sharp and shrill resembling that of young gull, like the word *skua* or *skui* (McGillivray).

BREEDING. — On sea-islands but not in colonies. *Nest:* On rocky cliffs or tundra, of grasses, lichens, mosses, etc. *Eggs:* 2 or 3; 3.00 by 1.99 to 2.45 by 1.55 in.; pale olive to brownish or deep olive-buff spotted with large and small brown markings of varying shades. *Dates:* May 5 to June 21, Greenland; May 20 to June 23, Iceland. *Incubation:* Period 28 to 30 days (Hantzsch); by both sexes. One brood yearly.

RANGE. — Coasts and islands of North Atlantic. Breeds in Iceland, Faroe, Shetland and Orkney Islands; believed to breed in Greenland and on Lady Franklin Island north of Hudson Strait; winters on fishing-banks off Newfoundland, Nova Scotia and Massachusetts; casual to Long Island and in interior; recorded at Niagara Falls, December 3, 1915;[1] in Europe from British Isles and Norway south to Gibraltar; casual or occasional on Madeira Islands and in Mediterranean and inland waters.

DISTRIBUTION IN NEW ENGLAND. — Rare visitor off shore in late summer or autumn; only one record of specimen taken on New England coast — at Pollock Rip.

SEASON IN MASSACHUSETTS. — The Skua has been considered mainly a winter visitor on the fishing banks off the Massachusetts coast, but Capt. J. W. Collins says that Skuas are "most plentiful on the Grand Banks [of Newfoundland, Ed.] in July, August, and September; while Mr. Walter H. Rich found Skuas from June 19 to November 5 on the fishing grounds off Nantucket (in the "south part of the channel" 35 miles east of south from Sankaty Head, 68° 42' W.; 41° 20' N.) where its period of greatest abundance was from August 12 to September 10. Mr. Rich says that these facts have suggested to Mr. Arthur H. Norton the possibility that these summer Skuas may be Antarctic Skuas which come north to summer here, and which breed in the far south in the Antarctic summer, while the winter Skuas come from the northern breeding grounds.[2] If some ornithologist would collect and examine a few summer Skuas, this question might be settled.

Following are the only definite records of the Skua: One captured alive on a fishing vessel on Georges Bank was found dead July 18, 1878, at Gloucester, where it had been left by its captor (this has been cited as a Massachusetts record, but the bird was taken about 100 miles offshore);[3] one seen at Ipswich Bay, September 17, 1878, by Raymond L. Newcomb;[4] two noted October 17, 1883, on Nantucket Shoals;[5] female taken September 10, 1884, at Pollock Rip.[6] This species appeared at Woods Hole August 30, 1890, and September 19, 1889 — both probably sight records by the late Vinal N. Edwards who reported them, according to H. C. Oberholser.[7]

HAUNTS AND HABITS. The Skua is a bird of the wide seas or the fishing banks far out of sight of land. Chamberlain describes it as a sea-falcon preying upon weaker and smaller birds, robbing those it cannot kill, subsisting on fish and flesh, with a partiality for eggs; piratic, daring, strong and bold; living solitary as the eagle, and defending its nest as few eagles dare; showing so fierce a front in defense of its offspring that few dogs care to close with it. Its attacks in defense of its young are so swift, savage and reckless

[1] Reineke, Ottomar: Oölogist, Vol. XXXI, 1916, p. 13.
[2] Bent, A. C.: Bulletin No. 113, Smithsonian Institution, United States National Museum, 1921, p. 6.
[3] Brewer, T. M.: Bulletin, Nuttall Ornithological Club, Vol. III, 1878, p. 188.
[4] Allen, J. A.: Bulletin, Nuttall Ornithological Club, Vol. IV, 1879, p. 128.
[5] Collins, J. W.: United States Commission of Fish and Fisheries, Report of the Commissioner, 1882, pp. 323, 324.
[6] Goss, N. S.: Auk, Vol. I, 1884, p. 395.
[7] Cooke, W. W.: Bulletin No. 292, United States Department of Agriculture (Biological Survey), 1915, p. 6.

that even the Golden Eagle is compelled to retreat, and for this reason it is believed to guard from the attack of the king of birds the flocks of sheep on some of its island homes. On the fishing banks it follows the fishing fleet and pounces upon any refuse thrown overboard. Powerful of wing, it rides unharmed upon the storm, and so it keeps the sea — a great, dour, somber bird, the embodiment of predatory might. It is not very rare on the fishing banks off the New England coast.

Mr. Walter H. Rich, who has often observed it, thus excellently describes its appearance in flight:

"When on the wing, which is the greater part of the time, the skua shows in the air hawk like, rather than like the gulls, with whom we rather expect to find its resemblances. Its appearance in the air is somewhat like the buteonine hawks, except that its wing action, in its seemingly restrained power and forceful stroke, suggests the unhurried flight of a falcon, or, perhaps, more accurately — since the wings are at all times fully opened, employing their full sweep in their action, their primaries slightly separated at the tips and slightly recurved — the majestic flight of an eagle. The wing spread is ample, the wing well balanced in its proportions of length and breadth, well combined to produce both power and speed. The figure is somewhat burly and chunky as compared with the lighter appearance of the gull and the more racy lines of the yager. The impression of muscularity is heightened by the short, square-cut tail, carried somewhat uptilted, giving the fowl an appearance unmistakable in the eyes of one having once recognized it. This peculiarity of tail, which to me seemed slightly forked instead of having the central feathers lengthened, as in others of this group, together with the broad white patch across the bases of the primaries, furnishes a good field mark for the identification of the species." [1]

Sometimes it may be driven by storm or attracted by food to the shores of Cape Cod, Marthas Vineyard or Nantucket. At such times gunners and fishermen have told of visits of a large, dark bird which from the description they give may have been the Skua.

ECONOMIC STATUS. See page 50.

Stercorárius pomarínus (TEMMINCK). Pomarine Jaeger.

Other names: JIDDY HAWK; GULL CHASER.

Plate 4.

DESCRIPTION. — Jaegers are smaller and not so robust in form as Skuas; bill weaker; middle tail-feathers of all except very young birds extend considerably beyond others; a light or whitish band usually across primaries (white basal parts of inner webs) fading toward ends; plumage very much varied, but upper plumage always darkest; flight hawk-like; all have a light and a dark phase. *Adults (sexes alike):* Cere straight and smooth; unguis not longer than cere; bill shorter than head, about ¾ length of tarsus; upper mandible convex and hooked; head with slight appearance of crest; feathers of

---

[1] Bent, A. C.: Smithsonian Institution, United States National Museum, Bulletin No. 113, 1921, pp. 3–4.

neck rigid and narrow; 1st primary longer than 2d; tail (excluding middle feathers) less than half length of wing; all tail-feathers broad to tips, shafts projecting slightly beyond them; middle pair much lengthened, projecting 3 to 4.75 inches beyond others and twisted at tips to an angle of at least 45 degrees; webs of this middle pair also broadened near tip; hind toe extremely short; webbing of toes very full and slightly convex on edges. There is *great individual variation in coloration* but little seasonal variation; description of all individual variations is impossible; three principal phases may be described as follows (somewhat abridged from Ridgway):

Adults, light phase: Forehead, top of head and front face, together with upper plumage, except lower nape and hindneck, plain dark sooty-gray; rest of head and neck and under plumage white, ear-region and sides of nape and throat more or less tinged with straw-yellow forming a yellow collar; region of vent and under tail-coverts brownish-gray, sometimes intermixed with whitish; bill whitish, its terminal third (approximately) black; iris dark brown; tarsi and feet blackish, upper part of tarsi pale bluish. *Adults, intermediate phase:* Similar to light colored phase but chest and hind neck barred or spotted across with dusky; sides and flanks irregularly barred same.* *Adults, dark phase:* Entirely plain, dark, sooty, grayish-brown, with a slaty cast in certain lights, ear-region sometimes tinged yellowish. *Young in first winter plumage, light phase:* Very little if any elongation of middle tail-feathers; head, neck and under plumage dull buff or white, elsewhere barred dusky; upper plumage dusky, grayish-brown, scapulars and interscapulars tipped buff, rump and upper tail-coverts spotted or tipped same. *Young in first winter plumage, dusky phase:* Entirely sooty grayish-brown; breast, abdomen and sides narrowly and rather indistinctly barred buff; under and upper tail-coverts broadly and sharply barred same. *Immature:* Varying in each phase; lighter phases grow lighter below and the dark phase grows darker; middle tail-feathers increase in length year by year; in lighter phases buffy barring on upper plumage fades into whitish during second winter. *Downy young:* Immaculate grayish-brown passing into paler and tending toward drab on chin and under parts of body; bill brownish, legs and feet much paler brownish.

MEASUREMENTS. — Length about 20.00 to 23.00 in.; spread about 48.00; folded wing about 14.00; tail about 5.00, middle feathers projecting 3.00 to 4.00 more; bill 1.45 to 1.75; tarsus 2.00 to 2.10.

MOLTS. — Juvenal plumage seems to be practically continuous with first winter plumage which is worn with slight change to about end of first year; from June to October of second year birds are undergoing first postnuptial molt; (if there is any spring molt it is partial); many birds in third year plumage (at about two years of age) are practically in adult plumage, but seem to perfect this later. "I have never seen a specimen in which the neck, breast and shoulders were entirely free from dusky mottling. The prenuptial molts of both young and adults are probably incomplete" (A. C. Bent). Length of central tail-feathers varies with age; in juvenal plumage they project very little, if at all, beyond the others, and in other early stages they project more but are not noticeably twisted.

FIELD MARKS. — Largest of our jaegers; adults have elongated central tail-feathers twisted so that ends standing out beyond rest of tail are set vertically and appear spatulate like the blade of an oar; immature birds closely resemble those of Parasitic Jaeger and though larger are indistinguishable in the field unless the two species can be compared side by side.

VOICE. — Usual call "a sharp *which-yew;* also a squeaky whistle; occasionally a squealing note like the *week-week* of the Herring Gull" (Walter H. Rich); "a low, harsh chattering cry" (E. W. Nelson).

BREEDING. — On sea-islands, on the mainland, and by preference in colonies, but nests not very close together. *Nest:* A mere hollow in the moss of some knoll in marsh or tundra; eggs sometimes deposited on a cliff-ledge. *Eggs:* 2 or 3; 2.85 by 1.77 to 2.32 by 1.57 in.; color variable, from light or dark olivaceous or greenish to brownish, spotted more or less heavily with dark brown and sometimes with underlying blotches of gray or drab. *Dates:* June 10 to 28, Alaska. *Incubation:* No data. One brood yearly.

---

* "The majority of specimens are of this intermediate phase, the two extremes being comparatively rare. A large series shows every gradation between the two extremes" (Ridgway).

RANGE. — Northern part of Northern Hemisphere and south to Peru, South Africa and Australia. Breeds in North America from Banks, Melville and North Somerset Islands and central Greenland south to northern Alaska, northern Mackenzie, Melville Peninsula and Baffin Island, in Europe from Iceland to Spitzbergen and Novaya Zemlia, and in Asia along the coast of Siberia; winters on Atlantic coast to Florida, Gulf of Mexico and probably much farther south, and on Pacific coast south to the Galapagos and Peru; reported in European and Mediterranean waters, south Africa and northern Australia; occasional in winter in Orkney Islands, off southern coast of England and off Japan; casual in interior of United States.

DISTRIBUTION IN NEW ENGLAND. — Uncommon spring, not very common fall, migrant off or along coast from Maine to Rhode Island; uncommon or rare to casual in midsummer, but plentiful in the great flight of 1886, from Pt. Judith to Buzzards Bay;[1] on Maine coast occurs throughout summer (May 29 to September 22). — A. H. Norton states that "almost any day in summer spent at sea three or more miles beyond the bays, will usually show one or more Pomarine Jaegers";[2] not recorded from Connecticut.

SEASON IN MASSACHUSETTS. — Spring, usually in May; July 5 to October 20; not recorded in June; occasional in July; more common in late August and September.

HAUNTS AND HABITS. Probably the Pomarine Jaeger is not so common on New England shores as is the Parasitic Jaeger but, like all our jaegers and shearwaters, it comes in some numbers when mackerel and bluefish are numerous in August and September off our coasts. When the mackerel fishermen are making great catches, then is the time to look for the Pomarine Jaeger and other jaegers and shearwaters, for the birds follow the fish. In seasons when mackerel-fishing does not pay, few birds are to be found. The fishermen say: "No fish, no birds." In autumn when the fish move southward, these birds go with them. This large species is rather less bold and active than the smaller species and a little heavier in flight.

Dr. E. W. Nelson says that whenever a Pomarine Jaeger crosses the path of one of the smaller jaegers, the latter commonly gives chase and beats its antagonist off the field. Regarding this he writes as follows: "This attack embarrasses the large bird, so that it flinches and dives, and often alights and watches an opportunity to escape from its nimble assailant. One that was driven to alight in the river thrust its head under water at every swoop of its assailant, and exhibited the most ludicrous terror. When on the wing they usually ward off an attack from one side by a half closed wing, and if above, both wings are used, forming an arched shield above the back."[3]

The Pomarine Jaeger may be seen not uncommonly along the Massachusetts coast, particularly on Cape Cod, in its southward migration, but as the shore line turns and recedes westward toward Long Island Sound, the species grows rare. It seems to move south into the broad Atlantic, and so far as I know has never been recorded from the coast of South America. About May 9 the species again passes northward along our coast. It moves rapidly and a month later appears 2,000 miles north of our latitude. A few stragglers return early in July.

Although this Jaeger is depicted as a coward in its relations to its smaller and more

---

[1] Baird, Spencer F.: Auk, Vol. IV, 1887, p. 71. [2] Auk, Vol. XXXIII, 1916, p. 376.
[3] Nelson, E. W.: Report upon the Natural History Collections made in Alaska, 1887, p. 46.

active congeners, it nevertheless does not hesitate to attack gulls of all sizes, even the great Glaucous Gull and the Black-backed Gull, in its attempts to rob them of their food. The swarming Kittiwakes seem to suffer more than any other species from its persecutions while off our coasts. On its breeding-grounds over the wide and desolate tundra or on its tremendous island cliffs within the Arctic circle this, like other species of the genus, is a notorious nest-robber, taking eggs and young birds alike, but it is constantly on the watch for insects. At sea it has been known to pursue and kill small sea-birds and it continually robs shearwaters of their food. Its evolutions in attacking shearwaters are graphically told by Mr. Walter H. Rich, who says that on several occasions he has seen the Pomarine Jaeger turn a complete somersault in the air while diving down upon some piece of food which the sweeping gale had caused it to overrun. Mr. Rich says that the "Gull Chaser," coveting some dainty morsel which the shearwater has seized, rises against the breeze, turns upside down, and then, with wings half closed, falls on its victim like a lance. The squealing, choking "Hag" gulps mightily to swallow its spoil in time; but if the Jaeger has any luck, he may secure a fragment.[1]

The piratical bird is so persistent in its attacks that it often forces the Hag to disgorge. Terns also are pursued by the Pomarine Jaeger, but it is not quite so successful in robbing them as are its smaller congeners.

At Nantucket, Chatham or almost any outlying point or island on the New England coast in September this bird may be seen chasing gulls or terns to make them drop or disgorge food; it is, however, much more common on the fishing-grounds miles from shore. Two or three or even more sometimes join in the chase of a single gull or shearwater, and when the victim disgorges, they fight over their ill-gotten booty. Yet this Jaeger does not merely exploit the labor of others; it hunts for itself, sweeping over wide waters with steady flight as it searches the waves for any smaller creature that may come within its ken.

ECONOMIC STATUS. This bird has no known economic value.

Stercorarius parasiticus (LINNÆUS). Parasitic Jaeger.

Other names: RICHARDSON'S JAEGER; JIDDY HAWK; GULL CHASER.

Plate 4.

DESCRIPTION. — Nasal sheath or false cere much longer than chord of rest of mandible; wings moderately long, strong, pointed; 1st primary longest; others regularly and rapidly graduated; *shafts of three outer primaries white, those of other primaries growing gradually darker;* lateral tail-feathers graduated only .50 inch, middle pair tapering and pointed, projecting 3 to 4 inches only and beginning to taper about 4 inches from their pointed tips; feet rather short and quite slender; tarsus as long as middle toe and claw. *Adults, light phase (sexes alike):* Top of head, and region in front of and surrounding eyes grayish-brown; rest of head, together with neck and under plumage (except partial collar on sides of neck, and under tail-coverts) white; sides of head more or less strongly tinged straw-yellow; upper-plumage brownish-gray, becoming darker or dusky on primaries and tail; basal part of inner webs of

---

[1] Bent, A. C.: Smithsonian Institution, United States National Museum, Bulletin No. 113, 1921, p. 12.

primaries white which shows when wing is spread; region about vent, and under tail-coverts brownish gray; bill light horn color, terminal part dusky or blackish; iris brown; legs and feet mainly black "upper part of tarsus light bluish" (E. H. Eaton); adults in autumn have chin, throat and neck clouded more or less with light drab, and cap not so dark as in spring. *Adults, dark phase (sexes alike):* Entirely plain, dark, sooty-grayish-brown, neck often more or less tinged straw-yellow. *Young in first winter plumage, light phase:* Head and neck streaked dusky-brown and cinnamon or cinnamon-buff, latter usually predominating; whitish under plumage more or less distinctly barred or cross-spotted with dusky-brown; upper plumage dusky-grayish-brown, feathers tipped or terminally margined cinnamon, cin-namon-buff or whitish. *Young, dark phase:* General color dusky-grayish-brown or brownish-gray; wings and tail darker; middle of neck streaked indistinctly all round grayish-white; under plumage except chest and upper breast, barred with grayish-white, bars broad and distinct on under tail-coverts; scapulars, wing-coverts, upper tail-coverts and most of feathers of back and rump narrowly tipped or terminally margined pale dull buff. In all the above plumages an interrupted band of white or whitish (composed of white basal parts of inner webs) shows across primaries when wing is spread. (This can be seen from above or below.) *Downy Young:* "Sooty brown above, paler below; but the downy young of dark parents are darkest."

MEASUREMENTS. — Length about 15.50 to 21.00 in.; folded wing 11.80 to 13.50; tarsus 1.50 to 1.87; bill 1.15 to 1.50; tail 4.90 to 6.05, long middle feathers up to 9.00.

MOLTS. — The sequences of molts and plumages are practically the same in both light and dark phases as in the case of the Pomarine Jaeger, except that the Parasitic Jaeger seems to mature earlier, normally acquiring its adult plumage when not much over two years old; adults and young have a complete postnuptial molt in August, September and October; probably there is an incomplete prenuptial molt also (A. C. Bent). The Practical Hand-book of British Birds, edited by H. F. Witherby, gives immature plumages up to the "third" summer when the bird is about three years old.

FIELD MARKS. — The long, middle tail-feathers which in adults project 3 to 4 inches beyond rest of tail are not broadened, twisted or rounded at ends as in the case of Pomarine Jaeger but are tapering and pointed; young of the year are hardly distinguishable in the field from either the preceding or succeeding species, although *pomarinus* is larger and *longicaudus* smaller; note in the lighter phase the *downward extension of dark upper color* on sides of neck where it forms a partial or even complete collar; the adult Long-tailed Jaeger lacks this. *Recognition marks:* Immature birds of this species and of the Long-tailed Jaeger so closely resemble each other, their measurements so frequently overlap and their tails are often so nearly alike that it is well to point out dependable recognition marks for the bird in hand; in museum specimens measure the distance direct from front edge of nostril to tip of bill, then compare this with length of false cere or nasal shield, measuring along ridge of mandible; in *longicaudus* these two measurements are about equal; in *parasiticus* cere is much the longer; in birds in the flesh *parasiticus* has legs usually black or mainly blackish, while *longicaudus* usually has them bluish-gray or grayish-blue.

VOICE. — Loud wailing cries interspersed with harsh shrieks; on cloudy days or in dusky twilight vicious screams (W. Elmer Ekblaw); on our coast the bird seems rather silent (E. W. Nelson).

BREEDING. — On Arctic tundras or on or near shores of rivers or lakes. *Nest:* A mere hollow, some-times scantily lined, in bare soil, grass, moss or other low-growing vegetation or among rocks near sea or lake or on an island. *Eggs:* 2, rarely 3 or 4; 2.42 by 1.62 to 2.20 by 1.50 in.; like those of the Long-billed Curlew and quite as variable but not quite so pear-shaped; olive-green or gray, sometimes deeply tinged with yellow or reddish-brown (sometimes brown), marked with sepia and differing shades of drab, brown and lilac. *Dates:* June 10 to July 18, northern Alaska. *Incubation:* Period 24 days (Faber); by both sexes. One brood yearly.

RANGE. — Northern part of Northern Hemisphere. Breeds in North America to about 80° North latitude; from northwestern Alaska, Melville and other Arctic islands and northern Greenland south to southwestern Alaska, Aleutian Islands, southern Mackenzie, northeastern Manitoba, northern Hudson Bay and northern Labrador, and on Arctic islands of Siberia and northern Europe south to Commander

Islands and north coast of Scotland and Hebrides; winters from southern California south to Argentina and occasionally to Straits of Magellan, and from Florida south along eastern coast of South America; also from European coast to Cape of Good Hope, Persian Gulf, and occasionally in Australia, Tasmania, New Zealand and Chatham Islands; accidental in winter in Massachusetts and Maine; casual in interior of North America to Great Lakes, Missouri, Kansas and Colorado.

DISTRIBUTION IN NEW ENGLAND. — Rather rare spring and common fall migrant along New England shores except in Connecticut where very rare; more common on fishing-banks; occasional or casual in midsummer, but plentiful in the great flight of 1886;[1] accidental in interior (Portland, Connecticut) and in winter.

SEASON IN MASSACHUSETTS. — May 31 to November 1, but most common in spring and fall; occasional in summer; accidental in winter.

HAUNTS AND HABITS. Dark hawk-like birds chasing terns or smaller gulls may be seen most commonly in August, decreasing in October on our Massachusetts shores. They are seen most often near Cape Ann, Cape Cod, Marthas Vineyard and Nantucket, and are nearly always common at this season on the fishing-banks. The Jaeger singles out some tern that has just caught a fish, perhaps, and darts after it, following every twist and turn of its victim, menacing it with hooked beak and clutching at it with strong, curved claws until the tern either drops or disgorges the fish, when the dashing robber catches its ill-gotten booty in the air. Probably the Parasitic Jaeger is the commonest jaeger off our coast and along shore when the terns are moving in their autumnal migration. On the fishing-banks the Kittiwake Gull seems to be the victim most often selected by this species. Jaegers seem to be as well equipped as any tern for swimming and diving, but their powerful hawk-like pinions, hooked bills and strong hooked claws fit them for a predatory life, and they prefer to profit by the labor of others. At times when food is abundant, however, and easily obtained they do not rely on the labor of others, but help themselves to anything that they fancy. At such times they so gorge themselves with food as to be unable to fly until they have disgorged at least a part of the feast.

The majority of the birds of this species seen on our coasts in late summer and early autumn seem to be adults of the lighter phases. Birds of the dark phase are rather seldom seen. At a distance these seem almost as black as a crow.

The Parasitic Jaeger passes northward off our coast in May but is then rarely observed; in the latter part of May or in June it arrives on its breeding-grounds in Arctic regions. Its principal flight along the Massachusetts coast occurs on its southward migration. Now and then one rarely appears in July, but the majority come in late August or September. October usually sees the last of them, but there are November and winter records.

In addition to its fish and shellfish diet this species seeks the eggs and young of gulls and terns, kills small rodents, small birds and large insects; while Chamberlain says that in extremity, it will feast on crowberries. Also like all jaegers it is an ignoble scavenger, feeding on offal, ordure or garbage.

ECONOMIC STATUS. This species is of no economic importance in New England.

----

[1] Baird, S. F.: Auk, Vol. IV, 1887, p. 71.

Stercorarius longicaúdus Viellot. Long-tailed Jaeger.

Other names: BUFFON'S JAEGER; WHIP TAIL.

(Also share their names with the two preceding species.)

Plate 4.

DESCRIPTION. — Bill shorter than head, less than middle toe without claw, higher than broad at base, its sides regularly converging; nasal sheath or false cere, covering basal portion of mandible, equal in length to chord of unguis; encroachment of feathers on bill greater than in other species; on upper mandible extending within .50 inch of the outer end of cere, having a broad, rounded termination, feathers of the two sides meeting on and covering ridge of upper mandible at some distance from its real base; feathers on sides of lower mandible extend nearly as far as on upper; wings long; 1st primary longest, rest rapidly graduated; tail longer, both absolutely and relatively, than in any other jaeger, being half as long as wings, graduated .75 inch; middle pair of feathers projecting 7 to 10 inches beyond others, rigid at base, being there much stiffer than other feathers, but gradually becoming flexible, and at length very slender; feet quite slender; tarsus equal to middle toe and claw. *Adults, light phase (sexes alike):* A black cap extends over forehead, lores, eyes and top of head, and down below eyes and upper part of nape; rest of head and neck, including hindneck and lower part of nape, straw-yellow, paler on chin and throat; upper plumage, except as described, plain deep brownish-gray, flight-feathers and tail-feathers darker, becoming nearly black towards ends; *two outer primaries with shafts white or yellowish-white, others usually abruptly darker* (but this abrupt change not always plainly evident); chest (sometimes breast also, more rarely even upper part of abdomen) white, shading into grayish behind; under tail coverts, region about vent, flanks and (usually) abdomen neutral gray; bill blackish toward tip, basal part brownish or horn color; iris dark brown; legs and basal parts of toes and webs light bluish-gray, remaining parts of toes and their webs black. *Young in first winter plumage, light phase:* Ash-brown above, head darkest, cap streaked; feathers of back, fore wings, throat and fore neck grayish-white streaked ash-brown; tail-coverts tipped buff, these tips increasing in width on scapulars and upper tail-coverts; other under plumage dull grayish-white, barred ash-brown.[1] *Young in first winter plumage, dark phase:* Entirely dark, dusky-brown with narrow buffy or whitish feather tips which grow wider on abdomen, tail-coverts, sides and flanks; feet and tarsi of young birds more or less clouded and variable in color. *Downy Young:* Brown, head paler with few if any markings.

MEASUREMENTS. — In size this species is decidedly less than Parasitic Jaeger, but extreme elongation of middle tail-feathers makes its total length as much or even more — 20.00 to 23.00 in. in some cases; folded wing 11.55 to 12.85; tail about 6.25, its middle feathers 10.50 to 16.00; bill (chord) 1.15; cere .60; unguis about the same; from feathers on sides of bill to tip .90; tarsus 1.50 to 1.80.

MOLTS. — There seems to be a light and a dark phase among the young birds but possibly not among adults; first year plumage seems to be worn with little change until first postnuptial molt in second summer; at second postnuptial molt when a little over two years old, bird becomes indistinguishable from adult; adults have partial prenuptial molt in spring and complete postnuptial molt in August, September and October (A. C. Bent). (The Practical Handbook of British Birds describes immature plumages up to the fourth summer.)

FIELD MARKS. — Small size, slimmer form and exceedingly long, tapering tail distinguish adult from other jaegers, but young of the year have short central tail-feathers like those of the others and are indistinguishable in the field except by size.

VOICE. — A shrill *pheu-pheu-pheu-pheo*, often followed by a harsh *qua;* a rattling *kr-r-r-r, kr-r-r-r, kr-r-r-r, kri, krĭ-krĭ-krĭ*, latter syllables shrill and querulous and sometimes followed by the long-drawn *pheu-pheu-pheu* in the same tone (E. W. Nelson).

---

[1] Saunders, Howard: Catalogue of the Birds in the British Museum, XXV, 1896, p. 337.

PLATE 5

Louis Agassiz Fuertes

BREEDING. — On tundra or barren plain or on an island; in colonies. *Nest:* A mere slight hollow in ground lined with a little grass or a few bits of moss or leaves. *Eggs:* Commonly 2; indistinguishable from those of preceding species; average smaller but measurements overlap; 2.41 by 1.67 to 1.90 by 1.40 in. *Dates:* In various parts of breeding range June 6 to July 12 (A. C. Bent). *Incubation:* Period 23 days (Manniche); both sexes incubate (A. C. Bent). One brood yearly.

RANGE. — Northern part of Northern Hemisphere. Breeds on Arctic coasts and islands of Europe and Asia, northwestern and northern coasts of Alaska, in northern Mackenzie and east probably in Keewatin to northern Hudson Bay, north to Grinnell Peninsula, Ellesmere Island and northern Greenland, south to northern Labrador and probably in northeastern Manitoba; winters south to Gibraltar and Japan; recorded in winter in South Carolina and Florida and in migration in Chile and Argentina; not rare in migration off New England coast; casual on Pacific coast south to California; migrates in interior as well as on both coasts; reported in British Columbia, Manitoba, Missouri, Iowa, Indiana and Illinois.

DISTRIBUTION IN NEW ENGLAND. — Rare migrant on New England coast; not rare offshore; casual in Rhode Island and Connecticut; accidental in interior.

SEASON IN MASSACHUSETTS. — Spring and autumn migrant; mainly late August and September; casual in winter.

HAUNTS AND HABITS. The Long-tailed Jaeger is the most northerly in range of the jaegers. It breeds largely within the Arctic Circle and perhaps seldom wanders so far south in winter as the others. It is the rarest of the jaegers on our coast and keeps mostly well offshore. I have never knowingly seen it alive. Its habits are similar to those of other jaegers. In power of flight it rather exceeds its congeners. It is so much superior to the gyrfalcon in the air that in defense of their young a pair of Long-tails will drive off the much larger and more powerful falcon.

It arrives on our coast in September, but authentic records here in the spring migration are rare indeed. In late May and June it reaches its Arctic breeding-grounds.

The Long-tailed Jaeger is almost omnivorous, and takes all sorts of animal food, garbage, insects and even berries.

ECONOMIC STATUS. See page 50.

FAMILY **LARIDÆ**. GULLS AND TERNS.

Number of species in North America 42 ; in Massachusetts 23.

This family consists of long-winged swimmers with horny covering of bill continuous (no false or so-called cere such as is seen in skuas and jaegers) and tail without especially elongated central feathers. This is a large and important group with about a score of genera and over 100 species. It has a world-wide distribution. It is divided into two subfamilies — *Larinæ* (Gulls) and *Sterninæ* (Terns).

SUBFAMILY **LARINÆ**. GULLS.

Number of species in North America 26 ; in Massachusetts 12.

Gulls differ from terns in having bill more or less hooked and tail even or rounded, rarely forked. Gulls average much larger than terns and are more robust in form; their feet are larger and their wings relatively shorter and wider. When on the wing in search of food, they commonly *carry the head horizontally*. They are more at home on the water than terns, but most gulls are not so skilful as terns in diving. Sexes are alike; young generally darker. Apparently they molt twice a year; some of the larger species require at least three seasons to reach full plumage. Gulls feed largely on fish, but are scavengers also, and are continually flying and circling over water and picking up floating garbage or dead fish which they seek also on shore. At low water they frequent tidal flats where they feed.

ECONOMIC STATUS. Gulls are more or less omnivorous, but prefer animal matter as food. The quantity of fish consumed by them is relatively unimportant, as the live fish which they eat are mainly small surface-species. Gulls feed more on dead, injured or dying fish, offal, carrion and small forms of animal life exposed by outgoing tides. They are valuable as scavengers, as they dispose of vast quantities of garbage thrown into the sea or into harbors, and consume shoals of fish and other sea-animals that are sometimes stranded on the shore. Some species visit agricultural lands and follow the plow for grubs and other destructive insects. They destroy many grasshoppers and locusts, as well as field-mice and other rodent pests, and should be protected and conserved. Gulls often are of some value to fishermen in cases where their presence indicates the arrival of food-fish. In foggy weather mariners and fishermen locate dangerous rocks and ledges by the cries of gulls which breed upon them. In war time gulls show the location of drifting mines by perching upon them, and by following submarine boats these birds betray the presence of the submerged craft.

Pagóphila álba (GUNNERUS). Ivory Gull.

Other names: SNOW BIRD; SNOW GULL; ICE PARTRIDGE.

Fig. 3.

DESCRIPTION. — Bill much shorter than head, about equal to tarsus, very stout; feet very short and stout (webs deeply incised); wings very long and pointed; form robust. *Adults in breeding plumage* (*sexes alike*): Pure white; shafts of primaries straw-yellow; bill greenish-gray or slaty at base, rest yellow, changing to yellowish-red at tip; feet black; iris dark brown; edges of eyelids red. *Adults in winter plumage:* White, similar to breeding plumage. *Young in first winter plumage* (variable): Similar, white, but front and sides of head and throat clouded or mottled dusky-grayish, upper neck spotted same; scapulars and both upper and under wing-coverts and tertials spotted brownish-black; spots most numerous along lesser coverts; primaries, secondaries and tail-feathers spotted near or at tips with dusky; a row of spots along under surface of wing near edges. "Bill blackish with yellowish clouding" (Ridgway). *Downy young:* White at first, later gray.

MEASUREMENTS. — Length 15.00 to 19.50 in.; spread about 41.00; folded wing 13.00 to 14.37; tail 5.50 to 6.25; bill 1.15 to 1.40; tarsus 1.40 to 1.50. Female smaller than male.

MOLTS. — Molts and plumages of this species not yet fully known; authorities differ regarding time required to reach maturity; Dr. Jonathan Dwight gives it a three-year plumage cycle, indicating that bird becomes adult at its second postnuptial molt when somewhat more than 2 years old; "adults apparently have but one complete annual molt — in July and August" (A. C. Bent). (Practical Handbook of British Birds gives molting dates June to October.)

FIELD MARKS. — Small size; near that of Kittiwake, much smaller than Glaucous or Iceland Gulls;

FIG. 3. — YOUNG IVORY GULL IN WINTER PLUMAGE

From specimen in Museum of Boston Society of Natural History

Courtesy of Dr. Frank M. Chapman

FIG. 4. — GULL-BILLED TERN ON EGGS

From Camps and Cruises of an Ornithologist

Page 95

snowy whiteness; extreme restlessness; runs rapidly on ice suggesting action of large plover (A. H. Norton); wings *well extended in flight*, long for size of bird but with little bending of carpal joint, broad and wedge-shaped in comparison with those of Herring Gull; *black feet;* flight much like that of tern or jaeger; *immature* show blackish spots on head, neck, wings, back and tail.

VOICE. — A "short, loud, harsh scream," something like that of the Arctic Tern.

BREEDING. — In colonies; usually on rocky, boulder-strewn shores, sometimes on cliffs, sometimes on low ground. *Nest:* If on low ground, a bulky, flat-topped pile of mosses, algæ, lichens, etc., with a few feathers, splinters, etc.; if on cliff, a slight depression lined with a little moss, grass, feathers, etc. *Eggs:* 1 or 2; 2.23 to 2.73 by 1.56 to 1.75 in.; olive-buff or olive-drab marked with varying shades of brown and gray; more glossy than those of Kittiwake. *Dates:* Late June and early July in various parts of range, but no accurate data available. *Incubation:* Apparently by both sexes. One brood yearly.

RANGE. — Probably circumpolar. Breeds in high latitudes from Arctic coast of North America to Prince Patrick Island, Melville Island, northern Baffin Island, northern and northeastern Greenland (in large numbers) and on Arctic islands of Eastern Hemisphere; winters mainly in Arctic regions south to Labrador and casually British Columbia, Lake Ontario and Long Island; in Europe south casually to northern France.

DISTRIBUTION IN NEW ENGLAND. — The Ivory Gull is accidental in winter during or after north-easterly storms. *Records:* A bird was shot December 1, 1886, on Monomoy at the elbow of Cape Cod, by a member of the Monomoy Life Saving crew.[1]

A bird was taken in December, 1894, in Penobscot Bay, Maine, and is now in the National Museum at Washington.[2]

Messrs. Arthur H. Norton and Walter H. Rich observed an Ivory Gull January 5, 1918, in Portland Harbor, Maine.[3]

Dr. C. W. Townsend notes that the late George O. Welch of Lynn told him that an Ivory Gull was shot near the middle of the last century by a fisherman at Swampscott and that the bird was mounted.[4]

HAUNTS AND HABITS.   Where countless crowding icebergs rear their snowy pinnacles; where dark blue, racing seas, flashing and roaring in the clear sunlight, dash their foaming crests high up the pallid slopes of crashing ice; there we may find the Ivory Gull. When leaden waves run sullenly to dash upon the floes; when driving snow-squalls whiten the pack ice; there amid the tumult, its lovely form touched now and then with a gleam of sunlight from a rift in the maelstrom of whirling snow, standing out in strong contrast against the murky clouds, the snowy bird sails serene.

In spring dawns, fair and rosy, when the sun rising over the blue Arctic, magnificent with floating ice, reveals a scene of gorgeous splendor; where ice lies in innumerable shapes, some sparkling like gems and prisms, others rearing vast, white, phantasmal forms; on the edge of the ice pack where the wind opens vast sea-lanes; where the mirage shows towering mountains that never were on land or sea; in summer or winter, in storm or sunshine, there dwells the white Gull, bird of the ice and snow.

The Ivory Gull is abundant in summer on its breeding-grounds in the Arctic seas. It sometimes remains in the far north until the sun has gone and the long Arctic winter night has come.   Forced southward at last by winter conditions during the rest of the

[1] Cahoon, John C.: Ornithologist and Oölogist, Vol. XII, 1887, p. 206.
[2] Cooke, Wells W.: United States Department of Agriculture, Bulletin No. 292, 1915, p. 16.
[3] Norton, Arthur H.: Auk, Vol. XXXV, 1918, p. 220.
[4] Townsend, C. W.: Birds of Essex County, Massachusetts, 1905, p. 88.

year, it follows the pack ice often far from any land. It appears to prefer as a perch the highest pinnacles of ice, and is rather rarely seen on the water. The bird seems to be generally rare in North America below the Arctic Circle, though at times it is common or even abundant for a short time in November or December on the Labrador coast. Boardman reports two examples from Grand Manan, and Chamberlain notes one off the harbor of St. John, N. B.[1]

This lovely white bird is courageous, attacking even the polar bear in defense of its young; but it is a voracious scavenger, a foul feeder, subsisting on blubber, dead fish, dead whales, shellfish, small rodents, garbage thrown from ships and even the excrement of seals. It is a ravenous and omnivorous feeder and no animal food seems to come amiss.

ECONOMIC STATUS. This Arctic species has no known economic value.

Ríssa tridáctyla tridactyla (LINNÆUS). Kittiwake.

Other names: FROST-BIRD; SNOW GULL; WINTER BIRD; HADDOCK GULL; WINTER GULL; JACK GULL; PINNY OWL OR PINYOLE; METERICK.

Plate 5.

DESCRIPTION. — The Kittiwake has but three toes; hind toe usually absent or rudimentary and without claw (but sometimes fully developed); wings longer in proportion to its size than those of Herring Gull. *Adults in breeding plumage (sexes alike):* Head, neck, rump, tail and under plumage, including axillars and under wing-coverts, white; back, scapulars, wing-coverts, tertials and secondaries except white tips light pearl-gray ("between light and pale neutral gray"); primaries a paler gray than back, first five with black ends; 1st, very pale gray without white tip, entire outer web and inner web for about 2.50 inches from tip, black; 2d, like 1st but without black outer web, tip black for nearly same distance as on 1st but having a tiny white spot at extreme end; on 3d and 4th black sometimes grows shorter while tips usually show more white; base of black wing-tip thus extends in a nearly straight line across closed primaries; 5th primary breaks this line, having a white tip with a little black on one or both webs; markings of primaries may vary somewhat; 6th sometimes has black subterminal spot on outer web; white tips sometimes wanting on 1st, 2d and 3d; bill light yellow tinged more or less with greenish; iris dark reddish-brown; edges of eyelids and inside of mouth orange or red; feet black or blackish. *Adults in fall and winter plumage:* Similar to breeding plumage but hind head, nape, hind neck and rarely more or less of breast and belly clouded with color of back; a slaty spot in ear-region which sometimes extends across back of head but may disappear in February; usually a small, dark crescent in front of eye and partially surrounding it; bill a trifle more clouded greenish than in summer. *Young in first winter plumage:* Similar to winter adults but all tail-feathers except outer pair tipped with a broad, black bar; large, prominent, dusky patch in ear-region; broad bar or patch across back of lower neck and large patch on fore wing near bend (usually including most of lesser wing-coverts and part of tertials) dusky or blackish; first four or five primaries have outer webs, outer half of inner webs together with ends for some distance black, rest mostly grayish-white; 5th and 6th usually have some black toward end; bill black; feet dusky-brownish. *Downy young:* Head, neck, wings and under plumage white; back, rump and thighs shaded with yellowish-gray and buff; grizzled, but not spotted like young of Herring Gull.

MEASUREMENTS. — Length 16.00 to 18.00 in.; spread about 36.00; folded wing 12.00 to 13.00; tail 5.25 to 5.75; bill 1.40 to 1.50; tarsus 1.25 to 1.30. Female smaller than male.

---

[1] Chamberlain, Montague: Ornithology of the United States and Canada, based on Nuttall's Manual, 1891, Vol. II, p. 245.

MOLTS. — Juvenal plumage is succeeded by first winter plumage with little molt; immature birds have partial molt usually in early spring (February or March), but sometimes as early as December, in which most of dusky feathers on head and black lesser wing-coverts disappear; most immature birds become as winter adults after first postnuptial molt in August when a little more than one year old (this is a complete molt); a partial prenuptial molt involving head, neck and body-feathers produces adult nuptial plumage; adults have partial molt in spring and complete molt June to December, after which they take on winter plumage.

FIELD MARKS. — *Adults:* Smaller than Herring Gull or Ring-billed Gull; otherwise much like them, except that at a distance ends of wings appear pure black; the black is cut nearly straight across at its base as if the wing-tips had been dipped in black paint; *feet black* (Herring and Ring-billed Gulls have feet of *pale flesh* color and *greenish-yellow,* respectively). *Young:* Broad, black, terminal band on tail; dark bar on back of neck; blackish patch on upper wing; in flight when seen from above, outer primaries form wide, black border at end of each spread wing; bill black or dark; young Kittiwake resembles young Bonaparte's Gull but is much larger and shows white hind-border and black fore-border to spread wing when seen from above; young Bonaparte's Gull has both wing margins black and no black patch on back of neck.

VOICE. — This bird derives its name from its common note *kit-ti-wake* or *kitti-aa* (Montague Chamberlain); "their cry resembles *keet keet wack, wack*" (Ralph Hoffmann); *ka-ake;* sharp, piercing *ki, ki, ki* rapidly repeated and a harsh, rattling *kaa, kaa, kae, kae, kae* and *kaak kaak* (C. W. Townsend).

BREEDING. — In colonies; on ledges of rock and cliffs overhanging salt water. *Nest:* Usually of seaweed, grasses and mosses. *Eggs:* Usually 1 or 2, sometimes 4; about 2.09 to 2.46 by 1.47 to 1.70 in.; not distinguishable in color from those of other gulls but rather lusterless. *Dates:* May 23 to June 26, Gulf of St. Lawrence. *Incubation:* Period 26 days (Evans); 21 to 24 days (Hantzsch). One brood yearly.

RANGE. — Coasts and islands of northern regions. Breeds in North America principally if not wholly east of longitude of Mackenzie River north and east to north Greenland, south to Gulf of St. Lawrence, and from Arctic islands of Europe and western Siberia to northwestern France; winters from Gulf of St. Lawrence south to New Jersey, south in Atlantic to 25° north latitude, and casually or occasionally to Virginia, Bermuda, Great Lakes and Florida; accidental in Ontario, Michigan, Pennsylvania, Illinois, Missouri, Colorado and Wyoming, and in Eastern Hemisphere to Canary Islands, Azores and Mediterranean, Black and Caspian seas.

DISTRIBUTION IN NEW ENGLAND. — Common to abundant fall, winter and early spring visitant offshore except on Connecticut coast where it is generally rare; recorded every month in year off Maine coast; casual in interior; has been noted or taken in Vermont, and at inland localities in Maine.

SEASON IN MASSACHUSETTS. — September 2 to April 7; usually most numerous November to February during cold rough weather.

HAUNTS AND HABITS. Out on the heaving sea of the Grand Banks, where dripping bowsprits rise and fall; where plunging bows of fishing-craft throw off the foaming waves and dash aloft sheets of blinding spray which, torn by the wind, descend upon the icy planks in freezing showers; where roaring, foaming crests overleap the bulwarks and flood the rocking decks; there the Kittiwake rides the wind. Where fishing-vessels ride to taut cables, when dories are hoisted aboard and the splitting and cleaning of the fish begins, there our little gulls gather to the feast.

The Kittiwake is a sea-bird. It is not so commonly seen in our harbors and estuaries as is the Herring Gull, but keeps more at sea, drinking salt water and sleeping on the waves. It is quite tame, comes close to schooners and dories, and thousands have been caught in the past by fishermen with hooks and lines baited with pieces of fish offal. The birds thus taken were eaten or used for bait. Kittiwakes follow ocean steamers and fishing and coasting vessels, sometimes for long distances. At times, particularly after severe winter storms, they may be seen in harbors like those of Rockport, Gloucester, Provincetown, Nantucket and Marthas Vineyard where they find food and shelter. At such times they also visit the outer beaches. Kittiwakes fly over the sea in loose flocks or in company with other sea-birds. Their exceedingly long wings and long, broad tails fit them for powerful flight, and they are among the most graceful of the gull family as they circle and glide on fixed and stable wing, or flutter easily above their prey, maintaining always a perfect mastery of the air. Mr. J. A. Farley tells me that he once saw at Plymouth Beach a flying Kittiwake drop a mussel and then shoot downward easily and gracefully and catch it in the air before it had fallen many feet. The Kittiwake is extremely affectionate toward its mate and young and companions of its own species. If one is shot down, others gather and hover over it and clamorously lament its fate, singularly indifferent to their own peril.

The Kittiwake rarely appears in numbers off the Massachusetts coast until about the middle of October and sometimes not until well into November. It begins to move northward toward its breeding grounds in February.

The Kittiwake feeds largely on the smaller fishes of the sea, on crustaceans, mollusks and other marine animals, and like other gulls it is more or less of a scavenger. It follows whales to pick up the fragments that escape the cetacean's jaws. Dr. Hatch remarks that in Minnesota it eats small snakes.

ECONOMIC STATUS. See page 60.

Lárus hyperbóreus GUNNERUS. Glaucous Gull.

Other names: BURGOMASTER; ICE GULL; OWL GULL; WHITE MINISTER.

Plate 5.

DESCRIPTION. — Very large and powerful; as large as Black-backed Gull; bill large and strong, nearly as long as middle toe and claw; primaries without dark subterminal areas; tarsus longer than middle toe and claw. *Adults in breeding plumage (sexes alike):* Back, scapulars and wings very pale pearl-gray; primaries white or with tinge of pale gray, fading to white toward tips; shafts yellowish-white to pale yellow; otherwise pure white everywhere; bill mostly lemon or gamboge-yellow; vermilion spot near angle of lower mandible; iris yellow; naked skin around eye orange-yellow; feet pale flesh-color or pinkish. *Adults in winter plumage:* Similar; edges of eyelids yellow; feet paler than in summer. *Immature in second winter plumage:* Some white all over; bill flesh-colored, black-tipped; feet as in adult. Other second-year birds more or less mottled ashy or brownish-gray and some have light gray backs and tails quite white but mottled brownish. *Young in first winter plumage:* Impure grayish-white tinged and mottled pale grayish-brown; variable; upper plumage more or less tinged buffy; sometimes quite dusky on back; under plumage pale brownish or grayish; wings and tail slightly barred with same (primaries, white below, fade toward spring to nearly white above); iris yellowish-brown; bill blackish; feet brownish-flesh color. *Downy Young:* Grayish-white above; white below, tinged buff on throat and breast; back marked with smoke-gray; head and throat spotted sooty-black.

MEASUREMENTS. — Length 26.00 to 32.00 in.; spread 57.00 to 65.00; folded wing 16.75 to 18.75; tail 7.40 to 8.50; bill 2.15 to 3.00; tarsus 2.30 to 3.25. Female smaller than male.

MOLTS. — These occur in the following succession: Juvenal plumage barred or mottled with brown seen in August or in early September; partial postjuvenal molt in November or later, which includes mainly part of body plumage while quills of wings and tail are retained; partial prenuptial molt which often begins about end of February when birds have faded and become much whiter than in previous autumn; these two molts seem to overlap and this obscures the question whether all birds have one or two molts at this time; first postnuptial plumage assumed in second autumn is lighter but still more or less mottled; in this plumage also some birds become pure white all over; practically adult winter plumage apparently is assumed in some cases in autumn of bird's third year, but some birds may require more time; The Practical Handbook of British Birds gives progressive plumages up to the fifth winter, admitting, however, that some birds may become fully adult the fourth winter; adults have a complete molt (July to winter) and a molt of body-feathers beginning in March or April.

FIELD MARKS. — *Adults: Great size and no black marks; white primaries very conspicuous in flight* (Herring Gull and Black-backed Gull have blackish or black-ended primaries); may be distinguished at close range from Iceland Gull (which it resembles in all plumages and sometimes closely in size) by its larger head and *longer, heavier bill.* (A Glaucous Gull, a trifle smaller in most of its measurements than an Iceland Gull compared with it, had a much longer and heavier bill.)

VOICE. — Hoarse cry like raven (Nuttall); *kuk-lak* or *cut-leek* (Montague Chamberlain); *kuk-kuk* (C. W. Townsend); hoarse cries *kû-kû-kû, kû-kû-kû, ku-lēē'-ōō, kû-lēē'-ōō, kû-kû-kû, kû-kû-kû — kû-kû* in a hoarse nasal tone, the rest a shrill screaming cry (E. W. Nelson).

BREEDING. — Usually in colonies; commonly on cliffs, sometimes on low islands or sandy beaches. *Nest:* Often mere depression on beach; sometimes mound composed of moss, seaweed, grass and almost any available material. *Eggs:* 2 or 3, rarely 4; 2.75 to 3.34 by 1.91 to 2.25 in.; variable; stone-drab, umber-brown, olive-buff, sometimes pale buff or pale bluish-green, marked with different shades of brown (mostly dark) and ashy-gray. *Dates:* From May 12 to July 6, Arctic coasts and islands. *Incubation:* Period variously recorded as 3 to 4 weeks; 28 days (Evans); 27 to 28 days (Swenander). One brood yearly.

RANGE. — Arctic regions mainly. Breeds on practically all Arctic coasts and islands from northwestern Alaska, Melville Island and northern Greenland south to Pribilof Islands, northern Mackenzie, James Bay, eastern Labrador and Newfoundland, and on Arctic coasts and islands of Eastern Hemisphere; winters from Aleutian Islands and Greenland south to Monterey, California, the Great Lakes, and Long Island, and casually to Bermuda, North Carolina, Texas and Hawaiian Islands; in Europe and Asia north to the limits of open water and south to Azores, Mediterranean, Black and Caspian seas and Japan.

DISTRIBUTION IN NEW ENGLAND. — Uncommon but regular winter visitant on coast; but not recorded from Connecticut.

SEASON IN MASSACHUSETTS. — November to April. (May 26.)

HAUNTS AND HABITS. The Glaucous Gull or Burgomaster is much on the wing, and apparently does not rest on the water as often as do many other gulls. In the Arctic regions it seems to prefer to alight on icebergs and cliffs, but in New England it is sometimes seen along the beaches where fish refuse is thrown into the sea. Even in harbors such as Boston, Gloucester, Rockport and Woods Hole where such food abounds, this species should be looked for among the many Herring Gulls that frequent such places. Since ornithologists along our coasts have begun to look carefully for it, the bird has been seen during every winter in small numbers on the sea-coast of Massachusetts.

The Glaucous Gull often reaches Anticosti Island in August, but does not usually appear in Massachusetts until late November or early December. In spring it reaches southern Greenland and Baffin Land in March or April, and appears in May at the northern limits of its range.

This is one of the largest, most powerful and most predatory of all gulls. It not only robs other gulls, guillemots and other sea-birds of choice morsels and of their eggs and young, but it also actually kills and devours many of the smaller species such as Dovekies. It eats shell-fish, starfish, sea urchins, dead water-birds, dead fishes and other carrion, garbage, and even the droppings of large animals, and is said to feed also on crowberries.

ECONOMIC STATUS. See page 60. This bird has little economic importance in Massachusetts.

Larus leucópterus FABER. Iceland Gull.

Other name: WHITE-WINGED GULL.

Plate 5.

DESCRIPTION. — Bill commonly shorter, smaller and more slender in proportion to size of bird than in Glaucous Gull (according to Dwight, this species averages only 16 per cent smaller than Glaucous Gull, but its bill averages 33 per cent smaller); tarsus usually not longer than middle toe and claw; in corresponding stages of plumage closely resembles Glaucous Gull, but smaller; considerable variation in *first winter plumage,* some birds being quite white but all more or less shaded and mottled and all growing whiter as spring approaches; in *second year plumage* some birds are practically white all over, while others have upper plumage much like adults; according to Dwight, back, scapulars and fore wings are slightly darker at maturity than those of Glaucous Gull; tarsi and toes in fully adult *leucopterus* often *orange-red* and not flesh-colored as in *hyperboreus* (L. Kumlien); in juvenal stage "the primaries more frequently have white or brownish shafts untinged with the yellow so prominent in *hyperboreus;* some birds, too, are in the mottling perhaps more black and white than brownish" (Jonathan Dwight). Mr. Charles R. Lamb took an adult at Rockport, January 22, 1916, which had a bill of a "delicate shade of light green" with a yellow spot, almost orange, on lower mandible and a lighter yellow spot on upper.[1] Young in juvenal plumage have the bill blackish, as in Glaucous Gull.

MEASUREMENTS. — Length 24.00 to 26.00 in.; often less, rarely more; folded wing 14.75 to 17.00; bill 1.56 to 1.87; tail 6.00 to 6.75; tarsus 2.05 to 2.50.

MOLTS. — About like those of Glaucous Gull.

FIELD MARKS. — Most individuals seen on our coast are young of the year in mottled plumage with an occasional older white but still immature bird; nevertheless adults sometimes appear; Iceland Gull resembles Glaucous Gull but averages much smaller; head and bill more slender and smaller in proportion to the bird's size than in the case of Glaucous Gull; seen with Herring Gulls, Iceland Gull usually seems a trifle smaller, whereas Glaucous Gull usually is larger than Herring Gull (but measurements of Glaucous Gulls and Iceland Gulls may approach closely or even overlap; size alone cannot be depended upon always as a field mark); Iceland Gull may be distinguished from Herring Gull by its white or light primaries with no black markings, and from Glaucous Gull by its relatively longer and more pointed wings; in first winter plumage Iceland Gull is indistinguishable from young Kumlien's Gull.

VOICE. — This species seems rather silent here in winter but when pursuing living fish it is said to be vociferous.

BREEDING. — In colonies, sometimes with other species. *Nest:* Varying from mere grass-lined hollow on beach to compact grass, moss and seaweed structure on cliff. *Eggs:* 2 or 3; 2.66 to 2.97 by 1.55 to 2.02 in.; light or dark buff or clay color; variable; more or less tinged with green; some nearly

---

[1] Auk, Vol. XXXV, 1918, p. 233.

"olive drab"; marked with browns and grays like those of Glaucous Gull. *Dates:* May 29 to July 2, Greenland and Iceland. One brood yearly.

RANGE. — Arctic regions. Breeds from Victoria Island to central Greenland and east to Jan Mayen Land; winters regularly from southern Greenland south to Long Island; occasionally on Great Lakes as far west at least as Chicago; casual south to Cape Hatteras, west to Nebraska; recorded in California and at Point Barrow, Alaska; winters in Europe from Iceland to British Isles, Scandinavia, Baltic Sea and coast of France; casual or accidental in Madeira Islands and Italy.

DISTRIBUTION IN NEW ENGLAND. — Common to rare but regular winter visitor locally along the coast; most common in Maine; very rare in Connecticut.

SEASON IN MASSACHUSETTS. — (September 15) November 4 to April 19 (May 13).

HAUNTS AND HABITS. The Iceland Gull, like the Glaucous Gull, is a boreal bird, descending to the latitude of Massachusetts during its winter migration only. Comparatively few specimens are seen annually off our coast. Occasionally, though, it is common locally. At Eastern Point, Gloucester, 32 were reported December 24, 1917, by Barron Brainerd, and Judge C. F. Jenney found 14 at the same spot January 19, 1918.[1] Wherever along our coast fish-cleaning is done or garbage is thrown into the sea, there gulls congregate, and there this species may be looked for. It is reported each winter at Gloucester, Swampscott and Lynn, and occasionally at Boston. It is seen regularly in small numbers about Block Island and Long Island. White-winged gulls are reported in winter from Cape Cod, and may belong to either this or the preceding species. The bird is not very shy, and I have seen it about the fish wharf at South Boston, seemingly quite as tame and confiding as any Herring Gull. Apparently it is not so predatory as the Glaucous Gull. Its habits are like those of the Herring Gull, as it commonly accompanies many of the latter species and feeds with them. The mottled young birds which greatly predominate here might easily pass unrecognized among young Herring Gulls were it not for their generally lighter hue and their white or whitish primaries. Some of them resemble the young of Kumlien's Gull so closely that it is impossible to distinguish the two species.

The food of this species while here is similar to that of the Herring Gull. The bird is a scavenger and a feeder on small marine animals. It is said to eat vegetal matter including grain. Hagerup asserts that in Greenland the young eat crowberries (*Empetrum nigrum*).[2]

ECONOMIC STATUS. See page 60.

Larus kúmlieni BREWSTER. Kumlien's Gull.

Other names: GRAY-WINGED GULL; LESSER GLAUCOUS-WINGED GULL.

Plate 5.

DESCRIPTION. — Similar to Iceland Gull, but four outer primaries of adults with subterminal space of deep brownish-gray on outer webs and two or three of primaries with cross bands of same color near tips. *Adults in breeding plumage (sexes alike):* Back, scapulars and wings uniform pallid to pale neutral-

---

[1] Townsend, C. W.: Memoirs of the Nuttall Ornithological Club, No. V, Supplement to the Birds of Essex County, Massachusetts, 1920, p. 34.   [2] Hagerup, Andreas T.: The Birds of Greenland, 1891, p. 15.

gray; primaries and secondaries tipped white, five outer primaries broadly so tipped; 2d, 3d and 4th, or 2d and 3d, or 3d and 4th, with subterminal band (either extending across both webs or broken or confined to inner web) of brownish-gray (sometimes a trace of this band on 5th); bands on 2d or 4th, or both, sometimes imperfectly developed or obsolete — more rarely only that on 3d complete; four outer primaries with outer web brownish-gray toward end; this color sometimes connects with subterminal band on inner web, but sometimes is separated from band by a white area; inner webs of primaries pure white (except when subterminal brownish-gray band is present) passing into delicate pale gray basally, outermost primary sometimes with narrow subterminal stripe of gray on inner web along shaft; head, neck, rump, upper tail-coverts, tail and under plumage, including axillars and under wing-coverts, white; bill yellow, lower mandible with subterminal spot of red on each side; iris cream color; eye-ring reddish-purple; legs and feet flesh color. *Adults in winter plumage:* Similar, but head, neck and throat rather faintly spotted and streaked brownish or grayish. *Young in second winter plumage* (variable): Similar to winter adult; head and neck mottled brownish-gray; first four primaries dark brownish-gray, darkest on outer webs, wing generally darker than in *leucopterus*, tail largely white (may show gray patches); bill yellowish but somewhat clouded. *Young in first winter plumage:* Light brownish-gray or grayish-brown, nearly uniform on breast and abdomen but upper plumage mottled dull white and indistinctly mottled and irregularly barred brownish-gray; head and neck paler and indistinctly streaked; primaries brownish-gray above, darker on outer webs, whitish below; tail nearly brownish-gray mottled whitish; tail-coverts brownish-gray or grayish-brown, more coarsely mottled or blotched whitish; bill darker than that of adult; iris gray; legs and feet dull flesh color (I have examined many specimens labeled *L. leucopterus* which showed no constant difference from other specimens labeled *L. kumlieni*. If these were correctly labeled, the two species in *first winter plumage* are sometimes indistinguishable). *Young in juvenal plumage:* Kumlien, who collected the type specimen of this species, asserts that young early in September are even darker than young of Herring Gull and that primaries and tail are very nearly black, but I have seen no specimen in this plumage.

MEASUREMENTS. — Length 23.00 to 24.00 in.; spread about 50.00; folded wing 15.00 to 17.00; tail 6.00 to 6.50; bill 1.56 to 1.90; tarsus 2.06 to 2.40.

MOLTS. — Dr. Jonathan Dwight who has examined a considerable number of birds of this species says that first winter plumage is very similar to juvenal, and that plumage assumed in following spring doubtless still closely resembles that of first winter (but birds may be expected to become whiter about head and with a few gray feathers on back); after second autumnal (first postnuptial) molt species attains a considerable amount of adult plumage; "the gray mantle, clouded white head and body, and white tail indicate a close approximation to the adult plumage," but primaries and other feathers of wing not very much paler than in first winter plumage; tail and wings may show some gray patches; bill becomes yellow but often clouded and lacking red spot; second nuptial plumage shows some renewal of body plumage at second prenuptial molt, but individual bird does not become indistinguishable from adult until after second postnuptial molt, when it finally assumes adult winter plumage during third winter, and in next spring after third prenuptial molt when nearly three years old it appears in full nuptial plumage.

FIELD MARKS. — *Adults:* This is well called the Atlantic "Gray-winged" Gull to distinguish it from the "White-winged" Iceland Gull; it is slightly smaller, with considerably smaller bill, than Herring Gull; its lighter back and wings and its *dark gray markings* toward ends of white-tipped primaries which replace *black markings* on wing of Herring Gull are good field marks to separate it from that species. *Immature:* Birds in their *second* winter may be distinguished from immature Iceland Gulls by their darker and grayer primaries but in *first* winter plumage the two species are indistinguishable.

BREEDING. — Nothing is known of its breeding habits since Kumlien found this gull in 1878 nesting "on shelving rocks on high cliffs"; the single egg known to science (now in the United States National Museum) is badly broken; elongate oval in shape; olive-buff with small spots of various shades of brown and brownish-drab.

RANGE. — North Atlantic coast of North America.   Known to breed only in Cumberland Sound; south in winter from Gulf of St. Lawrence rarely to New York, Connecticut and Long Island.

DISTRIBUTION IN NEW ENGLAND. — Rare winter visitant to coast of maritime states.

SEASON IN MASSACHUSETTS. — October 27 to March 24, Essex County (C. W. Townsend).

HAUNTS.   I have never seen this bird in life and can say nothing of its habits, but I have camped for days at a time on islands where its slightly larger Pacific congener *Larus glaucescens* breeds.   Both these species seem to resemble the Herring Gull rather closely in habits.   The bird was first taken in 1878 by Kumlien who believed it to be identical with *glaucescens*.   It was unknown to science as a distinct species until 1883 when it was described by Brewster.   Since then specimens have been seen and taken rarely about the Bay of Fundy and along the New England coast.   Dr. C. W. Townsend has over twenty records of observations of this bird in Essex County [1] and I have nearly as many, several of which doubtless refer to the same bird or birds.   On February 22, 1905, Mr. Francis H. Allen took, in Boston Harbor, an adult male, the first specimen recorded from Massachusetts.[2]   Mr. C. J. Maynard also has reported it not infrequently.   An adult female was taken January 31, 1913.[3]   Other specimens have been taken in New England.   The bird has been noted at Ipswich, Gloucester, Swampscott, Lynn, Nahant, Boston and a few other Massachusetts localities.   In the late fall and early winter it wanders southward sparingly along the New England coast.   Its haunts seem to be similar to those of the Herring Gull and it seems to feed on similar food.

ECONOMIC STATUS.   See page 60.

Larus marínus LINNÆUS.   Great Black-backed Gull.

Other names: BLACK-BACK; SADDLE-BACK; COFFIN-BEARER; MINISTER; TURKEY GULL.

Plate 5.

DESCRIPTION. — *Adults in breeding plumage (sexes alike)*: Bill very stout and heavy, upper mandible very concave; back, scapulars and wings dark slate, nearly black, with purplish reflections; secondaries and tertials broadly tipped white; primaries variable, but all black or blackish, white-tipped; 1st (outer) primary, black, tipped white for 2.50 inches; 2d, black, but more grayish at base with a little less white at tip, the white tip usually interrupted by a broad black bar on one or both webs; 3d, 4th and 5th, broadly tipped white, their bases successively lighter than that of 2d, and fading into white at junction with a broad black subterminal bar; remaining primaries dark slate, tipped white; head, neck, tail and under plumage (including under wing-coverts and axillars) white; bill bright chrome-yellow or pale yellow, tip paler; most of terminal half of lower mandible bright vermilion and often a little of upper mandible; edges of jaws and eyelids vermilion; iris very pale lemon-yellow; feet pale bluish-flesh color.   *Adults in winter plumage:* As in summer, except top of head and hind neck which are slightly streaked dusky.   *Young in first winter plumage:* Upper plumage mostly dark dusky-brown with buffy edgings on back and buffy indentations on wing-coverts which fade to whitish toward spring, when back appears to be barred transversely dusky and white; head heavily streaked dusky in autumn, becoming much whiter before spring; primaries brownish-black; dusky tail basally white, mottled with fuscous, narrowly tipped white, and crossed near tip by a narrow band of brownish-white or whitish, thus mark-

---

[1] Townsend, C. W.: Supplement to the Birds of Essex County, Massachusetts, 1920, p. 35.
[2] Auk, Vol. XXII, 1905, p. 205.   [3] Auk, Vol. XXXV, 1918, p. 233.

ing off a broad dark subterminal band; outer tail-feathers mottled white and some primaries slightly tipped white; under plumage (except white throat) mottled white or whitish and dusky; bill blackish, sometimes paler at base (where pinkish on lower mandible); iris brown; feet whitish. *Downy young:* Pale, olive-gray, lighter on head and flanks, and white on middle breast; upper parts mottled with deeper dusky-gray and head spotted with blackish.

MEASUREMENTS. — Length 28.00 to 31.00 in.; spread about 65.00; folded wing 17.60 to 19.50; bill 2.40 to 2.60; tarsus 2.70 to 3.10.

MOLTS. — The following description (condensed) from Bent (who had access to a large series of specimens) of the molts and sequence of plumages of this bird shows the gradual changes which indicate that the species does not normally assume full adult nuptial plumage until after the third year.

The half-grown young bird is nearly fledged in its dusky and buff juvenal plumage; change from juvenal to first winter plumage is gradual and not very well marked, as the molt is limited; such changes as occur in coloration in this plumage are largely due to fading and wear; in late winter and early spring the first spring molt occurs and the bird then assumes second year plumage showing only slight advance toward maturity, evidenced by more or less dark, slaty feathers in back, scapulars and wing-coverts; other feathers here show both adult and juvenal colors while still others appear like those of the first year; under plumage and tips of wing-feathers grow white; in third year back becomes more than half blackish, and primaries show more black and white; at next postnuptial molt some birds, now a little over three years old, probably assume adult plumage; others (probably a large majority) retain traces of immaturity in primaries and tail, and only become indistinguishable from adults after the postnuptial molt in fall of next year; both adults and young have incomplete prenuptial molt in winter and early spring and complete postnuptial molt in August and September.[1] (Practical Handbook of British Birds gives progressive molts and plumages up to the fourth winter.)

FIELD MARKS. — Larger than Herring Gull. *Adult:* Unmistakable when back is seen in a good light; dark back (much darker than that of other large gulls) contrasts strongly with white head, neck, breast and tail. *Immature in second winter:* Begin to show some resemblance to parents, being evidently "black-backs." *Young of the year:* Difficult to distinguish at any distance from some immature Herring Gulls, but average larger, are more buffy and less gray, are lighter below and head and bill are larger and heavier; may be distinguished from young Glaucous Gull (which has very light wings and tail) by blackish primaries and wide, dark band near tip of tail.

VOICE. — *Cak, cak, cack* (Nuttall); "a very noisy bird on its breeding grounds, indulging in a variety of loud, harsh cries or raven-like croaks; has a long drawn-out scream — *keeaaw* — on a lower key than that of Herring Gull; also a short, more quickly uttered note — *kow, kow, kow* — very much like other gulls; also a high pitched *ki ki* and a hoarse laughing *ha, ha, ha*"; courtship note *kowaat* softer and more prolonged — also humanly varied (A. C. Bent); notes uttered while in Massachusetts waters are generally limited to a hoarse *cow cow cow* and a harsh *ha ha ha;* in Labrador, *cow cow, carcas-sonne, au-par-a-vant, help help,* and *ma-ma* (C. W. Townsend).

BREEDING. — In single pairs or in colonies; on sea-coasts or islands on coast or in lakes. *Nest:* Mere depression lined with moss, grass, seaweed or similar material, or pile of grass, moss and seaweed. *Eggs:* 2 or 3, rarely 5; 2.83 to 3.43 by 2.00 to 2.25 in.; olive-gray, buffy-gray or pale drab to deep buff, sometimes blue or tinged with olive, blotched with brown, blackish and gray; sometimes spotted with purplish or neutral tints darker than those of Glaucous Gull. *Dates:* May 15 to June 13, Nova Scotia; May 25 to June 28, Labrador. *Incubation:* Period said to be 26 to 28 days; by both sexes. One brood yearly.

RANGE. — Coasts and islands of the North Atlantic. Breeds from North Devon Island and central western Greenland south to Nova Scotia and to 50° north latitude on European coasts; winters from southern Greenland (rarely) south to Great Lakes and Delaware Bay (casually to northern Florida), northern Africa and Canaries; accidental in Nebraska, Bermuda, Kerguelen Island and Japan; occasional in interior to Ohio.

---

[1] Bulletin 113, Smithsonian Institution, United States National Museum, 1921, pp. 81, 82.

DISTRIBUTION IN NEW ENGLAND. — Common spring and fall migrant and winter resident coastwise except in Connecticut and Rhode Island waters where rather rare; occasional and sometimes locally common in summer in Maine and Massachusetts.

SEASON IN MASSACHUSETTS. — September 3 to May 11; non-breeders seen irregularly in summer.

HAUNTS AND HABITS.   This great, dark-backed, powerful, wary bird is locally common in winter along the New England coast, and a few individuals may be seen for days at a time in all the summer months on some Massachusetts bars and beaches.   Occasionally in June or July scores appear at outlying points on the Massachusetts coast, such as Cape Ann, the tip of Cape Cod or Monomoy, but nearly all these seem to be immature and probably non-breeding birds.   The species begins to increase in number here in late July and early August and by September it is here in considerable force.   Sometimes a hundred may be seen at once, but usually they are much fewer and often appear in the company of the more numerous Herring Gulls.   They frequent sand-bars and beaches, rocky ledges and isolated points and take good care to keep out of gunshot.   Indeed they are so shy that a powerful telescope is needed to make any intimate study of their habits except in places where they are seldom molested, or are protected or fed in winter, such as the fish pier at South Boston and in Plymouth Harbor.   On their breeding-grounds they may be watched from a "blind."   While here their behavior is much like that of the Herring Gull.   Commonly they are slow fliers but when in pursuit of other birds they exhibit both speed and agility.   In March or April they begin their journey from New England to their northern breeding grounds.

The Black-back feeds on fish or flesh, living or dead.   It is a robber among the sea-fowl, sometimes pursuing smaller birds until they drop their prey, which it appropriates. It kills and devours Dovekies and other small birds, young ducklings and the eggs and young of other birds, young mammals such as mice, rats and rabbits, drives other gulls and crows away from their finds upon the beaches, and takes shellfish and crustaceans. Mr. Allan Keniston of Vineyard Haven states that this gull devours Coots (*fulica*). In a letter (Nov. 30, 1924) relative to the great numbers of Coots or "Blue Peters" in Edgartown Great Pond he writes: "A daily toll is taken by several Black-backed Gulls; these gulls hover over the rocks, dip down and take one every few minutes, then leave to come back again when hungry . . . these Blue Peters seem to lose all idea of escape, just rush around on top of the water and it's only a matter of time or the number of Black-backs that will put the whole bed of fowl out of the running."   "It eats dead ducks and sometimes crippled ducks that it has killed.   It can carry a full-grown scoter."   (Isaac Hills, 3d.)   It has even been accused of eating eggs of its own species.

ECONOMIC STATUS.   This gull, like the Herring Gull, is a scavenger, and as such may be of some service in cleaning up carrion, refuse and garbage.   On the other hand as it kills and eats wild ducks and some other birds it must be included among the enemies of birds.   As no thorough investigation of its food habits has been made, we do not know to what extent, if any, it destroys harmful rodents and insects or useful land birds, and its economic status therefore is doubtful.

Larus argentátus Pontoppidan. Herring Gull.

Other names: SEA GULL; HARBOR GULL; GRAY GULL; WINTER GULL.

Plate 6.

DESCRIPTION. — *Adults in breeding plumage* (*sexes alike*): Back, scapulars and wings mostly pale bluish-gray ("between pale and pallid neutral gray"), darker than those of Glaucous Gull and much lighter than those of Laughing Gull; primaries somewhat variable in markings, their bases colored much like back or a little lighter, this color very short on 1st primary, barely reaching within 6 or 7 inches of tip, not lighter at its juncture with black and extending no farther on central part of feather than on edge; first six primaries with small rounded white spots at tips and black from these spots to gray bases;* black grows narrower from 1st to 7th where it often becomes a mere point on outer web; basal gray of primaries extends about same distance on 2d, 3d and 4th (within about 4 inches of tip of 2d), runs farther up on centers than at edges and grows much lighter where it meets black; white spot near tip of 1st primary rounded and slightly more than an inch long, this mark sometimes wanting on outer vane; in oldest birds spot so enlarges as to include white tip of feather; on 2d primary this subapical spot usually either wanting or very small; primaries from 7th inward gray with white tips; head, neck, rump, upper tail-coverts, tail and under plumage white; bill yellow with transverse spot of red above angle of lower mandible; iris silvery-white to pale yellow; bare ring around eye yellow; legs and feet pale flesh-color. *Adults in winter plumage:* Similar to summer adults but head and neck streaked gray; bill duller in color. *Immature in second winter plumage:* Lighter than in first winter; feathers of back more or less pearly gull-gray; primaries largely dark or blackish, tipped white; head, neck, rump and breast more or less spotted and streaked; tail sometimes dark, sometimes light (when light with imperfect bar of dusky near end). *Young in first winter plumage:* Prevailing color rather dark, brownish-gray, or grayish-brown, more or less variable; upper plumage mottled with irregular small patches of light grayish or grayish-buffy; head and neck streaked whitish; tail and flight-feathers mostly brownish-black; no prominent white spots near tips of primaries; tail sometimes mottled slightly with whitish; breast and belly ashy-brown; bill flesh-colored, blackish toward tip; iris brown; feet dull or pale flesh color. Juvenal plumage assumed by fledglings is dark gray tinged brown, more or less mottled above with whitish and buffy and streaked whitish on head and neck. *Downy young:* Buffy, fading into whitish below and darkening on back, more or less mottled with angular dusky spots; feet dusky-pink.

MEASUREMENTS. — Length 22.50 to 26.00 in.; spread 54.00 to 58.00; folded wing 16.25 to 18.00; tail about 7.50; bill 1.95 to 2.50; tarsus 2.30 to 2.80.   Female a little smaller than male.

MOLTS. — Young have a partial autumnal molt and another in spring, but first winter plumage and first nuptial plumage do not differ very greatly from dark juvenal plumage; at this age bird is widely known as Gray Gull; it has a complete molt in fall when it assumes its second winter plumage which is lighter than before, with more white below and much light gray above; a partial molt in the next spring into the second nuptial plumage lightens the dress still more; not until third year (or later) does bird seem ever to molt into fully adult nuptial plumage; (Astley who has kept European Herring Gulls in captivity says that they do not assume the bright yellow bill until later,[1] and the Practical Handbook of British Birds asserts that young birds become like adults in the fourth winter); adults have two molts yearly — a limited prenuptial in spring and a complete postnuptial in August and September.

FIELD MARKS. — Compared with other gulls the Herring Gull is larger than Ring-billed Gull and smaller than Glaucous Gull or Black-back, but size is very deceptive unless species can be compared side by side.   Young of these other species resemble young Herring Gulls and all at some age may have (or appear to have) a black band or bar near end of tail; but young Black-backed Gull is more streaked and buffy and lighter below than young Herring Gull, while young Ring-billed Gull is generally lighter in

---

* White spots at tips of outer primaries wear away during summer, leaving extreme tips black.
[1] Astley, H. D.: My Birds in Freedom and Captivity, 1901, p. 160.

PLATE 6

PLATE 6

RING–BILLED GULL

Page 80

YOUNG, JUVENAL COMING INTO FIRST
WINTER PLUMAGE

HERRING GULL

Page 72

ADULT IN BREEDING PLUMAGE

ADULT IN BREEDING PLUMAGE

YOUNG IN FIRST WINTER PLUMAGE

SABINE'S GULL

Page 93

ADULT IN BREEDING PLUMAGE

BONAPARTE'S GULL

Page 89

ADULT IN BREEDING PLUMAGE

LAUGHING GULL

Page 82

ADULT IN BREEDING PLUMAGE

ADULT IN WINTER PLUMAGE

YOUNG IN JUVENAL PLUMAGE

YOUNG COMING INTO FIRST
WINTER PLUMAGE

All one-eighth natural size.

color both above and below, with very distinct blackish subterminal bar on tail; adult Herring Gull may be distinguished from white-winged gulls by black ends of its primaries and from Kittiwake by longer and more irregularly shaped black markings on same, as well as by its flesh-colored feet. This latter character will serve also to distinguish it from Ring-billed Gull, with its yellowish-green feet, if the two birds are not too far away.

VOICE. — The usual alarm note *kak-kak-kak*, or a series of *ha ha has* (C. W. Townsend); a challenge or trumpeting call *queeeeah-ah, quak, quak, quak, quak, quak, quak, quak, quak, quak, quak* (A. C. Bent); also many other calls which perhaps express various emotions, as a peculiar, mournful, wailing cry when its young are threatened, and strange hissing whistles.

BREEDING. — Usually in colonies on islands in sea or in fresh water. *Nest:* On ground (sometimes on a bare shoal or on rocks or cliffs, sometimes in thick vegetation); rarely among or *in* trees; usually composed of eel-grass or other seaweeds when on shore, but often of marsh-grasses, weeds, sticks, chips, sometimes a few feathers, shells and tree-mosses. *Eggs:* 3, rarely 4 or 5; 2.70 to 2.90 by 1.80 to 2.05 in.; commonly elongate-ovate but variable; very variable in color and markings — "light sky blue, dead blue, light blue-gray, light gray-blue, dark lilac-gray, light gray, light pea-green, green, drab, warm drab, ochre drab, pink drab, light brown, and cinnamon," with spots and blotches of chocolate-brown, rich brown, light brown, snuff brown, asphalt, black, lilac and mauve (William Dutcher and W. L. Baily);[1] spots and blotches of various shades and many sizes distributed sparsely or thickly as the case may be. *Dates:* May 4 to August 8, Maine (C. W. Townsend). *Incubation:* Period, 24 to 28 days (C. W. Townsend); by both sexes. One brood yearly.

RANGE. — Northern Hemisphere. In America its western and northern limits are rather uncertain but it has been reported as breeding from south central Alaska, Melville Island, southern Ellesmere Island and Cumberland Sound south to southern British Columbia, Saskatchewan, northern North Dakota, central Minnesota, northern Wisconsin, Lake Michigan, southern Ontario, central New York, northern Vermont and Massachusetts, and in Eastern Hemisphere from Iceland and western Siberia south to northern France and east to White and Baltic seas; winters from southeastern Alaska south to Lower California and western Mexico, and from Gulf of St. Lawrence and Great Lakes south to Bahamas, Cuba, Yucatan and coast of Texas; in Europe from British Isles to Mediterranean and Caspian seas and casually to Canary and Madeira Islands.

DISTRIBUTION IN NEW ENGLAND. — Abundant winter resident and migrant coastwise where uncommon to abundant locally in summer; breeds on islands (mostly) on coast and in lakes of Maine;* nests on islands in Lake Champlain; a rare breeder on Massachusetts coast; common to rare locally in migration on interior rivers and lakes.

SEASON IN MASSACHUSETTS. — Resident on coast throughout year; most abundant in migrations or in winter; breeds in a few localities.

HAUNTS AND HABITS. South of Marthas Vineyard lies a little isle of the sea, a mere sand-bar thrown up by the waves, known as Skiffs Island. It is all that shows above water of a long, dangerous shoal that extends far offshore. Strong tides run swiftly about it and angry waves beat on its sloping sands. It is a place for the mariner to avoid. There are ugly tide-rips about it, and often the pounding surf makes landing difficult. High storm-tides tear it down and rebuild it. In August, 1888, it was 1,200 feet long

---

[1] Auk, Vol. XX, 1903, p. 417.

* Arthur H. Norton, Field Agent for Maine of the National Association of Audubon Societies, in his annual report for 1921 said that the Herring Gulls had increased "enormously," having in the past ten years "extended their breeding range on our [Maine, Ed.] coast nearly sixty miles to the westward, with many large colonies" (Bird-Lore, Vol. XXIII, 1921, pp. 355–356). Mr. Norton in 1923 said: "The Herring Gull breeds today as far west as Casco Bay. It has extended its range westward from Matinicus, once its farthest west."

and 290 feet wide in its widest part, and was more or less covered with weeds and beach-grass. In July, 1908, it was but a small sand-spit swept clear of all vegetation. In July, 1917, there were two islands, one of which had a pond with beach-grass growing around it. In January, 1919, there were three islets; in April there were two; and in July there was only one. In July, 1920, there appeared a long island like that of 1888, but narrower. For many years Skiffs Island has been occupied more or less, summer and winter, by Herring Gulls, and in 1919 I found them breeding there. Probably they had been domiciled there for several years. In 1919 they nested in the most primitive manner on the island. The outer beach had been reared high by surf, and usually the sand sloped a little toward the center. Over this outer rampart the sea during storm-tides threw sea-wrack and eel-grass, and in bunches of this stranded seaweed the gulls made their nests. These were mere hollows shaped by the bird in the seaweed and lined with a little of the same material. Young birds that had left the nest squatted and tried to hide from intruders. Larger young ran away over the bare sand until they reached the water into which they boldly plunged to be washed about by the surf.

Probably the Herring Gull once nested on small islands all along the coast of New England; but many years ago most nesting sea-birds were driven away from our southern coasts by continued persecution, and it is only within recent years since protection has had some effect that they have begun to come back. Mr. Allan Keniston of Vineyard Haven sent me a photograph of a nest and eggs of the Herring Gull that he found in 1912 on a "neck" extending out into Edgartown Great Pond. This is the first recent record of the breeding of the species in Massachusetts. The last prior and only known earlier record is that of a pair nesting on middle Wepecket Island in 1888 which is recorded in an interesting paper on the Herring Gull by Mr. George H. Mackay.[1] Mr. Vinal M. Edwards, a thoroughly reliable observer, found the nest and downy young. Captain W. H. Proctor informs me that about 1913 a small colony of these birds nested at Edgartown on the beach-ridge between the herring creek, which flows from the Great Pond, and the sea. The next record is mine for Skiffs Island where at least 20 pairs were nesting in 1919 and 1920, and where I found 14 nests in 1921 though some evidently had been washed away by high seas.* In 1920 Mr. W. Sprague Brooks found two nests with eggs on sand-spits near Muskeget which I saw later; and Dr. John C. Phillips informs me that in 1921 more than a dozen pairs nested there. In 1924 a nest was reported on Marthas Vineyard and several nests on Monomoy. In 1919 Mr. Freeman B. Currier of Newburyport reported a large colony of gulls on one of the Isles of Shoals off the New Hampshire coast which he said was continually robbed by fishermen. He sent me a colored drawing of one of the eggs which unquestionably was that of the Herring Gull. It is improbable that the Herring Gull can long maintain itself anywhere on the coast of southern New England. All habitable islands will be occupied sooner or later by "summer people"; and the gulls on most of the islets that they now occupy cannot be protected

---

[1] Auk, Vol. IX, 1892, p. 226.
* Mr. J. A. Farley found about 12 pairs nesting in 1922.

from the depredations of fishermen and collectors.   However, there are gull-colonies on islands in lakes in the interior, such as Lake Champlain and some of the Maine lakes; while there are islands off the Maine coast where Herring Gulls breed and where they are more likely to prosper.   Says Mr. Arthur H. Norton, of the Portland Society of Natural History, the accredited authority on the birds of Maine: "By a conservative estimate, it seems probable that *upwards* of 60,000 pairs of Gulls bred this year [1921] on the coast of Maine" (Bird-Lore, Vol. XXIII, 1921, p. 356).

I have visited several of the Maine islands which are comparatively large, with high, dry breeding-grounds which have been guarded for years by wardens appointed by the National Association of Audubon Societies.   On all these islands there are weeds and shrubbery and on some, spruce and fir-trees, all of which offer protection and conceal-ment for nests and young.   Most of the islands are uninhabited or occupied only by lighthouse keepers who are concerned to protect the birds.   One of the largest colonies is situated on Great Duck Island off Mt. Desert Island.   This is a rocky island sparsely forested with coniferous trees but there is much relatively open land used as sheep-pasture which supports a good growth of grasses and shrubbery.   The sheep probably do no great injury to the gulls' nests for the birds are well able to defend their eggs and young against these timid creatures.   Duck Island is nearly two miles long and perhaps three-quarters of a mile wide at its widest part.   The gulls build their nests over the greater part of it.

When we approached Great Duck Island in early July, multitudes of white-breasted gulls were seen sitting on stumps or dead branches or on their nests; for in the most thickly settled part of the colony the trees are dead and many have been cut or have fallen, leaving only stumps and dead branches where the forest once stood.   Our intru-sion disturbed hundreds, if not thousands, of birds which rose high in air with a continu-ous, complaining clamor.   The avian host presented a wonderful spectacle as they floated on widely-extended pinions, some wheeling, others darting downward, and all calling and crying with all their might.   Presently many of the more distant birds settled like white doves on the branches of the dark trees, their snowy breasts in bold relief against the blue summer sky.   Numerous nests lay scattered about, some in the open, others concealed, some with eggs, others with newly hatched young.   Downy young were running about and many more were hiding beneath the weeds or shrubbery.   By setting up a blind among the nests one is able, while concealed, to watch at close range the habits of the birds and to observe their manner of incubating their eggs and brooding and feeding their young.   The material used in the nest (largely green grasses, seaweeds, etc.) shrinks and settles under the weight of the incubating bird and is added to and re-placed from time to time with more fresh green material.   Formerly many nests were placed in trees, and I have seen a few in such situations; but under protection compara-tively few gulls now nest in trees.

While the young gulls are small and tender, the parents brood them and protect them from sun, rain and their natural enemies.   The parent bird swallows the food intended for its young.   On reaching its offspring it bows its head until it succeeds in regurgitating the food which is either in a fresh undigested condition or partially digested according to the length of time since it was swallowed.   The bowing of the parent sometimes brings

up the food at once; at other times it seems as if an emetic would be necessary to produce any visible results.   In such cases digestion perhaps has gone a little too far.   However the youngster seems to receive thankfully whatever comes and does not require actually to be fed; for though it receives its food occasionally from the parent's bill, it takes it more often from the ground. The gull chicks as they grow stronger wander about more or less, and some no doubt "get lost" while the parents are away hunting for food; but the adults seem to be able to find and recognize their offspring.   The young, however, do not care by what bird they are fed so long as they get their fill; they beg from any parent that appears near them with food.   Dr. C. W. Townsend avers that both parents feed the young and that they are fed for at least five weeks.[1]

Dejection

While watching the feeding of the young, I saw several insistent, begging, young birds attacked and killed by adults which were probably not their parents.   This murderous habit may come from irritation at the insistent demands for food made by strange youngsters.   In these instances the adult not only pecked the young bird on the head but followed up the frightened and fleeing little thing, sometimes even grasping it by head or neck and shaking and pecking it until it was stretched dead or dying on the ground.   Such savage birds were believed by the warden to be irritable old males who had acquired this habit, which is not uncommon.   Downy young of various ages and sizes are the usual victims.

Somnolence

It is difficult to determine just when the southward migratory movement of the Herring Gull begins in Massachusetts as many of the species remain in summer on our coast.   A large proportion of these birds are immature but by no means all; most adults seen here in June and early July, however, may be barren or unmated birds.   They roost on islands, sand-bars, marshes, beaches or sand-hills, in isolated and quiet nooks and corners of the coast. Where the shore is unsafe, they sometimes sleep on the water; but on islands where they breed, they roost on land, go out at daylight and return before dark.   In early July I have known about 500 birds to sleep nightly in a valley among the sand-dunes

Joy

ATTITUDES OF YOUNG
HERRING GULLS

Expectation

[1] Bulletin No. 113, Smithsonian Institution, United States National Museum, 1921, p. 107.

of Cape Cod.   More than half of them were adult or nearly adult birds.   Gulls are seen also not only on the coast but occasionally about the larger rivers, lakes and ponds, mostly during migration.   Their numbers have increased largely since they have been accorded general protection under State and Federal laws, and have had special care on their breeding grounds by the National Association of Audubon Societies.

The Herring Gull is a master of the air.   It can fly forward or backward, veer gracefully in any direction, soar with stiffened pinions or shoot downward like an arrow, sail on steady wing against the wind and perform numberless evolutions with grace and ease. In calm weather it flaps along much like a heron, and ordinarily when traveling this is its mode of progression; but when the wind blows, it sails, wheels, rises and falls with great speed and power.   Large flocks sometimes swing in wide circles and rise to immense heights.

Naturalists have much discussed the power possessed by these gulls of following without wing-motion a steamer for a considerable distance against a strong head wind.   Some believe that gulls are able to do this because of an upward current of air deflected from the hull of the boat; but this does not explain how gulls can sail thus into the wind when distant from a vessel.   Dr. C. W. Townsend has observed that in flight the feet of this gull are usually carried behind under the tail, but are sometimes brought forward and buried in the feathers of the breast or belly.

Herring Gulls are excellent swimmers; but although commonly seen on the water, they do not swim very far when able to fly.   They do not seem to dive commonly or deeply, but in case of necessity they can dive like terns from on the wing.   I once saw one at rest on the Wankinco River that dived from the surface in less than six feet of water and apparently brought up some food from on or near the bottom.

This species, like many other sea-birds, can drink salt-water, but evidently it must drink fresh water also, as there are many colonies on fresh-water lakes.   During the seasons of migration when fresh-water ponds are unfrozen, many Herring Gulls visit such ponds that are near the sea.   It is a common sight to see them flying over Boston in numbers in autumn, winter and spring, on the way to and from the Back Bay Basin, Fresh Pond in Cambridge, or other ponds about Boston where shooting is forbidden. At times so many gulls collect in some of the reservoirs supplying Boston or nearby cities with water that the authorities have feared that these birds from the water-front might contaminate the drinking water with typhoid bacilli from sewage discharged into the harbor; and men with guns have been employed to drive the gulls from the reservoirs. Perhaps eventually we may come to realize the folly of casting into rivers and harbors the sewage of our cities, and thus wasting invaluable fertilizer for the land, befouling pure waters, destroying or polluting valuable fisheries and endangering the lives of citizens.

About the second week in August when the breeding season is nearly over and many young are on the wing, the Herring Gulls scatter from their breeding-islands in Maine and the Provinces.   Late in July their numbers begin sometimes to increase on the Massachusetts coast and on the fishing-grounds, and before the end of September they have scattered all along the coast of southern New England, and have reached New Jersey. From late March until well into May flocks may be seen on their return flight.

The natural food of the Herring Gull consists of fish, shell-fish and other marine or fresh-water animals, together with many insects, supplemented in times of scarcity by eggs and young of other sea-birds. A scavenger, however, the bird always has been, for the reason that it is not skilful in diving and swimming under water, and so finds it difficult to catch large, healthy, active fish except under particularly favorable circumstances — as where many fish are crowded together in a limited space in a net or weir or in a narrow, shallow stream. Therefore it lives more on dead, dying, stranded or disabled fish and fish-refuse than on the products of its own skill in fishing.

The Herring Gull watches diving ducks and mergansers as they dive for food; and when a successful bird comes up, the gull hovers overhead and very often is quick enough to snatch the morsel from the diver's bill as soon as the bird reaches the surface. Mr. John A. Farley, who has spent considerable time in watching Herring Gulls, has been kind enough to supply me with his notes on this subject. See also "The Gulls and Terns of Sagadahoc County" by Capt. Herbert L. Spinney for a description of this habit.[1] It is able often to secure clams and other shell-fish, especially after storms when the bivalves are washed upon the beach. By care and dexterity it now and then seizes the neck of a buried clam and bites off its head. It has learned the crow's plan of rising high in air and dropping the clam or mussel on a rock or other hard object to break the shell, following quickly as it falls to take advantage of a break in the shell, or to guard the morsel from thieving crows. Often the gull does not fly high enough the first time to break the shell. However, if the shell remains unbroken, the bird picks it up again and carries it higher. If the second drop is ineffective, the mollusk is taken higher still, until finally the impact of the fall smashes the shell and the bird descends to its hard-won repast. The gulls have learned that the automobile road between Vineyard Haven and Oak Bluffs on Marthas Vineyard offers an excellent surface for smashing shells. As a consequence the roadway is constantly strewn with broken shells much to the disgust of motorists.

There is some complaint that these gulls destroy scallops, but probably most of these shell-fish taken by them are such as are cast up by the waves or have gotten into shallow water where, if not picked up by the gulls, they probably would be destroyed by the frost and ice of winter.

When the crews of fishing-vessels are dressing their catch, Herring Gulls lose most of their characteristic caution, and crowd around the sterns, and drop to the water with extended feet and spread tails to pick up any morsels they can reach. When thus they swarm about the stern of a fishing-boat, in their eagerness to secure their share, they sometimes approach within two or three yards of the men at work. Throughout the fishing-season the gulls visit the traps and pounds of the shore-fishermen where they cap-

---

[1] Journal of the Maine Ornithological Society, Vol. I, 1899, p. 17.

FIG. 5. — YOUNG HERRING GULLS LESS THAN THREE DAYS OLD
SKIFFS ISLAND

FIG. 6. — NEST OF HERRING GULL. SKIFFS ISLAND

ture many fish that are dead, dying or disabled. In herring ponds and creeks, also, where the fish become massed in shallow water, the gulls catch many, especially the weaker or injured ones, and feed also on the dead and dying. They kill and eat mice, rats and other rodents. Chamberlain says that "their formula for disposing of a rat is unique." They first break the bones by crunching with the bill; then dip the rat in water and soak it thoroughly; then swallow it entire, head first. It is a habit of this gull to soak dry or salted food, or to rinse food in water before eating it. I saw traces on the sands of Monomoy showing that a gull had dragged some object, probably a dry fish, nearly 150 yards to the water, and Dr. C. W. Townsend tells of a fish that he found on Ipswich Beach that had been dragged 134 yards.[1] On islands where insects are abundant, young Herring Gulls secure many of the larger species. Adults sometimes pick up worms and grubs behind the plowman.

During hard winters when harbors and flats are iced over and food is hard to get, Herring Gulls eat dead ducks, and even pursue and kill the wounded or starving of these or other birds, thereby usurping the prerogative of the crows. Mr. Horace Bearse of Chatham says that during the hard winter of 1919–20, when the crows and gulls, both on the verge of starvation, clashed at a garbage-heap in that town, he saw a crow attack a Herring Gull. The crow was more active and vigorous than the gull and succeeded first in blinding its enemy and then in killing it. This could not have happened except to a gull weakened by starvation.

ECONOMIC STATUS. Civilization has diminished the natural food for gulls in our harbors and rivers by decreasing the supply of fish and shell-fish, but has substituted offal, garbage and sewage which are eagerly sought by these birds. The Herring Gull has become valuable therefore as a scavenger. It gathers in flocks in harbors wherever fish are dressed or thrown away, at canning factories, fish-freezers or fish-wharves and quickly devours all offal or fish-waste thrown into the water. It flocks in thousands where sewage is discharged and where garbage is dumped at sea, and cleans up much filthy, floating refuse that might otherwise be cast back by winds and tides on beach and shore. Wherever fish, killed in thousands by disease, frost or other causes, are cast up in countless multitudes upon the shore to poison the air with the offensive effluvia of decay, there the gulls gather and in an astonishingly short time succeed in abating the nuisance. Sometimes the zeal of the gulls in disposing of such noisome fare brings them into disfavor with the farmers who, having hauled loads of dead fish to their fields for fertilizer, fail to plow them under, and soon find that they have vanished, the gulls having flown away with them. Not long ago a farmer in Rhode Island bought for fertilizer some tons of starfish that had been dredged up by the oystermen; but he let them lie too long and when he got ready to haul them, they had disappeared. The gulls knew where they went.

Mr. Arthur H. Norton reports (Auk, Vol. XXVI, 1909, p. 438) that the Herring Gull

---

[1] Bent, A. C.: Bulletin No. 113, Smithsonian Institution, United States National Museum, Life Histories of North American Gulls and Terns, 1921, p. 111.

destroys the beach snail (*Polinices heros*) which is a well-known and common enemy of the clam.

Herring Gulls are very noisy during the breeding season, and in foggy weather on the Maine coast their clamor serves to mark the islands on which they breed. The birds thus serve the purpose of the stationary fog-horn. In thick weather local fishermen heed the loud voices of the birds to correct their course. Small coasting steamers threading devious channels in a fog often stop while the pilot listens for the gull-chorus which may indicate the need of another turn of the steering-wheel to clear the rock.

Larus delawarénsis Ord. Ring-billed Gull.

Plate 6.

DESCRIPTION. — Bill quite stout, nearly equals length of middle toe without claw; middle toe and claw hardly more than three-quarters length of tarsus. *Adults in breeding plumage (sexes alike)*: Head, neck, tail, upper tail-coverts and under plumage including axillars and under wing-coverts white; back, scapulars and wings light pearl-gray fading gradually into white at ends of secondaries; primaries (subject to some variation) — 1st black, basal part of inner web very pale gray, almost white, with spot of white about 1.25 inches in length near end and of about equal extent on both webs, divided by black shaft; 2d primary similar but with inner web whitish basally for a longer space and small white spot near end; whitish on bases of primaries increases inward and black decreases until on 5th or 6th, it becomes a mere bar or spot; tip of 1st primary black, others white, white terminal spot being very small on 2d, gradually increasing on others (but these terminal spots sometimes wanting); 7th and last primaries like secondaries pale gray with white tips and no black; bill chrome-yellow at tip, sometimes tinged orange, greenish-yellow elsewhere, except wide band of black which encircles it at angle (some specimens have only a transverse spot of black); inside of mouth deep orange-red; edges of eyelids red or yellow; iris straw-yellow or cream; feet pale greenish-yellow, "light yellow" or "chrome-yellow" (but usually with a greenish cast); "dusky-green" (J. H. Langille). *Adults in winter plumage:* Similar but head and neck (except chin, throat and sometimes fore neck) spotted or streaked slightly with dusky; feet greenish. *Immature in second winter plumage:* Back mainly light gray, feathers narrowly edged whitish, greater wing-coverts similar; lesser wing-coverts mottled dusky; much dusky on primaries, tertials and sometimes on secondaries; primaries brownish-black; tail whiter basally but still has broad, dusky, subterminal band; head and hind neck streaked and spotted dusky; below mainly white; basal half of bill yellowish, terminal half black; iris grayish-yellow; feet becoming greenish. *Young in first winter plumage:* Similar to juvenal plumage. Above irregularly mottled with dusky-brown and "gull gray" of adults; during winter buffy and dark markings of feathers wear away and fade leaving bird generally much lighter colored than in juvenal plumage; head and neck mottled dusky; many new feathers, partly light gray with dark markings, appear on back; primaries largely blackish, inner ones basally light gray slightly tipped white; basal half (about) of secondaries light gray; tail very pale gray, basally whitish, lighter in color than in juvenal plumage, mottled with grayish-brown, a broad, dusky band near end, and slightly tipped whitish; below white with more or less mottling; iris brown; naked eye-ring bluish; feet pale flesh color or "purplish gray"; bill blackish, base (more or less) flesh color or yellowish, extreme tip light. *Dark Phase:* Apparently two phases are seen in juvenal and first winter plumages. Some young birds in September are nearly as dark as juvenal Herring Gull with blackish tail (no dark bar) and only a few light marks toward tips and on lateral feathers; some variation in tail-pattern; feathers of back and scapulars broadly margined and tipped pinkish buff or whitish; lower abdomen shading into whitish; closely resembles young of California Gull but smaller. *Young in juvenal plumage:* Resembles juvenal Herring Gull but much smaller; tail dusky or blackish (not light with subterminal black band as in later immature plumages), with usually a little more white about tip than in Herring Gull; relatively broader whitish margin on feathers of back, scapulars, tertials, rump and upper tail-coverts. *Downy young:* At least two color phases; some individuals smoke-gray; others buffy, all distinctly spotted dark brown on head and neck, and less distinctly mottled or clouded with same on back; lighter, sometimes nearly white, below.

MEASUREMENTS. — Length 18.00 to 20.00 in.; spread about 47.00 to 49.50; folded wing 13.60 to 15.75; tail 5.20 to 6.00; bill 1.42 to 1.63; tarsus 1.95 to 2.45.

MOLTS. — Juvenal plumage complete when bird is nearly full grown and partial molt of body-feathers later when bird goes into first winter plumage; in spring partial prenuptial molt and in autumn full postnuptial molt; molt thus continues, partially in spring and wholly in autumn, until bird is two years old when "the fully adult plumage is perhaps assumed by some birds," but many "still retain signs of immaturity during the third year" (A. C. Bent); there is complete postnuptial molt of both adults and young in August and September and partial prenuptial molt (of body-feathers) mainly in March.

FIELD MARKS. — A little larger than Kittiwake or Crow. *Adult:* Black ring or partial black cross-bar on bill, seen only at close range unless with a powerful glass; tarsi and feet greenish-yellow or grayish-yellow-green, instead of black as in Kittiwake, or flesh-colored as in Herring Gull; black of primaries has distinct terminal white spots (see under Kittiwake); back a little lighter than that of Herring Gull; smaller and tamer "with a lighter and more sprightly carriage" (L. A. Fuertes). *Bird of first winter:* Not usually so slaty-gray as in Herring Gull but lighter; its lighter color and very distinct, well-defined, dark band on tail should separate it from Herring Gull, immature of which, however, sometimes has, or appears to have, a broad, dark tail-band.

"The fact that they may fly along the beach directly by or over an observer without sheering off out of gunshot as Herring Gulls do has always given me a hint as to the species, for they appear to have a very confiding nature" (C. W. Townsend).

VOICE. — When alarmed, a piercing note of protest — *kree, kreeee* — like the cry of a hawk, softened and modified when its excitement has subsided; subdued *kow, kow kow* often heard from a flock floating overhead; while pursuing its ordinary vocations rather silent except for a short mellow *kowk* (A. C. Bent).

BREEDING. — In colonies; sometimes with other water-birds, on islands in inland lakes or on sea-islands or cliffs. *Nest:* Much like that of Herring Gull; usually on ground or rock, rarely in small tree. *Eggs:* Commonly 3; similar to those of Herring Gull but smaller; average 2.35 by 1.67 in. *Dates:* May 9 to June 22, North Dakota; June 4 to 23, Saskatchewan and Manitoba. *Incubation:* Period about 21 days (A. C. Bent). Presumably one brood yearly.

RANGE. — North America. Breeds (mainly in southern Canada) from southern Alaska, central British Columbia, Great Slave Lake, northern Manitoba, northern James Bay and Hamilton Inlet south to southern Oregon, northern Utah, Idaho, southern Colorado, northern North Dakota, southern Ontario, northern New York (casually) and Canadian Labrador (southeastern Quebec), and (formerly at least) in Minnesota, Wisconsin and northern Michigan; not known to breed on Atlantic coast in New Brunswick, Nova Scotia or New England; winters from British Columbia, Colorado, Idaho, Montana, Great Lakes and Maine (rarely Gulf of St. Lawrence), south to Bermuda (casually), Gulf of Mexico, Cuba and southern Mexico; accidental in Hawaii.

DISTRIBUTION IN NEW ENGLAND. — Not uncommon migrant coastwise; locally and irregularly common to rare or casual migrant inland; irregular winter resident coastwise.

SEASON IN MASSACHUSETTS. — July (17) to late May or early June (June 5); apparently winters rarely (though perhaps regularly) except in mild winters when more common; "common at Plymouth in a very severe winter" (J. A. Farley).

HAUNTS AND HABITS. The Ring-billed Gull which was described by Audubon as the "Common American Gull" is no longer the common gull of New England. It does not breed now on the New England coast, if it ever did, and has not been noted very recently as breeding very commonly even in Labrador where formerly it was abundant. It has also forsaken several islands in the Great Lakes and has retired to regions where it is less persecuted by man.   Apparently it cannot stand such persecution as has followed the Herring Gull, and it has been driven to breeding-haunts farther north or in the interior which are remote from thickly populated districts.   For many years it has been seen on the New England coast only in migration or in winter; but it is still the common gull on the lakes of the prairies and plains of the northern United States and Canada where it far outnumbers the Herring Gull.   Since gulls have been given continuous protection under the laws of State and Nation, this species seems to have increased in migration along the Atlantic coast;   recently it has been reported in greater numbers, and more often, in New England.   It is seen singly, in small flocks or with Herring Gulls, mainly during the migrations.   In appearance, flight and behavior the Ring-billed Gull resembles closely the Herring Gull.   Many of its notes are similar to those of that species; and when seen in flocks of its own kind, it might be (and probably often is) mistaken for its larger congener.   It is sociable and gregarious, associating not only with those of its own species but also with other gulls.

It is a very clever bird on the wing.   Mr. J. A. Farley notes that once in the Gulf of St. Lawrence he saw a Ring-billed Gull which was flying in the wake of the vessel, and which scratched its face with its claw as it flew.

The Ring-billed Gull is rarely seen in Massachusetts waters before September or early October when young birds appear among flocks of Herring Gulls.   Most individuals pass southward and comparatively few winter north of Cape Cod.   In March and April they appear on their return; by the middle of April they have reached their breeding-grounds in North Dakota; and during the latter part of the month they arrive in the Canadian Northwest.

This gull frequents the outer bars and beaches where it feeds largely on dead fish and other aquatic animals, small rodents and insects.

ECONOMIC STATUS.   The Ring-billed Gull performs the part of a scavenger by assisting the Herring Gulls in cleaning up floating refuse in the harbors, or wherever garbage from the cities is dumped at sea or about the lakes of the interior.   It sometimes robs the nests of other birds but has a useful habit on its breeding grounds, that of catching flying insects, particularly grasshoppers.   On the whole it is a gentle, confiding and beautiful species, and may be regarded as ordinarily more beneficial than injurious.

Larus atricilla LINNÆUS. Laughing Gull.

Other names: BLACK-HEADED GULL; BLACK-HEAD; BLACK-HEADED MACKEREL GULL.

Plate 6.

DESCRIPTION. — Bill about as long as middle toe and claw; shorter than tarsus or head; outline of lower mandible concave in front of angle; tip of upper mandible well decurved; middle toe about three-quarters length of tarsus. *Adults in breeding plumage (sexes alike):* Head mostly dark sooty-gray or nearly black which extends farther down on throat than on nape; eyelids more or less white, posteriorly, their edges red; neck (all around), broad tips of secondaries, tertials and inner primaries, upper tail-coverts, tail and under plumage white, latter sometimes with more or less rosy, peach-blossom tinge; back, scapulars and wings rather dark leaden-gray, much darker than usual gull-gray; outer six (five sometimes) primaries more or less black, usually white-tipped, their bases for short distance on inner web of 1st and for increasing distance on both webs of others, colored like back; bill dark brownish-red shading into blood-red or carmine toward tip of upper mandible; feet dusky-red, webs darkest; iris very dark brown. *Adults in winter plumage:* Similar but white below, never rosy; no hood; head white with some blackish marks on top and back of head and about eye- and ear-regions; bright coloring of bill and feet obscured. *Young in first summer plumage:* Similar to winter adult but secondaries largely grayish-brown; primaries dark grayish-brown and unspotted; tail white with some dark feathers or marks. *Young in first winter plumage:* Back, scapulars and smaller wing-coverts grayish-brown, broadly edged pale grayish-buff or clay color; greater wing-coverts gray with edges lightening to pale grayish-buff toward ends; secondaries dusky (mainly on outer web) white-tipped but grayish basally; primaries and their coverts dull slaty-blackish, some narrowly tipped white; upper tail-coverts and sides of rump white; rest of rump light brownish-gray; other hinder parts, except tail, white; basal half of tail light gray, rest black, narrowly tipped white; head, neck, breast and sides brownish-gray or grayish-brown, darkest on top of head and nape and somewhat tinged dull buffy on breast and sides; upper breast and abdomen grayish-white or very pale brownish-gray; bill and feet obscured with blackish. *Young in juvenal plumage:* Similar to that of first winter but darker, some dark gray or drab on head, neck and breast, almost as dark as young Herring Gull. Such birds may be seen in August on our coast. *Downy young:* Buffy-brown or dark above, sometimes more or less tinged with tawny-olive and variegated with dusky or dark brown; lighter below.

HALF GROWN DOWNY YOUNG
LAUGHING GULL
About ½ natural size.

MEASUREMENTS. — Length 15.50 to 17.00 in.; folded wing 12.25 to 13.75; tail 4.62 to 5.40; bill 1.42 to 1.65; tarsus 1.82 to 2.07. Female smaller than male.

MOLTS. — Apparently the Laughing Gull assumes winter plumage of adult in its second autumn, although a few individuals may still show signs of immaturity; in spring of next year all take on for the first time fully adult nuptial plumage; Bent says that juvenal plumage is complete before the young bird is fully grown, and that a gradual postjuvenal molt takes place during the first autumn and winter, which is practically continuous with the first prenuptial molt of first spring; the bird afterward molts fully in fall and partially in spring.

FIELD MARKS. — *Adults:* Not likely to be confused with any gull commonly found in Massachusetts except Bonaparte's Gull, which is smaller, has a much lighter back, a black bill and is rarely seen here (except in spring) in full nuptial plumage with black head; black outer primaries distinguish Laughing Gull from Bonaparte's Gull which has outer primaries mainly white with black tips. *Young:* No other small gull in New England has breast as dark as this species.

VOICE. — '*Haw 'ha 'ha 'ha 'haw, oh oh agh agh* (Nuttall); *half, half, half* (A. C. Bent); a deep *ha ha ha* followed by rapidly repeated sounds as of rippling laughter, complaining cries *ai ai* and *kai kai* (C. W. Townsend).

BREEDING. — In colonies; sometimes in company with terns; usually on sea-islands. *Nest:* On ground; sometimes mere hollow in sand without concealment; usually rather well built of grasses, sea-weed, sticks, etc., and more or less concealed among rather thick, low vegetation. *Eggs:* Two to five, usually three; 2.10 by 1.55 in. (Coues); ranging in shape from elongate-ovate to short-ovate; brown to olive-buff or cream-buff or even pea-green, with spots, blotches and sometimes scrawls varying from seal-brown to raw-umber; often with underlying spots of different shades of gray or pale purplish. *Dates:* April 8, Texas; May 26, Cobb's Island, Virginia; June 7, Muskeget Island. *Incubation:* Period about 20 days (A. C. Bent). One brood yearly.

RANGE. — Tropical and temperate coasts of America. Breeds from Maine and Massachusetts (formerly Nova Scotia) south on Atlantic and Gulf coasts to southern Texas; winters (mainly in Gulf of Mexico and Caribbean Sea) from coast of South Carolina south to Chile and Brazil; casual in New Mexico, Colorado, Kansas, Nebraska, Wisconsin, Iowa, Quebec and Ontario; accidental in Lower California, Bermuda and Europe.

DISTRIBUTION IN NEW ENGLAND. — Rare summer visitant along most of New England coast but fast increasing in numbers; breeding plentifully on Muskeget Island and in smaller numbers on Western Egg Rock in Muscongus Bay, Maine;* former nesting-places of the bird in Maine were Matinicus Seal Island, Metinic Green Island and Little Green Island, the latter colony being of long standing; a straggler in Vermont; more or less common in summer on coast within 20 miles or more of its breeding places; a bird of this species was seen early in October, 1923, by R. O. Morris at Southwick Ponds, Massachusetts.[1]

SEASON IN MASSACHUSETTS. — April 12 to October 23 (November 10).

HAUNTS AND HABITS. South of the peninsula of Cape Cod lies a sandy island which is now the chief breeding-place of the Laughing Gull in New England. The Indians named this islet Muskeget and it still bears the name. Lying on the boundary of Nantucket Sound and surrounded by treacherous shoals, it is one of the graveyards of the Atlantic and is avoided by mariners. Often its shores are strewn with the timbers and wreckage of lost ships. Strange sea-creatures frequent the deeps and shallows that surround this island. Small fish often abound in the adjacent waters and these are pursued by larger fish and sea-birds. Thousands of gulls and terns breed and rear their young upon the sands of the island. It is one of the largest bird nurseries on the New England coast. Muskeget Island consists mainly of sand built up by wave and wind and appears to be of comparatively recent origin. It is roughly crescent-shaped and is about one and one-half miles long. Sand spits rising above the waters near its northwestern face defend it against the sea and provide a harbor for small boats. Tides run fiercely over the shoals about it and in windy weather, particularly at low stages of the tide, foaming breakers roar for miles along the tide-rips and break in fury on the shore. Treeless, Muskeget is a succession of low, rolling dunes and hollows or sandy levels covered more or less with beach-grass, poison-ivy, beach-peas and other low-growing plants and with stunted bayberry and beach-plum bushes. Formerly its vegetation was very sparse; but within a few years this has increased in quantity and luxuriance, making conditions more favorable for the Laughing Gulls, which prefer to hide their nests, and less so for the Common Terns which affect more open sandy land. The only permanent domicile on the island is the United States Life Saving Station, but there are also a number of

---

* Western Egg Rock is near New Harbor, a small fishing hamlet and summer resort in the town of Bristol. It is owned by the Cumberland County Audubon Society. "In Muscongus Bay some of these birds have nested from times unknown. There they have occupied the Shark, the Eastern and the Western Egg Rocks, at times scattering to all, at other times resorting to one or two of the three stations" (Arthur H. Norton in Maine Naturalist, Vol. IV, 1924, p. 65).

[1] Bagg, A. C.: *in litt.*

shanties and camps occupied from time to time by gunners, sportsmen or fishermen. The Laughing Gulls usually arrive in numbers about the second week in May on their nesting grounds here.

When I first visited Muskeget in 1908 with two companions, we were lost in wonder at the enormous numbers of its feathered inhabitants. As we approached the nesting grounds, we were soon in the midst of a veritable storm of darting, diving, sailing, fluttering, screaming terns, while high above our heads in the blue and cloudless sky floated innumerable black-headed gulls, their clear cries mingling with the harsher sounds given out by the storming terns. Nests were there in thousands; but while those of the terns were usually quite open and unconcealed on the sands, those of the gulls were more often made beneath the shelter of high beach-grass or that of umbrageous plants like the poison-ivy, a path beneath the vegetation leading in at one side of a nest and out at the other. The eggs, therefore, usually were well hidden, and the downy young (which do not remain long in the nest) were mostly lying concealed under the dense foliage. Most of the nests contain eggs by the middle of June; and early in July there are many half-grown young, many of which may be seen running to shelter whenever an intruder appears.

I am told that about the year 1850 Laughing Gulls were abundant on the island, but that the depredations of the eggers greatly reduced their numbers; and that about 1876, when the demand for the feathers of native birds was at its height, this colony of gulls was nearly extirpated. Mr. George H. Mackay, who is responsible for the preservation of the colony, tells me that at one time there were not over 12 pairs of Laughing Gulls left on the island. In 1880 they were still scarce although a few pairs bred. The species would soon have vanished but for Mr. Mackay's influence in state legislation for the protection of birds, and in the town affairs of Nantucket. Mainly through his good offices the town authorities were induced to employ a warden to guard the birds during the breeding season on the island, and the captain of the life-saving crew took an active interest in their protection. Since this guardianship was assumed, the birds have increased, slowly indeed for the first ten years but more rapidly since, until now (1923) there are thousands of Laughing Gulls on the island; and they appear during the summer in numbers not only for miles around but also on the coasts of the three southern New England states, in places where for many years they were seldom or never noted. Nuttall reported great numbers on the coast of New Jersey; and in Giraud's day there were colonies of the species along the coast of Long Island. Now, however, the bird is practically extirpated as a breeder from the region between Muskeget and the coast of Virginia, with the exception of two colonies in New Jersey which have thrived under the protection of the National Association of Audubon Societies. In the breeding season of 1919 I saw this species with young on Monomoy where, Mr. George W. Bloomer informed me, a few nests were built and a few young reared. They, however, have not nested there since, and I know of no other nesting-ground in New England but Muskeget excepting the Maine islands mentioned on page 84.

Apparently the name Laughing Gull is a misnomer. The bird certainly produces syllables that simulate laughter, but those who hear in its notes anything closely resembling the quality of human mirth must draw largely upon their imagination. There is nothing about the notes suggesting risibility or likely to promote mirth in the listener. Some of them seem sad and complaining and these are most commonly heard.

In April Laughing Gulls appear all along the Atlantic coast of the United States even to their "farthest north" in Maine where a few of the birds arrive late in the month. In late August and September they are again on their way southward and October sees most of them in the "sunny South."

The food of the Laughing Gull consists of almost anything edible that it can find on sea or shore. Insects, worms, small fish, crabs and their spawn, various other marine animals, garbage, offal, etc., make up a large part of their food in our waters. Several times I have observed Laughing Gulls standing in small, shallow, tidal-streams which flowed at low tide over the flats, and apparently dancing. Close observation showed that they were actually dancing backward in water, sometimes up to their bellies but usually more shallow, evidently for the purpose of dislodging some creature from the sand or mud. When successful each bird made a quick lunge into the water apparently with the object of catching some lively little animal. What they secured I could not see even with a telescope. This gull at times eats many insects, and where insect pests are numerous it often goes inland to secure them. In the summer of 1923 when there was an outbreak of the seventeen-year cicada (*Tibicina septendecim*) on Cape Cod, great numbers of these gulls, as well as many terns, fed on the insects. The Laughing Gulls apparently carried many cicadas to Muskeget Island to feed their young. The nearest outbreak of the insects was fully 20 miles distant from the island. Mr. Allan Keniston who visited the island at this time asserted that about a dozen of the young birds that he examined there ejected the remains of cicadas.[1]

In August when flying ants are abundant, I have seen these gulls in numbers near shore circling about like swallows over the waters of Buzzards Bay and catching the ants in air or picking them up from the surface of the water. They follow the fishermen for the offal thrown overboard, go far to sea for floating refuse, search river-shores near the sea, and resort to flats and beaches for animal food uncovered by the tide. They often follow the steamers upon Nantucket and Vineyard Sounds, and feed upon whatever edible matter is thrown overboard. In summer it is only necessary to toss out a few small pieces of bread or fat to attract numbers from far and near. They hover over or near the stern of the boat, dipping gracefully to the water with extended legs and expertly picking up the fragments. Often they may be attracted in the same way about the wharves of Marthas Vineyard, Nantucket and Cape Cod. When pieces of fish-liver are thrown to them, they become very bold and sometimes will come within a few feet of the observer. With a low sun shining upon their lovely breasts, the wheeling flock makes a very attractive picture, not soon to be forgotten. I have never seen this bird dive

---

[1] Auk, Vol. XLI, 1924, pp. 468–470.

FIG. 7. — HEAD OF LAUGHING GULL
½ natural size

FIG. 8. — HEAD OF FRANKLIN'S GULL
½ natural size

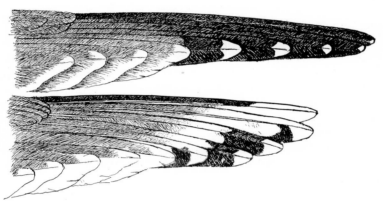

FIG. 9. — ABOVE, PRIMARIES OF LAUGHING GULL.   BELOW, PRIMARIES
OF FRANKLIN'S GULL
½ natural size

FIG. 10. — HEAD OF MALE MASKED
DUCK
½ natural size

FIG. 11. — HEAD OF FEMALE MASKED
DUCK
½ natural size

Page 283

under water for food like the terns or some of the other gulls, but it may do so in case of extreme necessity.   It has been seen to chase viciously a tern and rob it of its fish.   Mr. A. C. Bent quotes Mr. Stanley C. Arthur to the effect that in Louisiana the Laughing Gull takes a heavy toll of the eggs of Cabot's and Royal Terns.   He also quotes Audubon in proof of the egg-eating habit and says that he himself has seen some evidence of it.[1] I have seen no direct evidence at Muskeget that this gull destroys the nests and eggs of the terns, but apparently the number of terns on the island has decreased much in recent years while that of the Laughing Gulls has increased.   One of its peculiar habits in the South enables it to get sustenance at the expense of a larger bird.   It watches the Brown Pelican at its fishing and when the latter raises its head awkwardly from the water with fish in its pouch or beak, the gull coolly alights on the pelican's head and snatches from its partly closed beak a share of the prey, while other gulls flutter about to pick up the pieces that fall from the pelican's capacious food receptacle.

ECONOMIC STATUS.   The Laughing Gull's fondness for insects may cause it to render some service to the farmer, as for example in the destruction of the cicadas on Cape Cod. Otherwise, its economic value has not been demonstrated, except as a scavenger.

Larus fránklini RICHARDSON.   Franklin's Gull.

Other names: PRAIRIE PIGEON; PRAIRIE DOVE.

Figs. 8 and 9.

DESCRIPTION. — *Adults in breeding plumage (sexes alike)*: Similar to Laughing Gull, but bill smaller and much shorter and hood of similar size but darker — deep slaty-black; upper surface of body similar but a mere shade more bluish and usually not quite so dark as in Laughing Gull but considerably darker than in Bonaparte's Gull; primaries marked as follows (but somewhat variable) — 1st with outer web black to within about 1 inch of tip, inner web white, crossed by a black bar about 2 inches wide near end, leaving about 1 inch of whole tip white; next five primaries white-tipped, colored basally like back, paler on inner webs and all fading into white toward black bar which crosses each feather near its end, this bar about as wide on 2d primary as on 1st, narrowing on successive feathers (toward inner edge of wing) to small bar or one or two little spots on 5th or 6th; rest of primaries and secondaries colored like back, all fading into white at tips, shafts of all white (sometimes black where feather is black); tail white, tinted very pale bluish-gray on several central feathers; neck all round, rump, tips of secondaries (broadly), tips of longest scapulars (usually) and all under plumage white, latter with rosy wash which fades after death; bill dark red with band of darker red near tip; naked eye-ring, legs and feet dark red or "claret color." *Adults in winter plumage:* As breeding plumage, but hood wanting or indicated by only a few dark feathers; head largely white with dusky-gray about top and back of head, darkest from just before eye to ear-region; bill and feet darker, duller red than in breeding plumage, bill tipped orange-red.   *Young in first winter plumage:* Variable; forehead white, top of head and hind head mottled gray and dusky, darkest on sides of head under and behind eye, much as in winter adult; nape and sides of head mainly dusky or slaty-black; back and scapulars mostly plain gull-gray, otherwise resembling juvenal plumage especially on wings; tail with broad subterminal bar of dusky; under plumage white. *Young in juvenal plumage:* Head mottled dusky and whitish above; back, scapulars and lesser wing-coverts brown and drab, feathers edged light brown; greater wing-coverts gray; primaries blackish, tipped white; secondaries gray basally, black centrally, broadly tipped and edged white; tertials black-

---

[1] Smithsonian Institution, United States National Museum, Bulletin No. 113, 1921, p. 160.

ish, broadly edged white; upper tail-coverts white; tail light gray with broad, subterminal blackish band; under plumage white from chin to tail, rarely faintly tinged rosy. *Downy young:* variable; two color phases, the first largely brown, spotted or marbled with black above; throat and upper breast buffy; white below; other phase similar but brown and buffy replaced by gray.

MEASUREMENTS. — Length about 13.50 to 15.00 in.; spread about 35.00; folded wing 11.25 to 11.35; tail 4.00 to 4.50; bill 1.25 to 1.30; tarsus 1.60 to 1.70.

MOLTS. — After a partial postjuvenal molt (September to December) first winter plumage is acquired; there is a complete molt in the ensuing spring, followed by first summer plumage; after postnuptial molt in autumn immature birds appear to be indistinguishable from adults, except by primaries which still show signs of immaturity, outer primary being black for about 3 inches, with less black on each succeeding primary and tips of all white; as bird grows older black in primaries decreases at each succeeding molt and white increases until bird becomes fully adult; adults have a prenuptial molt (March to May), and a postnuptial molt (August to October).

FIELD MARKS. — I have never seen this bird alive, but it may be difficult to distinguish it from Laughing Gull, which however has *more black and less white on primaries.*

VOICE. — A soft *k r r r u k* or a low clucking call (A. C. Bent); a shrill *kuk, kuk, kuk, kuk;* a more plaintive cry *pway pwa-ay*, rather musical, also *weeh-a weeh-a weeh-a* and *po-lee polee polee polee* (Thomas Miller).

BREEDING. — About lakes fringed with marshes. *Nest:* A mass of dead reeds or rushes in water, on bottom or afloat. *Eggs:* 2 to 4, very variable in size, shape and color, average 2.05 by 1.45 in. (Coues); ground color various shades of buffy and greenish-buffy, with all sorts of markings of various browns and lavender. *Dates:* May 18 to June 4, Minnesota and North Dakota. *Incubation:* Period probably 18 or 20 days (T. M. Roberts); probably by both sexes.

RANGE. — North and South America. Breeds from southeastern Alberta, central Saskatchewan and south-central Manitoba to northeastern South Dakota, Iowa (formerly) and southern Minnesota; winters from Gulf coast of Louisiana to Peru and Chile; accidental or casual in California, Keewatin, Hudson Bay, Utah, Colorado, Illinois, Michigan, Ohio, Ontario, Massachusetts, Virginia, Lesser Antilles and Hawaii.

DISTRIBUTION IN NEW ENGLAND. — One record: Female taken October 28, 1885, at Salem; placed for years with the gulls in Peabody Museum, Salem, and supposed to be a Bonaparte's Gull, but finally identified by Prof. Albert P. Morse, the present curator.[1]

HAUNTS AND HABITS. Franklin's Gull in life is one of the most beautiful of the gull tribe. It is a great wanderer and should occasionally reach New England, as although it breeds in the far interior and migrates up and down the middle and western sections of the continent, it has occurred on both the Atlantic and Pacific coasts. We have but one authentic record for New England. Although the species has been reported several times in Massachusetts, it resembles the Laughing Gull so closely that no dependence can be placed on sight records. Franklin's Gull seems to have a better disposition than the New England gulls, for often it has been known to feed and care for stray young ones belonging to other gulls of the same colony. Its habits resemble somewhat those of the Laughing Gull, but it feeds much more inland and commonly follows the plow to pick up worms and grubs, and it nests about or in bodies of fresh water in the interior. In autumn it follows the inland route to the Gulf of Mexico, and passes the winter largely along the western coast of South America, returning by the same route in reverse as spring comes on.[2]

---

[1] Morse, Albert P.: Bulletin Essex County Ornithological Club, 1921, p. 69.
[2] Job, Herbert K.: Bird-Lore, Vol. XII, 1910, p. 127.

Economic Status. This is a very useful bird on its western breeding-grounds, as it feeds largely on insect pests of the farming country. In the breeding season insects seem to constitute a very large part of its food. Small fish, frogs, crawfish and small mollusks, as well as destructive grasshoppers, locusts and many other insects have been found in the stomachs examined. Where numerous, this species destroys immense quantities of grasshoppers.

Larus philadélphia (Ord). Bonaparte's Gull.

Other name: FROST GULL.

Plate 6.

Description. — Bill shorter than head or tarsus; very slender for a gull, curve of ridge less than in most species; slight distinct notch on each mandible near tip; nostrils very narrow; length of tarsus about equal to middle toe and claw. *Adults in breeding plumage (sexes alike):* Hood (including about all of head, but not extending so far back as in Laughing Gull) leaden-slate; white of eyelids extending behind eye but not in front; back, scapulars, greater part of wings and upper plumage to middle of rump, delicate pale neutral-gray, much lighter than that of Laughing Gull; ends of inner secondaries and scapulars barely lighter than back; shafts of first four or five primaries white except extreme tips, others darker; 1st primary, outer web and extreme tip black, rest white; 2d, mainly white, with longer black tip than first, feather usually bordered narrowly for a greater or less length on either or both webs with black; 3d to 6th have black ends, each for about same distance, and light tips, black bordering each inner web farther than on outer web; inner webs of 3d and 4th and both webs of 5th and 6th colored much like back; other primaries match color of back; 7th and 8th have spot of black near tip; 3d to 6th with white or light speck at tip; markings of adult primaries vary somewhat but generally quite constant in this species; unlike Laughing Gull primary wing-coverts and bastard quills largely white, giving fore wing a white border; neck and all under plumage, including lining of wings, white; breast and belly often with rosy tint; bill black; lining of mouth and eyelids carmine; iris dark brown; legs and feet orange-red or orange-vermilion. *Adults in winter plumage:* Similar, but head and neck white; back of head more or less mottled with grayish-black and white; a blackish patch in ear-region; little crescent before eye and patch below ear dark slate; back of neck washed with color of back; lower base of bill light colored; feet paler or flesh color. *Young in first winter plumage:* Similar to winter adult; head mainly white with dusky patch in ear-region; patch on lesser wing-coverts and tertials brownish-gray or dusky-brown; seen from above spread wing seems to be margined all around black or blackish, as secondaries are blackish near ends; white tail with subterminal dusky or blackish bar and very narrowly tipped white; bill dark flesh color; in this plumage juvenal wing and tail are retained but upper plumage becomes much grayer and head whiter. *Young in juvenal plumage:* Top of head, and hind neck clouded with dusky bluish-gray, becoming light grayish-yellow on sides of neck; sides of head mainly white with dark crescentic spot before eye, and dark ear-patch; scapulars and feathers of middle back basally like those of adult but tipped broadly grayish-brown (fading into white at extreme tips) and thus nearly hiding basal color, leaving prevailing color of upper plumage brown with pale edgings; a band along lesser wing-coverts, tertials and inner secondaries brownish-black, latter edged like feathers of back; feathers along outer edge of wing variegated black and white; primaries black; outer two-thirds of inner vanes of first three or four, bluish-white to near end; both vanes of others same color toward end; extreme tips of most of them light gray or whitish; secondaries light, their ends largely blackish, continuous with black ends of inner primaries; tail white, with broad subterminal band of black, very narrowly tipped buffy or whitish; below white excepting brownish wash on sides of neck and breast;

bill more or less dusky or blackish; feet black. *Downy young:* Much like that of common tern. "Yellowish with dusky mottling above" (Jonathan Dwight).

MEASUREMENTS. — Length 12.00 to 14.50 in.; spread about 32.00; folded wing 9.50 to 10.75; tail 3.75 to 4.25; bill 1.05 to 1.25; tarsus 1.15 to .42. Female smaller than male.

MOLTS. — Young apparently assume adult winter plumage in autumn of second year and full adult breeding plumage in spring of third year; succeeding juvenal plumage, there is partial molt in September and October, involving body plumage, after which first winter plumage is assumed; again there is partial molt in March and April when plumage of head is renewed, but in some cases partially black head is acquired, even amounting to nearly complete dark hood; tail still retains its broad, dark subterminal band; next comes complete postnuptial molt lasting from July or August until September or October; adults have partial prenuptial molt in spring and complete postnuptial molt beginning in August.

FIELD MARKS. — Small size, slender bill, much lighter coloration of back and wings and black outer border of white-ended wing distinguish this species when in full plumage from Laughing Gull; spread wings have white back-edges and much black on primaries; young Bonaparte's Gull has black band near tip of white tail, white breast and wing margined about with black or blackish, while young Laughing Gull has neck and sides of breast clouded with gray and banded tail darker than that of Bonaparte's Gull; young Bonaparte's Gull except for size, resembles young Kittiwake; both show some black on side of head and black subterminal band on tail, but Kittiwake has black patch on back of neck also; Bonaparte's is smaller than Kittiwake and its feet are red or flesh-colored while those of young Kittiwake are yellowish or dusky-brownish.

VOICE. — A harsh, rasping cry (C. W. Townsend); plaintive, shrill cry, almost a whistle (Neltje Blanchan); usually rather silent in Massachusetts.

BREEDING. — In colonies; on forested islands in lakes or in the forested interior near some lake or stream. *Nest:* On logs, stumps or bushes, but usually in coniferous trees from 4 to 20 feet from ground, built of sticks, twigs, leaves, etc., and lined with mosses or down. *Eggs:* 2 to 4; 1.80 to 1.95 by 1.30 to 1.34 in. (Coues); ground color, varies from "olive gray," "grayish olive brown" or "Dresden brown" to "dark olive buff," spotted and blotched, rarely scrawled, with chocolate and various shades of brown, "brownish olive" and "brownish drab." *Dates:* June 10 to July 15, Anderson River region (A. C. Bent). One brood yearly.

RANGE. — North America. Breeds from northwestern Alaska and northern Mackenzie south to southeastern British Columbia (but few breeding places actually known); winters from Massachusetts, (Maine very rarely) to Florida, on Gulf coast southward to Yucatan, and on Pacific coast from Washington south to Lower California and western Mexico; occurs in migration west to Kotzebue Sound and east to Ungava (northern Quebec); casual in Peru, Bermuda and Bahamas; accidental in Laysan Island of Hawaiian group, in Chile and in Great Britain, France and Heligoland.

DISTRIBUTION IN NEW ENGLAND. — Common migrant near coast but visiting both coast and interior waters; irregular resident or visitant coastwise in mild winters.

SEASON IN MASSACHUSETTS. — July 25 to June 10, but most common in March, April and May and again in September and October; rare and irregular or local in winter.

HAUNTS AND HABITS. With the first warm days of April when the alewives begin to run up our streams comes the lovely, graceful, little Bonaparte's Gull. Arrayed in its gay nuptial plumage, with black head and snowy vesture, it wings in graceful flight along the coast or up the great river-valleys of the interior, spurred on by the urge of the reproductive instinct, toward the great forests of the North where it nests in dark coniferous trees. In autumn the immature birds appear — dainty tern-like creatures — with their slender bills, trim forms and long wings; but the rounded tail with the broad black bar near the tip serves to distinguish them at once from the terns. Their flight is airy, buoyant, easy and graceful like that of the terns. They frequently dip down to the water, but I have never seen one go under as terns so often do.

A loose flock of these charming birds wandering along shore or over river marsh, performing their sprightly evolutions while catching insects, or fluttering poised over the water as they stoop to pick up some tidbit, perhaps a living fish which they secure by a lightning-like dart, adds life and beauty to the landscape. Although this delicate creature seems fitted only to play in the sunlight amid summer zephyrs, it has wonderful powers of flight and is hardy enough to breast the storms and raging seas of winter along our coast. Although it is not often seen during the most inclement seasons on the New England coast, yet it is not uncommon locally during mild winters and a few may be found here irregularly at this season where rivers or estuaries remain ice-free so that the birds can secure food. In winter in our waters it seems to be a rather silent bird; but while feeding in flocks, particularly in spring, individuals sometimes keep up a continual chattering.

Bonaparte's Gull feeds largely on small "fry" but during the summer is more dependent on insects than are most gulls. It seeks insects in marshes, on cultivated fields, on seaweed stranded on shore or floating on water; and its stomach is often filled to repletion with such food. Flies, ants, moths and their larvæ, and other insects are eaten, also many small crustaceans and marine worms.

ECONOMIC STATUS. Apparently this species does no harm as it is not known to feed on any of man's crops, and as an insect eater it no doubt has some share in the regulation of insect life.

Larus minútus PALLAS. Little Gull.

DESCRIPTION. — Tail nearly even at end. Similar to Bonaparte's Gull, but smallest of its tribe, much smaller than any American gull. *Adults in breeding plumage (sexes alike):* Hood black; back and wings very pale pearl-gray; primaries shading darker toward margins of inner webs, very broadly edged (toward end of inner web) and tipped white; secondaries also tipped white; no black marks on wing;

ADULT IN BREEDING PLUMAGE AND YOUNG OF LITTLE GULL
About ½ natural size.

upper tail-coverts and tail white; below white, rose-tinted; under wing-coverts and under surface of flight-feathers (except white tips) dark smoke-gray; axillars white; bill dark reddish-brown or lake-red; iris dark brown; legs and feet vermilion. *Adults in winter plumage:* Similar but lacking black hood; forehead white, with more or less gray and dusky (or slaty) about eyes, ears and hind head; legs and feet reddish-brown to flesh-color. *Young in first winter plumage:* Resemble adults in winter, but with much dark brown above, with white or buffy feather-tips; wing-coverts and inner quills tipped white; secondaries mainly white; inner webs of outer primaries chiefly white; inner primaries gray, their tips white; tail with broad, black terminal band; bill blackish; feet yellow to flesh color. *Downy young:* Above dark grayish-buff, marked irregularly and rather inconspicuously with brownish-black; below buffy-gray.

MEASUREMENTS. — Length 10.40 to 11.50 in.; folded wing 8.70 to 9.10; tail 3.55 to 3.75; bill .82 to 1.20; tarsus .98 to 1.10.

MOLTS. — Juvenal body plumage is molted August to October, and young bird then assumes first winter plumage; young birds probably become as adults or closely resemble adult in second winter; adults have a complete molt in autumn and a partial molt in spring.

FIELD MARKS. — Smallest of gulls; shorter than Common Tern. *Adult:* Pale gray back, and primaries tipped white; broad white hind border to wing; no black on primaries; *under wing-surface dark gray or dusky, hind border white;* adults and young resemble Bonaparte's Gull or terns in flight, but lack the black margin about wing seen in Bonaparte's. *Young:* Have wide dark band extending entire length of upper surface f spread wing, bordered before and behind by white; pale fore margin extends outward on fore wing from body to bend, and a broad white border extends similarly outward on hind wing to tips of middle primaries; black band at tip of tail.

VOICE. — "Its voice is described by Naumann as short and screeching and as different from that of any other Gull or Tern" (Seebohm).

BREEDING. — Usually in colonies; sometimes with other gulls or terns on small islands in fresh-water lakes or on tussocks in marshes. *Nest:* Of dead sedges, rushes, etc., among rushes, reeds or grasses in the water or close to it. *Eggs:* 2 to 5; smaller than those of Bonaparte's Gull, about 1.66 by 1.25 in., resembling eggs of Common Tern; ovate. *Dates:* Late May to mid-June, northern Europe. *Incubation:* By both parents. One brood yearly.

RANGE. — Europe and parts of Asia and Africa. Breeds chiefly in northern Europe and Asia from Iceland to the sea of Okhotsk; in winter migrates south to coast of north Africa and mouth of Amur River; casual in northern India, Faroe Islands and interior of central Europe; accidental in Bermuda and eastern United States.

NOTE. The Little Gull (*Larus minutus* Pallas), the smallest of all gulls, has not been recorded within the limits of Massachusetts. Since, however, it has been taken twice on Long Island and twice in Maine, it is not improbable that it may have visited Massachusetts, and it may yet be recorded here. An Eurasian species, the Little Gull must cross the Atlantic to reach our coast. Records: An adult male in nuptial plumage but with worn primaries and traces of postnuptial molt on head was taken August 12, 1904, near Mosquito Island, St. George, Maine;[1] the other Maine specimen was also an adult male and was taken July 20, 1910, at Pine Point, Scarborough.[2]

HAUNTS AND HABITS.   The smallest of all gulls, a mere straggler from across the sea, the Little Gull is a *rara avis* in New England.   It feeds on small fish and other small aquatic life and is an indefatigable insect catcher; its flight in pursuit of insects much resembles that of the Black Tern; probably it is quite as graceful and active in flight as are any of the terns.   It might be mistaken for Bonaparte's Gull by anyone unacquainted with the field marks, but it is actually much smaller.

ECONOMIC STATUS.   Probably the Little Gull is useful in Europe because of its insectivorous habits there, however as an accidental visitor it is of no economic importance in America.

---

[1] Norton, Arthur H.: Auk, Vol. XXXIII, 1916, p. 377.   [2] Norton, Arthur H.: Auk, Vol. XXVII, 1910, p. 447.

Xéma sábini (J. Sabine). Sabine's Gull.

Other name: FORK-TAILED GULL.

Plate 6.

DESCRIPTION. — Bill not slender; tail forked. *Adults in breeding plumage (sexes alike):* Hood clear, dark, slaty-gray bounded behind by narrow collar of black; neck (all around to edge of collar), lower rump, tail, upper tail-coverts, under plumage, four inner primaries, most of greater wing-coverts, most of exposed parts of secondaries (except tips of innermost), wing-linings and axillars white; back, scapulars, upper rump and wing-coverts (except greater) slaty-gray, somewhat lighter than in Laughing Gull; dark line around bend of wing including bastard quills; first five primaries black except tips and broad margins of inner webs which are white to near ends; rest of primaries white, 6th with mere touch of black on outer web; bill black from base nearly to angle, terminal part abruptly orange or yellow; inside of mouth orange or vermilion; naked edges of eyelids orange or red; feet dusky-gray. *Adults in winter plumage:* Similar but without hood or collar; head mainly white, usually with more or less touches of dark gray or dusky on back, nape and ear-region. *Young in first winter plumage:* Similar to juvenal plumage but lighter above, a paler, more uniform grayish-brown; primaries dull blackish, tail white, tipped black, and bill dusky. *Young in juvenal plumage:* Smaller than adult; tail forked according to age — at first very little, more later; no dark hood or collar; above, including back of neck and most of head, slaty grayish-brown or deep brownish-gray, cross-waved by brownish-white or buffy tips of feathers; on longer scapulars, tertials, etc., lines of dusky precede light tips; rest of plumage mainly white, but tail has subterminal bar of black about 1 inch wide on middle feathers, growing gradually narrower at each side, sometimes reaching only inner web of outer feathers; wings similar to those of adult, with white secondaries but less white on inner webs of primaries, and white tips, sometimes barely noticeable or wanting; bill rather dusky, smaller and weaker than that of adults. *Downy young:* "Rusty yellow," ochraceous-tawny, "tawny-olive" or "deep brownish-buff" above and on throat (paler on chin) and pale pinkish-buff or still paler "whitish-gray" on belly; top and sides of head heavily spotted black; back and often rest of upper down, mottled blackish.

MEASUREMENTS. — Length 13.00 to 14.00 in.; folded wing 10.10 to 11.15; tail 4.50 to 5.00, forked .60 to 1.25; bill .95 to 1.04; tarsus 1.25 to 1.47.

MOLTS. — First winter plumage a continuation of juvenal, becoming paler above by fading and wear; first spring or prenuptial molt is partial, and young bird assumes part of its black collar and gray hood; first postnuptial molt in August or September is succeeded by adult winter plumage; adults have partial or perhaps complete prenuptial molt in late winter or early spring and acquire hood and collar before May, and a complete postnuptial molt in August and September which is succeeded by winter plumage.

FIELD MARKS. — *Adults:* Distinguished by hooded head and forked tail, black line around bend of wing, large white patch on hind wing and yellow or orange end of bill. *Young:* Also plainly show white patch on wing and forked tail with a graduated (apparently terminal) bar of black. Does not resemble closely any other gull or tern.

VOICE. — A harsh, grating cry similar to that of Arctic Tern but harsher and shorter (E. W. Nelson).

BREEDING. — On islands or on shores of ponds. *Nest:* On ground; a mere depression, sometimes lined or partly lined with stems and blades of grass. *Eggs:* 2 or 3; 1.75 by 1.25 in. (Coues); brownish-olive, Dresden-brown, deep olive-buff and other shades, usually sparsely and rather faintly and irregularly spotted with various shades of brown. *Dates:* May 28 to July 10, northern Alaska and northern Mackenzie (A. C. Bent). *Incubation:* Both parents apparently take part. Probably only one brood yearly.

RANGE. — Arctic regions to South America. Breeds on St. Lawrence Island, coast of Bering Sea, in northern Alaska, northern Mackenzie, northern Keewatin, northern Hudson Bay, Boothia Peninsula,

Victoria Island, on eastern and western coasts of Greenland, and in Spitzbergen, northeastern Europe, and Siberia; occurs in summer but not known to breed in many Arctic and subarctic lands in both hemispheres; in migration on both coasts of United States and casually over greater part of interior; winters on coast of Peru; occasional in winter in British Isles and northern France; accidental in Holland, Heligoland, Middle Europe and Bermuda.

DISTRIBUTION IN NEW ENGLAND. — Accidental transient visitor to Maine and Massachusetts coasts. Records: *Maine:* Scarborough, bird taken May 31, 1877;[1] Portland (Brothers Island), immature female taken September 22, 1899;[2] Saco Bay (near Bluff Island and locality of first Maine record in 1877), bird seen September 11, 1912.[3] *Massachusetts:* Boston Harbor, immature bird taken by H. W. Diamond, September 27, 1874,[4] and now in the collection of the Museum of Comparative Zoölogy at Cambridge; Cape Cod, immature bird taken in 1888;[5] North Truro, adult female taken August 21, 1889;[6] Chatham, two adult males in winter plumage taken September 2, 1912.[7]

SEASON IN MASSACHUSETTS. — August 21 to September 27.

HAUNTS AND HABITS. Sabine's Gull is a boreal bird and usually haunts the vicinity of cold seas. It is rarely seen in temperate or tropical regions, except on the coast of Peru to which it migrates in winter. On that coast there is a very cold Antarctic current, and in this current Arctic and Antarctic zoölogic forms meet. To this region of cold currents Sabine's Gull annually finds its way over the broad Pacific. As there is no such region of cold waters in the Atlantic, this bird does not migrate in any numbers down the Atlantic coast, and so cannot be regarded as other than a rare or accidental visitant to New England. It has been recorded in many places in the interior of the continent, which fact may indicate that some individuals normally reach the Pacific coast of South America by the overland route. This bird's habits are much like those of Bonaparte's Gull. According to Mr. F. S. Hersey, the species is usually rather solitary, and at low tide it spends much time feeding on the flats where it runs about like a plover. In appearance and flight it resembles a tern, and the forked tail adds to the illusion; especially if the bird appears late in September without the hood and in winter plumage.

Toward the end of September Sabine's Gull becomes scarce over its breeding range as most individuals of the species are then on their way south. In April they begin to move northward and they arrive at their subarctic and Arctic breeding grounds from the latter part of May until late in June.

In the Arctic regions this species feeds much like other gulls on various aquatic forms of life, and insects. Little is known of its food elsewhere. It picks up much of its food from the surface of the water, not flocking much, but seeking its subsistence singly and attending chiefly to its own affairs. Occasionally two or three are seen together and sometimes they feed with other gulls.

ECONOMIC STATUS. See page 60.

---

[1] Smith, Everett: Forest and Stream, Vol. XX, April, 1883, p. 205.
[2] Knight, O. W.: Journal Maine Ornithological Society, Vol. II, 1900, p. 2.
[3] Norton, Arthur H.: Auk, Vol. XXX, 1913, p. 574.
[4] Brewster, William: American Sportsman, Vol. V, 1875, p. 370.
[5] Ornithologist and Oölogist, Vol. XIV, 1889, p. 95.
[6] Miller, G. S., Jr.: Auk, Vol. VII, 1890, p. 227.
[7] Hersey, F. Seymour: Auk, Vol. XXX, 1913, p. 105.

Subfamily **STERNINÆ**. Terns.

Number of species in North America 17; in Massachusetts 11.

Terns may be distinguished from gulls by their different shape. As a rule they are of slighter build and of more graceful form. The bill is slender, long and narrow, and its upper mandible is not sharply curved toward the point nor almost hooked like that of the gull. The wings are very long, narrow and pointed and give terns a swift and dashing flight surpassing that of gulls. Terns average much smaller than gulls, though some species reach the dimensions of medium-sized gulls. The tail is usually more or less forked while that of the gull is commonly even or rounded. The feet are small and relatively weak, indicating that terns swim and walk but little. In seeking food terns fly habitually with the bill pointing downward and pounce headlong from the air upon their prey in the water; hence the name "Striker," applied to several species in the South.

Most of the species when in full plumage are white or nearly white below with a black-capped head. They are more or less maritime, but are coastal rather than seabirds.

Economic Status. Many terns that feed on destructive insects are undoubtedly useful. Others which feed on fish follow the schools, and so guide the fishermen to their catch. From time immemorial the eggs of terns have been used for food by man; but the gathering of birds' eggs for food is now illegal in the United States.

Gelochelídon nilótica aránea (Wilson). American Gull-billed Tern.

Other names: marsh tern; nuttall's tern.

Fig. 4.

Description. — Bill stout, somewhat gull-like but not hooked; head crested; wings very long and acute; tail short, deeply forked; tarsus shorter than bill, longer than middle toe and claw; hind toe remarkably developed. *Adults in breeding plumage (sexes alike):* Cap, including long crest, greenish-black, taking in eye and leaving only narrow white line on side of upper mandible; other upper plumage, including tail, mainly pale gray; sides of head up to level of lower eyelid, and all under plumage, including wing-linings and axillars, white; tail-feathers darkest at tips, fading to almost pure white toward bases on that part of each covered by next; color of back reaches to tips of inner secondaries; primaries grayish-black (darkest on outer web of 1st) but frosted over so as to appear much lighter, the shafts very pale yellow; space of white on each inner web, largest, purest and extending farthest on 1st primary where distinctly defined; white space diminishes in length and width with each successive primary until inconspicuous on last; bill black, tip rarely yellowish; iris dark brown; "legs and feet dark reddish-brown, soles of toes pinkish-brown" (Ridgway); "legs and feet greenish-black" (Coues); "bill and feet black" (Witmer Stone). *Adults in winter plumage:* Similar but cap very light, almost white, slightly mottled blackish posteriorly and on eye and ear-regions, usually dark crescent before eye and dark patch in ear-region; sometimes head all white, except more or less dusky in eye and ear-regions. *Young in first winter plumage:* Similar to winter adult; bill slightly smaller; forehead white and crown mostly white but sometimes streaks on hind head and upper neck; back and scapulars rarely streaked dusky; traces of dusky on tail; brownish-black bar on lesser wing-coverts; bill dusky-brownish; feet reddish to dusky-brown. *Young in juvenal plumage:* Head darker, more mottled; upper plumage largely pale gray, with markings of brownish on feathers, giving bird general brownish appearance. *Downy young:* Pinkish-buff, light grayish-buff or creamy-buff above; a distinct dusky stripe on each side of hind neck and upper back; usually more or less mottled, spotted or streaked above; white on breast and belly; "feet dull brownish orange" (Ridgway).

MEASUREMENTS. — Length 13.00 to 15.25 in.; spread 33.00 to 37.00; folded wing 11.75 to 12.25; tail about 5.50, forked 1.20 to 1.75; bill about 1.40; tarsus, average 1.30.

MOLTS. — Partial postjuvenal molt begins early in September followed by quick change to first winter plumage; probably species assumes plumage like adult in the next spring when about one year old; adults have two complete molts each year — prenuptial in late winter mainly and postnuptial in August and September (A. C. Bent).

FIELD MARKS. — Tern-like tail, shorter and less deeply forked than that of Common Tern, and stout, somewhat gull-like, black bill should distinguish this species, but only at close range.

VOICE. — On breeding grounds *katydid, katydid* or *kadid* or *killy* or *killy-kadid* (A. C. Bent); *kay-wek, kay-wek* (Montague Chamberlain); *che-ah* and *af, af, af* (Yarrell).

BREEDING. — Singly or in colonies of other terns or of its own species; on low sandy sea-islands. *Nest:* Varies from mere depression on sandy shores or among grasses to a large pile of sedges or grasses; sometimes also lined with shells. *Eggs:* 1 to 4; 1.74 to 2.00 by 1.27 to 1.42 in.; usually shorter, rounder and lighter-colored than those of the more common species and thus more or less distinguishable; very variable in color like eggs of terns in general — varying from different shades of buff to "ivory" and marked with many shades of brown and drab. *Dates:* June 2 to July 8, Virginia; May 3 to June 10, Texas (A. C. Bent). One brood yearly.

RANGE. — Species nearly cosmopolitan as closely allied forms breed in or visit many lands. The American form, recently separated, breeds on coasts of Mexico, Texas, Louisiana, North Carolina, Virginia (rarely), (New Jersey formerly) and in Bahamas, Cuba and at mouth of Amazon River; casual north to New Brunswick, Ohio and Illinois; winters in Texas and Louisiana (rarely), also in southern Mexico and southern Guatemala, but mainly in South America from Brazil south to Patagonia and Chile.

DISTRIBUTION IN NEW ENGLAND. — Records: *Maine:* Scarboro, three taken in September, 1868, and one shot, May 21, 1881;[1] Portland (near), accidental straggler taken March, 1885.[2] *Massachusetts:* Ipswich, bird taken by C. J. Maynard in September, 1871,[3] now in the Museum of Comparative Zoölogy at Cambridge; bird seen by Judge Charles F. Jenney and Dr. William C. Mackie August 8, 1909, at close range, and identification was positive.[4] Probably less rare formerly.

HAUNTS AND HABITS. The earlier writers knew this species as the Marsh Tern for it once frequented salt marshes of the Atlantic and Gulf States and bred there. Apparently the few left on the Atlantic coast now nest on sandy beach-flats. This tern possibly was a victim of the trade in birds for millinery purposes, and late in the last century it nearly disappeared from the Atlantic coast. Probably it always was rare in New England.

This species is believed to feed almost entirely on insects and spiders; but it also feeds to some extent on small fish and aquatic life.

ECONOMIC STATUS. The Gull-billed Tern has become so rare as to be of no economic importance in the Northeast.

---

[1] Smith, Everett: Forest and Stream, Vol. XX, April, 1883, p. 205.
[2] Allen, Glover M.: Auk, Vol. XXV, 1908, p. 234.
[3] Brewster, William: American Naturalist, Vol. VI, 1872, p. 306.
[4] Maynard, C. J.: Records of Walks and Talks with Nature, Vol. II, 1909, p. 157.

PLATE 7

PLATE 7

BLACK SKIMMER
Page 130
Adult in Breeding Plumage

SOOTY TERN
Page 126
Adult in Breeding Plumage

COUES' CASPIAN TERN
Page 97
Young in Juvenal Plumage

Adult in Nuptial Plumage

ROYAL TERN
Page 99
Adult in Winter Plumage
Adult in Nuptial Plumage

All one-sixth natural size.

Stérna cáspia imperátor (Coues). Coues' Caspian Tern.

Other names: IMPERIAL TERN; SQUAWKER.

Plate 7.

DESCRIPTION. — Largest of terns; bill extremely large, thick, heavy; tail short with no long, streaming, lateral feathers; folded wings extend much beyond its tip. *Adults in breeding plumage (sexes alike):* Entire top of head, including crest, glossy greenish-black, extending lower than eye; lower eyelid white; back of neck, back and upper wings pallid neutral gray fading invisibly into white on upper tail-coverts and on sides of neck; sides of head below cap, neck all around, rump and under plumage white; tail (particularly middle feathers) more or less grayish; primaries hoary grayish-black (when new so heavily frosted as to appear light, hoary gray, especially when seen from above), their shafts yellowish-white; often a narrow, central, light field on web of each primary growing narrower from first to last or disappearing on inner primaries; inner webs of secondaries white, outer webs gray; bill deep coral or vermilion-red, lighter ("orange or yellowish") toward tip; legs and feet black. *Adults in winter plumage:* Similar, but forehead white; crown white, with narrow distinct streaks of blackish; on sides of head, both before and behind eye, the black is mixed with white; nape only slightly touched with white; bill orange-red, lighter toward tip. *Young in first winter plumage:* Similar to winter adult but upper plumage more or less mottled dusky. *Young in early autumn:* Similar, but feathers of fore back heavily tipped dusky, scapulars and tertials marked with same; lesser wing-coverts and tail toward tip mottled dusky, most so on middle feathers of latter. *Young in juvenal plumage:* Much smaller than adult; bill smaller, weaker and duller in color; entire upper half or more of head blackish, mottled or streaked whitish, blackish cap running from gape well below eye; gray feathers of upper plumage so broadly tipped buff as to give bird a buffy appearance; scapulars banded black, two bands on each feather; feathers of back and coverts more or less marked black; under plumage white. *Downy young:* Pale grayish-white to dark grayish-buff above, sometimes unspotted but usually more or less mottled or spotted blackish; as bird grows, color gradually fades until nearly white; white below, except throat which is dusky, or black.

MEASUREMENTS. — Length 19.00 to 23.00 in.; spread 50.00 to 55.00; folded wing 15.00 to 17.40; tail 5.00 to 6.75; forked about 1.50; bill 2.45 to 3.00; tarsus 1.60 to 1.90.

MOLTS. — Partial molt of body-feathers of juvenal plumage (September to winter); ensuing plumage soon changes by wear, fading or molt into first winter plumage, with pearl-gray back and wings; complete molt from January to July after which practically adult nuptial plumage appears to develop in some birds (usually in March); others seem to resemble adult in winter plumage; "adults have two complete molts — prenuptial in February or March and postnuptial in August and September," the latter sometimes beginning as early as June (A. C. Bent).

FIELD MARKS. — *Adult:* Great size, nearly twice that of Common Tern; very large red bill; tail much less deeply forked than that of smaller Royal Tern and primaries much darker when seen from below. *Young:* Blackish on top and sides of head and forehead which runs back from gape well below eye and lower and farther forward than in young Royal Tern; bill deeper in color; tail less forked.

VOICE. — *Adult: ca-arr, ca-arr, ca-arr, ca-arrrrrrr* (S. C. Arthur); loud, hoarse, rasping cry something like that of a barnyard goose (C. W. Townsend); "the adult rather infrequently gives a loud, coarse squawk or croak, one of the harshest bird-notes I have heard. It has such carrying qualities, it may often be heard before the bird is fairly in sight. . . . I have several times heard [from other birds (immature?)] a whistling note rather suggestive of a Black-breasted Plover, but with considerably less range between the high and low notes, and in a weak, sibilant tone, which nevertheless carries rather well" (J. A. Hagar).

BREEDING. — In colonies; on sandy or gravelly islands or coasts. *Nest:* Hollow in sand, lined or unlined, or in dead reeds; sometimes no nest. *Eggs:* 1, 2 or 3; 2.65 to 2.75 by 1.80 to 1.90 in. (Coues); ovate or elliptical-ovate, broad, more like gulls' than terns' eggs; usually some light shade of buff and somewhat sparingly marked with rather small spots of brown and gray of varying shades. *Dates:* May 25 to July 1, Lake Michigan; April 8 to June 18, Texas (A. C. Bent). *Incubation:* Period said to be about 20 days. One brood yearly.

RANGE. — Species nearly cosmopolitan, but the American form is now regarded as a subspecies; breeds at Great Slave Lake, Mackenzie; Lakes Winnipegosis and Winnipeg, Manitoba; Klamath Lake, Oregon; in Saskatchewan (probably), central California, on islands of northern Lake Michigan, coast of southern Labrador and coasts of Texas, Louisiana, Mississippi, South Carolina and Virginia; winters from coast of central California to Lower California and western Mexico and on south Atlantic and Gulf coasts of the United States south to Mexico; casual in migration throughout most of North America north to Alaska, mouth of Mackenzie river, James Bay and Newfoundland.

DISTRIBUTION IN NEW ENGLAND. — Formerly a not uncommon migrant coastwise, but now rare and local in the spring migration, although in autumn it is sometimes not very rare locally; "of occasional occurrence along Maine coast" (A. H. Norton); not recorded from Connecticut.

SEASON IN MASSACHUSETTS. — (April 30) May 3 to 13; "August 8 to October 2," Essex County; "a fairly regular transient in autumn at Ipswich" (C. W. Townsend); "I believe Caspian Terns are regular and not uncommon migrants on this coast ["South Shore"] and that if an observer could be along the shore daily, he would never fail in any year to see at least a small number" (J. A. Hagar).

HAUNTS AND HABITS. The Caspian Tern is the largest and most powerful of the terns. It might well be called the Imperial Tern, since it surpasses in strength the Royal Tern, nearest it in size. Audubon relates how on its breeding grounds in (Canadian) Labrador it masters even the Pomarine Jaeger. Mr. A. C. Bent says of it: "Among the vast hordes of sea-birds nesting in the great colonies of the southern Atlantic and Gulf coasts, this king of terns may be seen climbing the air on its long, strong wings, its big, red bill wide open, yelling out its loud raucous cry of defiance. As the dominant, ruling spirit in tern colonies it scorns the companionship of humbler fowl, holds itself aloof and lives a little apart from the others." [1]

In its great power of flight and the arrowy velocity of its dive from airy heights above the sea it resembles the great white Gannet of the North Atlantic. Formerly the Caspian Tern must have been rather common along the New England coast, on its migrations to and from its summer home in Labrador. In May, 1875, Mr. William Brewster found it common at Chatham; but probably its nesting places on the coast of Labrador have been broken up by the natives and fishermen so that now it is rather rare in migration in New England. If the Canadian authorities find it possible under the migratory Bird Convention Act to protect this species on its Labrador breeding grounds, it may again be commonly seen in migration on the New England coast.

Mr. Joseph A. Hagar writes from Marshfield Hills: "They are so strictly a bird of passage, that I had never seen one alight until the morning of Sept. 9, 1921, when the flock of three circled about and lit for a brief moment on the sand bar off Trouant's Island. They had scarcely folded their wings when they were up again and passing down the river to the southward."

A peculiar action of the Caspian Tern was observed by Capt. B. F. Goss at Nueces Bay on the Texas coast where the birds, on the approach of his party, rose about eight

---

[1] Smithsonian Institution, United States National Museum, Bulletin No. 113, 1921, p. 202.

feet, and hovered and circled over their nesting grounds, and then began plunging to the ground. The captain's companion, who had observed the habit before, exclaimed: "They are breaking their eggs!" On landing it was found that "at least one-quarter of the eggs were broken," and that in some cases the bill of the plunging bird had passed entirely through the egg. Captain Goss' companion believed that the birds did this to prevent their eggs from falling into the hands of the intruders.[1] An illustration of the instinct of birds to seek the protection of deceptive appearances is afforded by the nesting of this species on the Gull Islands in Lake Michigan where among a number of gravel ridges they have selected only one on which to breed, that one being characterized by pebbles which match their eggs in size and color.[2]

The Caspian Tern flies much like other terns, but on account of its large size, large bill and head, and short tail seems heavier and more gull-like than any of the smaller species. When engaged in fishing it flies swiftly and rather low over the water, with bill pointed downward; when resting on beach or bar it occasionally raises its black crest. Mr. A. C. Bent contrasts its note with that of the Royal Tern: "The cry of the Caspian tern is entirely unlike that of the royal tern and quite different from that of any of the Laridæ. Its ordinary note is a hoarse, croaking 'kraaa' on a low key, loud, harsh and grating. A shorter note sounding like 'kow' or 'kowk' is often heard on its breeding grounds, where it also utters, when angry, a loud, vehement, rasping cry of attack." [3] This species is most likely to be found on the New England coast early in May and during September.

The Caspian Tern feeds on small fish, and it takes various forms of surface-swimming aquatic life, also mussels; it is said to eat the eggs and young of other birds.

ECONOMIC STATUS. See page 95.

Sterna máxima BODDAERT. Royal Tern.

Plate 7.

DESCRIPTION. — Bill nearly or quite as long as in Caspian Tern, but more slender and differently shaped; tarsus not longer than middle toe and claw; tail deeply forked, middle feathers broad to rounded tips, others successively elongated, narrowing toward tips, outer pair slender; a prominent (when raised) nuchal crest. *Adults in nuptial plumage (sexes alike)*: Cap glossy greenish-black but, unlike that of Caspian Tern, not extending below eye and narrowing in front of it, leaving a broad stripe of white feathers along base of upper mandible (below cap) and extending as far forward as black; in most individuals complete black cap worn but a short time in spring and early summer and succeeded soon after pairing by black and white cap of breeding plumage (see below); tail white with faint gray tinge, especially on middle feathers and inner webs of others; back, scapulars and wings pale gray ("pallid neutral gray" or paler), fading into white on rump, upper tail-coverts and ends of inner secondaries; most of secondaries white except space (mainly on outer web) near tip which is darker than back; outer web of 1st (outer) primary also darker than back; inner web with blackish space from base to tip, narrow at base and widening toward tip where for about an inch or more it occupies whole web; rest of web white, separated

[1] Bent, A. C.: Smithsonian Institution, United States National Museum, Bulletin No. 113, 1921, p. 205.

[2] Van Winkle, E.: Oölogist, Vol. X, 1893, p. 114.

[3] Bent, A. C.: Smithsonian Institution, United States National Museum, Bulletin No. 113, 1921, p. 209.

by straight edge from black; 2d to 5th primaries similar but white space rapidly narrows and shortens and runs out farther in center of web than along edge, leaving border of blackish along outer margin near end; other primaries pearly blue-gray, their inner edges white; under plumage and sides of head and neck all round white; bill coral or orange-red with lighter tip; feet black or blackish, soles yellowish. *Adults in breeding plumage:* Similar to nuptial plumage, but whole forehead and part of crown white, rest of cap black. *Adults in winter plumage:* Similar to breeding plumage but bill duller with dull yellowish tip; front of cap white; crown black and white, black increasing toward nape which is often nearly or quite black; black often extends forward rather narrowly on sides of head including eye; tail much less forked than in summer plumage, tinged gray like back and darkening toward tip into dusky leaden-gray (may be pure white in very old birds). *Young in first winter plumage:* Similar to adult winter plumage but wings and tail are those of juvenal plumage. *Young in juvenal plumage (August):* Bill much smaller than in adult, tip less acute, mostly reddish-yellow, lighter at tip; cap resembling that of winter adult but crest not noticeable; upper plumage mainly white with faint, creamy tinge, feathers centrally tinged with light gray and with brown or dusky spots or shaft-streaks; primaries and secondaries slaty-gray, edged with white, much like those of adults, but wanting sharp definition; tail white at base of inner webs, then dusky or lead-colored, then brownish, and white at extreme tip; under plumage pure white. *Downy young:* Variable; from light pinkish-cinnamon to "cartridge buff" above, much lighter below where sometimes nearly white; some birds almost unspotted; others heavily spotted with black above; bill "pale yellowish or dull ivory whitish, more horn-colored at tip; legs and feet grayish"; also a dusky type, with ground coloration concealed on head, throat, upper parts and flanks by dusky filaments.

MEASUREMENTS. — Length 18.00 to 21.00 in.; spread 42.00 to 44.00; folded wing 14.00 to 15.00; tail 6.00 to 8.00, forked 3.00 to 4.00; bill 2.25 to 2.50; tarsus 1.35 to 1.45.

MOLTS. — Juvenal plumage acquired before young birds reach full growth; postjuvenal molt of body-feathers (quills being retained) begins late in August; complete prenuptial molt in March after which young birds resemble adults but black cap may be imperfect; adults molt completely both spring and autumn, postnuptial molt occurring mainly in August and September though often prolonged into October or November; prenuptial molt in March, which is succeeded by black cap, is usually followed in turn by partial molt of head, producing white forehead; only small proportion of incubating birds retain full black cap.

FIELD MARKS. — *Adult:* Distinguishable from gulls by slim, sharp bill and deeply forked tail; resembles Caspian Tern but distinguishable at close range by deeply forked tail extending about to wing-tips where *caspia* has short forked tail, and wings extending beyond its tip; bill lighter red than that of *caspia;* black of head does not run beneath eye as in *caspia;* nor over forehead which is white and unstreaked where young (juvenal) *caspia* has it streaked with blackish and whitish. *Young:* Almost indistinguishable from *caspia* in field but *maxima* is an accidental *summer* visitant to Massachusetts while *caspia* comes chiefly in *spring* and *autumn;* tail more forked than that of immature *caspia.*

VOICE. — Not so loud and raucous as that of *caspia* and pitched in higher key; a squawking cry, like the syllables *quak, kak* or *kowk;* another note in lower key like bleating of a sheep; a soft liquid, musical rolling whistle — *tourrreee* — suggestive of the rolling whistle of the Upland Plover (A. C. Bent).

BREEDING. — In colonies; on low sandy islands or sand-bars. *Nest:* Slight hollow in sand. *Eggs:* 1 or 2, rarely 3, very rarely 4; 2.60 to 2.70 by 1.70 in. (Coues); rougher, narrower and usually more pointed than those of the Caspian Tern from which they may be distinguished; commonly very light, from white to ivory or dull yellow; darker or more greenish specimens not common; markings large or small, mostly dark brown of different shades, some almost black; some eggs have spots of various shades of gray also, and a few are unspotted. *Dates:* April 8 to June 28, North Carolina, South Carolina and Gulf states (A. C. Bent). One brood yearly.

RANGE. — Tropical American coasts and islands mainly; north to United States. Breeds in West Indies and Bahamas, on southern Atlantic and Gulf coasts north to Virginia, west to Texas, and on

Pacific coast of Lower California and Mexico; casual in summer north to Massachusetts, Michigan and Wisconsin; not rare in that season from San Francisco Bay south to western Mexico; winters from central Florida, Louisiana coast and Gulf of Mexico south along Atlantic coast to Patagonia; on Pacific coast from central California to Peru; also on west coast of Africa from Straits of Gibraltar to Angola.

DISTRIBUTION IN NEW ENGLAND. — Accidental summer visitant in Massachusetts. Records: Nantucket, two birds (a pair) taken by Brewster and Maynard July 1, 1874;[1] Chatham, female taken July 29, 1889;[2] Ipswich (beach), adult male taken by C. Otto Zerrahn, July 17, 1904.[3]

HAUNTS AND HABITS. The Royal Tern is one of the largest species of the family. In eastern North America it is second in size only to the Caspian Tern which, because of a more deeply forked and longer tail, it nearly equals in length but not in size. This species nests in such massed colonies that in one of the Breton Island Reservations (Louisiana) Mr. Bent counted 100 nests in a space four yards square. The birds on their nests sat so close together that they could hardly spread their wings without mutual interference. He says that the full black cap seems to be the courtship plumage, and the white forehead is the prevailing nesting plumage.[4] Therefore most of the Royal Terns which wander north in summer may be expected to appear in the latter plumage. The species might be mistaken easily for the Caspian Tern, though it is of lighter and more slender build than the other, while its flight resembles more that of the much smaller Common Tern. It is not improbable that nomadic Royal Terns may reach New England more frequently than records show.

ECONOMIC STATUS. See page 95.

Sterna sandvicénsis acuflávida CABOT. Cabot's Tern.

Other name: SANDWICH TERN.

DESCRIPTION. — Bill much longer than head, often exceeding combined length of tarsus, middle toe and claw; rather slender, tip very acute; hind toe very small. *Adults in breeding plumage (sexes alike)*: Cap glossy greenish-black, extending just below eye, forward to bill and backward over nape, much as in *maxima;* slightly crested; black cap usually worn but a brief period in spring and early summer; upper parts "pallid neutral gray to nearly pale neutral gray," fading to pure white on hind neck, rump and upper tail-coverts and tail; first four primaries colored much like those of Royal Tern (see page 99); heavily frosted when new; other primaries pearly bluish-gray with broad white margins for whole length of inner webs; sides of head below cap, and all under plumage white; bill black; tip bright yellow for .50 to .75 inch, sharply defined; iris dark brown; inside mouth dark

STERNA SANDVICENSIS

This head and bill is almost an exact counterpart of that of Cabot's Tern. About ½ natural size.

[1] Brewster; American Sportsman, Vol. V, 1875, p. 249, Howe and Allen. Footnote erroneous, but record correct; one specimen now in museum of Boston Society of Natural History, the other in Museum of Comparative Zoölogy, Cambridge.

[2] Ornithologist and Oölogist, Vol. XV, 1890, p. 110.

[3] Townsend, C. W.: Birds of Essex County, Massachusetts, p. 102.

[4] Bent, A. C.: Smithsonian Institution, United States National Museum, Bulletin No. 113, 1921, pp. 214, 216.

blue; feet black. In late May or June black cap usually becomes speckled with white. *Adults in winter plumage:* Similar, but frontal part of cap white, in some cases speckled with black; top of head white with narrow black or blackish shaft-streaks; crest usually brownish-black and a streak of same color running from crest to and through eye; tail less forked than in breeding plumage because of shortening of lateral feathers, usually slightly grayish near end; yellow at tip of bill duller and less in extent. *Young in first winter plumage:* Similar to winter plumage of adults but juvenal wings and tail retained. *Young in juvenal plumage:* Cap more or less black, variegated with white, forehead nearly or quite white, top of head with black markings and back of head nearly black; back and scapulars pale gray, with irregular but well-defined spots of brownish-black and V-shaped markings which are largest on scapulars; grayish band on lesser wing-coverts; greater wing-coverts with pale gray wash; flight-feathers of wings slaty-gray with white edges; tail grayish-white, with dusky areas or black spots near tip, very slightly forked; under plumage white; bill and feet either flesh-color or dusky, bill sometimes lighter toward end. *Downy young:* Usually buffy, whitish or white; unspotted; some individuals however are marked slightly with dusky on back and others in addition over top of head; bill and feet flesh-color.

MEASUREMENTS. — Length 14.00 to 16.00 in.; spread about 34.00; folded wing 11.00 to 12.15; tail 4.50 to 6.00, forked 2.25 to 2.50; bill 1.90 to 2.25; tarsus about 1.00.

MOLTS. — Juvenal plumage assumed gradually as down is shed, while bird is still growing; partial postjuvenal molt (not including wings and tail) begins in September when first winter plumage appears; following early spring prenuptial molt, most immature birds, then about one year old, probably assume plumage practically indistinguishable from adult nuptial; adults molt completely twice each year — prenuptial between March and May, and postnuptial beginning in early July and continuing through August and September (A. C. Bent).

FIELD MARKS. — *Adult:* Slightly larger, paler and relatively more slender than Common Tern; recognizable (at close range) by long, slender, black bill with *clearly-defined, bright yellow tip* and *black feet;* after breeding season yellow of bill dulls and diminishes somewhat in extent.

VOICE. — Loud, sharp, grating, heard half a mile (Audubon); hoarse grating cry, *cree* or *pink* (Morris); *kirhitt, kirhitt* (Yarrell); very noisy when in flocks or on breeding-grounds.

BREEDING. — In colonies; on sandy islands, often in company with Royal Terns. *Nest:* Mere hollow in sand; sometimes no hollow. *Eggs:* 1 or 2, rarely 3; 2.10 by 1.40 in. (Coues); often somewhat pointed; beautiful in both shape and color; various shades of olive-pink and buff (some eggs white), with an endless variety of markings of various browns, grays, lavender and black. *Dates.* April 25 to June 14, Texas (A. C. Bent). *Incubation:* Period about 3 weeks; shared by both sexes. One brood yearly, possibly two.

RANGE. — North and South America. Breeds from Virginia (casually) and North Carolina south to Florida, Texas, Bahamas, Antilles and British Honduras; winters from Bahamas, Florida and Louisiana south to Central America, Greater Antilles, Colombia, southern Brazil and on Pacific coast of southern Mexico and Guatemala; accidental in Ontario, Massachusetts and New Jersey; a few summer in Brazil.

DISTRIBUTION IN NEW ENGLAND. — Accidental visitor to Massachusetts. Record: Chatham, immature bird taken August, 1865.[1]

The record of a Cabot's Tern taken October 2, 1888, at Monomoy, Chatham, by John C. Cahoon, seems to be based on an error, since the authority for this record, as given in Howe and Allen's "Birds of Massachusetts," is William Brewster in Vol. VI (1889) of the Auk, pp. 66, 67. But this reference mentions only the capture of Forster's Tern by Mr. Cahoon on the same date and at the same place as mentioned in the case of Cabot's Tern. Nor does Mr. Cahoon record the taking of the Cabot's Tern on this date or any other.

It is of interest to know that Mr. A. W. Higgins, a competent field ornithologist, saw on July 10, 1918, at Sandwich, at the mouth of the Cape Cod canal, flying and also perched close by on the mooring pilings

---

[1] Allen, J. A.: American Naturalist, Vol. III, 1870, p. 644.

two terns which he is confident were Cabot's Terns. They had black bills (with light tips) and black feet and when they flew, were notably whiter than the Common Terns with which they were associated. Mr. Higgins saw these terns through a good glass; they were, in short, so near that their markings were distinctly discerned.

HAUNTS AND HABITS. Cabot's Tern seems to be the friend and companion of the larger Royal Tern. It breeds in colonies of Royal Terns and lives amicably beside them. In form it appears slender and rather frail, but nevertheless it is strong, swift and daring, a master of the air and capable of battling successfully with wind and storm. Apparently it is not one of the vanishing species. Under protection it seems to be pushing its way northward. Not until recent years has it been known to breed in North Carolina and Virginia. If it continues to increase, it may be looked for during late summer and early autumn as a casual visitant on the outer bars and beaches of Cape Cod.

ECONOMIC STATUS. See page 95.

Sterna fórsteri NUTTALL. Forster's Tern.

Other name: HAVELL'S TERN.

Plate 8.

DESCRIPTION. — Similar to Common Tern but a little larger; *bill longer and stouter; tail longer;* feet larger. *Adults in breeding plumage (sexes alike)* : Black cap not extending so far down on sides of head as in Common Tern; lower lid of eye white; rest of upper plumage except lower rump and upper tail-coverts and tail "pallid neutral gray"; primaries not dark like those of Common Tern but heavily frosted or silvered; outer web of 1st not black but frosted like others; no such distinct white space on inner webs of primaries as are seen in Common and Arctic Terns, but indication of it on three or four outer ones, others gray and frosted; tips of secondaries, anterior upper tail-coverts, sides of head and all lower plumage including wing-linings and axillars white, with hardly trace of leaden-gray evident on Common Tern and still deeper on Arctic Tern; "tail slightly lighter than back" (Coues); *long outer tail-feathers white on outer web and dusky on inner* (exactly the reverse in Common Tern); bill orange or orange-yellow with more or less black toward end; iris dark brown; feet bright orange, often nearing vermilion. *Adults in winter plumage:* Similar but forehead white; black of cap mostly replaced by whitish; dark, broad, ill-defined, crescent-shaped, dusky bar across nape, and distinct broad black stripe beginning before eye, inclosing it and ear, and extending well toward back of head; white of neck often extending round like a white collar; outer tail-feathers shorter than in summer, no longer than summer tail of Common Tern; iris dark brown; bill dusky or black except base of under mandible and space toward tip; feet dark orange; sometimes whole top of head grayish-white, darkening toward nape (this is the plumage described by Audubon as *Sterna havelli*). *Young in first winter plumage:* Similar to winter adults, with broad blackish stripe on side of head, but tail less deeply forked and somewhat mottled brownish; primaries darker and less frosted and their white spaces more sharply contrasted with dark. *Young in juvenal plumage:* Darker and browner above and below than young of Common, Arctic or Roseate Terns; pearl-gray of back and scapulars almost concealed by buffy or brown feather-ends of varying shades; top of head snuff-brown; sides of neck heavily clouded and fore-breast and rump lightly clouded same, which shows also on wing-coverts and tail, the whole giving bird a brown appearance above; black patch on each side of head similar to that on winter adults and young. *Downy young:* Vary from light clay-color to pinkish-buff, fading into whitish below; darker on throat, which is sometimes drab but not so dark as in Common Tern; heavily spotted or streaked above with blackish, spots largest on back.

MEASUREMENTS. — Length 14.00 to 15.00 in.; spread about 30.00; folded wing 9.50 to 10.50; tail 5.00 to 8.00, forked 2.30 to 5.00; bill 1.48 to 1.75; tarsus .90 to 1.00.

MOLTS. — Juvenal plumage acquired as young bird comes to full size, but browns fade or wear away as season advances and (with a partial molt of body feathers) young bird assumes its lighter winter plumage; complete prenuptial molt in February or March, succeeded by first nuptial plumage, which usually is as adult, but sometimes shows traces of first winter plumage, bird being nine or ten months old; two complete adult molts, prenuptial beginning in February and postnuptial beginning in July or August.

FIELD MARKS. — *Adult in breeding plumage:* Indistinguishable (except by cries) at a distance from Common Tern, but at close range seems slightly larger; *white or nearly so below* where at same season Common Tern is darker; wings shorter; primaries much lighter than those of Common Tern, as seen from above; bill orange-yellow toward base, black toward tip; tail longer and more streaming than in Common Tern. *Adult and young in winter plumage:* With much white in cap; fore part of head all white and *distinct broad blackish stripe along side of head,* beginning just before eye, including eye and ear.

VOICE. — Quite distinctive, rendering identification easy and certain; young in juvenal plumage gives shrill, high-pitched squeal, quite different from those of other Gulls and Terns; notes of adult harsh and grating on low key, *tza-a-ap, zreep, zrurrr* — a rasping, buzzing, nasal sound suggesting the cry of a Nighthawk; also a shrill peeping, *pip pip pip pip pip,* rapidly given (A. C. Bent).

BREEDING. — In colonies; on salt marshes, sandy sea-islands or marshy borders of inland lakes. *Nest:* Varies from well-made structure on assembled heap of vegetation to mere hollow in pile of reeds or on muskrat house; sometimes buoyed up by dead reeds or flags in several feet of water; sometimes a mere hollow on muddy shore. *Eggs:* 2 to 5; indistinguishable from those of Common Tern. *Dates:* In South early May to late June or early July; in North mostly in June and July. *Incubation:* Period 23 days; probably by both sexes (A. C. Bent). One brood yearly.

RANGE. — Mainly temperate North America. Breeds in interior California, southern Oregon, Nevada and Utah and from southwestern Saskatchewan, central Alberta and Manitoba south to northern Colorado, northern Nebraska, Minnesota, northeastern Illinois and southern Ontario, on coasts of Texas, Louisiana, Virginia and (formerly) New Jersey; winters from southern California, Gulf coast and South Carolina south to southern Guatemala; in migration on Atlantic coast casually north to Massachusetts; accidental off coast of Brazil.

DISTRIBUTION IN NEW ENGLAND. — A straggler; definite records are in fall. *New Hampshire:* Seabrook, September 24, 1872, immature male taken by William Brewster and now in collection of Boston Society of Natural History.[1] *Massachusetts:* Ipswich, September, 1870, bird taken by C. J. Maynard;[2] Gloucester (Magnolia), August 28, 1877, male taken;[1] Chatham, August, 1885, a number seen by Dr. J. A. Allen;[3] Chatham (Monomoy), October 2, 1888, immature bird taken by J. C. Cahoon,[4] and now in collection of Boston Society of Natural History; Ipswich, August 3, 1920, bird seen by H. L. Barrett;[5] Chatham (Monomoy), September 1, 1924, immature bird in first year plumage, seen by A. C. Bent.[6]

HAUNTS AND HABITS.   Forster's Tern is so much like the Common Tern in appearance, habits and behavior that Audubon did not recognize the breeding adult as a different species, though in a quite different winter plumage he named it Havell's Tern. Swainson and Richardson described it as the Common Tern while Wilson never recognized the species.   George N. Lawrence, in 1858, was the first to differentiate the bird in breeding dress from the Common Tern; and Coues, still later, described for the first time its various plumages.   Considering its resemblance to the Common Tern it is probable that

---

[1] Smith, J. D.: *in litt.*   [2] Brewster, William: American Naturalist, Vol. VI, 1872, p. 306.
[3] Allen, J. A.: Bulletin of the American Museum of Natural History, Vol. I, 1881–86. Revised List of Birds of Massachusetts, 1886, p. 227.   [4] Brewster, William: Auk, Vol. VI, 1889, p. 66.   [5] *In litt.*   [6] *In litt.*

PLATE 8

PLATE 8

ARCTIC TERN
Page 115
ADULT IN BREEDING PLUMAGE

ROSEATE TERN
Page 118
ADULT IN BREEDING PLUMAGE

FORSTER'S TERN
Page 103
ADULT IN BREEDING PLUMAGE

COMMON TERN
Page 105
ADULT IN BREEDING PLUMAGE

YOUNG IN FIRST WINTER PLUMAGE

YOUNG IN FIRST WINTER PLUMAGE

BLACK TERN
Page 128
ADULT IN BREEDING PLUMAGE
YOUNG IN FIRST WINTER PLUMAGE

LEAST TERN
Page 122
ADULT IN BREEDING PLUMAGE
YOUNG IN JUVENAL PLUMAGE

All one-fourth natural size.

Forster's Tern is a less rare visitant to Massachusetts than the records indicate; therefore it should be looked for during the migrations. Except by its dissimilar cries the adult in breeding plumage may be distinguished from the Common Tern only at close range; but in the immature and adult winter plumages (in one or other of which it may occur here in late summer or early autumn) the distinct black patch on side of head should enable a close observer with a good glass to recognize the bird. Like the Black Tern it breeds in the latitude of Massachusetts and wanders here in late summer and fall. Unlike the Black Tern, however, it may easily escape recognition. When terns are seen catching insects in autumn on our coast it is well to observe them closely as some may be of this rare species. Forster's Tern usually comes north in May and moves southward in August and September; rarely a few remain until about the middle of October.

This species feeds more on insects than does the Common Tern. It catches them on the wing and picks them up from the water. It also eats fish and frogs (both alive and dead) and other aquatic animals.

ECONOMIC STATUS. See page 95.

Sterna hirúndo LINNÆUS. **Common Tern.**

Other names: WILSON'S TERN; TEARR; MACKEREL GULL; SUMMER GULL; SEA SWALLOW; MEDRICK.

Plate 8.

DESCRIPTION. — Bill as long as head, about equal to tarsus and middle toe without claw. *Adults in breeding plumage (sexes alike)*: Whole top of head, forehead and nape deep black, extending slightly below level of eyes but leaving lower eyelids white, black so broad in front of eyes that white feathers along side of bill barely reach forward as far as black; rest of upper plumage "pale neutral gray" except tips of secondaries, lower part of rump, upper tail-coverts and greater part of tail which are white; below pale lavender-gray or "pallid neutral gray" to grayish-white; on neck, throat, chin, sides of head and under tail-coverts, color of under plumage fades insensibly into white; wing-linings and axillars white; shafts of primaries white, darkening toward tips; outer web of 1st (outer) primary black; first four or five primaries grayish-black and frosted silvery-gray, their inner webs with space of white along inner margins (on 1st primary this occupies entire web at base, narrows as it ascends and either ends or narrows to a line about 1 inch from tip); this white less extensive on other primaries, on each web running up center farther than on edge, and on innermost primaries forming only a narrow margin to web; inner primaries lighter, mostly of color of back, edged white on inner web and at tip; secondaries mostly white, their outer thirds bluish-gray and ends whitish or white; tail largely white, not very deeply forked, folded wings reaching an inch or two beyond it; *inner* web of outer tail feather *white*, *outer* web *dusky*, darkening toward tip; outer webs of remaining tail-feathers (except middle pair, or in some cases, four feathers) pale gray; bill bright coral or vermilion, with more or less of terminal half black (rarely only a little black near end of upper mandible), extreme tip slightly yellow or yellowish; iris dark brown; feet rich orange-vermilion. *Adults in winter plumage:* Similar, but black of cap imperfect, replaced by white on fore part of head and crown, black only on back part of head; *below lighter, usually white;* tail shorter than in spring; red of feet and bill duller (base of upper mandible usually red, rest black, lower mandible vermilion at base, crimson at angle, black at tip). *Young in first winter plumage:* Region about eye, and back of head (occiput) dull black, crown mixed with black and grayish-white; other upper plumage pale gray, rather lighter than in adults; scapulars, back and tertials, with subterminal crescent-shaped marks of dusky or grayish-brown and tipped pale buff; distinct blackish bar on fore wing formed by dusky lesser wing-coverts; fore part of head, upper tail-coverts, inner webs of tail-feathers, tips of secondaries and all under plumage white; bill dusky with brownish tinge, base of mandible lighter and more reddish than dusky; feet rather pale reddish; as season advances young bird becomes more like winter adult except that feet are dark or blackish, tail is less forked and darker, and traces of dusky still remain on wing-coverts. *Young in juvenal plumage:* Forehead pale brown blending into dull black on back of head; upper plumage more or less pale gray, with many dusky margins and buff edgings; dusky band on fore wing caused by darker lesser wing-coverts; white below; iris dark brown; bill and feet flesh-color; tip of bill blackish. (Dwight says flesh-colored bill and feet first brighten, then darken.) *Downy young:* Vary above from pale yellowish to deep buff, clay-color or gray, mottled with various shades of rather dark brown or blackish; throat varies from blackish or sooty-gray or dusky to nearly pure white and is usually dark (rarely very light and unspotted); under plumage white; feet flesh-color, pinkish or reddish.

MEASUREMENTS. — Length 13.00 to 16.00 in.; spread 29.00 to 32.00; folded wing 9.75 to 11.75; tail 5.00 to 7.00, forked about 3.50; bill 1.25 to 1.50; tarsus .66 to .87. Female smaller than male; young smaller, down to 9 inches. (Above measurements indicate great variation in size among individuals of same species.)

MOLTS. — Downy young slowly acquire juvenal plumage early — before full growth; first winter plumage assumed usually after September, following postjuvenal molt (August to November) of body-feathers and sometimes some of lesser wing-coverts, leaving wings and tail substantially as in juvenal plumage; in next spring complete prenuptial molt (February to June), followed by adult nuptial plumage which often is not fully assumed until June when bird is nearly one year old; sometimes full adult plumage is not assumed until the next spring; A. C. Bent referring to this delayed development says, — "Occasionally in young birds the first nuptial plumage, described above, is not assumed, but instead a plumage like the adult winter plumage is acquired by a late prenuptial or an early postnuptial molt. This plumage is worn throughout the spring and summer, probably by the less vigorous birds which do not breed. It is the plumage which was once described as a species under the name *Sterna portlandica.*" [1] Adults molt completely twice annually.

DOWNY YOUNG COMMON TERN
½ natural size.

FIELD MARKS. — *Adults:* In summer darker than Roseate Tern; bill bright coral or light vermilion with more or *less black toward end* and longer than that of Arctic Tern; tail usually shorter than in Arctic or Roseate Terns; folded wings reach beyond its tip. *Newly-fledged young:* Indistinguishable in field from those of Arctic or Roseate Terns except perhaps by an expert. *Downy young:* May be distinguished from those of Roseate Tern by flesh-colored feet; the former have blackish feet; *downy young* of *lighter phases* of Common Tern may be separated from those of Arctic Tern by absence of dusky in forehead.

VOICE. — Most commonly *tee' ar-r-r*, uttered harshly, but often much varied in length, enunciation and pitch, thus expressing different emotions or moods; "a sharp vibratory *tut tut* or *kik kik kik*, followed by a piercing, screaming *tear*" (C. W. Townsend). (See also page 111.)

BREEDING. — On islands in lake or sea or on shores. *Nest:* Varying from mere hollow in beach-sand or pebbles, lined with a few bits of shell or small stones to well-built hollowed mound of grasses and seaweeds; sometimes of fish-bones; sometimes a hollow in stranded eel-grass; sometimes on bare rock; usually in the open, but often among weeds or grasses and sometimes even amidst shrubbery. *Eggs:* 2 or 3, sometimes 4, rarely 5 or even 6; 1.55 to 1.65 by 1.20 to 1.25 in. (Coues); short ovate to elongate-ovate; exceedingly variable in size, shape and color; ranging from immaculate white (rarely) through various shades of pale brown, buff, olivaceous and green, spotted and blotched with various browns, grays and lilacs; often eggs found in same nest differ widely in shape and color. *Dates:* May 15 to

[1] Smithsonian Institution, United States National Museum Bulletin No. 113, 1921, p. 245.

July 20, Massachusetts; May 29 to July 26, Maine. *Incubation:* Period 21 days (Lynds Jones); by both sexes. One brood yearly; no conclusive evidence of more than one in New England, but two broods may be reared in South.

RANGE. — Both Hemispheres. Breeds from near northern coast of Mackenzie, Great Slave Lake, northern Manitoba and probably well into Keewatin, west coast of Hudson Bay, southern Ungava (central Quebec) and Newfoundland south to southeastern Alberta, southwestern Saskatchewan, northern North Dakota, southern Minnesota, southern Wisconsin, southeastern Michigan, northern Ohio, western Pennsylvania, northern New York and North Carolina; some breed in the Bahamas, on coast of Venezuela, on Florida Keys, Dutch West Indies, and coasts of Alabama, Louisiana and Texas; breeds also in Europe, Asia and northern Africa and in Azores, Canary and Madeira islands; some bred formerly in Bermuda; winters from Florida south along both coasts of South America to Straits of Magellan and in southern Asia and Africa; appears in migration through interior of North America, on Atlantic and Pacific coasts and in Bahamas and Bermuda.

DISTRIBUTION IN NEW ENGLAND. — Summer resident coastwise; common to abundant locally; abundant near its colonies in Maine, Massachusetts, Rhode Island and Connecticut, but rather rare visitant in interior, especially in Vermont (seen by Dr. L. H. Ross, May 30, 1907, at Bennington[1]).

SEASON IN MASSACHUSETTS. — (April 20) May 1 to November 23 (December 2 and 22); accidental in winter.

HAUNTS AND HABITS. A June morning in 1908 found me marooned on a sandy islet near the elbow of Cape Cod. My skiff had been filled and my oars carried to sea by the surf of the stiffest "sou-wester" of the season; and with back to the gale and the flying, cutting sand-drift I watched the rising sea gradually march up the streaming strand until the wash began to pour over the seaward bank and race across the sand to my feet. The attraction which drew me that morning to the islet was an immense concourse of birds resting on its sands or hovering above them, most of which proved to be Common Terns. There was nothing to do but await a rescue; so crouching in the stranded boat I watched the birds and the sea. The flying terns soon discovered a "school" of fish, and then all was wild excitement among them. Instantly the island was birdless, as they all launched upon the gale and rode down to leeward intent upon their prey. When mackerel or bluefish, coming in great hordes, find a school of "bait," the larger fish chase the little ones until the latter, in their efforts to escape, break water in all directions and skip over the waves like little flying-fish, or else "mill" about in a dense mass at the surface. Then the water all about fairly boils under the savage onset of their pursuers. The sharp-eyed terns, too, spying the commotion, flock from afar to feast on the luckless "fishlings." To see the terns thus fishing is a sight to stir the blood. High in the sunlight they hover above the surging sea. Below the blue waves roar on, to break in foam on the yellow sand. The whirling, screaming, light-winged birds, strongly contrasted against the smoky murk to seaward, alternately climb the air and plunge like plummets straight down into the waves — rising again and again, fluttering, poising, screaming, striking. So now like birds gone mad the terns flashed from sky to sea. It fairly rained birds; hundreds of them were shooting down into the angry waves. They played with gale and sea. Rising, they shook the brine from their feathers and,

---

[1] Vermont Bird Club Bulletin, No. 3, 1908, p. 32.

towering high, hovered a moment, breasting the gale; then setting their wings like long, barbed spearheads, plunged again and yet again. This was the sight for which I had been waiting. The birds had given the signal to the fishermen to come out from shore. Soon three dories with their adventurous crews had passed out toward the foaming bar, and the men were dropping their lines near where the fishing birds were thickest. I had only to wait for a returning fisherman to take me off. Terns catching fish are a common sight, but that day they furnished a spectacle that illustrated, under stress, their power and address in taking prey — also their utility as guides to the fishermen of our coast.

TERNS FISHING

Mr. Franklin E. Campbell writes that on September 6, 1921, great schools of "sand eels" were massed in the North River at Scituate, and that a tern often had three or four at a time in its bill, holding them firmly and never dropping one. Neltje Blanchan, on the other hand, says that one tern sometimes drops a little fish as if in play, when another catches it in the air, until it has been passed from mouth to mouth several times before it is swallowed.

If one really wishes to see terns *en masse*, he should go in the breeding season to one of the greater tern colonies off the shores of Massachusetts or Maine, such as Muskeget or Machias Seal Island. In years past the human intruder upon the former breeding-ground was surrounded by a confused, gyrating "snow-storm" of birds and his ears were assailed by an almost deafening chorus of harsh, clashing cries. However, the fitness of Muskeget as a breeding-place for Common Terns is gradually lessening. Perhaps the vegetation over a great part of it is growing too dense for this species, which does not like thick cover; also the island is fast becoming a paradise for the increasing numbers of Laughing Gulls which rather prefer to hide their nests under rank grass or herbage. The Common Tern seems to select the naked sand in preference, especially when nesting on the mainland where it may be disturbed by enemies at night; and where new lands are building up from the sea, it promptly forsakes adjacent land on which it has bred (and which has become overgrown with beach-grass and other vegetation) and moves out on the bare sand which furnishes no cover for cats, skunks or other nocturnal enemies. The occupation of this land by the birds eventually increases its fertility; and when, therefore, vegetation becomes too rank, the terns must go elsewhere. Islands where sheep or cattle are kept, however, may be so closely cropped as to remain suitable for tenancy of the birds. Penikese Island which has long been occupied by terns, has become the most fertile island of its group — in part from the droppings of the birds. Terns prefer small islands well offshore whereon to breed, for here native predatory mammals are not likely to raid their nests. Wherever they breed on the mainland, they are attacked by dogs, cats, foxes, skunks and other night-prowlers. The birds are safer on islands well out to sea; but they also occupy islets in salt-water bays and harbors and in fresh-water ponds.

When I first visited Skiffs Island off the coast of Marthas Vineyard, it was a barren, wind-swept, wave-washed islet of sand without a sign of vegetation; yet terns were nesting everywhere above high-water mark. As we landed and our heads rose above the sloping bank, a multitude of downy young birds started up from the sand, marched to the opposite side of the island and there cast themselves boldly into the sea. Meanwhile overhead the darting, whirling multitude of parent birds filled the air with their clamor. We crouched down, and the young birds swam back to land little the worse for their bath; indeed some presently crept to our feet. Here was no vestige of any real nest beyond a few pebbles or bits of shell in slight hollows in the sand, with occasionally a few pieces of seaweed; yet here on this desolate, barren sand-bar the terns hatched, fed and reared their young in safety from cats or other nocturnal mammals.

Common or Wilson's Terns arrive in numbers from about the first to the tenth of May on their breeding grounds in Massachusetts. They begin making nests about May 20; and if all goes well, the young are hatching by June 16. If the nests are not disturbed, most of the young are on the wing by August 1 and have deserted the breeding-grounds; but if the nests are robbed, some young may still be found there through the month of August. The courtship of this species is well described as follows by Dr. Charles W. Townsend in "Beach Grass": "On this June day [June 12, 1921] I sat on the sand of Ipswich beach within sixty yards of a flock of over a hundred common terns that had alighted on the water's edge. It was at once apparent that the birds were preparing to breed, as many of them were engaged in active courtship. As the sexes are alike in plumage, one could distinguish the males from the females only by their actions, but these actions were distinctive. With short mincing steps a male would strut before a demure female. His puffed out neck and his head were stretched up to the full extent and his open bill was continually vibrating as he uttered rasping *crrrs*. His long tail was cocked up between the wings which were extended from the body so that the shoulders stuck out nearly horizontally. At times he side-stepped; at times he pirouetted. . . . Sometimes two would fly at each other like gamecocks, and continue the fight in the air. Again a male would return from fishing with a sand-lance drooped from his bill, and after eluding rivals who sought to take it from him, he would alight close to his beloved one and present her with the choice morsel, following up his gift with courtship antics. She, meanwhile, calmly and apparently without the least concern for him, swallowed the tidbit."

Nest building on the open sand is but the work of a moment. The bird alights, selects the spot, crouches slightly and works its little feet so rapidly that the motion seems a mere blur, while the sand flies out in tiny jets in every direction as the creature pivots about.   The tern next settles lower and smooths the cavity by turning and working and moving its body and wings from side to side.   Occasionally, where nesting-material is abundant, quite an elaborate nest is built — a pile of grass, seaweed or other drift some six inches high.   Other nests are mere hollows sparsely wreathed about with a little beach-grass.   Sometimes the nests are more or less concealed under beach-grass or other vegetation.   When the eggs or young are destroyed, a second set of eggs is commonly laid, and sometimes perhaps a third.   Occasionally, as in 1920 at Nauset, a large number of terns arrive late in the season and deposit their eggs and rear young in late July and August.   Probably such late comers have lost elsewhere in some way their eggs or young.

Some of the older ornithologists would have us believe that terns leave their eggs in fair weather to be hatched by the heat of the sun, but probably this is an error.   I have never seen the slightest sign of such a habit.   No doubt there are hours when their eggs can be left safely, for all wild-birds' eggs will bear some neglect and still hatch.   But to leave them long exposed to the hot summer sun or to cold wind and rain probably would be fatal, and I have never known terns to desert their eggs in any weather unless driven off by intruders.   Let the watcher lie down and remain quiet where terns are incubating, and soon he will see them settle on their eggs all about, coming as near him as they dare. When photographing or camping among them, I have seen them come back to their eggs within a few feet of my (concealed) face.   The female usually performs most of the duties of incubation, but she is occasionally relieved for brief periods by the male.   Terns that nest on the sand must cover their eggs carefully when the young are hatching, particularly if a "sou'wester" is blowing, which often happens during the breeding season. Mr. David Gould, who has guarded the tern colony at Nauset, tells me that he once approached the nests on a windy day when many young were hatching, and the dry sand blown by the strong wind adhered to the wet plumage of the newly-hatched birds so that within fifteen minutes many were buried alive — smothered in drifting sand. Eggs also may be buried at such times; but some of the birds are intelligent enough to dig them out again and place them in new nests, or to continue to brood eggs dug out of the sand by the warden.   On such days people should not be allowed to disturb the sitting terns.   The female tern must stay by her eggs to protect them against crows, gulls and other enemies; and for mutual protection the community sometimes joins forces when all *en masse* will assail and drive away a hawk or other foe.   Some of these birds are so devoted to their eggs and young that they will even strike a human intruder.   Many times terns have struck my head with their beaks, and a few times with such force that the effect of the blow was felt for some time afterward.   When the young are safely hatched, the parent usually flies off with the empty egg shells and drops them at a distance.

On July 6 and 7, 1921, I camped in a small shelter-tent in the heart of a colony of several thousand terns at Chatham.   The birds became so indifferent to my shelter that they alighted upon it.   Fledglings climbed to its top while I helped their progress with my hand beneath the canvas. All about me males wooed their mates, while parents incubated their eggs and fed one another and their young. They were vocal all day, very noisy at sundown and more or less so through the night, with many variations of the common *tee' arr*, such as a guttural *éorrr*, which was very common. There were many low guttural *rrrs* and a faint plaintive *pee'-ope* which may have been a call of the fledglings. Their notes were in much greater variety than I had supposed and many of them cannot be adequately indicated by the pen. They uttered many hen-like calls, and one resembling a note of the cuckoo; also a fast repeated *cack* or chuckle, sometimes given so rapidly and by so many birds in unison that it sounded almost like a pattering of many feet or the combined fluttering of the wings of a large flock. This occurred mainly at dusk or even after dark. The birds seemed to be quietest about 3 A.M., but with the awakening day they grew noisy again.

The male constantly attends the sitting female and brings food to her, largely "sand eels" or similar small, slender fish which are rarely over five or six inches in length. The food-call of the female is recognizable, and is frequently repeated when the supply arrives, for which she begs with uplifted head and wide-open mouth. Sometimes when the male brings a fish, another bird tries to steal it and seizes one end. Then comes "the tug of war." The two pull each other back and forth and sometimes others join in the strenuous struggle, but in the end the owner usually retains his booty. Often he does not feed the female at once, but turning a cold shoulder walks into the grass and drops the much-desired morsel. She follows, begging piteously, and finally picks it up from the ground, and with seeming difficulty swallows it. Now and then as I watched, a male, having fed his mate, stretched his neck to full length, with head horizontal or with bill pointed skyward, and then, with tail jauntily cocked, bowed gravely several times. The males appeared to do most of the fishing. A constant flight of them passed out to sea and returned with fish.

Young terns are very precocious and self-reliant and can (soon after hatching) run about and swim and hide in moments of danger. Yet they differ totally from the young of Shore Birds (*Limicolæ*) in that they depend upon their parents for food and have no notion of securing it for themselves. On a hot July day I watched a hatching chick break its shell and emerge into the sunlight. The extreme heat of the sun distressed it almost immediately. It crept

THE COMMON TERN
FROM NESTLING
TO LAST STAGE
OF THE DOWN

three feet away into the shadow of a little plant. After resting there in the cool shade it returned to the nest where the mother came and brooded it. Its down, still bedraggled with the moisture of the egg, had not yet assumed the fluffy appearance, even, of the day-old chick. As soon as the young birds become strong, they leave the nest and wander at will, except as they are driven about by adults other than their own parents. The young will beg from any tern coming in with food, as they do not seem to be able to recognize their own parents. Apparently, however, every parent knows its offspring, though on account of the frequent wandering of the little ones it may not be able always at once to find them. I noticed that these little strays were chased by adults other than their parents and were buffeted about from one bird to another. In consequence they early became very meek in the presence of an elder, and sneaked self-effacing by or squatted with head held to the ground. Yet when pursued and struck at repeatedly, they seemed to outrun the adult bird which never followed far, seeming to be content with driving the youngling away. I have never seen an adult tern seize or kill a young bird of its own species (as Herring Gulls sometimes do); but Mr. Allan Keniston of Vineyard Haven has sent me a photograph of an adult Common Tern actually lifting a youngster from the ground and shaking it.

A struggle for existence is waged between terns and gulls in which the terns sometimes attack and kill young gulls. When Herring Gulls are driven off temporarily by visitors terns nesting near them are likely to attack any young gull that strays into their colony. I saw one such beaten down by repeated blows from many irate terns, and it saved its life only by creeping under the sheltering leaves of a low-growing plant and lying there as if dead. Dr. L. B. Bishop reports to Mr. Bent that at Stump Lake, North Dakota, he saw terns strike and kill young Ring-billed Gulls by darting down upon their heads while the young gulls were swimming. He concluded that the adult gulls had been eating the terns' eggs and young and that the terns took opportunity to retaliate.[1] Young terns are seen occasionally with heads pecked open, and this may be the work of gulls.

An enemy which has been known to attack young terns, as well as the young of some other ground-nesting species, is the ant. In 1922 and 1923 a colony of Common Terns nesting at the mouth of Pamet River, Truro, were beset by this enemy and most of the young were destroyed, being literally eaten alive. The matter was brought to the attention of the Massachusetts Audubon Society by Dr. C. P. Curley of Provincetown, and Mr. Winthrop Packard, Secretary of that society, took protective measures, using ant-poison and tobacco dust which apparently abated the nuisance.[2]

Professor Lynds Jones, a careful observer, who has watched Common Terns closely believes that they recognize their stray young by the sense of smell. His account indicates that the parent hesitates a moment and touches the youngster testingly with its forehead before feeding it. There is no doubt in my mind that Professor Jones saw exactly what he describes, but I have never seen the slightest hesitation or noted this touching of foreheads. When the searching tern gets sight of its young, it seems (in my experience) to recognize it at once. Mr. Stanley C. Arthur is quoted by Mr. Bent in an account of an experiment with two well-marked Cabot's Terns which he could easily distinguish one from the other by their differing plumage. During absence of the birds from their nests

---

[1] Smithsonian Institution, United States National Museum, Bulletin No. 113, p. 247.
[2] Bulletin Massachusetts Audubon Society, Oct. 1924, p. 5.

he exchanged their eggs; yet on their return each settled upon its own egg without showing "the slightest concern." Again he transposed the eggs with the same result. If in this instance the terns knew their own eggs by sight, is it not likely that they should know their own well-marked young by the same sense?

When the parent tern comes in with fish for the family, it utters a peculiar call, somewhat resembling the usual harsh *tee' arr* but higher in pitch and softer in tone. The young beg for food from any incoming fish-laden bird, and give a harsh rattling cry somewhat like the alarm-note of the adult. When a half-grown youngster sees a parent bird fluttering near with food, it cannot contain itself for eagerness. It dances about, flaps or flutters its wings and begs with open mouth in a most appealing manner. The parent, apparently recognizing its offspring while still in air, alights and proceeds unhesitatingly and in the most business-like and expeditious way to fill the yawning cavity with a small fish. The late Charles H. Weekes of Harwich once told me that he saw one very tiny young bird fed by regurgitation apparently from the parent's stomach. A watery substance seemed to be running from the beak of the parent into that of the little one. But from the very first day I have seen fish brought to the young. The youngsters soon learn to seek shelter from hot sun or cold wind. When photographing terns on a barren island, I found that two or three downy chicks had crept up under the shelter of my blind and one had ensconced itself comfortably in a hollow in the sand between my feet. As the day advances and the sun's rays strengthen, any object that provides shade or shelter is sought. A bit of driftwood or a dead skate on the beach, a bunch of beach-grass or any weed, will serve. Often under such circumstances I have seen a youngling crowd in between the stems of two plants that afforded it shade and concealment, and then, with flying feet, scoop out quickly a deep cavity for its body in the cooler sand below the surface and lie there hidden and comfortable. As their pinions develop, the young birds frequently stand facing the breeze and flap their wings until gradually, little by little, they become strong enough to raise themselves off their feet. Then it is only a few days before their wings sustain them for considerable flights. Now they make their way to the shore, and the parents feed them on the beach. A little later a parent passes food to its young while both are on the wing, or feeds the fledglings while the latter sit on the water.

It has been asserted that terns rarely rest on the water or swim. Although they do not swim or float as frequently as gulls, the Common Tern is, nevertheless, very fond of dipping, bathing and resting on water (either salt or fresh) on hot days; and I have seen hundreds flying daily to fresh-water ponds to bathe, during bright hot days and also in dull, foggy weather. Near Muskeget in calm weather great flocks thus seem to enjoy themselves on the surface of the sea; but when the water is rough, they dip into the waves singly and splash for a few moments only, and then rise again, as they do not seem to care to remain long in choppy waves. On July 17, 1921, at Chatham, I watched terns bathing in a fresh-water pond about half a mile inland from their main colony. Often birds coming in from the sea were so eager for their bath that instead of stopping first at the colony, they carried their fish with them, bathed, and then flew to their nests with their prey still held in their bills. They acted like boys out of school "going in swimming." Each one plunged in with wide-spread wings, but did not go wholly under, splashed about for a time, then rose, plunged again and splashed some more. I held my eye to individual birds and saw them rise and dive at least six times. As they flew away, they shook themselves like a dog just out of water. Several repeated this shaking two or three times while still in sight.

There is great mortality often among young terns. High storm-tides in June or July sometimes rise over the nests, wash away the eggs or drown the newly hatched young. Disease appears sometimes, and occasionally a protracted storm or a violent tempest kills young birds. Again sufficient suitable food is not always to be found within eight or ten miles of a large colony, and then some of the young perish from starvation. In 1921, at the large Chatham colony, there was great mortality among the smallest young. At this age they must have very small fish. As such fish (or "bait," as the fishermen call them) could not be found near the colony, the parents brought fish so large that the young could not swallow them; or else they failed to bring any. At Monomoy Point, about ten miles away, "bait" was plentiful. Here few deaths occurred. Also at the Nauset colony in Orleans there was no appreciable mortality. But on Muskeget famine prevailed. No one knows how far the parent birds will go from the nesting-ground to secure food for the young. While sailing once toward Muskeget in a fog, I saw right ahead a Common Tern dive and pick up a fish, and then start to return on the course we also were making for the island. There was no land nearer than Muskeget in that direction, and the boatman calculated that the bird had eleven miles to go. How the bird knew the direction and could keep it for eleven miles without chart or compass through thick fog is a question for the philosopher. If the parents were compelled to go ten or eleven miles for each fish taken, it is unlikely that they could get enough food to sustain both themselves and their nestlings.

Terns always show sympathy for a wounded comrade and gather about it as if lamenting its fate. Thomas Edward,[1] the Scotch naturalist, relates the following incident which, if a fact, shows quite clearly an altruistic tendency among terns. Edward says he shot a tern which fell screaming, with a broken wing, into the sea. The cries of the wounded bird brought together a considerable number of terns which surveyed their wounded comrade round and round, as they fluttered overhead. In the meantime the wounded bird was slowly drifting toward shore where Edward began to make preparations for capturing it. Then, to his utter astonishment and surprise, he saw two of the unwounded terns take hold of their disabled comrade, one at each wing, lift him from the water, and bear him seaward. The two were followed by two others. The first two having carried the wounded bird about six or seven yards, let him gently down, when the second two took him up in a similar manner, and thus they continued to carry him seaward until they had reached a rock at a considerable distance from the shore upon

---

[1] Smiles, Samuel: Life of a Scotch Naturalist, 1877, pp. 218–219.

which they landed him in safety. When Edward made toward the rock, he was observed by the terns and in a short time a swarm was about him. As he approached the rock, two terns took the wounded bird once more and bore him out to sea. Edward, viewing their devotion, did not molest them further.

Early in May practically all the terns of this species have left the coast of South America and a few sometimes appear in April on the coast of Massachusetts. Through-out most of May migrants are passing northward — after our resident birds have assembled at their breeding grounds. Early in August the terns begin to wander from their Massachusetts homes, and by the latter part of September a few have already reached South America; but they continue to pass in small numbers along the Massachusetts coast, sometimes well into November.

The food of the Common Tern varies more or less with locality and circumstance. Along the New England coast small slender fish, never over five or six inches in length, such as the sand-eel or sand-lance (*Ammodytes americanus*), form a large part of their food. Small herrings or alewives are eaten and even menhaden, together with shrimps and other crustaceans, aquatic worms and insects; in addition (in times of scarcity) the offal of fish thrown into the water by fishermen. In August and September the species is observed to catch on the wing such insects as flying ants, butterflies and cicadas.

ECONOMIC STATUS. The Common Tern, like the other species of this group, is a harmless bird. Its insect food includes species that are regarded as injurious. It never eats marketable fish, and it serves as a guide by which fishermen locate "schools" of bluefish and mackerel — also in times of thick fog to show them the way to and from the fishing-grounds.

Sterna paradisæa BRÜNNICH. Arctic Tern.

Other names: CRIMSON-BILLED TERN; LONG-TAILED TERN; SHORT-FOOTED TERN; MACKEREL GULL; MEDRICK.

Plate 8.

DESCRIPTION. — Bill shorter than head; about equals middle toe and tarsus together; slender, acute; feet very small. *Adults in breeding plumage (sexes alike)*: Cap (extending well down on sides of head) black; rest of upper parts mostly light silvery-gray; tips of secondaries and tertials, upper tail-coverts and greater part of tail (including whole of inner webs) white; outer web of elongated outer tail-feather deep gray, darker terminally (but white near tip) in strong contrast with white of inner web; outer web of next tail-feather pale gray; that of 1st primary dark gray or blackish, lightening at tip; inner webs of all primaries mostly white, each with stripe of silvery-gray next shaft, this stripe growing gradually wider toward inner primaries, where it extends across tip of inner web and runs near edge for a greater or less distance basally; three or four innermost primaries with inner webs light silvery-gray (like back) edged and tipped white; under tail-coverts, axillars, and wing-linings white; rest of under plumage light gray ("pale neutral gray"), slightly paler than color of upper plumage but slightly darker than in Common Tern, and fading into still paler gray on throat and chin and into white on sides of head next to black cap; bill carmine or nopal-red, rarely tipped blackish; iris dark brown; legs and feet intense red. *Adults in winter plumage:* Similar to summer adult, but forehead, crown and fore part of space before eye white, crown streaked black, only back part of cap and small stripe in front of eye uniform black; under plumage white, sometimes slightly tinged with gray; long tail-feathers much shorter in female than in male; bill and feet blackish. *Young in first winter plumage:* Very similar to winter adult but with juvenal wings and tail. *Young in juvenal plumage:* Like juvenal Common Tern, but *rump and tail-coverts white* without gray tinge and tail with more white; forehead and crown grayish, latter mottled with black which increases over ears and on hind head to practically clear black; back and wings "deep gull gray," feathers of back, scapulars and wing-coverts edged pale buffy, each with subterminal dusky band and fine dusky sprinkling; markings most conspicuous on scapulars; tertials, secondaries and inner primaries edged broadly white; considerable dusky and some pale buff near ends of tail-feathers; below white, washed pale brownish on sides, throat and breast; feet reddish-orange; juvenal plumage worn apparently until birds begin to migrate in September, but probably partially molted in fall to produce first winter plumage. *Downy young:* "Upper parts very pale buffy-grayish or grayish-buffy to wood-brown or bright 'avellaneous,' irregularly spotted or marbled with blackish, except on forehead" (Ridgway); *forehead, space before* and below eyes and throat grayish to sooty-blackish; *dusky frontal space distinguishes downy Arctic Terns from downy young of all other terns* (except dark phase of common tern); "chest white or brownish-white, passing into very pale buffy-grayish to light buffy-brown or drab on posterior and lateral under parts" (Ridgway).

The color of this tern varies so much with age and season that its various phases of plumage have been described from time to time and named as new species, as *S. pikei*, Lawrence, *S. longipennis*, Coues, and *S. portlandica*, Ridgway.

MEASUREMENTS. — Length (variable) 14.00 to 17.00 in.; spread 29.00 to 33.00; folded wing 10.00 to 10.75; tail 6.50 to 8.50, forked 4.00 to 5.00; bill 1.15 to 1.35; tarsus .60.

MOLTS. — Apparently similar to those of Common Tern (A. C. Bent); assumes adult nuptial plumage in spring of second year when nearly one year old, except that some individuals go through that year in immature plumage described erroneously as *Sterna portlandica*.

FIELD MARKS. — *Adult in summer:* Difficult to distinguish in field from Common Tern; bill shorter and more acute; carmine or blood-red (not coral or vermilion-red as in Common Tern), with *little or no black at tip;* tail often as long and trailing as that of Roseate Tern, extending beyond wing-tips when bird is at rest. *Young:* Practically indistinguishable in field from those of Common Tern.

VOICE. — When bird is enraged a rapidly repeated, vibratory *tut, tut,* or *kik, kik, kik,* followed by a piercing *táarr* (C. W. Townsend); shriller than that of Common Tern and ending in a rising inflection like squeal of a pig (William Brewster); also a harsh note similar to that of Forster's Tern; resembles syllables *creek, creek,* often repeated on wing (Audubon); a hawk-like squeal (Practical Handbook of British Birds).

BREEDING. — In colonies; sometimes with other Terns on rocky, sandy or pebbly islands or shores. *Nest:* Not distinguishable from that of Common Tern but usually less nesting-material used. *Eggs:* 2 or 3, usually 2; not distinguished by size or color from those of Common Tern, but seem to average, "a trifle darker in color and more rounded in shape" (A. C. Bent). *Dates:* June 8 to July 21, Maine and Nova Scotia. *Incubation:* Period probably about 21 days (Bent), 20 days (Paynter); by both sexes. One brood yearly.

RANGE. — Nearly cosmopolitan. Breeds from northern Alaska, Melville Island and northern Greenland south to Commander and Aleutian Islands, northern British Columbia, Lower Slave Lake, northern Saskatchewan, northern Manitoba, mouth of the St. Lawrence, Magdalen Islands, Maine and Massachusetts, and in Arctic regions of Europe and Asia; breeds north to 82° north latitude in both Hemispheres; in Europe south to 50° north latitude; in Asia south to 52° north latitude; winters on coasts of Brazil, Peru, Chile and South Africa and in Antarctic Ocean south to 74° south latitude; in migration, on Pacific coast south to southern California, Peru and Chile, and on Atlantic coast south to Long Island, rarely Delaware and eastern Pennsylvania, and in Argentina; accidental in interior of United States and in Hawaii.

DISTRIBUTION IN NEW ENGLAND. — A common summer resident coastwise in Maine and uncommon local summer resident in Massachusetts; recorded as migrant in Connecticut; undoubtedly occurs on coasts of New Hampshire and Rhode Island and occasionally inland.

SEASON IN MASSACHUSETTS. — (March 20) April 1 to October 24 (November 9).

HAUNTS AND HABITS. The Arctic Tern is one of the most remarkable birds of the world. It is the long-distance champion of avian migration. It nests at least as far north as the most northern Eskimos live, while in winter its tireless pinions beat along the distant shores of unexplored lands of the Antarctic continent. It sees more hours of daylight and of sunlight than any other creature on earth. On the arrival of the species at its northernmost nesting-site the midnight sun is shining and it never sets during the tern's stay; while for two months of its Antarctic sojourn the bird sees no sunset. For about eight months of the year it has twenty-four hours of daylight, and during the other four months more daylight than darkness.[1] Says W. Eagle Clarke: "It has the most extensive latitudinal range to be found among vertebrate animals."

According to Professor Cooke the Arctic Tern makes a round trip of 22,000 miles between its farthest north and farthest south, and he says that no man knows its pathway on the journey. When it disappears from New England, it seems to be lost in the vast immensity of the Atlantic; but within about 70 days its flocks are seen in the Antarctic Ocean. When summer comes to the Arctic fiords on the coast of Greenland; when the glacial streams begin to flow; when Arctic flowers are budding and the Snow Bunting, the Dovekie and the Burgomaster have returned; then, too, the flocks of Arctic Terns appear at their northern destinations.

This species seems to be more of a maritime bird than other common terns. Apparently it breeds in the interior less commonly than the others, and in migration keeps much offshore, as it is not commonly recorded on the Atlantic coast of the United States much south of Long Island. The southernmost breeding-place of the species on this coast is Muskeget Island where it bred formerly in considerable numbers. This is one of the birds that was sacrificed to the millinery interests in the latter part of the last century when it is said that about 40,000 terns were killed in a single year on or near Muskeget. Probably at that time the Arctic Tern was nearly extirpated from New England; now, happily, it is beginning to come back. In the summers of 1920 and 1921 I saw a few individuals of this species at Chatham and Monomoy, and Mr. A. C. Bent tells me that in 1921 there was a colony on the outer beach at Chatham. Their nests, however, were washed by a high storm-tide and skunks destroyed the eggs so that the birds finally deserted the place. During the same summer there were apparently a few Arctic Terns at Nauset Beach, Orleans; and I am told that some appear in summer at Penikese and the Wepecket Islands. Arctic Terns breed along much of the Maine coast. Knight (1908) gave Metinic Green Island, Machias Seal Island and Matinicus Rock as probably the bird's chief breeding places there.[2] Norton (1924) writes that "the

[1] Cooke, Wells W.: United States Department of Agriculture, Bulletin No. 185, 1915, pp. 10–11.
[2] Knight, Ora Willis: Birds of Maine, 1908, p. 60.

Matinicus Rock Colony thrives, so also apparently that at Machias Seal Island; but from Metinic Green Island they were driven some years ago by the Big Gulls." Arctic Terns also continue at some of the smaller colonies and probably at some of the mixed ones as well; they have also established new colonies. The species was found breeding in 1846 at Beverly by Cabot and between 1868 and 1870 at Ipswich by Maynard; but it is not known to breed now anywhere on the North Shore of Massachusetts. It is difficult to recognize this species among other summer terns. There is a slight difference in flight which may be noted by an expert (but is hard to describe), while the bill is more deeply and entirely red. This species seems to prefer to nest by itself though sometimes found breeding in colonies with other terns. Its habits seem to be almost identical with those of the Common Tern.

The Arctic Tern usually appears in late April in New England waters, but its arrival has been recorded on March 20 in Massachusetts and on April 12 at Davis Strait, 66° north. In early August a few stragglers, possibly returning migrants, appear on the shores of Essex County where the species is gradually becoming more common. A few birds remain until the very last of September on the Maine coast and the species has been recorded in October on Cape Cod.

The food of the Arctic Tern is similar to that of the Common Tern in this region, and consists chiefly of small fish and small crustaceans.

Economic Status. See page 95.

Sterna doúgalli Montagu. Roseate Tern.

Other name: Mackerel Gull.

Plate 8.

Description. — Elegantly formed; bill about length of head, quite straight and slender; wings shorter than those of Common Tern; tail much longer and more deeply forked with slender, streaming, outer feathers. *Adults in breeding plumage (sexes alike)*: Ample cap of uniform, deep, lustrous black reaching lower border of eye; rest of upper plumage mostly delicate, pale pearl-gray ("pallid neutral gray") passing into silvery-white on upper tail-coverts and tail, including both webs of outer tail-feathers which sometimes have a faint pearly tinge; inner secondaries tipped white, and inner webs of others and of primaries broadly edged same; outer web of outermost primary dark gray or blackish-slate; inner webs of three outer primaries white, with stripe of silvery-gray next shaft, white extending to extreme tip; sides and lower parts of head and neck, lower hind neck, and entire under plumage, including axillars and under wing-coverts, white, usually more or less deeply tinted pink, especially on under parts of body; bill black, usually more or less red (vermilion) at base (often about .50 of upper mandible and .33 of lower); iris dark brown; legs and feet vermilion-red or scarlet. *Adults in winter plumage:* Similar to summer plumage, but tail less forked and no rosy tints; fore part of head white; crown largely shaded with grayish, and indistinctly streaked darker; eye-region, hind head and nape uniform black; lesser wing-coverts brownish; bill dull black, base brown, tip yellowish; feet orange-red. *Young in first winter plumage:* Similar to winter adult but usually showing on upper plumage some trace of white edges or dusky markings of young bird; wings and tail as in juvenal plumage. *Young in juvenal plumage:* Unlike Common Tern; more boldly marked black and white; feathers of back, scapulars and tertials subterminally barred with brownish-black or heavily marked with U-shaped or V-shaped spots of same;

Photograph taken at Harwich by the Author

FIG. 12. — YOUNG ROSEATE TERN PASSING FROM THE DOWN TO JUVENAL PLUMAGE

Photograph taken on Marthas Vineyard by the Author

FIG. 13. — NEST OF COMMON TERN IN SEAWEED

these feathers at first broadly margined or tipped pinkish-buff, which later fades to white; buffy areas often sprinkled with dusky; outer tail-feather unmarked, rest more or less dusky near tips; breast faintly rosy and feet black or blackish to pale orange-red: (Common Tern at same age has white breast and pale flesh-colored or dull reddish feet — A. C. Bent). *Downy young:* Variable in color, with at least two color phases, of which the following is one: "Above pale grayish-buffy or buffy-grayish, thickly flecked or irregularly streaked with dusky" (Ridgway), presenting a grizzled appearance unlike that of young of other common species; differing from young of Common and Arctic Terns by coarse or matted appearance of down, caused by a number of filaments being joined together at tips (Practical Handbook of British Birds); front of forehead uniform dusky; throat and sides of head and neck dull (or pale) grayish; rest of under plumage dull white; bill brownish, tipped blackish; legs and feet dark brown, dusky or blackish.

MEASUREMENTS. — Length 14.00 to 17.00 in.; spread about 30.00; folded wing 9.25 to 9.75; tail 6.00 to 8.00, forked 3.50 to 4.50; bill 1.40 to 1.55; tarsus about .85. Female smaller than male.

MOLTS. — Early in autumn partial molt of body-feathers of juvenal plumage leads to first winter plumage; in early spring complete prenuptial molt when most young birds assume adult plumage; adults molt completely in August and September, changing into winter dress; in early spring complete prenuptial molt makes way for full adult nuptial plumage (A. C. Bent).

FIELD MARKS. — *Adults in nuptial plumage:* Bill largely black, with red base, gives Roseate Tern different appearance from either of its red-billed associates, Arctic Tern or Common Tern; long, white, streaming, outer tail-feathers extending much beyond tips of closed wings help to identify sitting bird; on wing with a low sun lighting up under plumage, Roseate Tern shows much whiter below than the others; rosy tint of under plumage usually not noticeable at a distance and not often at close range (but gives a very *creamy* tint to under plumage as bird flies); when so seen exposed primaries are *light*, while those of *Common Tern* are *dark*. *Young:* Difficult to distinguish in field from young of Common Tern. *Downy young:* Grizzled and with dark or blackish feet, while young of Arctic and Common Terns are heavily spotted and have pinkish or flesh-colored feet.

VOICE. — Notes somewhat unlike those of other terns with which Roseate Tern associates; a harsh, grating, prolonged, rasping cry, *kreck, crack,* or *kraak,* louder and on lower key than cries of other terns (A. C. Bent); like sound made by tearing a strong piece of cotton cloth; also a soft, mellow *hew-it* (William Brewster); a variety of low, cackling, chattering notes; "rather sweet double-note suggestive of the call of the Semipalmated Plover; at times shortened and roughened so that it sounds like *chivy*" (C. W. Townsend).

BREEDING. — In colonies; chiefly on sandy islands, often in company with Common Terns. *Nest:* Sometimes a mere hollow in bare sand, often lined with grass or seaweed; more commonly placed amid beach grass and other vegetation than that of Common Tern. *Eggs:* 2 or 3; much like those of Common Tern but average a little longer and slimmer, lighter in color and less heavily spotted. *Dates:* May 20 to July 30. *Incubation:* Probably by both sexes. One brood yearly.

RANGE. — Temperate and tropical regions. Breeds from Sable and Noddy Islands, Nova Scotia, locally south to Long Island and islands on the Virginia coast, in Bahamas and Bermuda; and from Florida (Tortugas) and Lesser Antilles south to Venezuela; formerly from Maine to Florida; rare migrant in Central America; winters from Louisiana (occasionally), Bahamas and Cuba south to Brazil, and on Pacific coast from southern Mexico south to Chile; accidental in Ohio and northwestern Indiana; occurs on coasts of large part of Eastern Hemisphere, including parts of Europe, Africa and Asia (the Australian breeding bird has been described as a distinct subspecies).

DISTRIBUTION IN NEW ENGLAND. — Rare summer visitant coastwise in Maine and New Hampshire; breeds rarely in Maine; common local migrant and summer visitor in southern New England; breeds in Connecticut and Massachusetts; now increasing in numbers.

SEASON IN MASSACHUSETTS. — May 1 to October 4.

HAUNTS AND HABITS.   The Roseate Tern has an elegant form that swells and tapers in lines of grace.   Its flight, as it rides at ease upon the gale, exemplifies the poetry of aërial motion.   Its lustrous plumage gives back the light in delicate rosy tints.   The exquisite blush upon its breast resembles the hue of the inner surface of some rare sea-shell, but it fades and passes as the love season wanes.

When, in Maytime, spring breezes blow on the shores of New England; when migratory fishes work up along our coast, then, urged on by the universal instinct of reproduction, and sailing upon the free wind as they speed toward their northern haunts, come the Roseate Terns, loveliest of all the graceful "swallows of the sea."   They glide high over the heaving flood, seeking their native isle; and when Phœbus dispels the mists of morning, they sight the well-remembered shore.   Then the glad birds glide gently downward, alight and rest on wave-washed sands.   What a picture they make as they stand in glistening rows, or flutter over the shallows, bringing beauty, action and clamor to the hitherto silent isle!   The male birds are a-tremble with amorous ardor — that magic which adds an extra gloss to their plumage, a new fire to their eyes, and fixes the effulgent glow of morning upon their breasts.   Soon they begin their wooing.   Watch them as they catch little fish which they present to their chosen mates; as they follow them in graceful, wavering flight over land and sea; or as they strut proudly about with upstretched necks, drooping wings and streaming tails held high.   Craned necks distended, they wheel with mincing steps and, bowing, exhibit all their graces.   There is much caressing, billing and preening of one another's plumage.   With it all goes screaming, chattering and much animated vocal exchange.   Little time is wasted in house-hunting or building; possessed by the same impulse, hundreds mate and begin their simple nests.   At first there are many little hollows made in the sand; next, lining material is added; a day later, many nests have one egg; the next, two; while a little later some have even three.   About three weeks later still we may see hundreds of little chicks.   Now all is bustle and activity. Parent birds are continually passing to and fro; some flying out to sea and others coming in with fish; while still others remain to brood and shelter the young.   Apparently this task falls mainly to the female; but the male occasionally stands guard, repels intruders of his own race and relieves his mate for a time on the nest.   I have watched these doings for days; have seen the lovely birds fishing, bathing, mating, incubating and feeding and brooding their young.   Their habits at the nesting-place seem to be essentially the same as those of the Common Tern, as hereinbefore described.   On the wing, however, they are more graceful than the other species.   Their wing-strokes seem a trifle slower, while their long, streaming, spotless tails add much to their aërial grace.   On land or water their little feet are of no great service, but their perfect pinions make the air their natural home.   At the slightest alarm they spring into their favorite element and give themselves to the winds.   They sport tirelessly above the waves and seem fitted for this alone. Often their nests are placed promiscuously with those of the Common Tern, although the tendency of each species seems to be to establish a settlement of its own.   Thus in certain parts of a tern colony nests will be mainly of one species; while not far off the other will predominate. The Common Tern seems to seek by preference the more open spaces, while the Roseate Tern seems to favor the tall grass or other vegetation. In feeding the young Roseate Terns the fish brought by the parent is sometimes too large to be entirely swallowed. As Professor Lynds Jones says, "A four inch fish could not manage to get wholly inside a four inch bird, so the tail was left sticking out for future consumption!"

When during the last quarter of the 19th century terns were being killed in great numbers on the Atlantic coast to secure their feathers for women's adornment, the beautiful Roseate Tern barely escaped extirpation. But the few terns remaining on Muskeget were saved, partly by the passage of laws protecting them, but principally by the efforts of Mr. George H. Mackay, who induced the people of Nantucket to elect an officer to guard and protect the birds. Later the National Association of Audubon Societies appointed a warden to guard the terns on the Wepeket Islands where some Roseate Terns settled and bred successfully. In recent years certain tern colonies along our coast have had special protection by wardens appointed by the Massachusetts Commissioners of Fisheries and Game and by their successor, the Division of Fisheries and Game of the Massachusetts Department of Conservation. Since such measures were taken, the species has increased greatly in numbers; and in 1921 it bred on Muskeget and some of the smaller islands near-by — also on Penikese and Gull Islands, the Wepecket Islands and Pine Island near Woods Hole, at Monomoy Point, Chatham, Nauset, and Ram Island in Buzzards Bay. It is seen occasionally in summer on the coast of Maine; it bred there formerly and may still do so, though I have seen no recent record.

In Massachusetts the Roseate Terns usually arrive during the second week of May and depart in late August when old and young begin to move southward; sometimes, however, they remain well into September, and a few stragglers have been noted in October. "On the Marshfield shore this fine bird has had during the last 10 years a history closely paralleling that of the Laughing Gull," writes Mr. Joseph A. Hagar. "By 1919 they were common from mid-July to early September, and have continued so to the extent that from 20% to 35% of all the Terns along the [North] River at any time are Roseates. They are rare before mid-July, however, and leave a month before the Common Terns, my last records each year falling between Sept. 5 and 10th."

So far as my observation goes, the Roseate Tern when nesting in company with the Common Tern (as it does in Massachusetts) feeds on the same sort of food; but I have never known the former to catch insects on the wing as the Common Tern does. However, as no bird is better fitted to pursue insects through the air, the Roseate Tern probably does this also.

ECONOMIC STATUS. As the Roseate Tern often breeds in company with the Common Tern and has similar food habits, its economic importance may be considerable. In New England, however, it is quite inferior in numbers to the latter although apparently increasing under protection. It is believed to be a harmless and beneficial species and its presence on our coasts tends to render them more attractive to summer visitors. See page 115 for economic status of the Common Tern.

Sterna antillárum (LESSON). Least Tern.

Other names: LITTLE STRIKER; OYT; POND TERN.

Plate 8.

DESCRIPTION. — Smallest of American terns. *Adults in breeding plumage (sexes alike)*: Forehead and sides of crown extending back as far as middle of eye white; rest of cap, upper part of nape and narrow stripe from bill to eye uniform deep black; rest of head and entire under plumage, including axillars and wing-linings white; upper plumage, including hind neck, rump, upper tail-coverts and tail plain, "pallid neutral gray," slightly deeper on back, scapulars and wings; two outer primaries dusky gray or blackish-slate, their inner webs broadly edged white; remaining primaries "pallid neutral gray" (like coverts, etc.), their inner webs edged white; bill bright yellow, usually tipped black; iris dark brown; legs and feet orange-yellow. *Adults in winter plumage:* Similar to summer adults but whole front and top of head grayish-white (purer white toward bill); crescent across hind head and stripe extending from this to and surrounding eye blackish; band of grayish-black on bend of wing; bill blackish or dusky; legs and feet dull yellow. *Young in first winter plumage:* Variable; somewhat like winter adult, but forehead not pure white and hind head not all dusky; upper wing (humeral region) with broad space of dusky-grayish; scapulars and back with V- or U-shaped submarginal markings of dusky; crown streaked and top of hind head mottled dusky; primaries and their coverts dark gray; bill dusky, basally more brownish. *Young in juvenal plumage:* Top of head, back and scapulars more or less suffused or washed buffy or light brownish more or less covering or hiding light gray of upper plumage; some black or blackish about eye-and-ear regions, often extending across nape; a dusky patch around bend of wing; secondaries mainly white or whitish; primaries dark gray, growing lighter from first to last with light tips and edges and parts of inner webs white or whitish; below mainly white with some clouding of buffy and dusky on sides of lower neck and fore breast; tail very short and gray, darkening toward tip, with light edges and tip. *Downy young:* Above white to deep pinkish-buff, sometimes nearly immaculate, but with one or more small irregular black spots on top of head, and a few small and indistinct spots or streaks of dusky on rump; below white or buffy-white, throat usually more buffy; some individuals rather heavily mottled or spotted on head and back with shades of gray or blackish, much darker than common light phase; bill pale yellowish-brown, tipped dusky; legs and feet pale yellowish.

MEASUREMENTS. — Much smaller than any of foregoing terns. Length 8.50 to 9.75 in.; spread about 20.00; folded wing about 6.60; tail about 3.50, forked about 1.75; bill along ridge about 1.10; tarsus about .60. Female smaller than male.

MOLTS. — Juvenal plumage which follows natal down is succeeded in August by first winter plumage as young bird gets its growth. There is a complete prenuptial molt in spring when most signs of immaturity disappear; at first postnuptial molt in July and August, young bird acquires winter plumage of adults and becomes indistinguishable from them; adults have complete prenuptial molt in spring and complete postnuptial molt in autumn.

FIELD MARKS. — *Adults in summer:* Recognized by small size and white patch on forehead, boldly contrasted against clear black of cap. *Young:* Has been confused with young of Black Tern but is smaller and has dark line around bend of wing where Black Tern has light one; tail is light where that of Black Tern is dark; bird is pure white below while young Black Tern has sides and flanks washed or tinged gray.

VOICE. — A shrill rasping cry *zree ee eep;* a variety of cackling and whistling notes; when attacking an intruder a sharp *yip* or a series of vehement notes like *kek, kek, kek,* rapidly repeated (A. C. Bent); when at ease a musical *pidink;* when alarmed a rather shrill *cheep.*

BREEDING. — Usually in colonies; on beaches; on sand flats back of outer sea beaches backed by lake, bay or harbor; also on exposed bars in rivers. *Nest:* Slight hollow in sand. *Eggs:* 2 or 3, rarely 4; 1.20 to 1.30 by .97 to .99 in. (Coues); varying from clear, light bluish-green or olive-buff to dull drab

Fig. 14. — Young Least Tern "Hiding"

Fig. 15. — Eggs of Least Tern in Situation

spotted irregularly and dotted lightly or heavily with varying shades of brown, drab and lilac or lavender; markings often wreathe about larger end; smaller end sometimes almost unmarked. *Dates:* May 29 to July 10. *Incubation:* Period said to continue 14 to 16 days (A. C. Bent). One brood yearly in New England; in the South two broods sometimes may be reared.

RANGE. — Tropical and temperate America. Breeds on coast of southern California and on Gulf coast from Texas eastward; also northward (up Mississippi and Missouri valleys) to Oklahoma, Missouri, southern Illinois, Iowa and South Dakota (formerly), northwestern Nebraska, southwestern Kansas and northern Indiana; recorded in Wisconsin and in Ohio; breeds also from coasts of Massachusetts (formerly Maine), Virginia, North Carolina and Florida south to Bahamas, Antilles, British Honduras and Venezuela; now mostly uncommon or rare where formerly abundant in breeding season from Florida to Maine; recorded in summer in Labrador, Newfoundland, Nova Scotia, Ontario and Minnesota, but some of the records are very doubtful; in migration on coasts of Lower California and western Mexico; winters from the Gulf south, down east coasts of Central and South America to Argentina and on Pacific coast from Gulf of California to Peru; reported in winter on Atlantic coasts of Africa. Birds of this species breeding on a part of Pacific coast are now considered subspecifically distinct.

DISTRIBUTION IN NEW ENGLAND. — Breeding to some extent in Massachusetts (in small colonies) on Marthas Vineyard, Nantucket and Muskeget (formerly), at Falmouth, Chatham (Monomoy), Truro, Cotuit and Sandwich on Cape Cod, north to Duxbury, and on coast of Bristol County; not known now (1923) to breed elsewhere in New England; formerly summer resident in Casco Bay, Maine, and at Ipswich and Beverly, Massachusetts, and once common resident along southeastern coast of Massachusetts; rare migrant and summer visitant on coasts of New Hampshire, Rhode Island and Connecticut.

SEASON IN MASSACHUSETTS. — (April 27) May 2 to October.

HAUNTS AND HABITS. Among the smallest and by far the most delicate and dainty of our sea-birds is the Least Tern. It inhabits sandy islands and barren shores. The south shore of the island of Marthas Vineyard has long been one of its chosen breeding-grounds. Along the stretch of beach extending about fifteen miles from Chappaquiddick to Squibnocket it has reared its young for many years on the "Great Sands" in such exposed places as it finds suitable.

Chappaquiddick reeks of the sea. Water-fowl and shore birds loiter along its shores or rest upon or about its inner waters. Flotsam of the sea strews the outer beaches — wreck-timbers, the remains of great blackfish, sharks, skates and other sea-creatures. Cape Poge lighthouse, tall and white, rises from a bluff at the northeastern point of the island promontory to mark for mariners the position of this dangerous cape, and to show them the way to shelter in the harbor of Edgartown. From near Wasque Point, at the southernmost end of Chappaquiddick, the great South Beach stretches westward for miles as far as the eye can see until its outline is lost in the misty spray of the distant surf.

Here we visited, on July 15, 1908, one of the few breeding-places of the Least Tern then left in the northeastern United States.* My companion and myself sailed from Edgartown across the shallows of Katama Bay, past a little fleet of "quahoggers." Steering our boat carefully over bars and along shallow channels, we landed on the beach.

---

* The beach at this point has now (1923) been swept away by the sea, leaving a wide gap through to Katama Bay; but probably this opening will be closed again by storm or tide.

This is, in fact, the outer beach, for it lies open to the mighty seas of southeasters that drive in from six thousand miles of ocean.   Here the Least Tern nests usually on the wide, open, sandy beach, on a neck of land or point between the ocean and some stream, bay or pond, in situations exposed to the full fury of the gale.   This beach is composed entirely of shifting sand and small pebbles held along its low ridge by beach-grass and other sparse vegetation.   Very high storm-tides break clear over it.   Here, on the barren, seaward sands, in the blinding glare of the sun, without the least cover and exposed to every enemy, this graceful little bird, about the size of a robin, lays its eggs on the sand and rears its tender young.

As we landed that day, a few of the little terns began to fly about, thirty or forty feet above our heads, "cheeping" complainingly; and by the time we had reached a wide, high, open part of the outer beach, bare of vegetation, fully thirty birds were flying overhead.   With angry cries some of them shot down almost to our heads fearful that their eggs and young were in imminent danger.   Menaced indeed they were unless we used the utmost care as we walked, for the color of both eggs and young so closely resembled the sandy beach or the scattered pebbles that it was exceedingly difficult to see them.   For this reason they are ever in danger of being stepped on when people walk upon the beach.   Usually there were but one or two eggs in each hollow, but occasionally three.   The tiny young squatted or lay so flat on the sand that they hardly cast a shadow.   Some were yellowish or about the color of the sand, while others were gray and mottled like a beach pebble.   This is the simplest form of protective coloration, and as the young ones lie motionless on the least alarm, they are likely to be overlooked by hawks or other winged enemies.

HALF-GROWN LEAST TERN
"HIDING"

Least Terns breed mainly in colonies and a threatening hawk may be attacked by all the enraged parents at once.   They follow it in a gyrating, screaming, assailing mob, individuals of which, constantly darting in, strike the enemy from every side.

In attempting to photograph these birds, we found that they were afraid of a device used in photographing birds (the umbrella blind); so we rigged up a less conspicuous place of concealment — with a camera bag, blind cloth and some sticks — and when they had become indifferent to this, I crept within.   Near me were two downy young, just hatched and their down hardly dry, yet able to run about a little.   Several other youngsters were near-by.   As I lay there propped on my elbows, several of the parent birds flitted back and forth, and soon their cheeping cries changed to a musical "*pidink*" (somewhat like the tinkling note of the bobolink).   Then the mother of the two nearest little ones alighted near-by, and running up settled gently upon them and shaded them from the sun's hot rays.   Next she turned her gaze upward and answered softly the tender notes of the male which circled overhead.   Later he alighted and took her place in shading the young, while she flew away to fish and bathe.   Far out over the sunny sea she arrested her flight, and for a few seconds remained poised in the air with beating wings; then suddenly and swiftly she plunged headlong into the waves. Presently she returned with a little "sand-eel" which she gave to one of the tiny ones who ran to her for it. Again she flew away and plunged into the sea and then returned to her nestlings and relieved the male. She stood over them this time with wet, ruffled feathers, and seemed to shake off some drops of water on their little panting bodies, while she raised her wings a trifle to shade them from the sun. I watched this scene from a distance of about seven feet and photographed some of it, the male meantime standing near-by.

YOUNG LEAST TERNS WITH THEIR MOTHER, ON THEIR FIRST MORNING

He took flight, and she nestled over the chick nearest me, coaxing it gently farther away by using her bill and calling the other which finally followed and settled by her side. Again the gentle twittering, and the male bird alighted with a tiny, bright, silvery fish. A little one stuck its head out from beneath the mother's wing, the father bird courteously passed the fish to the mother, and she fed the chick which begged with open mouth for it. Again the provider winged his way over the sunny sea to return with another fish. The little ones were now asleep under the breast of the mother. He offered her the fish; she refused it; he flew away, but soon alighted and politely proffered it again, only to be refused again. At last, having full assurance that his family needed no more, he swallowed the fish himself. Where shall we look to find

LEAST TERN — THE FIRST MEAL

a lovelier picture of happy, harmonious family-relations than that shown here on this sandy beach beside the roaring surf? [1]

In the early part of the final quarter of the last century this lovely little bird was abundant in summer on Buzzards Bay and the waters about Cape Cod. It was sacrificed to man's greed and woman's adornment, and now nothing but the most stringent protection can save it from extinction. Continuous persecution by crows, skunks, cats and other natural enemies, besides frequent disturbance by mankind, drive it yearly from place to place. For a time, under such protection as the Massachusetts Department of Conservation was able to afford, the species has increased; but probably there are not now (1923) breeding in New England over 300 individuals of the species.

Mr. Joseph A. Hagar of Marshfield Hills, writing of the Marshfield shore, says: "The Least Tern shows a marked yearly fluctuation in numbers, but has certainly

[1] From an unpublished manuscript. A part of above has been published by Mr. A. C. Bent in Bulletin 113, Smithsonian Institution, United States National Museum, p. 275.

increased to a gratifying extent, and if it has not already bred here, will surely do so in the near future."

Least Terns seldom appear much before the middle of May on the Massachusetts coast and then only in small numbers; and often they disappear rather early in August on the way to their winter homes.

The Least Tern feeds, like other terns along the coast, on small fish, small crustaceans such as shrimps, and on other forms of marine life — also on insects.

ECONOMIC STATUS. See page 95.

Sterna fuscáta LINNÆUS. Sooty Tern.

Other names: EGG-BIRD; WIDE-AWAKE.

Plate 7.

DESCRIPTION. — Bill as long as head; feet stout with short toes; webs much cut away. *Adults in breeding plumage (sexes alike):* Forehead (including extension on each side of crown as far backward as middle of eye), region below eye, lower half or more of ear-region, and entire under plumage, including axillars and wing-linings white; posterior under plumage (under tail-coverts especially) very faintly tinged pale gray; cap and broad stripe before eye uniform deep black, latter extending narrowly above eye and below forehead to bill; rest of upper parts, including hind neck, rump, upper tail-coverts, and tail, sooty-black, feathers of hind neck white beneath surface; a narrow white margin around bend of wing; outer pair of tail-feathers mainly white or grayish-white, with inner webs more or less extensively dusky toward end; next pair with inner web blackish toward end, passing into pale gray or grayish-white toward base; inner webs of primaries "neutral gray" with definite stripe of dusky next yellowish-white shaft; bill black; iris dark brown; legs and feet dusky or blackish. *Adults in winter plumage:* Similar to summer adults but with scattering white feathers in lores and crown. *Immature:* "Brownish-black above, darker on upper wing-coverts; outer tail-feathers nearly as sooty-black as the rest, except toward tips; tarsi and toes reddish-brown" (Howard Saunders). "I have seen birds in summer, apparently about a year old, with long wings and forked tails, in which the crowns and upper parts are 'fuscous black,' the foreheads white and the under parts white, heavily clouded with dusky." (A. C. Bent). *Young in first winter plumage:* Above deep sooty-brown, feathers of forehead and between eyes and bill fringed gray giving a hoary appearance; scapulars, tertials, smaller wing-coverts, feathers of back, and rump and upper tail-coverts tipped white or brownish-white, bars thus formed broadest on posterior scapulars, narrowest on back, rump, and upper tail-coverts; under plumage lighter grayish-brown, passing into much lighter grayish-brown or brownish-gray on region about vent and on under tail-coverts, where feathers are more or less distinctly tipped darker or more brownish; abdomen with more or less intermixed white; tail-feathers dusky; flight-feathers as in adult, but darker stripe next shaft on inner webs less distinct; bill small, brownish-black or dusky-brown; tail hardly or little forked. *Downy young:* Above varying from dark sooty, narrowly streaked pale grayish-buffy or dull buffy-whitish to pale buffy-grayish narrowly and indistinctly, but thickly, streaked dusky; sides of head and sides of neck and upper breast (usually chin and throat also) light brownish-gray, minutely flecked with paler; rest of under plumage dull white; bill brownish; legs and feet brownish or dusky.

MEASUREMENTS. — Length 15.00 to 17.00 in.; spread about 34.00; folded wing 10.75 to 12.00; tail about 7.50, forked 3.00 to 3.50; bill 1.73 to 1.90; tarsus .90 to 1.00.

MOLTS. — I am not aware that the sequence of molts and plumages of this species has been fully worked out; juvenal body-feathers and some wing-coverts are molted in winter; in some cases at least it seems to take more than a year to acquire adult plumage.

FIELD MARKS. — *Adults:* Nothing else like them; larger than Common Tern; white forehead, blackish upper plumage and white under plumage distinguish the species; head marked somewhat like that of Least Tern. *Young:* Entirely different; smoky-brown all over, but lighter below; white marks on back give bird a peculiar spotted appearance.

VOICE. — A squeaky *quack* and a high-pitched *ker-wacky-wack;* "nesting birds uttered a sharp, barking note, changing to a long-drawn *squawk*" (F. M. Chapman); a harsh *quanck, quanck* (C. J. Maynard); its cries are loud, shrill and piercing.

BREEDING. — In colonies, sometimes of enormous size; on sandy islands or rocky cliffs. *Nest:* Sometimes none; sometimes mere hollow in sand; sometimes on rocky shelf; occasionally wreathed about with a few leaves or pebbles. *Eggs:* 1 to 3; 2.00 to 2.12 by 1.40 to 1.50 in.; white, creamy or buff, sparingly spotted with light and dark shades of brown, purplish and vinaceous; very variable in color. *Dates:* April 10 to June 1, Gulf coast of United States. *Incubation:* Period 26 days (J. B. Watson). One brood yearly.

RANGE. — Tropical and subtropical Atlantic coasts. Breeds in America from Florida, Louisiana and Texas (formerly) throughout Bahamas and Antilles to tropical islands of Atlantic, at least as far south as equatorial Brazil; wanders north, usually after storms, on Atlantic coast rarely to Maine and Nova Scotia; in interior to Lakes Ontario and Champlain; also to Bermuda; casual in England, Germany and France; winters from Louisiana south to Patagonia; other closely allied forms of this species (which have been separated) are distributed widely in Pacific waters, and in Eastern Hemisphere.

DISTRIBUTION IN NEW ENGLAND. — Rare autumn visitant, but has been taken in every New England state; about 30 reports and records of this species in New York and New England, most of them in September and the latest in October (August 25 to October 29).* Records: *Massachusetts:* Williamstown (near Hoosic River) September, 1876;[1] Lawrence (Merrimac River) adult male taken October 29, 1876;[2] Chatham, 3 seen by W. A. Jeffries September, 1877;[3] Dennis, birds seen by Miss J. O. Crowell August 15 and 26, 1921;[4] Barnstable (Cotuit), 2 birds seen by Bowman Graton September 6, 1924.[5]

There is a mounted Sooty Tern in the Springfield Museum of Natural History which was shot by C. W. Bennett at Holyoke, probably in 1878.[6]

HAUNTS AND HABITS. In behavior this species is much like the Common Tern, but it may be distinguished from all the native terns by its black and white contrasts. Probably the Sooty Tern rarely, if ever, appears in New England unless it is blown here by one of the cyclonic storms or "West India hurricanes" that occasionally move up the Atlantic coast. Its various appearances here, so far as they are recorded, apparently coincide rather closely with these cyclonic disturbances. The fullest account of its nesting habits and behavior at the famous Bird Key in the Dry Tortugas is contained in a paper entitled "The Behavior of Noddy and Sooty Terns" by Professor John B. Watson.[7] An excellent history of the species may be found in the Life Histories of North American Gulls and Terns by A. C. Bent.[8]

ECONOMIC STATUS. See page 95.

---

* Newport, Rhode Island: Immature male taken January 8, 1908, now in collection of Harry S. Hathaway (Auk, Vol. XXX, 1913, p. 547).

[1] Tenney, Sanborn: American Naturalist, Vol. XI, 1877, p. 243.
[2] Deane, Ruthven: Bulletin Nuttall Ornithological Club, Vol. II, 1877, p. 27.
[3] Brewer, T. M.: Proceedings Boston Society of Natural History, Vol. XIX, 1878, p. 308.
[4] Crowell, J. O.: *in litt.*
[5] Graton, Bowman: *in litt.*
[6] A. C. Bagg *in litt.*
[7] Papers from the Tortugas Laboratory of the Carnegie Institution of Washington, Vol. II, 1908, pp. 187–255.
[8] Smithsonian Institution, United States National Museum, Bulletin No. 113, 1921, p. 279.

Chlidónias nígra surinaménsis (GMELIN). Black Tern.

Other names: SHORT-TAILED TERN; SEMIPALMATED TERN.

Plate 8.

DESCRIPTION. — Bill shorter than head, very slender and acute. *Adults in breeding plumage (sexes alike)*: Head, neck all around, and under plumage, except under tail-coverts and region about vent, nearly uniform sooty-black or grayish-black, varying rarely to deep purple-gray; under tail-coverts and region about vent white; back, scapulars, rump, upper tail-coverts, tail and wings "deep neutral gray or purple-gray," wings somewhat lighter than back; edge of wing, from body around bend, white; axillars and wing-linings "light neutral gray"; bill black "suffused with deep red" (L. A. Fuertes); angle of mouth "purplish red"; interior of mouth "lavender-pink"; iris dark brown; legs and feet "dusky livid-purplish" ("feet dark red nearly uniform," Fuertes). *Adults in winter plumage:* Head (in part), neck and under plumage white; eye- and ear-regions black; crown and hind head dusky, feathers with paler margins; upper plumage otherwise generally as in summer. While changing plumage, head and under parts patched with black and white. *Young in first winter plumage:* Similar to winter adults; smaller; upper plumage, especially scapulars, more or less washed or marked brown; anterior lesser wing-coverts, crown, back of head and nape dusky; a dark crescent before eye or a dark patch around it; a dark patch between eye and ear; sides and flanks often washed or tinged gray; feet light brown; bill blackish, base flesh-color below; inside of mouth yellow. *Young in juvenal plumage:* Upper plumage decidedly brown; beneath often with extensive brownish, drab or dusky wash on sides and flanks, sometimes on belly; back-feathers and scapulars margined clove-brown and tipped whitish; forehead whitish; crown and back of head mainly black; ear-region and eye-ring pure black. *Downy young:* Upper plumage "light sayal-brown, snuff-brown or verona-brown" (Ridgway); "cinnamon-drab on throat, neck and sides, shading off to pale 'drab-gray' on belly and cheeks" (A. C. Bent); rump with large irregular spots of blackish; back and hind head usually with similar but much smaller markings; under plumage paler brown, becoming much paler (sometimes dull whitish) on breast; sides of head (sometimes also fore part of forehead, sometimes only region before eye and ear) dull whitish or very pale brownish.

MEASUREMENTS. — Length about 9.00 to 10.25 in.; spread about 25.00; folded wing about 8.25; tail about 3.75, forked .90 to 1.00; bill along ridge 1.00; tarsus .55 to .65. Female smaller than male.

MOLTS. — Natal down disappears in July as juvenal plumage is assumed and young bird learns to fly; this dress is worn throughout August and September and birds wearing it may doubtless be seen in New England; the next later change is due largely to wear and fading, and probably there is also a partial postjuvenal molt; at first spring molt practically entire juvenal plumage is usually renewed. "Apparently a majority of the young birds acquire at this molt a plumage which is exactly or nearly like the adult nuptial, with more or less white in the black areas. Many birds, however, seem to wear the first winter plumage or a new one closely resembling it until the first postnuptial molt which occurs in June and July. This molt produces the adult winter plumage" (A. C. Bent). Adults have two complete molts — one early in spring and the other in July, August and September.

FIELD MARKS. — This species is so small that excepting the Least Tern no other New England tern could be mistaken for it. *Adults:* In dark breeding plumage are unmistakable, but if seen here in August or September (if molting) may be more or less pied with blackish and white, or may even be in nearly full winter dress; but they have dark bill and feet while those of Least Tern are yellow. *Young:* Back and tail darker than those of young Least Tern, and dark patch on either side of head.

VOICE. — *Craik-craik* and a soft *wheent-wheent-wheent* (F. M. Chapman); ordinary note *krik*; when much excited a shrill scream, *kreek* or *craik* (A. C. Bent); call note *klea* (W. F. Henniger).

BREEDING. — In colonies; in fresh marshes and sloughs or in wet meadows. *Nest:* Sometimes well built but often only a few weeds or mere hollow in or on pile of floating rubbish, old muskrat house, old nest of grebe or other waterfowl or on mud of bog or reedy marsh; sometimes nest is afloat on bit of driftwood or piece of board. *Eggs:* 2 or 3, rarely 4 or even 5; 1.35 by .95 in.; often somewhat pointed at end; brownish-olive, deep olive, buff, ivory-yellow, Dresden brown, etc.; a great variety of shades; many spots, dots and bold, large markings of various browns and neutral tints; tendency to aggregate at or wreathe around larger end. *Dates:* May 25 to August 4, Minnesota and North Dakota (A. C. Bent). *Incubation:* Period seventeen days (F. M. Chapman); by both sexes (Audubon). Possibly two broods yearly, in South; one brood in North.

RANGE. — North and South America. Breeds chiefly in interior of North America from central Alaska, Great Slave Lake, northern Manitoba and eastern Ontario south to inland lakes of California, Nevada, Utah, Colorado, Kansas, northern Missouri, Tennessee, northern Ohio, western Pennsylvania and west central New York; winters from Gulf of Mexico south to northern South America and from Mazatlan, Mexico, along Pacific coast south to Panama, Peru and Chile; rare spring migrant on east coast of United States, but rather regular locally in autumn; occasional in Prince Edward Island, Nova Scotia and New Brunswick; casual in Bermuda, Antilles and Bahamas.

DISTRIBUTION IN NEW ENGLAND. — *Maine:* Rare but nearly regular fall migrant August 14 to 28 ("fairly common in fall; very rare in spring" — A. H. Norton). *New Hampshire:* Rare summer and uncommon fall migrant mainly coastwise. *Vermont:* Rare migrant. *Massachusetts:* Rare spring and not uncommon fall migrant. *Rhode Island:* Rare spring and irregular fall migrant coastwise ("abundant, Pt. Judith, September 3, 1906" — H. S. Hathaway). *Connecticut:* Uncommon migrant coastwise mainly late in August. Unusual flights may appear rarely in any New England state.

SEASON IN MASSACHUSETTS. May 8 to June 10; July 19 to September 26; most individuals arrive here in August.

HAUNTS AND HABITS. The Black Tern is a bird of the prairie slough and the inland marsh. It rarely breeds near the sea or approaches it except in migration. It never has been known to nest in New England, though after the breeding season individuals wander to the Atlantic coast. While here it associates more or less with Common and Roseate Terns and has similar habits, but seems to fly about more over the land, especially over coastal marshes and flats wherever insects abound. The species is rare in spring and early summer in New England. Like other northern terns its breeding season normally ends in July, so it may be looked for here after that period.

The Black Tern is much more insectivorous than the Common Tern, and in its prairie home lives chiefly upon aquatic and land insects, including dragon-flies, moths, grasshoppers, locusts and other flying insects, most of which it catches on the wing, pursuing them in zigzag flight after the manner of the Nighthawk; also it follows the plow to pick up grubs and worms. On the Atlantic coast it often catches insects as they fly over fields and marshes. Fish, small mollusks, crustaceans and other small forms of aquatic life are taken.

ECONOMIC STATUS. A useful species where present in large numbers, but not common enough in New England to be of much importance.

FAMILY **RYNCHOPIDÆ**. SKIMMERS.

Number of species in North America 1; in Massachusetts 1.

The Skimmers are unique. The bill is extraordinarily specialized. The lower mandible is much longer than the upper and is compressed laterally. It has somewhat the shape of the blade of an oyster knife.   Its upper edge is as sharp as its lower and it fits into a groove in the upper mandible.   It is believed that these birds get much of their food mainly by sweeping low over the surface of the water, carrying the lower mandible immersed and catching in this way small marine animals floating on or near the surface. Skimmers are more or less nocturnal and their habits are not well known; at night they fly close to the water with slow strokes of their very long wings.   The formation of the bill is such as would seem to make it difficult for them to get their food in any other way than by skimming the sea.

Rýnchops nígra Linnæus.   Black Skimmer.

Other names: CUT-WATER; SCISSOR-BILL; SHEARWATER.

Plate 7.

DESCRIPTION. — Bill very thin; knife-like lower mandible about one-fifth longer than upper. *Adults in breeding plumage (sexes alike):* Forehead and sides of head to ear-region, entire under plumage (including linings of wings), outer upper tail-coverts, broad tips of secondaries and inner primaries, white; rest of plumage (except tail) including ear-region, chiefly sooty-black; tail mostly white, middle pair of tail-feathers dark sooty-brown edged white, rest white more or less tinged sooty-brown near shafts or at tips; basal half (approximately) of bill "bright vermilion red," "lower mandible more scarlet, passing into orange or yellow" on cutting edge; terminal half of bill black; iris dark brown; legs and feet "rich orange-vermilion." *Adults in winter plumage:* Similar to summer adults but upper parts a trifle duller and more brownish, interrupted by a broad white collar on lower hind neck. *Young:* Bill smaller, thinner and weaker than in adult; mandibles more nearly equal in length; tail shorter, less forked; variable according to season; light buff, each feather with central spot of blackish, sometimes tipped white, black spots largest on scapulars; region before eye and that below it, pale buff or whitish, with dusky space immediately before eye; greater wing-coverts blackish-gray or grayish-black, tipped white; secondaries white for most of their exposed part; primaries blackish, most of them margined light buff or whitish at ends, inner ones dusky, fading into white at tips; tail white, most of two middle feathers and parts of others grayish-brown, darkest on middle pair; below white; bill blackish toward end, dull horn-color at tip, flesh-color or reddish toward base; legs and feet dull, light or dusky reddish. *Downy young:* Above "pale grayish-buff" or vinaceous-buff irregularly and rather sparsely mottled blackish; below white.

MEASUREMENTS. — Length 16.00 to 20.00 in.; spread 42.00 to 50.00; folded wing 13.00 to 16.50; tail 4.00 to 6.00, forked 1.20 to 1.50; tarsus about 1.20 to 1.53; bill, upper mandible 2.20 to 3.00, lower 2.90 to 4.50.   Female smaller than male.

MOLTS. — During first winter juvenal plumage changes so as to resemble more closely that of adult, and in spring when bird is nearly a year old it molts and assumes a nuptial dress "practically indistinguishable from adults"; adults molt in February and March and in August and September; spring molt, however, "is not completed until about June 16–18 . . . only the under parts appear to be renewed" (Arthur T. Wayne).

FIELD MARKS. — *Adults* (and any Skimmer old enough to fly north as far as New England) should be recognized by their very long wings, large size when compared with Common Tern, reddish feet and peculiar red or reddish black-tipped bill, latter with under mandible longer than upper; at a distance adults appear pure black and white.

VOICE. — Peculiar nasal barking notes or grunting sounds; *kak, kak, kak,* or *kuk, kuk, kuk,* in a low guttural tone; also a variety of soft, low love-notes sounding like *kow, kow* or *keow, keow* (A. C. Bent); a cry almost the exact counterpart of the yelp of a hound (A. B. Howell).

BREEDING. — In colonies; on higher sand-flats near beaches or on shell-ridges. *Nest:* Slight hollow in sand, pebbles or shells of beach. *Eggs:* 3 to 5, usually 4; about 1.75 by 1.30 in.; white to pale greenish-blue or pale buff, spotted, blotched and splashed with dark browns, blackish and light grays or lavender; usually handsomely and boldly marked. *Dates:* May 15 to July 16, South Carolina; June 2 to July 26, Virginia (A. C. Bent). *Incubation:* By female mainly if not wholly. One brood yearly.

RANGE. — Tropical and temperate America. Breeds from New Jersey (sparingly) (formerly Massachusetts) south to Florida, Gulf coast and Texas; also summers and probably breeds on coasts of Yucatan and Venezuela; winters from Louisiana west and south along Gulf coast and Florida to Mexico and Costa Rica and along northern and eastern coasts of South America; straggles rarely to Long Island; casual north to Bay of Fundy and in West Indies; accidental inland to Tennessee, and also in Bermuda.

DISTRIBUTION IN NEW ENGLAND. — Formerly doubtless abundant locally in summer as far north as Massachusetts where it bred on Muskeget Island; now a mere straggler from the South, mainly on sea-coast after storms, as in August, 1879 and August, 1924. The earlier records are:

Maine: Ruthven Deane records that George A. Boardman, of Milltown, St. Stephens, N. B., under date of 31st of August, 1879, wrote to him that there had been a flight of Skimmers in that locality; that seven specimens had been killed off Grand Manan and Campobello Islands, New Brunswick; and that the birds were seen at St. Andrews, at the head of Passamaquoddy Bay off the Maine coast.[1]

Everett J. Smith in his "Birds of Maine," published in Forest and Stream, says of the Skimmer in Maine: "Of occasional occurrence only and no record of its appearance so far north as Maine previous to 1879. In the early autumn of that year a number were shot on our coast." He reports a Skimmer shot (one of two seen) August 28, 1879, at Wells Bay and, like Mr. Deane, quotes George A. Boardman to the effect that seven of the species were taken in the Bay of Fundy "where many were seen during the autumn of the same year." He also adds: "Mr. Harry Merrill informs me that a Skimmer was shot by a fisherman near Matinicus (Island), Maine, in the summer of 1881." [2]

Massachusetts: Three Skimmers taken August 19, 1879, at Sandwich[1]; and another on the same date at Woods Hole by John F. Carleton,[3] which was placed in the collection of the Boston Society of Natural History. (There is a second specimen in the collection of the Society which is labeled "Falmouth.") Still another was taken on August 20 of the same year in Boston Harbor.[1] A Black Skimmer was seen July 16, 1903, at the Wepecket Islands by Lynds Jones.[4]

"During the prevalence of an unusually severe gale the latter part of August, 1893, a Black Skimmer was found in West Springfield in an exhausted condition and taken by hand." Robert O. Morris in Auk, Vol. XI, 1894, p. 181.

Connecticut: A specimen was taken about June 16, 1883, in New Haven harbor. Judge John N. Clark reported to John H. Sage November 8, 1894, that a Black Skimmer was killed at Saybrook a few days before.[5]

Mr. Ruthven Deane, in his article (already cited) in the Bulletin of the Nuttall Ornithological Club for October, 1879, speaks of seeing August 31, 1879, a Skimmer about 10 miles off Saco, Maine, and says: "Is it not a little strange that a bird that has escaped our observation for years should appear so suddenly and at points along the coast from Cape Cod to the Bay of Fundy?"

NOTE. There is a brief reference to this famous Skimmer invasion of 1879 in "New England Bird Life" (Stearns and Coues) on p. 379 of Part II as follows: "There was evidently an irruption of Skimmers upon the New England coast in 1879," but no cause is assigned for this phenomenon.

The explanation of the 1879 Skimmer incursion is not far to seek. Reference to the records of the United States Weather Bureau and to local newspaper files reveals that a tremendous storm swept up the

[1] Bulletin Nuttall Ornithological Club, Vol. IV, 1879, p. 243.
[2] Smith, Everett J.: Forest and Stream, Vol. XX, 1883, p. 205.
[3] Brewer, T. M.: Bulletin Nuttall Ornthological Club, Vol. IV, 1879, p. 243.
[4] Jones, Lynds: Wilson Bulletin, Vol. X, 1903, p. 113.
[5] Sage, John H., Bishop, L. B., and Bliss, P. B.: Birds of Connecticut, 1913, p. 25.

Atlantic coast about August 20, 1879. On Monday, August 18th, 1879, in Boston, it rained heavily (especially from 3 P.M. to midnight) nearly all day, the rainfall for the day being 3.33 inches. At 7.30 P.M. a high northeast wind began blowing which before 11 P.M. had developed into a furious gale, reaching 44 miles per hour at 11.30 P.M. There were "floods of rain." The barometer fell with remarkable rapidity during the evening, touching 29 at 11 P.M. The humidity was nearly 100 all day and the weather was foul. Says the Boston Journal of August 19th: "Yesterday forenoon the weather became comparatively mild after the rainfall of Sunday . . . but the wind after the sun went down blew a furious gale, with incessant rain, which coursed the streets in torrents. . . ." Throughout the night this storm raged with great fury. Chelsea ferryboats stopped running at 10 P.M. and there were over 100 sail in the harbor. The high tide driven in by the wind swept over the wharves so that the next morning (19th) the waters of the harbor floated all manner of material as planks, cordwood, barrels, etc.

The rain continued till daybreak of Tuesday, August 19th, making a total fall of almost 5 inches since 3 P.M. of the day before. The wind continued to blow a gale from the northeast till noon when it died down for a brief period only to blow again with increased force, at 40 miles per hour, from the northwest and west. After several hours of this the gale at last gradually blew itself out, the barometer rose rapidly and there was clearing sky by 6 P.M. The weather report for the 19th closes thus: "The gale was one of the heaviest ever known all along the New England coast"; and on the next day it says: "To-day's (20th) press reports show the storm to have been extremely severe on the New England coast especially on Cape Cod."

This storm from the south which swept up the coast on Sunday and hit Boston on Monday probably spent its main force to the south and southeast over the Atlantic where the rainfall must have been unusually great. At Wilmington, N. C., the rainfall, between midnight and 8 A.C. Monday, reached the enormous quantity of 4.38 inches. Says a Wilmington despatch: "A terrific storm of wind and rain visited this section early Monday A.M., the velocity of the wind at 4 o'clock being 68 miles per hour." From this North Carolina point the storm covered the whole eastern coast up to Newfoundland and Nova Scotia.

Despatches from Newport and other points tell of the damage done by the storm. A Cottage City despatch of August 19 speaks of the gale as "the most terrific ever known at this season of the year"; while Provincetown reported that on August 19th "the storm last night can truly be called an August 'twister' for its like has seldom been seen in this vicinity."

The foregoing rather detailed report of the famous August storm of 1879 will apply as well to the various West Indian or southern hurricanes that more or less periodically in autumn strike the New England coast. A notable recent instance was the great storm of August 26, 1924, of tremendous wind-velocity, with the usual accompaniments of shipwrecks (as the bark Wanderer of New Bedford, "the last of the square-rigged whaling fleet"), uprooted trees and overturned or demolished buildings. This last southern hurricane was also notable in that it blew to our shores the greatest number of Skimmers yet known. Very few of these birds have been reported since 1879 in Massachusetts, and the invasion of that year sinks into insignificance when compared to this last case. There were more than 100 Skimmers reported, from New Brunswick and Nova Scotia to Nantucket, Long Island and New Jersey, and a number of these were taken, as the bird shot August 27, at Scituate (Fourth Cliff) by Joseph A. Hagar; the young male shot on the same date at Chatham (Monomoy) by A. C. Bent; the two immature females secured September 17 at Ipswich, by Charles Hodgkins; and the male taken September 1, at Lubec, Maine, by Spencer Hinson, a female taken September 3 at Jonesport, Maine, by John Wallace and immature bird, also on September 3, at Stonington, Maine, all in the collection of Clarence H. Clark, of Lubec, Maine.

The Skimmers remained in numbers on the Plymouth County (Massachusetts) coast for about one month.

Two Skimmers were seen September 1, on the Quonochontaug marsh, Rhode Island, and reported by Harry S. Hathaway, a recognized authority on Rhode Island bird-life. This is the first record of the species in Rhode Island.[1]

---

[1] Hathaway, H. S.: *in litt.*

The same storm also will doubtless account for other rarities in the bird line, as Forster's and Sooty Terns, which were seen on Cape Cod after the gale of August blew itself out. The latter species was also taken in Nova Scotia where it is exceedingly rare.

SEASON IN MASSACHUSETTS. — Accidental; July 16 to October 1.

HAUNTS AND HABITS. This most remarkable and highly specialized bird, known to ornithologists as the Black Skimmer, was undoubtedly one of the summer birds of Massachusetts when the Pilgrim Fathers settled at Plymouth. In 1605 Champlain voyaged to Cape Cod and visited what is now Nauset Harbor in Orleans. He found there in early July many of these unmistakable birds.* Possibly they were nesting there or at least not very far away. My old friend, Henry A. Purdie, who first called attention to this early record, recorded also the breeding of the species up to about 1830 on Muskeget Island.[1] This record was given on the authority of William Brewster who got his information from fishermen who claimed to have seen the birds breeding on Muskeget. Mr. Purdie also quoted old natives of the Cape to the effect that "them cutwater or shearwater birds used to be with us summer times" as proof that the species was found early in the century on our shores. Ebenezer Emmons also, in his "Catalogue of Massachusetts Birds" (1833), lists the Skimmer as follows: "Regular visitant and breeds on this coast." Since then there is no report of the breeding of the species in Massachusetts. Possibly it was extirpated by eggers. While its plumage was of no great value in the millinery market and its flesh was not valued as food, its eggs were prized on account of their large size. As Skimmers deposit their eggs without concealment on the open sands, the same fate overtook them along the northern coast of the Middle States where they have been extirpated within recent times. I have never seen them in the North, but on the estuaries and sounds of the South have witnessed their flights and heard their barking cries, particularly in the dusk or at night.

In flight the Black Skimmer is a strikingly individualized bird. Its very long but strong wings give grace and power to its flight and its broad, forked tail lends additional buoyancy. It seems especially adapted for skimming low over the water. The peculiar structure of the bill fits it for picking up fish and crustaceans from the surface while in flight. Mr. Howell asserts that the bird skims over water so near shore and so shallow that its bill strikes the bottom "every 20 feet or so," jerking its head back in a most comical manner.[2] If the bird desires to seize anything from the ground, it must turn its head to one side, but it wades into shallow pools and picks up small live fish out of the

---

* Champlain describes the birds as follows:

"We saw also a sea-bird with a black beak, the upper part slightly aquiline, four inches long and in the form of a lancet; namely, the lower part representing the handle and the upper the blade, which is thin, sharp on both sides, and shorter by a third than the other, which circumstance is a matter of astonishment to many persons, who cannot comprehend how it is possible for the bird to eat with such a beak. It is of the size of a pigeon, the wings being very long in proportion to the body, the tail short, as also the legs, which are red; the feet being small and flat. The plumage on the upper part is gray-brown, and on the underparts pure white. They go always in flocks along the seashore, like the pigeons with us." (Voyages of Samuel de Champlain, translated from the French by Charles Pomeroy Oles, Ph.D., with historical illustrations and a Memoir by Rev. Edmund F. Slafter, A.M., Vol. II, 1604–1610, Boston. Published by the Prince Society, 1878, pp. 87, 88.)

[1] Purdie, H. A.: Bulletin Nuttall Ornithological Club, Vol. VII, 1882, p. 125.

[2] Howell, A. B.: Auk, Vol. XXVIII, 1911, pp. 452, 453.

water. In the young birds the long, projecting lower mandible is not fully developed until after they have reached the flight stage. Therefore, until they are well able to fly, they can readily pick up food from the ground.

While it is known that the food of the Black Skimmer consists largely of small fish and crustaceans, I am not aware that any exhaustive study of its food has been made.

ECONOMIC STATUS. The Black Skimmer has no known economic value, but it appears to be harmless.

ORDER TUBINARES. TUBE-NOSED SWIMMERS.

Number of species in North America 40 ; in Massachusetts 6.

This order contains two families — *Diomedeidæ* and *Hydrobatidæ* — and more than 100 species. (The *Diomedeidæ* are not represented in New England, see note below.) All birds of the order may be recognized by their tubular nostrils. The wings are long, strong and pointed, with ten stiff primaries and usually numerous secondaries. The tail is short or moderate, ordinarily of 12 to 14 feathers, and the feet have long, fully-webbed front toes, with hind toe small, rudimentary or wanting. Members of this order are pelagic birds and roam the oceans of the world. The order includes birds of many sizes from the giant albatross with a spread of wing unequaled by any other bird to the little storm petrel no larger than a swallow. In long distance flight the *Tubinares* are perhaps unequaled and certainly unexcelled; and it is largely by reason of this power that they are enabled to exist upon the sea during the greater part of their lives.

NOTE. **Thalassarche chlororhynchus (Gmelin)**, Pink-footed Albatross or Yellow-nosed Mollymawk. A specimen of this bird, sex not given, was taken near Seal Island off Machias Bay, Maine, on August 1, 1913, by Mr. Ernest O. Joye, and is now in the collection of Dr. L. C. Sanford, in the American Museum of Natural History, New York City.[1] Dr. R. C. Murphy says that Seal Island is Canadian territory, that the bird was secured on the international border and that therefore the specimen belongs to the local avifauna of both New Brunswick and Maine. Mr. A. C. Bent says that the bird was killed off Machias Seal Island, Maine, near the entrance to the Bay of Fundy.[2] Dr. H. C. Oberholser records the specimen as taken "near Seal Island, New Brunswick."[3] Inasmuch as the locality probably cannot be determined with accuracy, and as the bird seems to have been taken at sea and possibly nearer to New Brunswick, than to Maine, it seems questionable whether it should be recorded as a New England species. This is the first record of the bird in North American waters. The occurrence of this sub-Antarctic species in the North Atlantic is purely fortuitous.

FAMILY HYDROBATIDÆ. FULMARS, SHEARWATERS AND PETRELS.

Number of species in North America 35 ; in Massachusetts 6.

In the *Hydrobatidæ* as in all the *Tubinares* the nostrils are united in a "double-barrelled tube" superimposed horizontally upon the upper mandible at the base of the bill. This character distinguishes these birds from all other swimmers found in New England waters.

[1] Murphy, Robert Cushman: Auk, Vol. XXXIX, 1922, p. 58.
[2] Smithsonian Institution, United States National Museum Bulletin, No. 121, p. 19. [3] Auk, Vol. XL, 1923, p. 678.

PLATE 9

PLATE 9

LEACH'S PETREL
Page 145

WILSON'S PETREL
Page 149

GREATER SHEARWATER
Page 140

SOOTY SHEARWATER
Page 142

FULMAR
Page 135
DARK PHASE

CORY'S SHEARWATER
Page 139

All one-fourth natural size.

Louis Agassiz Fuertes.

The upper mandible is always hooked at the end and in the shearwaters the lower mandible also. The covering of the bill is laid on in separate horny plates with sutures showing between. The *Hydrobatidæ* rarely visit the shore except to breed and are not known to go inland unless driven there by high winds. They nest chiefly on sea-islands and also on the Antarctic Continent. They spend most of their waking hours on the wing and gather their food largely from the surface of the sea. Nearly one hundred species of this family are distributed over the oceans of the globe. No member of the family is known to lay more than one egg as its nest-complement; yet these birds are reckoned among the most numerous of the world.

ECONOMIC STATUS. Most of the species of this family breed in rather inaccessible regions remote from civilization and are not of much economic importance. In some cases, however, their eggs are used as food and their feathers and down for bedding, etc. Some furnish valuable oil while others are used by fishermen as bait. So far as known they are harmless. Some species as the Storm Petrel and Wilson's Petrel have a certain economic value as foretellers of storms, as they are particularly active before such disturbances.

SUBFAMILY FULMARINÆ. FULMARS.

Number of species in North America 5; in Massachusetts 1.

Bill stout or very stout; nasal tubes high and prominent; end of under mandible not turned down nor hooked but with sharp angle near tip. Fulmars are gull-like birds and rather more robust in form than Shearwaters.

Fulmárus glaciális glacialis (LINNÆUS). Fulmar.

Other names: NODDY; OIL-BIRD; MARBLEHEADER; WHITE HAGDON.

BY JOHN A. FARLEY.

Plate 9.

DESCRIPTION. — Bill shorter than tarsus; shorter and more robust bill in proportion to size of bird than that of any jaeger, gull or shearwater, only about two-thirds as long as head, very stout, with high, prominent nasal tubes and swelling sides, its hook robust, very convex; folded wings about reach end of tail of 14 feathers, broad to their rounded ends; tail slightly rounded. *Adults (sexes alike or different; variable)*: *Light phase:* Head, neck and lower plumage white or whitish (in some birds gray or tinged gray); flanks sometimes with a slight wash of gray; above slaty-gray, flight-feathers darker; slaty-gray may be restricted to back and wings or may extend more or less on head and tail; bill yellow, especially at tip, with greenish-dusky tinge on ridge or at its base and on lower mandible (whole bill sometimes olive-brownish; *very variable*); legs and feet pale-gray (flesh or ash color; also variable); iris brown. There is considerable color-variation in this species — both sexual and individual (some birds are pure white, probably albinos). *Dark phase:* Nearly uniform smoky-gray or ashy-brown; bill dusky-brown. *Young:* Many are similar to adults in light phase; others are smoky-gray, much like dark phase, paler below; primaries as in adult; bill and feet obscured; slightly smaller than adult, and bill darker. *Downy young:* Whitish head and below, bluish-gray above.

MEASUREMENTS. — Length 18.00 to 20.00 in.; folded wing 12.50 to 13.50; tail 4.50 to 5.00; bill 1.37 to 1.60; tarsus 1.70 to 2.00.

MOLTS. — Apparently there is a second down, succeeding the first down, in which the young bird acquires a darker head and upper plumage; juvenal plumage succeeding the second down is as adult or somewhat paler; no seasonal change in color of plumage; adults have complete postnuptial molt in autumn beginning in July or August.

FIELD MARKS. — Though the Fulmar in its light phase somewhat resembles in coloration the Herring Gull, its flight is unmistakable; straight, stiffly-held, outstretched wings and long glides as the bird scuds along distinguish it from a gull; comparing with shearwaters, P. A. Taverner says (Birds of Eastern Canada) — "its light or grey coloration instead of dark brown as in the shearwaters which approach the Fulmar in size, should usually render the species recognizable in life"; dark phase resembles Sooty Shearwater but is lighter in color with much stouter bill.

VOICE. — The Fulmar is not usually a vociferous bird though noisy at times; its note is a "low croon" (Saunders); Dixon, in his vivid description of the swarming thousands of the St. Kilda Fulmars, says — "the silence of such an animated scene impressed me; not a single Fulmar uttered a cry;" Rev. Wm. Scoresby, as quoted by Yarrell, in describing the bird's voracity for food at the cutting-up of a whale, speaks of the "curious chuckling noise which in their anxiety for despatch they always make."

BREEDING. — In large colonies; on cliffs of Arctic mountains, or of sea-islands. *Nest:* A slight depression or excavation, with or without dried grass lining, in turfy soil or under some projecting tuft on grassy shelves of sea-cliffs; otherwise egg is laid on bare ledge or even ice-covered rock. *Eggs:* One; about 2.85 by 2.00 in.; ovate; white, rough, brittle and chalky, with strong odor of musk; the pure white egg becomes stained by contact with soil and is sometimes partly or wholly speckled with fine dots of reddish-brown. *Dates:* May 10 to July 1, Iceland; May 6 to June 15, St. Kilda. *Incubation:* Period said to be 50 or 60 days (A. C. Bent); by both sexes.

RANGE. — North Atlantic and Arctic Oceans. Breeds in Iceland, on Arctic islands of Europe, south to Ireland and Scotland and east at least to Franz Josef Land; in America from northern Greenland to Melville Island; ranges in summer to latitude 85° and west to Melville Island; one inland record for North American continent — Arnprior, Ontario, May 3, 1924;[1] winters south of Arctic Circle to Georges (fishing) Bank off Massachusetts coast and casually south to New Jersey; in winter a rather rare straggler on British coasts, except in Scotland where it is frequently observed; sometimes not uncommon on the southern shores of the British Isles; rarely as far south as the Mediterranean.

DISTRIBUTION IN NEW ENGLAND. — The Fulmar comes down in September from its breeding sea-cliffs in high latitudes to the Grand Banks of Newfoundland and to Georges Bank off the Massachusetts coast where it is fairly plentiful in winter. It usually leaves the Bank about the middle of March. Stragglers occur rarely on the New England coast; there are three definite records: *Massachusetts:* A fine adult Fulmar was picked up dead (but perfectly fresh and in fine condition) September 23, 1912, at Monomoy Point, Chatham, by Daniel E. Harrington.[2] A dead Fulmar was picked up December 28, 1918, on the beach at Sandwich, by Harry Torrey. This bird was not freshly killed, and may have died and drifted in after perishing at sea. *Connecticut:* A female Fulmar was shot October 10, 1909, off Stony Creek on Long Island Sound, by A. H. Verrill. This is the first really authentic record for Connecticut, as well as for all New England.[3] There is an indefinite record of a Fulmar taken some 12 years ago in Maine which was mounted for the owner by C. Emerson Brown, now director of the park of the Zoölogical Society of Philadelphia. Unfortunately all data of this specimen are missing.

HAUNTS AND HABITS. The gull-like Fulmar — beautiful, with its intelligent dark eye set in its pure white head, its yellow bill, clear gray mantle and snowy underparts — is one of the best known of North Atlantic sea-birds. It is littoral in the breeding season only, when it is extraordinarily abundant, literally in myriads, at some of its favorite

[1] Gormley, A. L.: Auk, Vol. XLI, 1924, p. 471.   [2] Brown, C. Emerson: Auk, Vol. XXX, 1913, p. 105.
[3] Bishop, L. B.: Auk, Vol. XXVII, 1910, p. 462.

nesting-places which are mostly in high latitudes. After nesting is over, the Fulmars scatter far and wide over the gray wastes of the North Atlantic Ocean. Like other petrels the home of the bird, except in the breeding season, is the open sea. With great powers of flight, it is a magnificent sea-bird, breasting the gale on sturdy wing or resting composedly on the water, no matter how high a sea is running. Fulmars are seen most often by whalers and fishermen upon whose ships the hungry birds are constant attendants. In Arctic and subarctic waters the offal from whalers and sealers attracts them. They crowd about and under the ship's stern, coming in greedy hundreds or even thousands from all quarters, when a whale is being cut up. Ravenous and audacious they swarm in the oily wake and come within a few feet of the sailors. Heedless of all else but the refuse, they may be knocked over often with a boathook, while they regard the discharge of a gun so little that their dead fellows float unheeded within a few feet. The Fulmar seems to like above all other food the blubber of the whale. For this it has a prodigious appetite, and sometimes it so gorges itself that it cannot rise from the water. Says Capt. Collins: "In former years many hundreds, if not thousands, of them were caught by the Grand Banks fishermen and used for bait. The voracity of these birds renders their capture by hook and line a comparatively easy task." [1]

Fulmars often associate with Shearwaters and with them "track" tirelessly the transatlantic steamships, both in midocean and nearer shore, following in their wakes, day by day, and picking up every bit of floating refuse cast overboard from the galley. The Fulmar usually feeds settled, albatross-like, on the water, though it sometimes "dives wholly beneath the surface to grasp food," a habit unusual among petrels. [2]

Fulmars have been much observed on their ancient breeding ground, St. Kilda, one of the Outer Hebrides, to which island they resort in vast numbers. Their young are fed with oil by regurgitation.

The food of the bird largely consists of mollusks, cuttle-fish material and any animal garbage or other animal food that it can pick up.

ECONOMIC STATUS. From time immemorial Fulmars have been an important source of subsistence to the St. Kilda islanders who hunt over their tremendous sea-cliffs for both eggs and birds, dangling far down by ropes along the faces of the precipitous crags. Birds, eggs and oil alike are utilized. Large numbers of birds are taken annually for their oil which is used for lighting as well as for medicinal purposes. In the one month of August some 20,000 fledglings have been taken. Both birds and their eggs furnish much of the subsistence of the St. Kildans, while the clear, yellowish or amber-colored Fulmar oil is one of the principal products of the island. The feathers and down of the birds also are utilized. The Fulmars on their eggs on the cliffs are literally a "sight to behold." An English writer, speaking of the Fulmars taking flight when alarmed, says that it seemed as if the cliffs were "dissolving" into birds.

---

[1] Collins, J. W.: Auk, Vol. I, 1884, p. 238.   [2] MacMillan, Donald B.: Four Years in the White North, 1918, p. 406.

Dáption capénse (Linnæus). Pintado Petrel.

Other names: CHECKERED PETREL; CAPE PIGEON.

Fig. 16.

Description. — *Bill short* (much shorter than head) and very *stout and wide* — *dilated toward base, dilated bill distinguishes this species from Shearwaters*. *Adults in breeding plumage (sexes alike):* Above spotted white and slaty-black (in some specimens brownish-black), the dark spots chiefly dark feather-tips; wings largely slaty-black with much white on inner webs and base of dark primaries; tail largely white with broad terminal band of slaty-black; head and neck slaty- or brownish-black, and un-marked or nearly so except throat which is more or less white; below white; iris very dark; "bill and feet black, much white on inner toes" (A. G. Bennett). *Downy young:* slaty-gray above, paler and sooty below.

Measurements. — Length about 15.00 in.; folded wing 10.00 to 11.00; tail 4.50; bill 1.33; tarsus 1.67.

Molts. — Not examined; plumage of juvenal birds appears to be similar to that of adults.

Voice. — Distinct cry, strong and raucous *cac-cac, cac-cac, cac*, increasing in rapidity; it also coos and clucks (F. D. Godman); when squabbling for food a grating chatter (J. T. Nichols).

Breeding. — On rocky cliffs on sea-islands. *Nest:* On ledges or in burrows or caves, made of earth and fragments of rock. *Eggs:* 1, averaging about 2.30 by 1.70 in.; oval to elongate-ovate — white.

Range. — Oceans of Southern Hemisphere. Breeds on South Georgia, South Shetland and Kerguelen Islands and on islands of Adelie Land; very rare to casual north of the tropic of Capricorn; accidental on coasts of Maine, California, England and Atlantic coasts of Europe.

Distribution in New England. — *Maine:* One record, Harpswell, 1873.

Note. The only New England specimen (now mounted in the collection of the Worcester Natural History Society) bears on its stand the following statement from the late Thomas A. Dickinson, former custodian of the collections of that society: "This bird was bought in Lewiston, Maine, of Levi Woolley, Taxidermist, in 1875. It was shot by Charles F. Nason, formerly of Lewiston, September, 1873, at Mooseluckmeguntic Lake (Rangeley). It was called by Woolley 'Manx Shearwater.' I am now satisfied that it was wrongly labeled at the time and is not 'Manx Shearwater' but 'Pintado Petrel *Daption capensis.*'"

This label does not state the facts. When the bird was obtained, I, a mere boy, through the kindness of Mr. Dickinson, was allowed the privileges of the museum and spent much time there after school hours in his company and assisted him in his work. He went in 1875 to Lewiston, Maine, where he purchased from Mr. Woolley the mounted bird in question. I was at the museum when the bird came in and saw it unpacked. Mr. Dickinson, who knew Mr. Woolley well, reposed the most implicit confidence in his veracity, and Mr. Woolley then gave Harpswell on Casco Bay as the place of capture, and June, 1873, as the date. The bird was wrongly identified however, and for some years stood in the collection labeled "Manx Shearwater." Finally in 1883 it was correctly identified by Henry A. Purdie at whose request I then wrote to Mr. Woolley, who replied from Sabattus (a suburb of Lewiston), Maine, certifying to the capture of the bird at Harpswell.

About fourteen years later, in 1897, Mr. Dickinson wrote to Mr. Woolley in regard to the bird, and received from him the incorrect statement that now appears on the specimen. Apparently Mr. Woolley's memory had become confused after a lapse of 25 years and he had some other bird in mind. The original record giving the locality as Harpswell, appeared in New England Bird Life (Stearns and Coues), Vol. II, pp. 386, 387. Arthur H. Norton, who has made a careful investigation of the case, says "the group of letters at hand from nearly every person connected with the matter show, it is believed, that the original record is correct." (Auk, Vol. XXXIX, 1922, p. 101.) Believing that this record is authentic, I include the bird in the New England list.

FIG. 16. — Pintado Petrel or Cape Pigeon
From a specimen in the Museum of Comparative Zoölogy

Photograph by courtesy of Henry W. Osgood

FIG. 17. — Black-capped Petrel
Page 144

HAUNTS AND HABITS. The Pintado or Spotted Petrel, commonly known as "Cape Pigeon," is well known to all who have rounded Cape Horn or the Cape of Good Hope. In the seas near these capes it is the most common petrel, is seen constantly and is very active, especially in windy weather. In flight it resembles somewhat the domestic pigeon, but sails much more than the latter, keeping its legs tucked away among its under tail-coverts. Its flight is exceedingly graceful, and at times it flies by night as well as by day. It is fearless and easily taken by means of hook and line, as it seems extremely fond of fat, which in the shape of salt pork is readily supplied on shipboard for baiting the birds. The Cape Pigeon is a mere straggler in the North Atlantic, and it may be long before another New England record will be made. It is believed that some of the European records were those of birds captured on ships in southern oceans and thus carried north where they escaped or were liberated. The Maine bird showed no sign of recent captivity.

ECONOMIC STATUS. See page 135.

SUBFAMILY **PUFFININÆ**. SHEARWATERS AND PETRELS.

Number of species in North America 19 ; in Massachusetts 3.

Bill variable in shape from slender and rather long to stout and rather short ; nasal tubes usually short and low, cut off obliquely in front ; both mandibles hooked or turned downward at ends ; tail with 12 feathers.

Púffinus boreális CORY.   Cory's Shearwater.

Plate 9.

DESCRIPTION. — *Adults (sexes similar)*: Above brownish-gray, feathers of back with pale tips, wings and tail darker ; first three (or four) primaries often with light ash on inner webs ; upper tail-coverts tipped white ; sides of head and neck ashy-gray, softly and inconspicuously mottled against white of throat and similarly barred against white of neck which gradually shades into white of throat — as in *P. kuhlii;* no distinct line of demarcation on side of head as in *P. gravis;* below white, washed sometimes on breast with grayish ; linings of wings white except on edges of wing where color of upper wing runs over ; under tail-coverts and flanks with ash mottling ; lower eyelid white contrasting with ashy of head ; bill yellowish with dark band and pale tip ; legs and feet yellow or yellowish-flesh color, darker (greenish-black) on outside of leg and outer toes ; iris brown. *Downy young:* Doubtless uniform, sooty-grayish-brown as with *P. kuhlii,* of which *borealis* appears to be a large race.

MEASUREMENTS. — Length 20.00 to 22.00 in. ; spread 40.00 to 49.50 ; folded wing 14.50 ; tail about 6.50 ; bill 1.95 to 2.28 ; tarsus 2.20 to 2.25.

MOLTS. — Apparently young shearwaters of all species are colored like the parent birds and probably reach maturity within the first year. Little is known regarding spring molt, but all adults molt completely in summer and fall.

FIELD MARKS. — Larger than Greater Shearwater. *Lack of sharp contrast of color between white throat and gray head* of Cory's Shearwater differentiates it from Greater Shearwater with its bi-colored head. Dark cap of "Greater" does not reach much below eye, while lighter ash mottling of "Cory's" extends much farther down side of head until it fades gradually into white of throat.

VOICE. — Male, *ia-gow-a-gow-a-gow;* female, *ia ia ia* (Ogilvie Grant).

BREEDING. — In vast numbers on sea-islands. *Nest:* A few feathers or bits of seaweed in holes and crevices, in among rocks or in caves, in stone houses built for these birds by the islanders, or in burrows excavated by the Shearwaters themselves. *Eggs:* 1; 3.28 by 1.93 to 2.80 by 1.80 in.; "ovate to elliptical-ovate"; white and smooth.

RANGE. — Atlantic Ocean. Breeds on Azores, Madeira, Salvage and Canary Islands; in migration south to at least 36° south; west to the coast of Brazil, and in North America from Newfoundland to North Carolina.

DISTRIBUTION IN NEW ENGLAND. — Off coasts of Massachusetts, Rhode Island [and Long Island] August to November; not uncommon; sometimes abundant locally; unrecorded from other New England states; in great numbers from Point Judith to Buzzards Bay in fall of 1886;[*] doubtless occurs off Maine coast as it has been recorded off western Newfoundland.[1]

SEASON IN MASSACHUSETTS. — August 2 to November 1 (A. C. Bent).

HAUNTS AND HABITS. Cory's Shearwater is the largest of the shearwaters on the New England coast. It does not differ from the Greater Shearwater (the next species) in habits. It flies similarly, is the same greedy bird, and enjoys the same sort of food. Ordinarily it is seen only at some distance from land; more rarely it appears along shore.

ECONOMIC STATUS. See page 135.

NOTE. Small specimens of "Cory's Shearwater" taken in North American waters are referable to the Mediterranean Shearwater *P. kuhlii*. Consequently the large shearwater described by Cory as *Puffinus borealis* becomes *P. kuhlii borealis*, as only a larger race of the Mediterranean bird — or *Calonectris kuhlii borealis* to be thoroughly up to date. (See H. C. Oberholser, Auk, Vol. XXXV, 1918, p. 201.)

The small specimens of "Cory's Shearwater" already noted in collections, with notably small bills, are therefore really representatives of the Mediterranean bird *P. k. kuhlii* (*C. k. kuhlii*) that, passing through the straits of Gibraltar, entered the range of the larger race — *borealis* — and so reached this side of the Atlantic. To quote Dr. Murphy: "The Mediterranean Shearwater should therefore be included in the next edition of the A. O. U. 'Check-list.'" Some of these aberrant "Cory's Shearwaters" (Mediterranean Shearwaters) have been taken so near the New England coast as Long Island waters,[2] and probably will be taken off our coast.

A good diagnostic feature of the Mediterranean Shearwater (*P. kuhlii kuhlii*) which is lacking in Cory's Shearwater (*borealis*) is the large amount of white on inner webs of outer primaries which makes a definite marking. This white on wing of *kuhlii* varies with the individual as it extends out much farther on the quills in some birds than in others.

Puffinus grávis (O'REILLY).　　Greater Shearwater.

Other names: WANDERING SHEARWATER; HAGLET; HAGDON; HAG; GRAY HAG OR HAGLET;
COMMON ATLANTIC SHEARWATER.

Plate 9.

DESCRIPTION. — *Adults* (*sexes alike*): Above sooty-brown, darkest on inner secondaries and rump; feathers of back, rump and wing-coverts with pale edgings of brownish- or whitish-ash; primaries and tail darker, inner webs of primaries lighter toward base; top of head and upper neck to below eye on line

---

[*] Professor S. F. Baird states (Auk, Vol. IV, 1887, p. 71) that toward the end of September, 1886, young sea-herring (*Clupea vulgaris*) came inshore in large numbers from Point Judith to Buzzards Bay and Vineyard Sound, and with them the mackerel which were feeding on them — also "enormous numbers of *Puffinus* and *Stercorarius*, the former proving to be almost exclusively *Puffinus borealis* Cory." Toward November 1st the birds were still with the herring, being very abundant off Gay Head, Menemsha Bight, Cuttyhunk and elsewhere.

[1] Griscom, Ludlow, and Janvrin, E. R. P.: Auk, Vol. XXXIX, 1922, p. 103.

[2] Murphy, Robert Cushman: Auk, Vol. XXXIX, 1922, p. 58.

with gape uniform dusky, this darker color sharply defined against white of throat which extends around on sides of head to hind neck, forming almost a collar; longer upper tail-coverts more or less white; below white, with zone (more or less extended) of smoky-gray spots on belly; flanks and under tail-coverts mostly dark grayish-brown, sides sometimes spotted with same; under tail-coverts white-tipped; lining of wings white, with dark mottling on outer border and axillars; bill blackish "yellowish-green" (Audubon) iris brownish; legs and feet (and webs) yellowish-pink, except outside of leg and outer toe which are brownish; strength and uniformity of color of upper plumage depend upon age, old and worn feathers being dullest and their grayish edgings less well-defined. *Young:* Similar to adult but with wash of sooty over white; a white half-collar nearly meets behind neck in young birds. *Downy young:* Sooty or gray in color.

MEASUREMENTS. — Length 18.00 to 20.00 in.; spread 42.00 to 45.00; folded wing 11.50 to 13.75; tail 5.00 to 5.90, graduated 1.00; bill 1.80 to 2.00; tarsus 2.20 to 2.40.

MOLTS. — See under "Molts" Cory's Shearwater (page 139).

FIELD MARKS. — Unmistakable two-colored effect on side of head. *Dark cap appears black by contrast with white of throat;* line of demarcation distinct and this, *together with white half-collar, contrasting with darker color above,* distinguishes this species from Cory's Shearwater; blackish bill of Greater Shearwater is more slender and shorter, while yellow bill of Cory's is longer and stouter. "Greater Shearwater" is a misnomer; for Cory's Shearwater is a larger bird in every way, although the difference in size is not enough to be depended upon as a field mark.

BREEDING. — Conditions almost unknown. *Nest:* Undescribed. *Eggs:* 1; 3.20 by 1.95 to 2.82 by 1.74 in.; pointed, oval, without gloss; white.

RANGE. — Atlantic Ocean; breeds on Inaccessible Island in the Tristan Da Cunha group in the South Atlantic; in migration from Greenland to Tierra Del Fuego and Cape of Good Hope; off east coast of North America June to November; common on Newfoundland Banks.

DISTRIBUTION IN NEW ENGLAND. — Common in summer and fall off coast; least common in Rhode Island and Connecticut waters.

SEASON IN MASSACHUSETTS. — As in New England; Essex County coast May 2 to October 12 (December 31); usually well outside (10 to 12 miles), but coming in closer to shore during fogs or heavy blows; summer, fall and early winter; commonest July to September; accidental in interior; August 10, 1887, Wellesley.

HAUNTS AND HABITS. The Shearwaters live most of their lives upon the sea. On the vast expanse of the Atlantic, where the mariner can see no land, where the sea heaves restlessly even in a calm or tosses and roars in wild commotion in the storm, there in the loneliness and desolation of the waters the Shearwaters are at home. I have never seen one very near land although sometimes they follow the fish near shore or even into some outlying harbor; but in summer on the banks of Newfoundland and New England, wherever fishing schooners anchor, there the "hags" are almost certain to be found. Notwithstanding the exceedingly great powers of flight possessed by this species, it cannot withstand the terrible, protracted tempests that sometimes occur on the Atlantic. The fierce gusts of a hurricane finally overcome the birds' powers of resistance, crumple them up and dash them into the raging sea. In the great hurricane of August 27–28, 1893, great numbers were cast up dead on the coast of South Carolina.[1]

The Greater Shearwater breeds in the Southern Hemisphere, and visits the North Atlantic when winter reigns in southern oceans. Anyone cruising in summer a few miles

---

[1] Wayne, Arthur T.: Birds of South Carolina, 1910, p. 8.

off isolated points, such as Cape Ann, Cape Cod, Marthas Vineyard or Nantucket, may see a large, rather gull-like bird flapping and sailing near the surface of the water. Its dark brown upper plumage and sharply contrasting white under plumage and its manner of flight at once identify it as the Greater Shearwater. To see these birds in numbers, one should go out to the fishing grounds where great "bottom fish" are hauled from the depths. Wherever the fish bite well, there these birds may be found; and a few fish-livers cut in pieces and thrown overboard are likely to bring this and other species about the boat, together with gulls and petrels that are also usually on the watch for such opportunities on the fishing-grounds.

Shearwaters are graceful birds on the wing, and in a high wind they scale about close to the water, with their long pointed wings slightly decurved. They circle and glide with the greatest ease. The Greater Shearwater often alights on the surface of the water to pick up floating food, swimming toward it with head erect and wings partially raised but not fully spread. In alighting it frequently strikes upon its breast with some force, but does not commonly plunge directly under water head first like a tern or a gannet. It can dive from the surface and swim well under water, and probably uses its wings beneath the surface in pursuit of sinking food or fleeing fish. Dr. J. E. H. Kelso writes me that he has watched many Manx Shearwaters diving to escape a sail-boat, and though unwounded they invariably used their wings under water. All manner of fish is food for the Shearwaters. They are particularly fond of the "gurry" or waste thrown overboard by fishermen. On this food they grow fat, and they consume quantities of fish oil. Dr. Townsend says that they are very fond of squids, as a Shearwater that he shot contained in its stomach the horny beaks of twenty-four of these animals.[1] Captain Collins says that he has opened many hundreds of these birds, and to his recollection never failed to find parts of squids in their stomachs.[2] "The hags feed on the squid, the gulls on the herring and the gannets on the mackerel," according to Cape Sable Island, N. S. fishermen.

ECONOMIC STATUS. See page 135.

Puffinus griseus (GMELIN). Sooty Shearwater.

Other names: BLACK HAGDON; BLACK HAG OR HAGLET.

Plate 9.

DESCRIPTION. — *Adults (sexes alike)*: Dark sooty-brown; darker (blackish) on wings and tail; grayer below, palest on throat; lining of wings mottled sooty-gray and whitish; bill dusky, tube, ridge and hook blackish; iris blackish; feet pale flesh-color, but blackish on under sides and elsewhere outwardly; "variation consists of the greater or less amount of *light color* beneath but this is doubtless due to age."[3] *Young in juvenal plumage:* Apparently like adult. *Downy young:* Sooty or gray.

---

[1] Townsend, C. W.: Memoirs of the Nuttall Ornithological Club, No. III, The Birds of Essex County, Massachusetts, 1905, p. 108.

[2] Collins, J. W.: Report of United States Commissioner of Fish and Fisheries for 1882 (1884), p. 216.

[3] Maynard, C. J.: Birds of Eastern North America, 1896, p. 35.

MEASUREMENTS. — Length 16.00 to 18.00 in.; spread 40.00 to 42.00; folded wing 11.15 to 12.75; tail 4.00 to 4.50; bill 1.60 to 2.25; tarsus 2.05 to 2.35.

MOLTS. — No material available to trace molts of young; adults apparently molt completely during spring, summer and early autumn.

FIELD MARKS. — At a distance bird looks black; this easily distinguishes Sooty Shearwater from other shearwaters.

BREEDING. — On sea-islands chiefly. *Nest:* In hole or burrow of varying depth (several feet) in ground. *Eggs:* 1; 2.60 by 1.60 in.; "round oval" or "ovoid elliptical"; white. *Dates:* February and March (Buller).

RANGE. — Oceans of both hemispheres. Breeds in New Zealand, on Norfolk, Stewarts, Kapite, Snares, St. Stephens, Auckland and Chatham Islands; on islands near Cape Horn; and probably on many others in southern oceans; occurs in summer on Kurile islands, on Pacific coast from southern Alaska to Lower California, and on Atlantic coast from southern Greenland and Labrador to South Carolina; occasional in British Isles; accidental in Alabama; not uncommon on Newfoundland fishing banks.

DISTRIBUTION IN NEW ENGLAND. — Summer and fall visitant; generally offshore; much less common than Greater Shearwater; accidental in interior (Vermont and New Hampshire); not recorded from Connecticut.

SEASON IN MASSACHUSETTS. — As in New England; Essex County, not uncommon summer visitor, March to October (Townsend).

HAUNTS AND HABITS. The Sooty Shearwater much resembles the Greater Shearwater in habits but is not so numerous off the coast of New England. Wherever many of the latter species are seen, however, some Sooty Shearwaters usually will be found. Captain Collins estimated that the numbers of this species did not exceed one per cent of the numbers of Greater Shearwaters on the Grand Banks. These Shearwaters are excessively greedy birds, and are very bold and combative in securing food from other birds. They often follow fishing dories when the fishermen are baiting trawls, and as the gear sinks in the water at the stern of the dory, the birds dive after the sinking bait and frequently succeed in tearing it from the hook. Some are so greedy that they swallow it hook and all. In former times the fishermen retaliated by catching them by means of a floating bait in which a light hook was concealed. Thousands of shearwaters were caught in this way, and their bodies were used by fishermen for bait or for food. Among the thousands thus caught were proportionate numbers of Sooty Shearwaters. Mr. Bent says that this species dives occasionally in pursuit of food "using its wings freely under water." [1]

The food of the Sooty Shearwater is similar to that of the Greater Shearwater but no exhaustive study of the food of either species has been made.

ECONOMIC STATUS. See page 135.

NOTE. Two subspecies of *griseus* are proposed — *Puffinus g. chilensis*, the Pacific bird; *Puffinus g. stricklandi*, the Atlantic bird. Following the classification given in the third edition of Check list of the American Ornithologists' Union the full range of the species in both hemispheres is given above.

---

[1] Smithsonian Institution, United States National Museum, Bulletin No. 121, 1922, p. 87.

Pteródroma hasitáta BONAPARTE. Black-capped Petrel.

Other name: DIABLOTIN.

Fig. 17.

DESCRIPTION. — *Adults (sexes alike)*: Upper plumage sooty, shading to bister-brown on back (where feathers often have lighter margins) and deepening on wings and terminal half of tail; upper tail-coverts, base of tail, forehead, sides of head and neck white (blackish cap of crown being thus isolated); black mark on side of head; below white, including lining of wings; brownish-gray wash sometimes on sides of chest; bill black; legs, together with bases of toes and webs, flesh-colored; rest of toes and webs black. *Immature:* Younger birds have less white on head and hind neck so that dark feathers here coalesce.

MEASUREMENTS. — Length 14.00 to 16.00 in.; spread about 39.50; folded wing 11.40 to 12.00; tail 4.80 to 5.30, central feathers longest, graduation being 1.25 to 2.00; bill 1.20 to 1.40; tarsus 1.40 to 1.45.

FIELD MARKS. — In flight and appearance very like Greater Shearwater, but the large, conspicuous white "wedge" of upper tail-coverts is a distinguishing field mark.

RANGE. — Warmer parts of North Atlantic Ocean, straggling to Haiti, southern coast of United States, and to England and France; casual inland in United States; not so rare in the Atlantic as was formerly supposed but appears to be a bird of warm latitudes; formerly bred in Lesser Antilles, but has disappeared from its former breeding haunts there; present breeding range seems to be unknown; bird is blown rarely into the interior of the United States by storms; at least four specimens have been recorded since 1849 in New York; may occur in Massachusetts at any time, but so far we have no definite record for this State.

DISTRIBUTION IN NEW ENGLAND. — The only definite record is that of an exhausted male bird, taken August 30, 1893, at Pittsfield, New Hampshire, 40 miles from the sea.[1] There is also a record from Vermont in late August of the same year, but place and date are lacking.[2]

NOTE. On the date that the New Hampshire bird was found, one was taken at Blacksburg, Virginia, 200 miles from the sea; and another, August 28, 1893, on Oneida Lake, New York.[3] Still another bird was taken about this time (September, 1893), in New York, at Cayuga Lake. Undoubtedly all these birds were blown far north and inland by the great hurricane of the last week of August, 1893. There is a late fall record (October 30) in this same year (1893) from Toronto, Ontario.

Records of *hasitata* from several eastern United States localities prove to be *diabolica* (Lafr.). (Noble: Bulletin Museum of Comparative Zoölogy, LX, 1916, pp. 370–374.)

HAUNTS AND HABITS. Nothing is known of the haunts and habits of this bird in our waters. There is quite a full biography in Mr. A. C. Bent's Life Histories of North American Petrels and Pelicans, Smithsonian Institution, United States National Museum, Bulletin 121, pp. 106–111.

SUBFAMILY PROCELLARIINÆ. STORM PETRELS.

Number of species in North America 9 ; in Massachusetts 1.

Smallest birds of the family; bill moderate in size, both mandibles well hooked at ends; tail of 12 feathers; leg-bones shorter than wing-bones.

---

[1] Allen, G. M.: A List of the Birds of New Hampshire, 1903, p. 69 (see also footnote 3).
[2] Allen, G. M.: Fauna of New England, List of the Aves, 1909, p. 24 (see also footnote 3).
[3] Allen, J. A.: Auk, Vol. XXI, 1904, p. 383.

Oceanódroma leucórhoa leucórhoa (VIEILLOT). Leach's Petrel.

Other names: LEACH'S FORK-TAILED PETREL; FORK-TAILED STORMY PETREL; FORK-TAILED PETREL; CAREY CHICKEN ("KERRY CHICKEN").

Plate 9.

DESCRIPTION. — Tail forked about 1 inch. *Adults (sexes alike)*: Sooty-brown, slightly browner below and slightly darker on crown; primaries and tail brownish-black; wing-coverts and inner secondaries light grayish-brown, sometimes edged and tipped whitish; upper tail-coverts white, generally more or less mixed with sooty-brownish; outer under tail-coverts white basally, and other under tail-coverts more or less so — also some white on adjoining feathers of abdomen and sides, amount of white varying with the individual; probably younger birds have most white; as in case of Wilson's Petrel, white feathers of upper tail-coverts join with (or meet) white lateral under tail-coverts, and thus make practically a zone of white nearly around basal third of tail (but there is never enough white under tail to make a white patch like that above it); iris brown; bill, legs and feet black. *Downy young:* Sooty or grayish; lighter in color than adults.

MEASUREMENTS. — Length 7.50 to 8.90 in.; spread 17.00 to 18.50; wing 6.00 to 6.50; tail 3.00 to 4.00, forked deeply .75; bill .62 to .70; tarsus .85 to 1.00. Female smaller than male.

MOLTS. — So far as known there are no material seasonal differences in the plumage of Leach's Petrel; the bird seems to pass from juvenal stage to winter plumage without any very material change in coloration (complete molt August to March), and to become fully adult in the summer of its second year when about one year old; complete annual molt of adults begins in August or September.

FIELD MARKS. — If seen close at hand, forked tail and short legs, which in flight do not show beyond end of tail, distinguish Leach's Petrel from Wilson's Petrel (with no forked tail but long legs), the only other common species off the New England coast; Leach's Petrel is a little larger and a shade browner than Wilson's Petrel; "an observer who once has had the good fortune of watching the two species together can thereafter distinguish them almost as far away as the birds can be seen." [1]

VOICE. — "When a nest was being disturbed, they kept up a constant squeaking like mice" (C. J. Maynard, describing a visit by day to a colony); at night at the nest a distinctly enunciated call of eight notes, not like the cry of any sea-bird and not to be compared with the notes of any bird "that I have ever heard" (Frank M. Chapman); by day at nest — "got any terbacker," or "Johnny get your hair cut" (O. W. Knight).

BREEDING. — In colonies; on outlying sea-islands. *Nest:* A slight collection of pebbles, short grasses, weeds, rootlets and perhaps a few feathers at the end of a burrow in the soil or beneath a rock; the burrows, like rat-holes and only a few inches in diameter, usually from 1 to 3 feet long, extend downward, then run along nearly horizontally not many inches below the surface and into a roundish chamber at end, slightly enlarged. *Eggs:* 1; 1.24 to 1.35 by .80 to 1.00 in.; a very small egg .99 by .78; oval, brittle and rough to touch; white, often dotted finely at large end with lilac and reddish, sometimes arranged in a ring. *Dates:* June 10 to August 19. *Incubation:* Period probably not far from 5 weeks (A. C. Bent); by both sexes; male incubates largely if not wholly in daytime. One brood yearly.

RANGE. — North Pacific and North Atlantic oceans. Breeds from Kurile Islands north to Aleutian and Commander Islands, Bering Sea and south along the coast of southern Alaska to Forrester Island,* and from southern Greenland and Iceland south to Maine and British Isles; "south in migration to the Equator and vicinity of Cape San Roque, Brazil"; [2] east to coast of Africa; in Pacific south of Equator near Galapagos Islands and west to Hawaii.

---

[1] Murphy, R. C.: Auk, Vol. XXXII, 1915, p. 171.

* Its southern subspecies breeds along the Washington, Oregon and California coasts.

[2] Murphy, R. C.: Auk, Vol. XXXII, 1915, p. 173.

DISTRIBUTION IN NEW ENGLAND. — Breeds in numbers on outlying islands off coast of Maine; common from May to October; "breeds as far west as Muscongus Bay" (A. H. Norton), on Eastern Egg Rock, Lincoln County; a rather common migrant offshore (Maine, New Hampshire and Massachusetts), but uncommon migrant off Rhode Island and Connecticut coasts; casual inland in migration; a few strays have been reported in winter from the Maine coast.

SEASON IN MASSACHUSETTS. — May 12 to June 21; September 1 to October 16.

HAUNTS AND HABITS.   In July, 1914, it was my good fortune to join Mr. T. Gilbert Pearson as a guest of Mr. William P. Wharton on the yacht Avocet for a cruise among the sea-bird colonies of the Maine coast.   On the evening of the 13th, having found a considerable number of Leach's Petrels nesting on a small island, we concealed ourselves by lying on the lowest branches of some of the scattering spruce trees that grew near the shore.   A higher layer of spruce limbs served us as cover, while the lower ones kept us off the ground.   Herring Gulls which bred on the island were then coming in for the night, and many hundreds were seen winging their way toward us from distant shores. They alighted on the heaving sea in great flocks, and sat in massed array along the dark ledges, their white heads, necks and breasts gleaming immaculate against the background of dun ledge and darkening waters.   As we lay concealed, their complaining cries died away in the air overhead, until dark brought comparative quiet, except that a few wakeful gulls kept up intermittent cries; but the Night Herons were awake, and they broke the silence with raucous croakings.

Softly the warm, balmy summer night settled down.   Eight o'clock, and still no sign of the petrels.   Time dragged on, and we had almost decided that it was useless to wait, when at nearly nine a dark, indistinct shape flitted silently in from the sea, fluttered bat-like back and forth, and then dropped in the shrubbery.   Soon another and another came, until the incoming was continual, while others seemed to be going out to sea, but may have been merely flying back and forth.   Now queer sounds arose, in the air, on the ground about us, and even in the earth beneath, for these strange birds had burrows in the earth under the tree in which we reclined, and they crept into their holes seemingly beneath our very bodies where we lay across the mouths of their passageways.   Tender chucklings, crowings, stammerings and formless sounds that seemed like billing and cooing filled the air.   Meanwhile there were flittings and flutterings, goings and comings, all about us.   This went on for a good part of an hour, when apparently the first excitement had passed, and we arose and departed, vastly entertained by the experience.   But it seems that we left too early in the evening to get the full benefit of the petrel concert.   My friend, Frank A. Brown, who visited the petrels on Machias Seal Island and camped there, writes that he dropped asleep to the monotonous chanting of their "staccato cooings," but awoke again about midnight to find these flight notes "succeeded by a different song apparently proceeding from the ground but probably uttered at the mouth of the burrow.   This song was softer, somewhat liquid and nearly continuous." [1]   Dr. Chapman says that "such a song might be uttered by elves or brownies," and Mr. Arthur

---

[1] Bird-Lore, Vol. XIII, 1911, pp. 243–245.

H. Norton, who probably knows these petrels as well as any man living, thus graphically describes his impressions of their night-life at their nesting place :

"Here within Night's dominion, in the midst of a no less funereally garbed throng of flitting forms, seeming to speak most earnestly in a subhuman, unknown tongue, which is answered by their encaverned mates in purring tones and pleading wails, the mind may readily picture a most animated gathering of the black elves of old, hurrying to and fro for the accomplishment of some important mission, ere dreaded Day begins to ride his shining steed through the pathway of the sky.

"The wide-ranging birds from the sea have returned to land to relieve their brooding mates, and the air seems full of them, calling on every hand ; the scene seems a hopeless chaos of activity, but soon by careful observation it is resolved to one of orderly purpose. As each flying bird passes over its nest, it calls in a hurried gibberish, to be answered by its brooding mate in an energetic purr often ending in a coaxing wail ; the flying bird dashes on and swings away to leeward again coming up the wind, and again as it passes its nest calls as before to be answered again ; time and again this is repeated, each passage over the nest finding the flying bird lower and lower in its flight, until it finally drops to the entrance of its burrow to meet its anxious mate. Now from the dank weeds and grass, like great June bugs, others are rising or crawling to a convenient place to rise. One is in the very midst of their activities. From one's feet to twenty feet over head they swarm, often dashing against one's person in their haste.

"But with the coming of the dawn, calm, damp and chill, this strange vision of the night has faded as a dream." [1]

Petrels are peculiar, eerie birds, and their habits are so strange that from time immemorial sailors have had a superstition that these small fowls are the precursors of storms and wrecks. There is some reason for such superstitions, as at the approach of a storm petrels often gather in great excitement about vessels. Our observations during the cruise of the Avocet seemed to prove that birds several times the size of the petrels have a strange, unaccountable fear of them. We took a petrel from its warm burrow in daylight and released it. It flew at once to the ocean, going toward a great flock of clamorous Herring Gulls sitting on a ledge near the island. Immediately every gull ceased its cries, took wing, and fled silently out to sea. Later we released petrels on other islands on which gulls or terns were breeding, and however numerous or clamorous were the birds immediately about us, the appearance of a petrel on the wing silenced their cries and caused a local exodus. No one has been able to account for this, so far as I know, and it may not be a universal experience ; but it was ours.[2] Let a hawk or an owl appear in one of these gull or tern colonies and the war cry is sounded, while the birds swarm from all directions to mob and harry the intruder until it is driven away ; let a cat appear in a colony of Herring Gulls in the daytime, and its appearance is the signal for a general attack ; but the small and apparently inoffensive petrel is avoided as if it were ghost or banshee.

---

[1] The Maine Naturalist, Vol. I, 1921, pp. 2–3.

[2] See also Mr. T. Gilbert Pearson's account, Bird-Lore, Vol. XVI, 1914, p. 388.

Dr. F. A. Lucas declares that Leach's Petrel stops at home all day in order to indulge in the reprehensible practice of staying out all night. This assertion has some foundation in fact. During the breeding season many Leach's Petrels (largely females) fly by day, and it may be mainly the males that are out at night; but there is proof that the male does most of the incubating while the female is the gadabout of the family.*

Leach's Petrel ranges widely at night. At midnight in July I found a petrel fluttering about the wharf-lights at Bar Harbor about ten miles from its nearest breeding-grounds. Travelers tell us that at night petrels often circle about the lights of ships at sea. Lights evidently attract these midnight wanderers. Dr. Joseph Grinnell, who passed a night in June, 1896, on the summit of the island of St. Lazaria, Alaska, says that it was "impossible to keep a fire alight in the middle of the night, as the petrels flew into it in such numbers as to extinguish it." [1] This was a favorite nesting place of petrels.

One of the most interesting facts in the life history of this ranger of the wide and stormy seas is that you may find its nest in a burrow under a commonplace barberry bush in an island sheep-pasture. It digs fast. How it disposes of the earth is a question unanswerable to one who has seen only the long-occupied burrows unless, as the boy said of the chipmunk, it begins at the other end! But some loose soil is often seen at the mouth of a new excavation. When the bird is disturbed in its unfinished burrow, it can dig itself in very rapidly, apparently using both bill and feet, and as the soil is light, it possibly packs it down with its feet, as it digs onward. During the burrowing and nest-building both male and female may be found in the nest through the day, but after the single egg is laid only one bird, usually the male, remains there in daylight. Like other petrels when disturbed in its burrow, it has a habit of ejecting from the mouth an oily liquid with an offensive odor. This odor often indicates the breeding-places of the birds.

From late in May until September we never see a petrel about the breeding-grounds during the day, for while one bird of each nest remains in the burrow, the other probably roams far away over the sea, and the young are fed mainly if not wholly at night. Owing to their nesting habits, petrels must needs nest on islands where there are no small burrowing animals, such as minks, rats or weasels, any of which would soon destroy a colony of these little birds. Any of man's destructive satellites, cats, dogs, or hogs, if at liberty, would soon extirpate them. It now seems that Leach's Petrel is doomed to destruction on the Maine islands wherever dogs or cats are introduced. In 1910 Mr. Wilbur F. Smith visited Wooden Ball Island where he found that the entire colony of petrels formerly breeding there had been destroyed by a wild house-cat and three cats kept by a

---

* "I have lately had quite a number of Leach's Petrels taken on the nests and find some things which are not mentioned in such books as I have access to. In the first place, the males do most, if not all, of the incubating. In a number received the 1st of June, five out of six were males. Thinking that, like pigeons, the males might perhaps all sit at the same time, I had another lot sent me about June 15, and again, of twelve specimens seven proved to be males. A careful examination showed that while the under plumage of the females was in every case perfect, each male had on the lower part of the breast a bare spot large enough to cover the egg." (Brewster, Wm. quoting Manly Hardy: Bulletin, Nuttall Ornithological Club, Vol. VI, 1881, p. 125.)

[1] Mailliard, Joseph: Auk, Vol. XV, 1898, p. 232.

fisherman. The ground was strewn with the remains of the petrels. On Machias Seal Island, Mr. Frank A. Brown found a dog kept as a pet by a little boy. This dog was digging out and killing about 10 petrels each day. Mr. T. Gilbert Pearson counted on less than an acre the bodies of 147 of these birds killed by this dog.[1] Unless these petrels are protected from such destructive enemies, the Maine islands will soon know them no more.

As a sea rover this species resembles the Wilson's Petrel, but it is now apparently rare in summer off the Massachusetts coast though still found in numbers on the Grand Banks. Its habits at sea are somewhat like those of the other species, but Dr. Murphy says: "Unlike Wilson's Petrel the Leach's Petrels settled frequently into the water, holding the tips of their wings high while they swam."[2] I have never seen this bird plunge or dive under water. On land it seems to alight only at the mouth of its hole into which it creeps or waddles on its tarsi, and in leaving the burrow it makes use of its wings at once.

I find little data on the migrations of the petrels along the Atlantic coast. They pass at night or far from land, and their flittings are noted only by those "who go down to the sea in ships." Captain Collins says that petrels generally leave the Banks late in October or early in November, and return in April or May.[3]

The food of Leach's Petrel seems to consist largely of oily matter which it gleans from the surface of the sea, together with small fish, mollusks, crustaceans and other small oceanic creatures found on or near the surface. Like other sea-birds it follows fishing-vessels and other craft for waste or garbage thrown overboard.

ECONOMIC STATUS. Leach's Petrel seems to be unimportant economically.

SUBFAMILY **OCEANITINÆ**. LONG-LEGGED STORM PETRELS.

Number of species in North America 3 ; in Massachusetts 1.

Bill and nasal tubes similar to those of Procellariinæ; only ten secondaries, fewest of any member of the family; 1st primary shorter than 2d, usually shorter than 3d; legs and feet very long; leg bones longer than wing bones.

Oceanítes oceánicus (KUHL). **Wilson's Petrel.**

Other names: LONG-LEGGED STORMY PETREL; WILSON'S STORMY PETREL; SEA MARTIN; MOTHER CAREY'S CHICKEN; LONG-LEGGED MOTHER CAREY'S CHICKEN; STORMY PETREL.

Plate 9.

DESCRIPTION. — Bill much weaker than that of Leach's Petrel; tail not forked. *Adults (sexes alike)*: Dark sooty-brown, somewhat lighter below; primaries and tail sooty-black; secondary wing-coverts pale gray, tipped with whitish, producing effect of narrow white line; upper tail-coverts white, shorter feathers marked with sooty; under tail-coverts mixed basally with white (basal third of outer under

---

[1] Bird-Lore, Vol. XIII, 1911, p. 276. [2] Murphy, R. C.: Auk, Vol. XXXII, 1915, p. 172.
[3] Collins, J. W.: U. S. Commission of Fish and Fisheries, Report of the Commissioner for 1882 (1884), p. 333.

tail-coverts white); also some white at base of tail, amount of white (more or less) depending upon the individual; iris brown; bill, legs and feet black, webs varying from dusky to yellow (or orange centrally). *Young in first winter plumage* (*in which young are seen here in summer*): Similar to juvenal plumage, but entire plumage dingy and threadbare; greater wing-coverts bleached and frayed; "white edgings of ventral feathers and white mottling of lores still discernible" (R. C. Murphy). *Young in juvenal plumage:* Similar to adult, but with conspicuous white edgings (of variable extent) to feathers of belly and whitish spot before eye; bill weaker than in adult. *Downy young:* Grayish-black or sooty. Irregular white markings (albinistic or not) often appear in the plumage of this species.

MEASUREMENTS. — Length 7.00 to 7.50 in.; spread about 16.00; folded wing 5.70 to 6.25; tail 3.00 to 3.25; bill .46 to .50; bare tibia 1.00; tarsus 1.30 to 1.35.

MOLTS. — An annual molt takes place during summer (between May and October) in the North Atlantic; apparently the species reaches maturity in one year; Dr. Robert Cushman Murphy, whose experience with this species probably is greater than that of any other living ornithologist, expresses the opinion that the bird does not molt during its first year.

FIELD MARKS. — Wilson's Petrel may be distinguished from Leach's Petrel at close range by its almost square-ended tail (tail of the latter species is distinctly forked); Dr. C. W. Townsend calls attention to longer leg of Wilson's Petrel (a difference of nearly an inch, which causes its yellow-webbed feet to project beyond tail in flight), as a good field mark; this is shown well in Alexander Wilson's plate; a keen eye will note (when both birds are seen at the same time) that Wilson's Petrel is a little darker and a little smaller than the other species, and that the wing beats of Wilson's Petrel are more quick and fluttering and that the species is more given to short periods of sailing.

VOICE. — Soft peeping or twittering notes when feeding on fish liver thrown overboard to bait the birds; cries harsher and more often repeated during boisterous weather (Giraud); resemble syllables *kee-re-kee-kee* and heard more often by night than by day (Audubon); a low "*weet weet*" and a low twittering "*pe-up*" or chirp by day, while at night, when disturbed (by a vessel), a singular guttural chattering like *kŭk kuk k'k, k'k* or something similar, ending usually in a low, swallow-like twitter (Nuttall).

BREEDING. — On sea-coasts and islands. *Nest:* In a rock-crevice or cleft or under rocks or in hollow made by bird; either no attempt at nest-making or else a flat structure of twigs and stalks. *Eggs:* 1; average about 1.30 by .90 in. (Nuttall); white, marked chiefly around larger end with fine spots of purplish or lilac and fine reddish-brown dots. *Dates:* Eggs have been taken from December to March. *Incubation:* Period 35 days (A. C. Bent); breeding and nesting period approaches 5 months (R. C. Murphy); by male.

RANGE. — All oceans except North Pacific; Antarctic regions north to Davis Strait; Labrador and British Isles. Breeds on Mauritius and Kerguelen Islands, in Indian Ocean, and on Antarctic islands and Antarctic continent; known to breed at Cape Horn, on Adelie Land, and Victoria Land and the South Orkney and South Shetland Islands and South Georgia Island; winters in northern summer mainly in western North Atlantic "between the latitudes of Bermuda and Greenland"; accidental inland.

DISTRIBUTION IN NEW ENGLAND. — Common, often abundant, from early May to middle of September off Maine coast; common to abundant from late May to September off southern New England coast; often in considerable numbers not very far offshore; casual or accidental inland (Maine and Vermont).

SEASON IN MASSACHUSETTS. — Late May to late September; more rarely seen in October south of Cape Cod.

HAUNTS AND HABITS. Wilson's Petrel was long a bird of mystery. In summer it appeared in the North Atlantic, but it was never known to breed or even to go ashore unless driven there by high winds. Time solved the mystery. This petrel is the smallest of New England sea-birds. Its length is less than that of the Purple Martin. It is too small and delicate to withstand severe winter storms, and so times its migrations, therefore, as to live in perpetual summer. But like the shearwaters it reverses the ordinary migratory movement of the Northern Hemisphere. It breeds during the Antarctic summer in the Southern Hemisphere; then wings its way far northward toward the top of the world making a journey of about 7,000 miles; and passes the period of extreme Antarctic winter in the North Atlantic Ocean. It keeps to the wide seas and is rarely seen ashore in our latitudes unless driven in by very severe, prolonged gales. That it cannot withstand such storms even in summer is shown by the fact that during the terrible gale that raged on the coast of North Carolina August 28, 29 and 30, 1893, many thousands of these birds were driven ashore on the beach extending from Beaufort harbor to Cape Lookout. In places the beach was covered with their bodies two or three deep, and the shore was littered with the dead, dying or exhausted birds, from the water up to the beach-grass, as reported by Mr. James Davis, a well-known business man of Beaufort.[1] Petrels live and die at sea. In company with Mr. A. C. Bent one day in the summer of 1921, I picked up from the surface of Cape Cod Bay a petrel of this species that was lying upon the water, apparently in its death struggles and unable to hold up its head. Our boatman said that petrels were sometimes taken in this condition by Banks fishermen.

Wilson's Petrel appears in numbers near our coast in June, July and August. Mr. E. P. Bicknell writes that on August 3, 1922, off the beach at Hewlett, Long Island, there was an enormous flock of "thousands and thousands, rising sometimes like a low, black cloud, about 1 mile long." The bird even penetrates into harbors; but commonly it is seen miles from any shore flapping and skipping along on the waves and often using both wings and feet at once, and thus both running (or skipping) and flying on the surface; hence, according to Dampier (1703), the name petrel (little Peter) after the Apostle Peter who also essayed to walk upon the waves. It seems credible, however, that the petrels were thus named in imitation of the notes of some species which resemble the word "petterel." Some photographs of this species show the bird apparently walking on the water, one foot after another. But usually it seems to hop or jump along with both feet habitually and I have never seen it walk. Dr. R. C. Murphy whose experience with the species is much greater than mine makes a similar statement.[2]

Wilson's Petrel may be seen during the summer from the deck of any vessel more than ten miles from shore. It is the common "Stormy Petrel" or "Mother Carey's Chicken" that follows steamships from American ports far out on the Atlantic, but unless viewed close at hand it is difficult to distinguish from Leach's Petrel except with a powerful glass. On a calm sea this species flies along close to the surface, flexing their wings like bats or fluttering almost like butterflies. In windy weather they sail more with set wings, using both feet at once and striking them down hard to leeward. They sometimes hop or bound from the surface of the wave, and appear to be tireless examples of perpetual

[1] Pearson, T. Gilbert: Auk, Vol. XVI, 1899, p. 249, and Birds of North Carolina, 1919, p. 44.
[2] Bulletin, American Museum of Natural History, Vol. XXXVIII, 1918, pp. 134–137.

motion as they often fly by night as well as by day; but Dr. Murphy, who watched them on a whaling voyage, says that at evening the birds dropped behind and he saw some settle on the sea. At about eight o'clock in the morning they appeared in the vessel's wake again. This indicates that the Wilson's Petrel rests at night on the sea.

It is remarkable that Wilson's Petrel seems to be unmolested by the Skua, that terrible foe of smaller birds, which Dr. Murphy says never attacks the species, though "quite ready to pounce upon or devour a dead or disabled *Oceanites*." Both species feed together at times and although Wilson's Petrel is much smaller than many of the birds that the Skua attacks and no swifter on the wing than others, it seems to enjoy complete immunity. Now and then one loses a leg, probably to some voracious fish, and one-legged birds are not rare.

Sometimes in daylight this species may be seen resting in flocks on the water. While they sometimes alight on its surface to pick up food, they usually gather this while flying and skipping along or while fluttering and stationary. They dance upon the sea, searching along the "slicks" and picking up any bits of oily matter that may float, and sometimes plunge or dive beneath the surface.[1] This Petrel when ashore is not only incapable of perching but even of standing upright unless by the aid of its fluttering wings. It walks on its tarsi; but by a powerful exertion of its wings it is enabled to run on its toes as it does on the surface of the sea.

Apparently Wilson's Petrel leaves its far southern breeding-grounds in March, and in April appears off the coast of Brazil. Early in May its hordes appear in the North Atlantic. The young birds seem to remain nearer the coast than the adults, and do not go so far north as the latter, for in northern regions they are in the minority. During summer the majority of the species seems to be distributed along the coast of North America and west of the Gulf Stream; but individuals may appear almost anywhere in the North Atlantic and some have been noted off the African coast. In September and October they all move southward toward their breeding-grounds and the Antarctic summer.

Wilson's Petrel feeds largely on fish oil and on small oily morsels, both of which it gleans from the surface of the waves. Often when taken in the hand it ejects this rancid oil from the stomach through the mouth or nostrils or both, and it always seems to carry the offensive odor of the liquid. Petrels gather about fishing-boats to feed on offal or bait or about whaling vessels for oil and scraps of blubber, and like other sea-birds may be attracted by throwing out pieces of fish liver for which they will come close to the boat. Dr. C. W. Townsend says that besides oil he has found in the stomachs of these petrels a few small stones and bits of charcoal.[2] Dr. Murphy reports fishes, maggots, seaweed, minute crustaceans and traces of algæ among the stomach contents of this species.[3]

ECONOMIC STATUS. See page 135.

[1] Murphy, R. C.: Bulletin, American Museum of Natural History, Vol. XXXVIII, 1918, p. 137. See also Spinney, Herbert L.: Auk, Vol. XX, 1903, p. 65.
[2] Townsend, C. W.: Memoirs of the Nuttall Ornithological Club, No. III, The Birds of Essex County, 1905, p. 111.
[3] Murphy, R. C.: Bulletin, American Museum of Natural History., Vol. XXXVIII, 1918, p. 145.

PLATE 10

PLATE 10

CORMORANT
Page 158

YOUNG IN FIRST WINTER PLUMAGE

ADULT IN NUPTIAL PLUMAGE

DOUBLE–CRESTED CORMORANT
Page 160

YOUNG IN FIRST WINTER PLUMAGE

ADULT IN NUPTIAL PLUMAGE

GANNET
Page 155

YOUNG IN FIRST WINTER PLUMAGE

ADULT

All one-sixth natural size.

Louis Agassiz Fuertes

ORDER STEGANOPODES — TOTIPALMATE SWIMMERS.

Number of species in North America 20 ; in Massachusetts 7.

Birds of this order differ from all other swimming birds in having four-toed feet *fully webbed*. The hind toe is large, placed slightly to one side and lower down than in other swimming birds, and is connected to the inner toe by a complete web reaching to the toe-tips. Thus these birds have three complete webs on their large feet, which are powerful swimming implements. The nostrils are very small, rudimentary or wanting. The bill in most cases is hooked, with a nail more or less distinct, and beneath it there is a pouch or sac connected with the throat. All the species are believed to feed chiefly on fish, which they pursue beneath the surface of the water, plunge for or scoop up with the bill. In some of the families the air-receptacles of the interior of the body are connected with air-cells situated beneath the skin of the breast and the abdomen. This pneumatic arrangement is seen at its best in the Pelicans and Gannets. When these pectoral air-cells are inflated, the birds ride very lightly on the water, and the air-cushion thus formed may serve as a "shock absorber" to deaden the force of the blow when these heavy birds plunge into the water from a height.

The order STEGANOPODES contains six families and not over seventy species (Coues). Two of the families — *Anhingidæ*, Darters, and *Phaëthontidæ*, Tropic Birds — are not represented in New England ; the other four families are the *Sulidæ*, Gannets, *Phalacrocoracidæ*, Cormorants, *Pelecanidæ*, Pelicans, and *Fregatidæ*, Man-o'-war-birds.

FAMILY **SULIDÆ**. GANNETS.

Number of species in North America 6 ; in Massachusetts 2.

The *Sulidæ* include the birds generally known as gannets or boobies. Gannets are sea-birds but do not ordinarily wander so far at sea as the TUBINARES. They seem to prefer coastal waters. All have a small, naked gular sac or throat pouch. The *Sulidæ* are large, goose-like, long-winged birds, but unlike geese in flight they alternately sail and flap, and they secure their prey by diving into the sea, usually from a height, somewhat in the manner of terns. The bill is rather long, straight and tapering, with sharp, irregularly serrated edges, but is not hooked. The short, stout, serviceable legs are placed near the center of the body. The feet as in all this order have three full webs. Birds of this family are gregarious and breed in large colonies. Eleven species have been recorded ; one northern and the others distributed along tropical and subtropical coasts.

ECONOMIC STATUS. Birds of this family feed almost entirely on fish, and fishermen generally believe them to be detrimental to the fisheries. No thorough investigation of their food has been made. It is very evident, however, that where gannets are numerous, fish also are abundant. The eggs and flesh of gannets are utilized for food in some parts of the world.

Súla leucogástra (Boddaert). Booby.

Other names: BROWN BOOBY; BOOBY GANNET.

Fig. 18.

DESCRIPTION. — *Adults* (*sexes alike*): Dark brown above; below white from base of neck backward; lining of wings dark brown and white, varying; axillars usually white; a grayish wash sometimes on breast and belly; head and neck of some individuals streaked brownish and white; bill and bare parts of head light colored or flesh-colored, bill varying to yellowish toward base; feet usually yellow; iris white. *Young:* Grayish-brown; lower breast and abdomen grayer; axillars lighter or whitish. *Downy young:* Born naked but soon clothed with white down.

MEASUREMENTS. — Length 28.00 to 31.00 in.; spread 50.00 or more; folded wing 14.50 to 16.50; tail 6.50 to 9.50; bill 3.25 to 4.00; tarsus 1.50 to 1.90.

MOLTS. — The molts of this species have not been carefully worked out; apparently the juvenal plumage is worn through the first winter and until the postnuptial molt of the second year, at which time the bird may assume adult plumage.

FIELD MARKS. — Easily known by small size and brown, unspotted upper plumage; adults show sharp contrast between dark neck and white breast.

VOICE. — Comparatively silent; when quarreling or alarmed utters hoarse, harsh screams.

BREEDING. — In large colonies; on islands in tropical seas. *Nest:* On ground; usually a slight lining of dry grass in a little hollow; rarely on bushes and made of sticks; sometimes no nest. *Eggs:* 2; 2.25 to 2.50 by 1.50 to 1.75 in.; chalky-white. *Dates:* January 14 to June 12, Bahamas. *Incubation:* Shared by both sexes; "sitting or brooding birds spend the night upon the nest, with their mate standing at their side" (Chapman). One brood yearly.

RANGE. — Atlantic coast of tropical America, and Pacific and Indian oceans. Breeds on Bahamas, some of West Indies and islands off coasts of Honduras, Costa Rica, Venezuela and Brazil and on St. Paul Rocks and Ascension Island in the tropical Atlantic; casual on south Atlantic and Gulf coasts of United States from South Carolina to Louisiana; accidental on Long Island and in Massachusetts (doubtfully); a rather irregular visitant to coast of United States.

DISTRIBUTION IN NEW ENGLAND. — Two records are the doubtful one recorded by Linsley at Guilford, Connecticut,[1] and the male estray from Cape Cod, recorded by Dr. T. M. Brewer in the Proceedings of the Boston Society of Natural History, Vol. XX, 1879, p. 277. This bird was found September 17, 1878, in the Boston market with some ducks from Cape Cod, by the Messrs. E. A. and Outram Bangs, and was supposed to have come from the same locality. But exact time and place, as well as name of gunner, are lacking in the record.

HAUNTS AND HABITS. The nearest breeding-place of the Booby is the Bahama Islands, and it is merely a casual visitant even to the coasts of Georgia and South Carolina. It gets its name from its apparently foolish habit of standing by its nest and defending its young. Therefore on its breeding-ground it can be killed with a club. Extermination will be its fate unless it is stringently protected on some of its breeding-grounds. It fishes like the gannet but does not fly so high. Often it sails along very low in the trough of the sea. Dr. Frank M. Chapman gives an excellent description of its nesting habits in "Camps and Cruises of an Ornithologist," pp. 210–217.

ECONOMIC STATUS. See page 153.

---

[1] American Journal of Science and Arts, Vol. XLIV, 1843, p. 271.

Courtesy of Dr. Frank M. Chapman

FIG. 18. — BOOBY

Male, female and young.   From Camps and Cruises of an Ornithologist

FIG. 19. — MAN-O'-WAR-BIRD
From a specimen in the Museum of Comparative Zoölogy

Móris bassána (LINNÆUS). Gannet.

Other names: WHITE GANNET; SOLAN OR SOLAND GOOSE.

Plate 10.

DESCRIPTION. — Bill longer than head, very stout at base, tapering but not hooked; wings very long; tail short and pointed. *Adults (sexes alike)*: White; head and hind neck washed with pale straw-yellow or cream color; primaries and spurious wing blackish; primary shafts white darkening toward tips; bill pale grayish, tinged with bluish or greenish; nasal groove, bare skin before eye and gular pouch blackish; mouth black (young as well as adults); legs and feet brownish-black; claws pale gray; iris white or very pale yellowish; a bright blue ring around eye; pale yellow of head varies in intensity with individuals — most intense in spring and summer, sometimes nearly wanting in winter. *Young in first winter plumage:* Dark brown above, including entire head and neck, feathers with small triangular white spots; below grayish-white, feathers with grayish-brown margins; flight-feathers and tail-feathers blackish, shafts of latter white; bill darker than in adult; feet dusky; iris pale brown, greenish or gray-ish; this dusky, spotted plumage gradually grows white, head, neck and under plumage changing first, while back still remains dark and more or less spotted; at 16 months of age a captive specimen had an unspotted dark back and white head and neck; at 22 months more white appeared on lesser wing coverts, back and scapulars; color of iris changes with age, through pale gray to purplish-gray at 12 months until at 24 months it whitens like that of adult; at 7 months ring about eye turns blue, but not so bright as in adult. *Downy young:* Newly hatched nestlings are black and almost bare, with mouth dark bluish-gray and a "sprinkling of powder-like down" (Gurney); twenty-four hours later more down begins to show, but a fortnight is required before it clothes the young bird with a thick white or pale yellowish coat.

MEASUREMENTS. — Length 33.00 to 40.50 in.; spread 72.00, more or less; folded wing 17.00 to 21.00; tail 9.00 to 10.00; bill 4.00 to 4.30; tarsus 2.00 to 2.25. Female smaller than male.

MOLTS. — "The prenuptial molt takes place in March, April and May, and the postnuptial molt in August and September" (Gurney). At least three years are required for the Gannet to attain its perfect plumage, and some individuals may take a longer time; European authorities differ on this, and estimates range from two years to six years; Gurney believes that the complete plumage is attained in two and one-half years, although "some individuals take three years." The Practical Handbook of British Birds describes progressive plumages up to the fourth winter.

FIELD MARKS. — Gannets when diving may be distinguished from gulls as far as the eye can see, for gulls do not habitually dive in the perpendicular manner of gannets; also the adult Gannet — a great white bird with black wing-tips — is unmistakable, while the equally unmistakable "shape" and habits will serve to identify the dark young or the pied immature bird.

VOICE. — The harsh call of the Gannet resembles the syllables "gor-r-r-rok" (Chapman); loud harsh cries of "carra-carra-carra" (Dixon); "karrack-kurruck" (A. C. Bent); there is also a softer note, "grog-grog."

BREEDING. — In large colonies; on precipitous sea-islands. *Nest:* Of seaweed chiefly (sticks also used in some cases), ranging from a bulky and well-made structure to practically no nest at all; usually on cliffs or summits. *Eggs:* 1; 3.00 to 3.30 by 1.80 to 2.10 in.; bluish-white overlaid with calcareous matter, more or less stained and soiled. *Dates:* May 5 to July 20, Bird Rock, Gulf of St. Lawrence. *Incubation:* Period 38 to 42 days, usually 42 days (Gurney), 39 days (Newton); by both sexes. One brood yearly.

RANGE. — Coasts of North Atlantic. Breeds on Bird Rock and Bonaventure Island in Gulf of St. Lawrence, on a rock off south coast of Newfoundland (near Cape St. Mary's), on an island off Hamilton Inlet, Labrador (54° 30′ N.), also on another island farther north, on various British islands and north to the Faroes and Iceland — in all not over a score of known breeding-places; winters from Virginia coast (irregular, rare to casual in winter to Maine) south to Gulf of Mexico, and on coasts of North

Africa, Madeira and Canaries; in migration off eastern United States coast; occasional in summer, off New England coast; casual north to Greenland, and in Indiana, Michigan and Ontario.

DISTRIBUTION IN NEW ENGLAND. — Common fall and spring migrant off coasts of Maine, New Hampshire, Massachusetts and Rhode Island; sometimes in summer; in winter off Massachusetts and (rarely) Connecticut coasts; accidental in interior.

SEASON IN MASSACHUSETTS. — March to June; September to December; commonest in fall; various summer dates; seen sometimes in winter off Cape Cod in mild seasons; said to be not rare in winter along south shore of Marthas Vineyard — "very common during onshore storms when they pass continually just out of gunshot feeding as they go and diving from considerable heights" (Allan Keniston, Vineyard Haven).

HAUNTS AND HABITS.   In fall and spring, rarely in summer, and sometimes in winter, great white birds with long, black-tipped wings may be seen fishing off our coasts.   They sail high over the sea, and at the right moment nearly close their pinions and shoot down like barbed arrow-heads into the waves with a resounding splash that sometimes tosses up spray eight or ten feet like a fountain.   To see such fishing is worth a trip to Cape Cod, Cape Ann or some other outlying point of the coast.   These birds are Gannets from the Gulf of St. Lawrence.   Captain Collins says that the height of their flight above the surface when they are fishing varies according to the depth at which the fish are swimming. By noting the elevation from which the Gannets plunge, expert fishermen can tell how deep to set their nets.   These birds often dive from a height of about one hundred feet, but a plunge of about 60 feet is more common.   Mr. W. Eagle Clarke says that in no case has he seen a Gannet drop more than 140 feet.[1]   The bird plunges from a height to get sufficient impetus to carry it to a considerable depth below the surface.   When the fish are near the surface, it sails close to the water and glides down diagonally upon them. But when small fish are at the surface, it sometimes rests on the water and pursues its prey on the waves, snatching them up with the bill.   We have little knowledge of the manner in which it chases its prey under water, but Mr. Booth says that his tame Gannets when diving used their wings beneath the surface after the manner of the guillemot.[2]

If a bird with wings as long as a Gannet's can use them to advantage under water, it seems probable that all birds that dive use their wings on occasion for propulsion beneath the surface.

No one knows how far down beneath the waves the Gannet pursues its prey.   Mr. William Thompson records in Charlesworth's Magazine of Natural History (1838, p. 19) that he learned from the postmaster of Ballantrae, a fishing village on the coast of Ayrshire, Scotland, that Gannets were commonly caught there in fishermen's nets which were set at depths of nine to twenty fathoms and sometimes at thirty fathoms (180 feet). Gould, in his "Birds of Great Britain" (Vol. V), tells the same story, which he had independently from some boatmen at Ballantrae.[3]   That a Gannet could force its way to a depth of 180 feet is, however, generally regarded by most naturalists as improbable.

---

[1] Studies in Bird Migration, Vol. I, 1918, pp. 302–303.   [2] Booth, E. T.: Rough Notes, 1883, pt. V, p. 14
[3] Gurney, J. H.: The Gannet, 1913, p. 409.

Gurney gives statements of competent witnesses to the effect that Gannets were taken at a depth of ninety feet.[1] Considering the buoyancy of a Gannet, increased as it is by great subcutaneous air cells, it would seem impossible for it to force itself down even ninety feet without using both wings and feet for propulsion. Certainly the impetus of its plunge would never carry it to such a depth.

The Gannet, it is said, cannot fish in a perfectly calm sea. Probably it is difficult, if not impossible, for so heavy a bird to rise from the water without help from the wind. Gannets have been washed ashore in numbers during a dead calm with a heavy swell running. The young leave the nest long before they are able to rise on the wing. They flutter or sail down from the cliff to the surface of the sea and there they remain until able to shift for themselves. Probably there is great mortality among them before the survivors gain full power of flight. They must keep at sea until they reach maturity as they do not appear on the breeding-grounds until in adult plumage.

From the deck of a coasting steamer in winter I have watched numbers of these great birds fishing far over the sea.   The feet are not used for steering in flight as in the short-tailed sea-birds like loons, grebes and auks but are carried under the tail. Gannets are active before a coming storm, and their snow-white forms contrasted against a murky sky as they sweep over the sea, now plunging, now rising again, always enliven the scene.

Both sexes of the Gannet participate in the "mating dance," which consists largely of bowing, with wings raised and partly open and tail raised and spread. This performance is described in detail by Dr. Charles W. Townsend in Bulletin 121 of the United States National Museum, prepared by Mr. A. C. Bent.

When the migratory fish begin their southward movement, the Gannets move with them and often between the middle of October and the 15th of December they may be seen in numbers by anyone walking on New England shores. Wherever fish on which the Gannets feed are abundant, there the birds may be found. They move southward slowly, following the fish. In January or February, in mild winters, some may be seen off Cape Cod, Block Island, Long Island, Nantucket and Marthas Vineyard, but usually they keep rather far from shore. From the latter part of March to early May, according to the season, they again become common on our coasts as they move slowly toward their homes in the Gulf of St. Lawrence.

Writing of the Gannets on Bird Rock in 1860, Bryant says: "The birds were feeding principally on herring but also on capelin filled with spawn, some fine looking mackerel, a few squids, and in one instance a codfish weighing at least two pounds." [2] Gurney, in his monograph of the Gannet (which see for a full account of this species) gives the following list of fishes eaten by this bird in European waters: Herring, Mackerel, Coal-fish, Pollock, Codling, Whiting, Haddock, Power Cod, Sand Eel, Salmon, Smelts, Sea Trout, Gurnards (any species), Garfish, Pilchard, Anchovy and Cuttlefish. He also mentions the Sild of Iceland and the Sardine of the Mediterranean. Gannets in captivity will eat

---

[1] Gurney, J. H.: The Gannet, 1913, pp. 410–411.
[2] Bryant, Henry: Proceedings of the Boston Society of Natural History, Vol. VIII, 1862, p. 69.

almost any fish and even fresh liver.　They have been known to catch and eat sparrows.[1]
Rev. J. H. Linsley in his "Birds of Connecticut" states that in the stomach of a Solan
Goose killed at Stratford, Connecticut, there was a bird "and in the stomach of the
latter was also a bird." [2]

ECONOMIC STATUS.　Though the Gannets have been accused of doing considerable
damage to the fishing interests, these harmful effects have been much overestimated
(P. A. Taverner).　No exhaustive study of the food of the Gannet and of its economic
status has been made.

FAMILY **PHALACROCORACIDÆ**.　CORMORANTS.

Number of species in North America 6 ;　in Massachusetts 2.

Cormorants are among the most powerful of swimming birds as the legs are short
and very strong and the feet large, strong and fully webbed.　There is an apophysis of
the tibia, shorter than in grebes, and a large free patella, both of which give extra points
of attachment for powerful swimming muscles that move the legs.　In under-water
progression cormorants use their large wings as well as their feet, in case of necessity,
and they dive to great depths.　The bill is almost as long as the head, stout or slim, with
upper mandible strongly hooked at the end.　Adults have no external nostrils but breathe
through the mouth.　The nostrils of the young close as they near maturity.　There is
a small naked gular pouch under the bill and naked skin about the eyes.　Unlike other
birds of this order the cormorant's legs are set far back on its body so that the bird is
forced to stand nearly erect or lie on its breast, thus resembling somewhat the Pygopodes
in structure and standing position.　The tail is strong and stiff, forming with the legs a
tripod for the support of the body when the bird is standing on earth or rock.　(In this
case, however, the tail is not always used.)　Cormorants are chiefly dark (although some
are white below) and densely feathered.

ECONOMIC STATUS.　Cormorants feed voraciously on fish, but their food and food
habits have not been fully investigated, and their economic status is not yet known.
The Chinese make use of cormorants by training the birds to catch fish.

Phalacrócorax cárbo (LINNÆUS).　**Cormorant.**

Other names: SHAG ; COMMON CORMORANT.

Plate 10.

DESCRIPTION. — Feathers of throat run up to a point in center almost reaching bill and so dividing
bare skin of throat-pouch as to make its posterior outline heart-shaped ; tail of 14 feathers.　*Adults in
nuptial plumage (sexes alike)* : Glossy greenish or bluish-black ; most of upper back, scapulars and wing-
coverts bronze-gray, feathers with glossy black edging ; flight-feathers and tail grayish-black ; conspicuous yellow pouch beneath bill bordered behind by broad encircling patch of white feathers ; large white
patch on flank ; numerous long, white, linear, filamentous feathers scattered on head and neck ; black

---

[1] Gurney, J. H.: The Gannet, 1913, pp. 386–393.　　[2] American Journal of Science and Arts, Vol. XLIV, 1843, p. 271.

feathers on hind head and hind neck elongated into slight crest; bill dusky, yellowish-white along edges and yellow at base of lower mandible; iris green; skin about eye dull greenish, beneath eye orange; legs and feet blackish; white patches on flanks sometimes begin to appear in January and disappear in July. *Adults in winter plumage:* Similar, but no crest and no white feathers on head and neck or on flanks; white of flanks well developed sometimes by March. *Third year (May):* Similar to adult but color of upper plumage less brilliant and under plumage not so rich glossy black; birds of this age (probably about 26 months old), do not breed but assume a partial breeding plumage; white, hair-like feathers on head and neck indicated, and white flank-patches partially acquired. *2nd year (September):* Upper plumage like that of adult but less brilliant and mixed here and there with feathers of first plumage; white feathers of breast and belly widely tipped brownish-black, presenting a mottled appearance. *Young in first plumage (September):* General color above dull brown, somewhat glossed on head, neck and back with bluish-green; feathers of back, scapulars and wing-coverts with wide dark margins; throat, front of neck, breast and belly white; sides, flanks, thighs and under tail-coverts dark brownish-black; as age advances, front of neck and chest become brown.[1] *Downy young:* Blackish although hatched naked with livid-slatish skin; feet dusky; legs yellowish-brownish; throat-pouch and mouth inside, flesh color.

MEASUREMENTS. — Length 34.00 to 40.00 in.; spread 60.00 to 62.00; folded wing 12.00 to 15.00; tail 6.00 to 7.75; bill 2.60 to 3.10; tarsus 2.25 to 2.50. Female a little smaller than male.

MOLTS. — The molting of the Cormorant seems not to have been fully worked out; Ogilvie-Grant says that among the birds of one or two years old, molt appears to be continuous throughout greater part of a year; immature birds probably assume adult nuptial plumage after prenuptial molt in spring of 4th year when about 3 years old; adults undergo a partial prenuptial molt in spring (beginning in February or March) and a complete postnuptial molt (July to November); the white neck-feathers are molted in May and June or July.

FIELD MARKS. — Size of a small goose; usually swims with bill pointed upward; distinguished from goose or loon in winter by much longer tail and darker coloration; difficult to distinguish *carbo* from *auritus* at a distance unless the two species are seen together, when *carbo* is known by greater size; white throat of adult *carbo* usually conspicuous and in spring white patch on flank may be seen; young *carbo* usually has belly much whiter than duller immature *auritus;* this may be noted when birds are sitting but not when they are on water except as one rises to flap its wings.

VOICE. — "A harsh croak" (C. W. Townsend); a *craw* reiterated, hoarse.

BREEDING. — In colonies; usually on precipitous sea-islands. *Nest:* Of sticks and seaweed; generally on shelves or in crevices of cliffs near sea; rarely in trees. *Eggs:* 4 to 6; 2.40 to 2.60 by 1.47 to 1.75 in.; bluish-green or bluish-white, with a chalky deposit. *Dates:* June 1–30, Labrador. *Incubation:* Period 28 or 29 days (Evans); by both sexes.

RANGE. — Northern Hemisphere. Breeds from central Greenland south to Nova Scotia, formerly Grand Manan and (probably) Maine; now rare or absent over much of its former range in North America; breeds also in Iceland, Scandinavia, North Russia and the British Isles; (European continental birds now regarded as subspecifically distinct); winters from southern Greenland south to Long Island, casually to Lake Ontario and South Carolina, and from the Mediterranean south to Canary Islands; a regular fall transient in small numbers off shores of Long Island.

DISTRIBUTION IN NEW ENGLAND. — *Maine:* Uncommon migrant and winter resident; *Vermont:* Rare migrant; *Massachusetts:* Uncommon migrant and winter resident coastwise; *Rhode Island:* Uncommon migrant and winter resident; *Connecticut:* Rare migrant and winter visitor coastwise.

SEASON IN MASSACHUSETTS. — (September 22); November to April; (May 14).

HAUNTS AND HABITS. If in the dead of winter one sees off our coast a large, dark bird flapping slowly along close to the water with outstretched neck and alighting on a

[1] Ogilvie-Grant, W. R.: Catalogue of the Birds in the British Museum, Vol. XXVI, 1898, p. 346.

spindle or a ledge where it stands nearly upright, probably that bird is the Cormorant. Once it was the "Common Cormorant." It is the common Cormorant of Europe and was common here also in winter long ago.　Today it is rather rarely seen as it has been nearly extirpated from its Canadian breeding-grounds; and as it is a hardy bird, it is probable that those breeding in Arctic regions rarely reach the latitude of Massachusetts. A cormorant seen in spring or autumn is much more likely to belong to the next species. The Cormorant may be looked for in late autumn, winter or very early spring on outlying ledges such as the Salvages off Rockport, and the Cormorant Rocks off Newport, Rhode Island; but often it may be looked for in vain.　Cormorants usually assemble in small numbers toward night to roost on such ledges.　There are several such islets of sea-washed rocks off the Maine coast where these birds formerly gathered in numbers, and where between October and May some still may be found.

The habits and food of the Cormorant are similar to those of the next species.

ECONOMIC STATUS.　See page 158.

Phalacrocorax aurítus auritus (Lesson).　Double-crested Cormorant.

Other names: SHAG; TAUNTON TURKEY.

Plate 10.

DESCRIPTION. — Hinder edge of throat-pouch nearly straight; *tail of 12 feathers;* tufts of elongated, narrow, curved feathers on head probably shed during nesting, as seldom seen after breeding season. *Adults in nuptial plumage (sexes alike)*: Glossy greenish-black; upper back, scapulars and wing-coverts bronzy-gray, feathers with glossy black margins and black shafts; flight-feathers and tail black; two lateral tufts of curly, black feathers on top of head, behind eye (double-crest); few (if any) white filamentous feathers over eye; bill dusky with yellowish markings; iris green; lores and throat-pouch orange; intense bluish-green dottings around eye; eyelids and mouth blue; feet black. *Adults in winter:* Similar, but no crests; eyelids dull; bill yellow, dusky along ridge; throat-pouch red in front, yellow-ochre behind. *Young in first winter plumage:* Top of head and adjoining hind neck brown; back, scapulars and wing-coverts dull, grayish-brown; feathers with brownish-black margins; rump black; sides of head and fore neck grayish; breast whitish darkening to blackish on belly; throat-pouch and base of bill yellowish; some young much whiter on fore neck and breast than others. *Downy young:* Dark brown or black, but hatched naked, black and shiny; down assumed in a few days.

MEASUREMENTS. — Length 29.00 to 35.00 in.; spread 50.00 to 53.00; folded wing 12.00 to 13.00; tail 6.00 to 7.00; bill 2.06 to 2.55; tarsus 2.25 to 2.55.　Female rather smaller than male.

MOLTS. — First winter plumage is completed in September, having gradually succeeded natal down, and is worn through winter with little change; molting begins in some cases in February but mostly not until late spring or summer; postnuptial molt begins probably in summer followed by second winter plumage, often not completed until late in winter when bird resembles adult but lacks double crest; molt and change have been almost constant until now the bird is ready to breed; adults have in late summer a complete postnuptial molt and in *early* spring a partial prenuptial molt followed by nuptial plumes or crests on sides of head (A. C. Bent).

FIELD MARKS. — Longer than any duck or brant; adult Double-crested Cormorant never has a white patch on throat like the common Cormorant, and its young has a light gray breast shading to black on lower belly while young of latter has a nearly white lower breast and belly; a cormorant on the water looks somewhat like a loon, but the adult is dark below (where loons are white) as well as above; does not fly like a loon but flaps like a heron; often alternates its flapping with brief sailing; its long tail and neck are then quite distinctive; a large, dark bird flying singly or in flocks of varying size — to quote Dr. Townsend (Birds of Essex County) — "in single file, in a perfect V, or in an irregular bunch"; when perched, the cormorant's shape — figure upright, neck long and slightly curved and tail used as a prop — is unmistakable; when sitting in "spread-eagle" style, with wings held out as if to dry, it may be recognized as far as the eye can see; on wing the dark cormorants have a general resemblance to geese or large ducks.

VOICE. — "Except for an occasional hoarse grunting croak when alarmed, I have never heard the Double-crested Cormorant make any vocal sound whatever and believe it is usually silent" (A. C. Bent).

BREEDING. — In colonies; chiefly on rocky sea-islands or on islands in lakes in the interior; sometimes in woods. *Nest:* Of sticks and weed-stalks or sticks and seaweed; sometimes large and well built; on ledges of cliffs, on ground or in trees or bushes. *Eggs:* 2 to 5; (many sets of 5 and 6 and several of 7 at Lake Winnipeg); 2.25 to 2.52 by 1.35 to 1.59 in.; greenish-blue overlaid with a chalky deposit. *Dates:* May 26 to June 19, Labrador; July 2, Maine coast; May 7, southeastern Minnesota; May 12 to July 11, North Dakota and Minnesota.

RANGE. — North America east of Rocky Mountains. Breeds from central Mackenzie (Great Slave Lake), south central Alberta, central Saskatchewan, southern Manitoba, James Bay, northeastern Quebec, Labrador and Newfoundland south to northern Utah (records here may mean *albociliatus* or two forms may intergrade), central northern Wyoming, South Dakota, southern Minnesota, central Illinois, northeastern Arkansas, west central Ohio (formerly?) and Penobscot Bay, Maine; casual in summer on Long Island; winters from New Jersey (casually north to Maine) south to Gulf coast; casual in Bermuda. (There is a southern subspecies *floridanus* and two western subspecies — *cincinnatus* and *albociliatus.*)

DISTRIBUTION IN NEW ENGLAND. — Common fall and spring migrant coastwise; rare or casual in interior or in midsummer; along Maine coast most numerous in fall and spring, but during summer individuals in numbers may be seen east of Rockland and a less number west of this point; a few have bred on Black Horse Ledge near Isle au Haut — the southernmost known breeding-place on Atlantic coast and the only known breeding-place in Maine; flocks of cormorants northward bound have been seen late in May in Long Island Sound off the Connecticut shore; there is a New Hampshire midsummer record — bird shot July 10, 1891, at Kingston.

SEASON IN MASSACHUSETTS. — April 4 to June 18; casual in summer; August 22 to November 24.

HAUNTS AND HABITS. The Double-crested Cormorant is now (1923) the only common cormorant of the New England seaboard. In spring, late summer or autumn long flocks of dark birds larger than Black Ducks may be seen almost anywhere along the New England coast, flying "in single file" close to the water with slow-flapping wings and outstretched necks. When seen passing diagonally at a distance close to the waves, the long wings of each seem to overlap those of the next in line, all rising and falling very nearly together. Often in the shimmering summer haze, which operates to deceive the eye, this spectacle will almost delude the credulous into the belief that they have seen the folds of a sea serpent rolling along the waves.

Now and then one of these birds may be seen sitting erect on a spar-buoy; and the inexperienced young sometimes are tame enough to alight on a spile near some wharf or bridge unconcerned by passing vehicles or people. Usually when a cormorant flies off from such a perch above the water, it descends nearly or quite to the surface before it gathers headway. From this habit has arisen the southern superstition that the "shag must wet its tail before it can fly." When resting on the water this bird somewhat resembles a loon, but unlike the loon it has no pure white fore neck and breast. The cormorant's tail is longer than that of a loon and the bird has a hooked bill. This cormorant is a remarkably expert swimmer and diver, and often uses its wings as well as its broad paddles in the pursuit of swift fish in the depths. I have never seen the submarine activities of this species in its natural environment, but Dr. Hatch who had abundant opportunity to watch the bird in its breeding-grounds in the clear lakes of Minnesota says: "Being principally fish eaters they spend most of the time in the water where their movements in pursuit of their prey are simply marvellous in velocity. With their totipalmated feet folded flatly into mere blades while carried forward and when struck out backwards opening to their utmost and the half-spread wings beating with inconceivable rapidity, they seem to fly through the waters at various depths in pursuit of their favorite food, the fish." [1]

That eminent ornithologist and close observer, Dr. Coues, says of the whole cormorant family: "They also, like the birds just mentioned (Pygopodes), dive and swim under water in pursuit of their prey, using their wings for submarine progression." [2]

I have published evidence from several well-known ornithologists who have seen these birds use their wings in subsurface progression and have more of such evidence not yet published. Doubtless both wings and feet are used for propulsion in deep diving or when in pursuit of swift prey; but where the bird is not hurried as when searching for food among rocks or in artificial tanks, the feet only are so used. [3]

It is thought that cormorants build (in part at least) their nests with seaweed that they obtain by diving. A statement by Dr. Charles W. Townsend in his "In Audubon's Labrador" (p. 113) lends color to this belief. Referring to a trading-schooner which was sunk off the Labrador coast, he says: "This summer, when some fishermen visited a cormorant island near by, they found that the birds had decorated their nests with pocket-knives, pipes, hairpins and ladies' combs — objects which they had obtained by diving to the wreck."

When Double-crested Cormorants have a good breeding season in the North, they sweep past the New England coast in great numbers in the autumnal flight. At times large flocks may be seen flying high overland. This was the case in the autumns of 1905 and 1921. The flight of 1921 was the greatest that I have ever seen. The birds began to come in late August and by early September there were days when many flocks were flying. There were enormous numbers in September and October, and the flight continued until winter set in. In migration these birds fly high, sometimes in very long lines and often in the "V" formation like Canada Geese, the "V" at times being very short on one side and long on the other. Sometimes such flocks are mistaken for geese but their dark color, longer tails, smaller size and silence in flight, while geese are vociferous,

---

[1] Hatch, P. L.: Notes on the Birds of Minnesota, 1892, p. 28.
[2] Coues, Elliott: Key to North American Birds, Vol. II, 1903, p. 960.
[3] Massachusetts Department of Agriculture, Bulletin No. 8, 1922, pp. 25–29.

should differentiate them at once. In the return flight numbers usually appear coastwise between the middle of April and the middle of May.

Mr. George A. Tapley of Revere shot in winter one of three cormorants which were eating a sculpin. Mr. George H. Mackay took in April, 1892, five of these birds at Cormorant Rock off Newport, Rhode Island. All of them had eaten small eels. On the flat top of the rock he saw a large number of curious balls which appeared to have been ejected by the cormorants. He collected fourteen of these balls which were composed almost entirely of fish bones, "chiefly those of young parrot-fishes (*Labroids*) and drums (*Sciænoids*) firmly cemented together with gluten." One of the largest of these balls was 5.25 inches in circumference and "contained three crabs."

ECONOMIC STATUS. "The danger of jumping at conclusions based upon superficial observation or common report was well illustrated by the outcome of a study of the food of these birds in the neighborhood of the Gaspé salmon rivers. Though commonly accused of damaging the salmon fisheries by devouring the small fish and fry, careful examination of about thirty specimens showed that the hundreds of birds present were eating fish of no economic value and no salmonoid remains were found in them. Probably the eels, sculpins and other fish taken by the Cormorant make the species beneficial rather than harmful to the salmon, and probably more than compensate for the few valuable fish that it occasionally takes. This is a good example of the caution that is necessary before condemning any species of birds." [1]

FAMILY **PELECANIDÆ**. PELICANS.

Number of species in North America 3 ; in Massachusetts 2.

Pelicans are large, long-necked birds, with long, large, straight bills, rather broad at base and toward the end, sharp-edged, with the upper mandible strongly hooked at the tip. They have very long wings, short broad tails, short, stout legs and large, fully webbed feet. Below the lower mandible and connected with the throat is a large, naked gular pouch capable of much expansion. The stomachs of pelicans are comparatively small. They feed mainly on small fish and the pouch is believed to be used as a dip-net and as a receptacle for storing or retaining an oversupply of fish until appetite prompts their consumption. Pelicans, like gannets, have layers of air-cells between the body and the skin of the breast and abdomen. Pelicans are gregarious birds and breed in large colonies.

ECONOMIC STATUS. Pelicans are commonly regarded as harmful because they eat fish, but such investigations of their food habits as have been made indicate that they are not injurious to the food-fisheries. Their bodies, eggs and feathers have furnished material of considerable economic value in times past.

---

[1] Taverner, P. A.: Memoir 104, Canada Department of Mines, Geological Survey, Birds of Eastern Canada, 1919, pp. 61, 62.

Pelecánus erythrorhýnchos Gmelin. White Pelican.

Fig. 20.

DESCRIPTION. — Tail of 24 feathers; wings very long. *Adults in nuptial plumage (sexes alike)*: General plumage white; primaries, primary coverts, spurious wing and many of secondaries black; shafts of quill-feathers white, darkening toward tips; feathers of hind head (a crest), breast and some of lesser wing-coverts, lengthened and pale yellow (hind head sometimes white); center of scapulars and tail-feathers salmon, this coloring very transient and varying in intensity with the individual; bill and pouch mostly reddish (lower mandible redder than upper and pouch paling terminally from red at base through orange and yellow); iris white, whitish or light bluish-gray (brown or dusky at times); eyelids red; bare skin about eye orange; feet intense orange-red; bill with horny elevation on terminal half; following the nuptial season (soon or late) horny appendage and crest are shed; hindhead has now a patch of soft, gray feathers which in their turn are lost, following (or at close of) breeding season; many breeding birds (possibly not fully mature) show no yellow on head but gray in its place throughout the breeding season. *Adults in winter plumage:* Similar, but hind head white; paler yellowish on breast and lesser wing-coverts; much less vivid color on face, bill, pouch and feet, all being yellow; iris brown. *Young in first winter plumage:* White; bill, face, pouch and feet pale yellowish; iris brown or dusky. *Downy young:* White; down soon appears on chicks, which are ruddy and practically naked when hatched, and clothes them completely in a few weeks' time.

MEASUREMENTS. — Length 54.00 to 70.00 in.; spread 8 ft. to almost 10 ft.; folded wing 20.00 to 25.25 in.; tail 6.00 to 7.10; bill 11.05 to 15.00; tarsus 4.50 to 4.75.

MOLTS. — First winter plumage, succeeding down, is acquired in autumn and resembles that of adult; in spring young birds do not have special adornments of nuptial season; heads and breasts are pure white and feet and bill duller colored than those of adults; at first postnuptial molt young become almost indistinguishable from adults but probably do not reach full maturity until 3d or 4th year; adults have incomplete prenuptial molt and complete (or nearly complete) postnuptial molt.

FIELD MARKS. — Size, shape and color of White Pelican make bird unmistakable; it is conspicuous at a great distance.

VOICE. — "A deep-voiced, not loud, murmuring groan" (F. M. Chapman).

BREEDING. — In colonies; on islands in lakes of interior. *Nest:* On ground; of sticks, reeds and grass, or mere depression in slight heap of sand or pebbles; eggs sometimes laid on beds of reeds with small attempt (or none) at nest-building. *Eggs:* 2 to 4; 3.15 to 3.45 by 2.20 to 2.30 in.; white, chalky, more or less stained and soiled. *Dates:* May 1 to June 25, Utah and Nevada. *Incubation:* Period "29 or 30 days" (Burns).

RANGE. — North America. Breeds from central British Columbia, and Great Slave Lake south to southern Manitoba, central North Dakota, northwestern Wyoming, northern Utah, western Nevada, southern Oregon and California; formerly to Wisconsin, Minnesota, South Dakota and Colorado; an outlying colony lies south of Corpus Christi, Texas; the White Pelican nested in 1904 40 miles north of Aitken, Minnesota, but there is no record of the species ever having bred east of the Mississippi; winters from southern California, southwestern Arizona, the Gulf States, Florida and Cuba south through the Antilles and on both coasts of Mexico and Central America, as well as in the interior, to Panama; casual east in migration to Atlantic coast, north to New Brunswick; has wandered in migration to nearly every Canadian Province and nearly every one of the United States; one was taken in June or July, 1900, by an Eskimo at Liverpool Bay on the shore of the Arctic Ocean, in Lat. 70° Long. 128°.[1]

DISTRIBUTION IN NEW ENGLAND. — Very rare or accidental straggler. Records: *Maine:* One shot May 28, 1892, on Passadumkeag Stream near Saponic Lake, Penobscot County; two seen during a heavy storm, June 8, 1897, at Eliot;[2] there is in the mounted collection of the Boston Society of Natural History

---

[1] Fleming, J. H.: Auk, Vol. XXIII, 1906, p. 218.   [2] Knight, O. W.: Birds of Maine, 1908, p. 75.

From Bird-Lore, Courtesy of Dr. F. M. Chapman

FIG. 20. — WHITE PELICAN

Photograph taken at Pelican Island, Florida, by Harry G. Higbee

FIG. 21. — BROWN PELICAN

Ceremony of changing places on the nest

a White Pelican in breeding plumage with "centerboard." It came from Matinicus Light and was shot by Francis Dana. The date of its accession is December, 1913, but other details are lacking. (There are one or two other more or less doubtful Maine records, as one seen at Calais (Geo. A. Boardman). *Massachusetts:* Adult male shot October 5, 1876, by Mr. George Pratt at North Scituate;[1] one taken in 1886 at Gloucester;[2] male in full nuptial plumage, with well-developed "center-board," found dead May 13, 1905, in beach-grass not far back from water's edge at Sandwich.[3]

HAUNTS AND HABITS. The White Pelican is a majestic bird. Awkward and grotesque though it be in captivity, it is, nevertheless, a master of the air and its aërial evolutions at great heights exhibit a power and dignity which can be equaled only by the eagle.

The Pelican is a curious survivor of an age that is gone. Dr. Frank M. Chapman well says: "We must accord to pelicans that respectful attention which is the due of extreme age. Pelicans became pelicans long before man became man." A study of the distribution of the eleven existing species leads to the conclusion that as late at least as the latter part of the Tertiary Period, our White Pelican presented much the same appearance that it does today.

In former days when Pelicans were abundant in North America, when the early settlers reported flocks on the Hudson River, there may have been many stragglers in New England; but now the White Pelican is a vanishing race and a mere accidental visitant to our section. In the spring of 1878 in Florida, I saw great flocks of these gigantic birds. When seen in the distance and magnified by the mirage, they presented the appearance of fleets of stately ships under sail on the calm lagoons. I never saw these birds, like the Brown Pelican, plunge from a height or dive for their food. On the coast they sat on the sands at low water, and as the tide flowed in, they sailed calmly and majestically out over the shallows, formed long lines at a distance from the shore and parallel to it, and then beating the water with their great wings, closed in toward the beach, driving before them the little fish, which they scooped up in their capacious pouches. Then after sitting sluggishly for a time the great white birds, with heads drawn backward on their shoulders, rose into the air in flocks and sailed grandly, sweeping in wide circles up into the blue dome, rising to enormous heights and floating there for long periods apparently to enjoy the cooling breezes of those high altitudes. In 1878 White Pelicans might be seen almost anywhere along the east coast of Florida. Now some birds perhaps may still be found about the Mosquito Lagoon near the Government Reservation, but the species is slowly disappearing. Some of its great feeding-grounds in the northwestern states have been drained; from others it has been driven away; and there seems little hope that the species can be saved to North America unless a number of its principal breeding-places can be made bird reservations and guarded for all time. The best opportunity for protection now is in the Canadian Northwest where Pelicans breed on some of the islands in large lakes. Dr. Chapman has immortalized the White Pelican in the account that he

[1] S. K., Jr.: Forest and Stream, Vol. VII, 1876–77, p. 186, and Howe and Allen, Birds of Massachusetts, 1901, p. 60.
[2] Allen, G. M.: Fauna of New England: The Aves, 1909, p. 28.
[3] Brewster, Wm.: Auk, Vol. XXVI, 1909, p. 185.

gives of his visits to several of its colonies, and by the excellent photographs that he took of young and old.[1]

Mr. William L. Finley secured a fine set of moving pictures of the Klamath Lake Colony in Oregon before the lake was ruined by a drainage project. Because of the enterprise of these two naturalists, future generations may have their only opportunity to realize how these wonderful birds appeared in life when they bred abundantly in the United States.

In March, April and May the White Pelicans move northward to their breeding-grounds; and in September, October and November they wing their way slowly southward to their winter homes. It is during these migrations that rare stragglers reach New England.

Mr. John F. Ferry states that inside the pouches of both old and young pelicans in a colony in Saskatchewan were clusters of parasites — "beetle-like insects with bodies striped with black and white." He further notes that some of the young pelicans disgorged from their pouches masses of salamanders (*necturus maculatus*); also occasionally a "jock-fish" and some brook sticklebacks (*Eucolia inconstans*).[2] Dr. P. L. Hatch says that whether the Pelican takes a minnow or a pickerel weighing three and a half pounds, the fish is grasped transversely, tossed in the air and received head first into the pouch.[3]

ECONOMIC STATUS. No exhaustive examination of the food of the White Pelican has been made. The species being accidental in New England is of no economic consequence here.

Pelecanus occidentális LINNÆUS. Brown Pelican.

Other names: COMMON PELICAN; AMERICAN BROWN PELICAN.

Fig. 21.

DESCRIPTION. — Tail of 22 feathers. *Adults in nuptial plumage (sexes alike)*: Head chiefly white with yellow tinge on top, white extending down neck and coming to a point on either side below pouch; rest of neck and hind head dark chestnut-brown, often lightening on hind neck; a small crest on nape; bristly feathers on forehead; rest of upper plumage dusky-brown or ashy-gray, many of smaller feathers with pale centers, the paler gray prevailing on wing-coverts; primaries black with white shafts blackening toward tips; secondaries dark, pale-edged; tail silvery-gray; below dark grayish-brown, with narrow white streaks on sides, flanks, axillars, wing-linings and under tail-coverts; lower fore neck chestnut, yellow and blackish; feathers here and of breast lengthened and narrow; bill with light and dark mottling, in places tinged carmine; iris white; eyelids red; bare skin around eye bluish; pouch dusky; feet slaty-black. *Adults in winter plumage (after breeding season)*: Similar, but hind head and neck white, with more or less yellowish mainly on head and lower fore neck; iris brown; colors of bill and soft parts vary with age or other condition. *Young in first winter plumage*: Much duller than adult; head mainly dark brown or brownish; elsewhere above brownish-gray, feathers with paler edges and tips; neck plain brownish; below white, gray-tinged on sides. *Downy young*: White; down appears in about 12 days on

[1] Chapman, Frank M.: Camps and Cruises of an Ornithologist, 1908, pp. 367–388. See also Sennett, George B.: Auk, Vol. XL, 1923, p. 629.

[2] Ferry, John F.: Auk, Vol. XXVII, 1910, p. 190.

[3] Hatch, P. L.: Notes on the Birds of Minnesota, 1892, p. 31.

young bird which has hatched black and bare, and in about a week clothes it completely; brownish flight-plumage which appears first on wings is complete when chick is about 10 weeks old — *i.e.*, at flying period.

MEASUREMENTS. — Length 44.50 to 54.00 in.; spread 74.50 to 84.00; folded wing 18.50 to 21.00; tail 5.50 to 7.00; bill 9.40 to 12.50; throat-pouch extends about 1 ft., more or less, along neck; tarsus 2.50 to 3.00; middle toe and claw 4.50.

MOLTS. — Complete molt ("first postnuptial") follows first-year plumage which probably has been worn for about a year; in second winter silver-gray feathers of adult above show in part; head and neck are similar to adult but with dusky mottling; brownish under plumage has still more or less white of immature; next dress, following partial molt of winter and spring, has under plumage still browner and head whiter while dark brown begins to appear on hind neck; following next complete molt (second post-nuptial) adult winter plumage apparently is assumed; adult's partial molt in late winter and early spring is followed by nuptial plumage while a complete postnuptial molt is succeeded by winter plumage; probably highest plumage, with yellow crown and breast-patch, is not assumed until bird is three years old or more.

FIELD MARKS. — Size of a large goose; long bill carried down front of neck; may be distinguished from White Pelican by its dark color and smaller size.

VOICE. — "The voice at first a choking bark passes through a rasping k-r-r-ring stage to a high piercing scream in the down-covered bird to a dignified groan in the bird in flight-plumage . . . the high scream is largely a feeding-note which the fledged young utter at least as long as they receive food from the parent" (F. M. Chapman); young Pelicans are very noisy but the adult is practically a silent bird.

BREEDING. — In colonies; usually on island in lake or lagoon; frequently in mangrove growth. *Nest:* In bushes or on ground; in latter case, of grasses almost wholly; in former, of sticks and grass. *Eggs:* 2 or 3; 2.80 to 3.10 by 1.80 to 2.15 in.; white and chalky. *Dates:* Pelican Island, Florida, December; Gulf coast, Florida, April 4; Louisiana coast, February; South Carolina, May 8 to 23, and extends even to August; November 5 (first eggs), Florida, in exceptional year of 1907–08; season begins December 1 practically, although some Pelicans on east coast of Florida begin laying in November; dates of incubation periods on east and west coasts of Florida differ widely; sometimes a few hundred Pelicans lay late in April on Pelican Island; whether this is a second brood is not known; egg dates ordinarily vary from December 1 to July 1. *Incubation:* Period about 4 weeks; by both sexes.

RANGE. — Atlantic coast of America, from South Atlantic and Gulf coasts of United States to coasts of Central and South America. Breeds in United States from South Carolina and Louisiana to southern Texas; probably breeds in Greater Antilles; said to breed in Bahamas, and on South American coast as far south as Brazil; regular in small numbers off North Carolina coast; has been observed in Virginia; accidental in Bermuda, Colorado, Wyoming, Nebraska, Michigan, Iowa, Illinois, Indiana, New York, New Jersey, New England, Ontario and Nova Scotia.

DISTRIBUTION IN NEW ENGLAND. — Accidental. Records: *New Hampshire:* Immature bird shot May 1, 1907, off Great Boar's Head, Hampton Beach.[1] *Massachusetts:* Bird shot out of flock during a heavy storm in 1867 by Mr. C. S. Martin near Brant Point lighthouse, Nantucket; two birds seen about the same time at Ipswich.[2] (The Ipswich record is in C. J. Maynard's "Naturalist's Guide," 1870 (Rev. ed. 1883, p. 149) viz.: "Mr. J. F. LeBaron is confident of having seen two of this species at Ipswich some years ago."); four seen June 7, 1922, at Ipswich Beach by C. J. Maynard. *Rhode Island:* Bird taken April 17, 1921, at Block Island.[3] *Connecticut:* Bird caught alive, June 6, 1902, off Guilford Harbor, by Mr. Levi Thrall.[4]

HAUNTS AND HABITS. In appearance Brown Pelicans are strange, weird creatures. Such peculiar birds have a great educational value. They seem like relics of a hoary past, alone in a modern world. They remind us of the flying reptiles of early ages, and

---

[1] Allen, G. M.: Auk, Vol. XXX, 1913, p. 22.
[3] Dickens, Miss Elizabeth: *in litt.*
[2] Allen, J. A.: American Naturalist, Vol. III, 1870, p. 640.
[4] Sage, Bishop and Bliss: The Birds of Connecticut, 1913, p. 28.

should be preserved to perpetuate their curious forms and habits for the benefit of future generations of mankind.   But it is only by dint of the strictest protection that they can exist side by side with modern civilization.

The Brown Pelican is a mere straggler in New England.   In the hot summer months following the breeding season some Pelicans wander northward.   They are not now known to breed north of South Carolina, but many appear in summer in North Carolina and occasionally some are seen farther north.   Thus one now and then may casually reach New England.   Brown Pelicans would be seldom seen by New England people were it not that many of our citizens pass the winter in Florida where some of the breeding grounds of this species have been guarded through the good offices of the National Association of Audubon Societies and the United States Biological Survey.   Dr. Frank M. Chapman tells us in his "Camps and Cruises of an Ornithologist" that when Pelican Island in Indian River, Florida, was first set aside as a Government Bird Reservation, the warden erected a great sign on the island which warned visitors not to land without permission.   This was in 1904.   Immediately the birds forsook the island and bred elsewhere that year.   The next year the sign was taken down and the birds came back.

But a second time the Pelicans left their Island where they had been recorded, with but one absence, for 65 years.   Disturbed, doubtless, by the new houses built on the nearby beach-ridge that divides Indian River from the ocean, they (many of them at least) went over 50 miles north, to an island in Mosquito Lagoon, on this same east coast of Florida.   Here they met shocking treatment.   Their new rookery was promptly raided (1924) by *human beings*, and at least 80 per cent of the young birds were killed (mostly clubbed to death), adding, to quote from Bird-Lore's editorial, "another black chapter to the history of bird-destruction in Florida."   (See Bird-Lore, Vol. XXVI, 1924, p. 207.)

Many years ago our camping-party landed by moonlight on Pelican Island.   The birds rose with a great uproar but one failed to awake, and my friend, the late C. K. Reed, walked up to the "sleeping beauty" and grasped it by the bill.   To all appearances he had captured a live traveling windmill that was bound to escape.   The antics performed by that bird and that man in the "mix-up" that followed were so ludicrous that the rest of the party became helpless with uncontrollable merriment.

In Florida Pelicans fish largely in the sea and in lagoons near the coast.   Often a long line of the great birds, each with a wing-expansion of more than six feet, may be seen flapping along over the waves of the incoming tide, flying parallel with the shore as they pass on the way to their fishing grounds.   With stiffened wings the leader sails low over the heaving sea, flaps a few strokes to get greater speed, and then sails again.   One bird after another in regular succession follows his example, sailing with wings widespread and heads drawn proudly back, the line falling and rising over the waves and just clearing their summits.   Usually in fishing the Pelicans scatter and fly from twenty to thirty feet above the surface.   When a Pelican sees a fish to its liking, it falls into the water with a splash like a barrel tossed from a ship's deck. The pneumatic cushion on its breast no doubt deadens the shock, but it also adds to the buoyancy of the bird which thus requires a great momentum to carry it well below the surface. The motions of the bird seem clumsy in the extreme. I saw one plunge, turn slightly in the air, catch its bill in the water and, tripping itself awkwardly, turn a complete somersault, but it landed right side up, and when the commotion had subsided, it had the fish.

The Ancients had a high opinion of the maternal qualities of the Pelican. One of the old chroniclers spake thus (freely translated): "The Pelican is the lovingest bird that is, for she feedeth her young on her heart's blood." This refers to the well-known habit of the young — that of reaching down the mother's throat for its food. Dr. Chapman explains that sometimes a Pelican's pouch is lacerated by the spines of fish and bleeds internally; and in such a case the young bird might well appear to partake of the blood of the devoted parent. He thus describes the feeding scene:

"With the utmost ease the croaking, wobbly little creature helped itself to the predigested fish, which, regurgitated by the parent into the front end of its pouch, was brought within reach of its offspring. This method is followed until at the age of about three weeks the young are covered with down, when, evidently requiring a larger supply of food than their parents can prepare for them, and no longer needing predigested nourishment, they extend their feeding excursions into the throat of the patient parent, finding there entire fish, which in some inexplicable manner they generally swallow before withdrawing their head. Two and even three young will thus actively pursue their search for food at the same time, and only their extended and fluttering wings seem to keep them from disappearing in the depths of the cavernous parental pouch. Not for a moment do they stop their high-voiced squealing, and the rise and fall of their partly muffled screams indicate the nature of their success in getting food. Occasionally the poor judgment of the parent allied to the greed of the young, leads the latter to attempt to swallow too large a fish, when the old bird saves its young from choking to death by forcibly pulling the fish from the throat it refuses to go down. More frequently the young Pelican secures a fish not too large, but too long for it, when it swallows it as far as it will go, and, with the tail sticking from its pouch, quietly waits for the head to digest before it can encompass the whole prize." [1]

Sometimes the spines of fish are dangerous to fish-eating birds. A Pelican was once found dying on Pelican Island with a cat-fish lodged in its throat, held there by the spines. Heavy fatalities among the young have occurred in the past on Pelican Island. Deaths have sometimes resulted from unfavorable weather conditions, while in other cases starvation has been the apparent cause.

Dr. E. W. Nelson, Chief of the United States Biological Survey, examined the remains of many hundreds of fishes dropped by Pelicans on Pelican Island. About 90 per cent were small menhaden, a few were anchovies, four or five were small fish known as "river menhaden" and two were known locally as "butterfish." He also visited the

---

[1] Chapman, Frank M.: Camps and Cruises of an Ornithologist, 1908, pp. 97–98.

reservation at Bird Key at Tampa Bay on the west coast of Florida where he found the Pelicans feeding "almost entirely *on menhaden and anchovies.*" [1]

ECONOMIC STATUS. Claims have been made by the commercial fishermen of Florida that Pelicans eat enormous quantities of food fishes. One estimate placed the daily damage to the fisheries at the ridiculous sum of $900,000. Dr. Nelson's examination noted above seemed to show that the quantity of food fish destroyed by the Pelicans was immaterial, and that they fed almost entirely on small fish not used for human food.

Mr. T. Gilbert Pearson, President of the National Association of Audubon Societies, was requested by the Federal Food Administrator to investigate the food of Brown Pelicans on their breeding-grounds. He made this investigation in the spring of 1918. Following is an extract from Mr. Pearson's Report:

"Regarding the food of the pelican at this season Dr. Hugh M. Smith, Chief of the United States Fish Commission, reported that every specimen sent him that was collected between Rockford, Texas, and Tampa, Florida, was the Gulf menhaden, a fish never used for human consumption. Neither the writer nor the state's representatives with me could find one single food fish. In south Florida menhaden were not so plentiful as farther west, and this may account for the fact that the fish collected there were of seven varieties, viz., common mullet, pigfish, Gulf menhaden, pinfish, thread herring, top-minnow and crevalle. Of the 3,428 specimens taken in Florida waters only twenty-seven individual fish were of a kind ever sold in the markets for food, and not a single specimen of the highly prized varieties, such as trout, mackerel, or pompano, could be discovered in the possession of any pelican. These large, grotesque-looking birds afford winter tourists much interest as they flop about the docks or scramble for fishheads thrown overboard, and many post-cards bearing pictures of pelicans are sent north every year. It is quite possible that the profits made on pelican post-cards at Florida news-stands exceed in value the total quantity of food fish captured by the pelicans in the waters along its charming coast. The Federal Food Administration has felt constrained to say that the charge against the brown pelican has been disproven." [2]

FAMILY **FREGATIDÆ**. MAN-O'-WAR-BIRDS.

Number of species in North America 1 ; in Massachusetts 1.

The Man-o'-war-birds are unique among water birds in that they have the greatest spread of wing in proportion to their size, a forked tail of extreme length and extremely small feet. The primaries are very powerful with stout squarish shafts. The long, pelican-like bill has both mandibles hooked downward at their ends, the pouch is comparatively small but capable of great distention and the long middle toe has a toothed or pectinated claw. The air is the element of these birds and they are seen often at sea, hundreds of miles from land. Few birds can even approach them in their command of

---

[1] A Defense of the Pelican, issued by the Florida Audubon Society, 1918, pp. 3–4.
[2] Pearson, T. Gilbert: American Review of Reviews, Vol. LIX, 1919, p. 511.

the power of flight and they soar at astonishing heights. They normally inhabit the warmer regions of the globe, but sometimes wander far into the temperate zones.

ECONOMIC STATUS. The food of the Frigate Pelicans is not well known and we have little information regarding their economic position.

Fregáta áquila (LINNÆUS). Man-o'-war-bird.

Other names: FRIGATE BIRD; HURRICANE BIRD; FRIGATE PELICAN.

Fig. 19.

DESCRIPTION. — *Adult male:* Black, glossed on head, lanceolate scapulars and interscapulars with greenish-bronze and purple; belly duller colored; usually gray or brownish on some wing feathers from wear; iris brown; legs and feet dusky or blackish. *Adult female:* Similar but less glossy; dull or brownish-black; lesser wing-coverts grayish-brown with pale edges; hind neck brownish; feathers of head, scapulars and interscapulars shorter and less lanceolate; fore neck, breast and sides white; iris brown; feet pink; bill varies with age and sex — of various shades of whitish, flesh-color, bluish or dusky (livid-bluish or dusky in old male); skin around eye livid; throat-pouch of male (inflated in nuptial season) orange-red or scarlet; mouth carmine. *Young in first winter plumage:* Similar to female but head and neck (sometimes mottled), together with most of under plumage, white; tail shorter and not so deeply forked; iris, bill, feet and face darkish-colored, livid-bluish. An immature male had "bill and feet bright blue." [1] *Downy young:* White; young hatch naked but become clothed with very fluffy, white down; interscapulars precede wing- and tail-feathers and cover back like black mantle; secondaries precede primaries.

MEASUREMENTS. — Length 37.50 to 41.00 in.; spread 84.00 to 96.00; folded wing 22.00 to 27.10; tail 14.25 to 19.25, forked for more than half its length; bill 4.25 to 6.00, tarsus 1.00 or less.

MOLTS. — Juvenal plumage which is practically continuous with first winter plumage appears to be worn with little change during first year after which the birds molt and the sexes become dissimilar; but date of this molt varies greatly; in third year, probably at second postnuptial molt when bird is a little over two years old, adult plumage is assumed (A. C. Bent).

FIELD MARKS. — Very deeply forked tail (like that of gigantic swallow), immense spread of long, pointed wings and dark coloration render the Man-o'-war-bird unmistakable; when soaring the long tail-feathers are held parallel and close together, but when the birds are fighting in the air, or courting or playing, they often open and shut like scissors.

VOICE. — Usually silent; utters "a loud grating cry" when fighting in air; "a clucking note" in mating season; also has a "rough croak."

BREEDING. — In colonies; on sea-islands. *Nest:* Of sticks, often flimsy and frail, slightly hollowed, in low trees or bushes, usually within a few feet of the ground (but sometimes high in mangroves), or on rocks. *Eggs:* 1 to 3, usually 1; 2.65 to 2.90 by 1.80 to 2.00 in.; white. *Dates:* February 3 to May 11, Bahamas (A. C. Bent). *Incubation:* By both parents.

RANGE. — Tropical and subtropical American seas and coasts; north to southern California, Texas, Louisiana and Florida; regular in Gulf states; north on Pacific side casually to Humboldt Bay, California, and on Atlantic side to Nova Scotia and Quebec; in interior to Kansas, Illinois, Iowa, Indiana, Wisconsin and Ohio; accidental in Bermuda; breeds from Florida, Bahama Islands, Antilles, Greater and Lesser, south to Venezuela.

DISTRIBUTION IN NEW ENGLAND. — Records: *Maine:* Bird recorded in Boston Evening Transcript for October 19, 1893, as having been shot "some time ago" at Machias, but date and other facts are lacking; another incomplete Maine record is that of a specimen taken but not preserved, "about 12 years

---

[1] Bowdish, B. S.: Auk, Vol. XIX, 1902, p. 359.

ago" [1871] at Boothbay.[1] *Massachusetts:* Young bird taken October 17, 1893, at New Bedford.[2] (This bird was undoubtedly blown north by the fierce West Indian hurricane that swept up the Atlantic coast a few days earlier — the second hurricane of the fall of 1893, the first being the famous August "blow.") *Connecticut:* Female shot in fall of 1859 at Faulkner's Island.[3]

NOTE. When the dates of the "Frigates" noted in the Province of Quebec (August, 1884) and at Halifax are compared with the foregoing New England dates, it will be seen that this species is a late summer and fall wanderer to this section, driven here probably by severe southerly gales. A specific annotation to the effect that it was driven there "by a strong southwest gale," it being "very warm weather for the time of year," accompanies the date of the adult male shot October 16, 1876, outside Halifax Harbor.[4]

HAUNTS AND HABITS. Of all the birds that sweep the skies none can excel the Man-o'-war-bird. Here is a bird with body about the size of that of a Red-tailed Hawk, but with wings spreading seven or eight feet! Its flight is wonderful. It has a marvelous capacity for sailing at great altitudes, and so calmly and easily does it ride the winds that it is even said to sleep on outspread wings above the storm. Walt Whitman, with a poet's license, has "somewhat exaggerated" its powers in these lines:

> "Thou who has slept all night upon the storm,
>   Waking renewed on thy prodigious pinions,
> Thou born to match the storm (Thou art all wings),
>   At dusk thou look'st on Senegal, at noon America."

On the coast of Florida I have seen these birds circling majestically up into the sky until they seemed like tiny specks in the blue, barely visible to the naked eye, and there they soared without apparent effort, up-borne by the passing gale. Sometimes they sail thus for many hours even after twilight falls. Scott says that at the Dry Tortugas he saw five of these "wonderful flyers" at eleven o'clock at night soaring in the moonlight, high above the lighthouse tower.[5]

The Frigate Bird is sometimes called the Hurricane Bird, as it appears outside its usual range chiefly when it comes riding on some great tropical storm. At such times it has wandered to New England and Quebec, and far into the interior of the United States. It frequents tropical and subtropical shores and islands where gulls, terns, cormorants, boobies and pelicans, fishing for their own needs or for their young, frequently are obliged to give up their booty to this merciless marauder. Its mastery of the air enables it to overtake them, and it easily swoops down and snatches any falling fish, relinquished by a terrified bird. It does not hesitate to attack even the Osprey, a bird heavier, more powerful and better armed than itself, but not so swift nor so skilful in flight.

The Man-o'-war-bird is so absolutely a "fowl of the air" that it is rather helpless on land. It seems to be unable to rise from the deck of a ship. Mr. H. H. Bailey, who visited Isabella Island in western Mexico where there is a colony of Frigate Birds nesting

---

[1] New England Bird Life, Vol. II, 1883, p. 342.
[2] Boston Evening Transcript, October 19, 1893, p. 10.
[3] Grinnell, George Bird: American Naturalist, Vol. IX, 1875, p. 470.
[4] Deane, Ruthven: Bulletin Nuttall Ornithological Club, Vol. IV, 1879, p. 64.
[5] Scott, W. E. D.: Auk, Vol. VII, 1890, p. 307.

in low bushes, found that numbers of the birds in alighting on their nests or in trying to rise from them became entangled in the bushes. Many remains of birds which had become thus entangled were hanging by wings, feet or head.[1] The wings are so long and the legs so short that the bird rises from such nests with difficulty.

Mr. A. W. Anthony found a Frigate Bird with one withered useless wing on the summit of the precipitous island of San Benedicte, Lower California. This bird, alone, at a distance from its fellows and unable to fly, had never left the top of the island, but it was fat and its stomach was well filled with flying-fish. Mr. Anthony believed that it must have been fed through all its life by its fellows.[2] On the other hand, this species has been known to eat the young of its own kind. The old males are pugnacious; they fight desperate battles in the air; and their evolutions at such times are astonishing. Some of the Polynesian natives take young Man-o'-war-birds from the nest, tame them and use them as we use carrier pigeons to convey messages from one island to another. Dr. Charles H. Townsend quotes Mr. Louis Becke, who says that these birds carry messages from 60 to 80 miles. When taken away from home and liberated, they soon return.[3]

Apparently this species does not migrate regularly. After the breeding season it goes where its favorite food abounds, or wherever it may be carried by the winds.

Professor Homer R. Dill has published a good description of the habits of this species in the Wilson Bulletin for 1916, pages 153–157.

The Man-o'-war-bird does not depend altogether on other birds for its supplies. It swoops down and picks up flying-fish and catches fish from the surface, but it is no diver. It will pick up dead fish and has often been caught by hooks baited with them. Evidently it subsists mainly on fish of which it consumes a great variety.

ECONOMIC STATUS. See page 171.

ORDER ANSERES. LAMELLIROSTRAL SWIMMERS.

Number of species in North America 57; in Massachusetts 42.

This order includes all swimming birds with lamellate bills. Both mandibles are fitted along the edges with series of tooth-like flutings or projections. These opposing *lamellæ* alternate and fit together forming a strainer through which a surplus of water and sediment may escape, while particles of food are retained. The tongue is fleshy and provided with serrations or *papillæ* along the edges, which correspond to the *lamellæ* of the bill.

---

[1] Auk, Vol. XXIII, 1906, p. 383. [2] Auk, Vol. XV, 1898, pp. 314–315. [3] Bird-Lore, Vol. X, 1908, p. 124.

FAMILY **ANATIDÆ**. DUCKS, GEESE AND SWANS.

Number of species in North America 57; in Massachusetts 42.

The order *Anseres* contains but one family, *Anatidæ* in which are comprised five sub-families — *Merginæ*, Mergansers, *Anatinæ*, River Ducks, *Fuligulinæ*, Sea Ducks, *Anserinæ*, Geese, and *Cygninæ*, Swans. In all these subfamilies the bill is more or less flattened and lamellated, except in the Mergansers which have the bill slender, rounded and toothed. In all species the bill has a membranous covering with a hard tip or nail at the end of the upper mandible. The body is flattened, tail usually short, wings moderately long, legs short and far apart but not placed quite so near the center of the body as in gulls and terns; toes four; front toes webbed, hind toe slightly elevated and free; neck usually long, plumage dense with a heavy undercoat of down. The family includes about 200 species and is represented in every habitable part of the globe. In most species of the ducks the male has an incomplete postnuptial molt in midsummer which gives it for a short time a temporary dress much like that of the female, called the "eclipse" plumage. During a part of the summer while the flight feathers of the wings are molted most ducks, geese and swans are unable to fly.

The increase of down in the nest as the eggs are laid is characteristic, more or less, of ducks.

Hybridism among ducks is well known; there are many records of hybrids of different species; "some of them between different genera, some even between birds we are accustomed to place in different subfamilies; and in these cases fertility of the mongrel progeny is the rule" (Coues).

ECONOMIC STATUS. Economically birds of this order are important. Wild-fowl, which swarmed in countless multitudes in America when the settlement of the country began, formed a very important part of the animal food of the early settlers, and still help to sustain life in the aborigines of far northern regions who in some measure depend upon the supply of flesh derived from these birds, preserved by salting or freezing to ward off starvation during the cold of winter. As game birds, wild-fowl help to maintain an immense trade in guns, ammunition and sporting goods, furnish employment to guides and boatmen, and bring custom to country hotels and boarding-houses; while their bodies supply a vast quantity of nourishing food. In the past in this country and even now in other countries great sums of money have changed hands annually in buying and selling these birds. The Fish and Game Commission of California estimated that in 1911, 250,000 wild ducks were sold in the San Francisco market, and that a million were killed in the same year in the state. The value of the ducks sold in 1911 in San Francisco is estimated at $125,000, while the value of those killed that year in the state is put at $500,000. The food value of water-fowl taken in the United States annually reaches the sum total of several millions of dollars.[1]

---

[1] Palmer, T. S.: Bulletin No. 1049, United States Department of Agriculture, p. 9.

PLATE 11

PLATE 11

HOODED MERGANSER
Page 187
Winter (Nuptial) Plumage

Adult Female   Adult Male

MERGANSER
Page 176
Winter (Nuptial) Plumage

Adult Female

Adult Male

RED-BREASTED MERGANSER
Page 181
Winter (Nuptial) Plumage

Adult Female

Adult Male

All one-sixth natural size.

The business of rearing ducks for sporting purposes is a large one in the British Isles and employs many gamekeepers. In the United States many wild ducks are now reared and sold, but as a business this has not proceeded much beyond the experimental stage.

All domesticated ducks and geese are descended from a few wild species. The rearing of domesticated ducks and geese for the market is a business which amounts to millions of dollars annually and will increase as population increases. The eggs and the flesh of ducks and geese form a large part of the annual poultry product from which the people of the world derive a portion of their food.

Wild ducks are destructive to certain insect pests such as locusts and army worms, and domesticated ducks in large numbers have been utilized to keep such pests in check. Ducks are very destructive to mosquito larvæ, eating them in untold numbers. Mosquitoes carry the germs of such diseases as malaria and yellow fever and with these germs infect human beings. These diseases cause the death of many people, also a great economic loss of labor, owing to intermittent illness. Millions of dollars are thus lost to the world every year. Wild ducks, if in sufficient numbers, greatly reduce the mosquito pest.

Subfamily **MERGINÆ**. Mergansers.

Number of species in North America 4; in Massachusetts 3.

This family comprises a small group of fish-eating ducks having the bill constructed especially for seizing and holding living, active and slippery prey. The mandibles are narrow and slender as compared with those of other ducks, the nail at the tip of the upper mandible overhanging and the lamellæ modified into tooth-like projections, sharp pointed and often turned backward like the teeth of a shark. (See figure.) The ducklike

BILL OF MERGANSER

form is modified to give exceptional ability to pursue fish under water. The feet are placed farther back than in river ducks but not so far as in loons, grebes, auks or cormorants, and are broadly webbed. The free hind toe is lobed. Nine species of this subfamily have been recognized, chiefly in the Northern Hemisphere, but some are found in South America. The head is more or less crested, although not always noticeably so; all species show some white in the wing in flight.

When in the air the long, slim neck, head and bill give these birds a long, narrow, rakish appearance in marked contrast to that of scoters or golden-eyes. They seldom fly very high and when once they have attained their altitude for horizontal flight, the head, neck and body are held in a straight line.

Mérgus americánus CASSIN. Merganser.

Other names: AMERICAN MERGANSER; BUFF-BREASTED MERGANSER; FISHDUCK; SAWBILL; SHELDRAKE; FRESH-WATER SHELDRAKE; POND SHELDRAKE; SWAMP SHELDRAKE; BRACKET SHELDRAKE; GOOSANDER; BREAKHORN.

Plate 11.

DESCRIPTION. — Bill toothed, with recurved or hooked serrations; *nostrils nearer middle than base of bill,* less than 1.50 inches from tip; tail of 18 feathers. *Adult male in winter plumage:* A short, rounded, bushy, *single* crest on top and back of head (not apparent unless erected); head and upper neck black, glossed dark green on top and sides of head and back and sides of neck; upper back and scapulars glossy black with purplish reflections; rump, upper tail-coverts and tail ashy-gray; outer surface of closed wing largely white, crossed on greater coverts by a bar of black; several inner secondaries edged black, primaries and outer secondaries brownish-black; axillars and under wing-coverts mainly white; middle secondaries white; inner secondaries and scapulars black and white; lower neck all round and under plumage creamy-white to salmon-buff (after death the salmon fades); iris carmine; bill red, its ridge and nail blackish; feet deep red. *Adult male in eclipse plumage:* Similar to that of female but without long crest; may be distinguished by white wing-coverts; chin white, throat brown, and usually some dark feathers on upper back; lower neck bluish-gray mixed with creamy-white; flanks with a few white or whitish feathers vermiculated with brownish-gray. *Adult female:* Slender feathers of *single* crest longer than in male, crest prominent and pointed; head and upper neck "tawny-brown or cinnamon," lightest on sides of neck; chin and throat white or whitish; above chiefly ashy-gray; lower hind-neck and sides of neck gray; sides and flanks faintly barred or mottled with whitish; middle secondaries white with sooty-brown border; below creamy-white to salmon-buff, except under wing-coverts and axillars which are mainly white; iris, bill and feet red, but duller than in male. *Young in first winter plumage:* Similar to adult female except that in juvenal plumage white of throat extends down nearly or quite to gray of upper breast; young male in first winter shows less crest than female and head slightly darker; sometimes there is a little dark edging about the neck and the salmon tint on under parts is deeper. *Downy young:* Above clove-brown, "bister" or "warm sepia" (mainly), with four prominent white spots — a white patch on hind border of each wing and one on each side of rump (sometimes a small white patch on either side of back); top of head and hind neck reddish-brown; face whitish with two dark stripes, one from bill to eye, another from gape below eye; below mainly white.

MEASUREMENTS. — Length 21.00 to 27.00 in.; spread 34.00 to 39.00; folded wing 9.22 to 11.00; tail 4.60 to 4.73; bill along ridge 1.74 to 2.30; tarsus 1.65 to 2.09. Weight — male averages 4¼ lbs., female ½ lb. less (Walter H. Rich); two males weighed respectively 3 lbs. 15 oz., and 3 lbs. 7 oz. (John C. Phillips). Female smaller than male.

MOLTS. — In juvenal plumage young are alike; during fall and winter molting is almost continuous; in spring tail is renewed; in late October young male, now nearly full-grown, shows an area of white passing nearly around lower neck, and some black feathers appear on back; in winter many whitish feathers vermiculated with brownish-gray appear in flanks, and black feathers on back increase; in spring tail is renewed and some black feathers come in on chin; young male probably has a partial eclipse plumage much like that of adult male but with gray wing-coverts; a molt takes place (August to November) after which, at about 17 months of age, young male becomes as adult; young female assumes adult plumage somewhat earlier — in 15 or 15½ months; A. C. Bent says that adult males have "a post-nuptial molt of contour feathers early in summer" in going into eclipse plumage, "a molt of the flight feathers in August or September," and a complete molt of contour feathers in going out of eclipse in the fall; "females," he says, "probably do not make the double molt of the contour feathers but have a complete molt late in summer."

FIELD MARKS. — Mergansers in short flights do not use the V-formation, but fly in long lines in single file one after the other or in elongated flocks; in flight Merganser shows more white especially in wing than Red-breasted Merganser. *Adult male:* Largest New England duck; as long as a Brant or longer; at a distance looks *black* and *white* (white sides and neck, black head); crest not often noticeable; white lower neck and white breast, sides and flanks distinguish it from Red-breasted Merganser, which has a reddish, striped band on breast; Merganser has a lower forehead and longer bill and is larger, longer and slimmer than Golden-eye which has a large head, short neck and chubby shape. *Female and young:* Usually distinguishable at some distance from corresponding plumages of Red-breasted Merganser; head and neck of Merganser slightly darker than that of Red-breasted; also grayish above where the other is relatively brownish; where throat can be seen, Merganser shows *white* contrasting sharply with color of head, while female and young of Red-breasted Merganser have whitish or pale brownish (on upper throat) shading gradually into deeper brown on sides of head and throat next to it; at close range single crest of female may distinguish Merganser from double-crested Red-breasted Merganser; young or female Merganser may be distinguished by long, slim bill from brown-headed female of Redhead or Golden-eye.

VOICE. — *Female:* A coarse, masculine quack (J. B. Law). *Both sexes* (*Goosander*): A harsh *karr-karr* (J. G. Millais); an unmelodious squawk (H. S. Swarth); hoarse croaks (Audubon).

BREEDING. — About woodland lakes and rivers. *Nest:* Usually in hollow tree or in top of broken stub; sometimes in hole in cliff or under rocks, in an uninhabited building, in a thicket or on ground; grasses, twigs, leaves, lichens, etc., lined with very light grayish-white down, mixed usually with white feathers and straw; when sheltered, nest may be entirely of down, as in case of Wood Duck and Hooded Merganser. *Eggs:* 6 to 17; 2.50 to 2.80 by 1.70 to 2.00 in., average 2.51 by 1.75; elliptical; pale creamy buff. *Dates:* Late May and June in northern Maine. *Incubation:* Period "28 days" (Burns and Evans); by female. One brood yearly.

RANGE. — North America. Breeds from southern Alaska, southern Yukon, southern Mackenzie, central Manitoba, southern Ungava (Northern Quebec), central Labrador and Newfoundland south to central Oregon, South Dakota, southern Minnesota (Cooke), central Michigan, central New York, Vermont, New Hampshire, Maine, formerly at least to Ohio, Pennsylvania and Massachusetts and in mountains south to central California, north central Arizona and northern New Mexico; winters at Aleutian and Pribilof Islands (rarely) and from British Columbia, Idaho, northern Colorado, southern Wisconsin, Great Lakes, southern Ontario, Maine, New Brunswick and Prince Edward Island (rarely) south to northern Lower California, northern Mexico and Gulf states; casual in winter in Canadian Labrador (southeastern Quebec). The Old World Merganser, *Mergus merganser*, which is practically identical with the American form, breeds in Europe and Asia and in one or other of its forms migrates south to northern Africa, India, China and Japan.

DISTRIBUTION IN NEW ENGLAND. — *Maine:* Common migrant and winter resident; less common summer resident. *New Hampshire:* Common migrant, winter resident in quick water of open streams south of White Mountains, and rather uncommon summer resident from White Mountains north. *Vermont:* Not uncommon migrant locally; occasional local winter resident; summer resident in northern parts. *Massachusetts:* Rather common migrant, less common winter resident; said to have bred formerly and may rarely breed still.* *Rhode Island:* Rather uncommon migrant and winter resident. *Connecticut:* Rather common migrant and less common winter resident.

SEASON IN MASSACHUSETTS. — October 10 to April 15; (May 25); (summer).

---

* My son, Lewis E. Forbush, saw, during the summer of 1907 in Westborough, three ducks which he describes as Mergansers. In June he saw one of these birds on a pond with her downy young. (Game Birds, Wild-Fowl and Shore Birds, 1912, p. 63.)

Capt. A. W. McGray of Brooklyn, New York, in a letter to Mr. Albert A. Cross of Huntington, states that during the last days of May, 1921 (and later) he and his family saw on three occasions at a pond in Huntington a mother sheldrake with a flock of nine young. By the "use of wings and legs the young birds were able to travel fast over the water," but by using a boat Captain McGray was able to get within 30 feet of them. He is positive that the mother was not a Red-breasted Merganser.

HAUNTS AND HABITS.   Few New England ducks are handsomer in life than an adult male Merganser.   After death the evanescent rich salmon tint of the breast fades and disappears.   The Merganser is a fresh-water fowl.   It is likely to appear in migration on any of the larger bodies of fresh water in New England.   The large black and white male is conspicuous, and therefore the species is better known to the country people than any other wild duck except the Black Duck.   It seldom is seen on the surface of the open sea unless it has been driven out of fresh water near the coast, but it frequents estuaries and backwaters where the tide runs in and out.   Wherever the species may be met with, individuals of both sexes usually are seen together, and the females and young are readily identified when in company with the unmistakable adult males.   They frequent fresh-water ponds and lakes near the sea, and some, if not molested, often remain in such bodies of water all winter or as long as the surface remains unfrozen.   They are seen commonly on the larger rivers and sometimes are the most numerous ducks on the Connecticut and the Merrimac.   They are vigorous, hardy, stout-hearted fowls.   Ice, snow and cold have no terrors for them. Sufficient food and open water are enough to insure their presence in New England in the severest winters.

An experience of my own may be related to exemplify the speed which these birds can attain at need when in flight.   Riding northward on a train in winter alongside the Merrimac in southern New Hampshire, I saw a small flock of Mergansers rise from some unfrozen rapids and fly upstream.   Their course was parallel with that of the train, which probably did not much exceed a speed of 30 miles an hour, and the birds maintained the exact speed of the train for some time and so kept nearly opposite my window. Suddenly the whistle of the locomotive sounded a loud blast.   At the sound those ducks shot forward at such a speed that they distanced the train immediately and soon disappeared from view.   Their startled flight must have carried them forward about twice as fast as the speed of the train.

In winter some of these birds frequent open reaches of swift water here and there, as on the Connecticut River and the Merrimac below Manchester, New Hampshire, the Winnipesaukee River, and between Haverhill and Lawrence.   In mild winters they remain in many open streams and ponds in southeastern Massachusetts.

The Merganser is an excellent swimmer and diver.   Like the grebes it can dive almost with the flash of a gun.   It either springs forward clear of the water, dips under with hardly a ripple or sinks quietly out of sight, employing the method that seems best suited to the occasion.   Sometimes in under-water swimming its wings are not used, but in pursuit of swift fishes it uses both its strong, webbed feet and its powerful wings to force it through the water, much in the manner of the fast-swimming loon.   Sometimes in shallow water it follows fish on the surface, using both wings and feet in the chase. At times it rises into the air, flies along over the water and flies down again into and under the water possibly in continued pursuit of swift fish.   Mergansers sometimes swim slowly on the surface with necks extended and heads partially submerged in the manner observed in surface feeding ducks, but whether they take in food in this manner or merely drink thus is still unknown.

Mr. Miles D. Pirnie writes that in February, 1916, while standing on a high bridge over a narrow channel at Pulaski, New York, he watched an unwounded male Merganser swimming under water to escape from a pursuing hunter. The bird was using both wings and feet to make headway against the current. Mr. Walter H. Rich writes of this species: "Seen under the water in pursuit of a breakfast or dodging about to escape capture when wounded the resemblance to some finny dweller of the sea is very marked; head and neck outstretched, every feather hugged closely to the body, the half-opened wings like large fins aiding the feet in their work, he goes shooting through the water like a flash." [1]

The Merganser is shy and is an expert in eluding the gunner. Also it possesses great vitality and often when severely wounded will escape by diving. In such a case it may hide in aquatic vegetation or may even seize in its bill grasses or weeds on the bottom and hold on until death.[2]

When rising from the water the Merganser has to use both wings and feet in running or pattering on the surface before it gets impetus enough to launch itself in the air.

Dr. Townsend thus graphically describes the courtship display of the male Merganser:

"The courtship of the Merganser . . . is fairly spectacular and differs widely from that of its red-breasted cousin, *M. serrator.* . . .

"A group of five or six male Mergansers may be seen swimming energetically back and forth by three or four passive females. Sometimes the drakes swim in a compact mass or in a file for six or seven yards or even farther, and then each turns abruptly and swims back. Again they swim in and out among each other, and every now and then one with swelling breast and slightly raised wings spurts ahead at great speed by himself or in the pursuit of a rival. . . . They frequently strike at each other with their bills, and I have seen two splendid drakes rise up in the water breast to breast, and, amid a great splashing, during which it was impossible to see details, fight like game-cocks. The pursuit is varied by sudden, momentary dives and much splashing of water.

"The smooth iridescent green heads, the brilliant carmine bills tipped with black nails, the snowy white of flanks and wing patches and the red feet, which flash out in the dive, make a wonderful color effect, contrasting well with the dark water and white ice. The smaller females with their shaggy brown heads, their neat white throat-bibs, their quaker blue-gray backs and modest wing patches, which are generally hidden, are fitting foils to their mates." The male frequently raises himself up almost on his tail and displays the beautiful salmon-yellow tint on the whole under surface of his body. "Most of the time he keeps his tail cocked up and spread, so that it shows from behind a white centre and blue border. Every now and then he points his head and closed bill up at an angle of forty-five degrees or to the zenith. Again he bows or bobs his head nervously and

---

[1] Rich, Walter H.: Feathered Game of the Northeast, 1907, p. 405.
[2] Grinnell, Bryant and Storer: The Game Birds of California, 1918, p. 81. See also Department Bulletin No. 8, Massachusetts Department of Agriculture, 1922, pp. 40 and 44.

often at the same time tilts up the front of his breast from which flashes out the salmon tint. From time to time he emits a quickly repeated purring note, *dorr-dorr* or *krr-krr*.

"The most surprising part of the performance is the spurt of water fully three or four feet long which every now and then is sent backwards into the air by the powerful kick of the drake's foot. . . ." [1]

Sometimes when the male is indifferent, the amorous female takes the initiative and pursues him with head and neck laid along the surface and half submerged.

Naumann asserts that the European Merganser carries the young to the water in the bill if the nest is in a tall tree and far from water; and Oswin Lee (Among British Birds in Their Nesting Haunts) says that he saw nine ducklings carried from the tree to the water by the female Merganser which held them partly in her bill and partly between the bill and breast. [2]

Sometimes when the nest is placed on the top of a very high stub, it may be possible, as Mr. W. L. Dawson suggests, that the mother carries the newly hatched young to the water in her bill, but I am not aware that this habit has been observed in this country while on the other hand the young have been seen to tumble into the water from nests high above it.

Although many Mergansers still breed in northern New England, probably most individuals that are seen here in migration come from much farther north. Apparently most of them leave northern Canadian inland waters by November 1. Rarely a bird of this species may appear on the Massachusetts coast in summer, but the average date of arrival is October 5. The first October arrivals are early birds, as Mergansers are late migrants and pass south only when forced by ice and cold storms. They do not usually become common in Massachusetts until late October and November. Even in December many may remain in the interior until ice closes most of the fresh waters and the ducks are driven south or to the sea. As soon as the ice begins to break up in March the Mergansers follow closely. In spring they migrate in numbers through Massachusetts in March and early April according to the season, resting for a time on the large ponds or streams as they go. In migration they usually fly very high in wedge-shaped formation, but in moving from place to place and especially up stream they commonly fly low over the water.

Mergansers feed on fish, destroying many small minnows, but are not confined to an exclusive fish diet. They feed also on shell-fish and nobody knows to what extent they may eat vegetal matter. Knight says that along the coast in winter they consume many mussels and other mollusks, swallowing shell and all. He finds that the shells are soon ground up in the stomach and in the process of digestion are reduced to "impalpable mud" at the end of the digestive tract. [3]

Dearborn found a bullfrog in one that he examined. The frog was so large that while its shoulders were in the bird's stomach its toes were still extended into the neck. [4]

[1] Auk, Vol. XXXIII, 1916, pp. 11–12.
[2] Millais, J. G.: British Diving Ducks, Vol. II, p. 97.
[3] Knight, Ora Willis: Birds of Maine, 1908, p. 78.
[4] Dearborn, Ned: A Preliminary List of the Birds of Belknap and Merrimac Counties, New Hampshire, 1898, p. 5.

Dr. E. Hartert (in a footnote) says of the European form of this bird that in summer at their breeding places they "eat caterpillars, cockchafers and burying-beetles." [1] Probably the American bird also eats insects.

Captain McGray in the letter to Mr. Cross hereinbefore mentioned relates that on December 2, 1921, Mrs. McGray scattered two or three pounds of yellow field corn in about three feet of water. Three days later the Mergansers found this corn and there was an "under-water scramble" for it. Captain McGray says that the submerged birds were so eager that they shouldered one another out of the way. The surface of the lake was glassy, and the movements of the birds under water could be plainly seen through the open window almost directly above. The birds carried their wings half open. While the corn-feast was in progress, two more flocks flew in and joined in the under-water meal, making nineteen birds in all. The Mergansers were drawn to the McGray shore in the first place by the many minnows which lay beneath a wharf.

ECONOMIC STATUS. No exhaustive investigation of the food of this species has been published; therefore no conclusive statement regarding its economic status can be made. It is said to eat small trout, but apparently it devours many more minnows and the latter destroy the spawn of trout. Also it feeds on crayfish which are believed to destroy spawn. If we could see what goes on under water among the fishes and could know how many of their enemies fish-eating birds destroy, we might cease to regard birds as enemies of food-fish. Fish are cannibalistic. Possibly the trout itself may be the greatest enemy of young trout.

Mr. A. C. Bent says that many sportsmen feel justified in killing the Mergansers on account of the large numbers of trout which they consume, but that this is hardly justifiable, for they destroy many predatory fish such as pickerel and thus help to preserve the balance of nature.[2]

As an article of food the Merganser which has a fishy flavor does not rank high. However, all fish-eating birds, if not too aged, are eatable and sometimes are excellent food, provided that the stomach and intestines are removed *immediately* after death. If this is not done, especially in warm weather, the fishy contents of the viscera, no longer subject to the processes of digestion, soon decay and the rank flavor quickly penetrates the flesh; then parboiling and other expedients must be resorted to in order to remove the taint and often with indifferent success.

Mergus serrátor LINNÆUS. Red-breasted Merganser.

Other names: SHELL-BIRD; SHELDUCK; SHELDRAKE; SALT-WATER SHELDRAKE; SAW-BILL; FISH DUCK; SEA ROBIN.

Plate 11.

DESCRIPTION. — *Nostrils near base of bill*, more than 1.50 inches from tip; hind head with a rather long *two-pointed* crest, in *both sexes;* tail of 18 feathers. *Adult male in winter plumage:* Head and a little of upper neck black, with metallic green reflections on sides; neck widely collared all round with white,

---

[1] Vogel Mitteleuropas, Vol. X, p. 296.

[2] Smithsonian Institution, United States National Museum, Bulletin 126, 1923, p. 11.

except a narrow black stripe down hind-neck; most of back and scapulars (except outer) and tertials black, outer scapulars white, some marked black; rump, upper tail-coverts and tail brownish-gray, with fine, broken black bars; outer surface of closed wing mainly white, crossed by two narrow, diagonal black bars; wing-coverts around bend of wing black; primaries and outer secondaries brownish-black; inner secondaries lighter; patch of white black-bordered feathers on each side of breast overhanging bend of wing; sides and front of lower neck and upper breast pale cinnamon, mottled black and streaked narrowly with fine, wavy lines of same; elsewhere below mainly white; bill red, dusky along ridge; inside of mouth orange; iris and feet red. *Adult male in eclipse plumage:* August 20. Head, neck and upper breast similar to adult female but distinguished by white wing-coverts and much less white on chin; upper plumage otherwise mostly blackish-brown with gray feather-edgings; wings like winter males; rump a mixture of ordinary plumage of male and female; breast dull brown; flanks and sides brownish-gray like those of female. *Adult female in winter plumage:* Head and neck cinnamon-brown on sides, darker on top of head and back of neck, growing blackish around eye, fading into whitish on chin and throat; elsewhere above mainly ashy-brown, feathers with darker centers, giving a slaty-gray appearance; flight-feathers largely blackish; closed fore wing like back, wing patch or speculum white, bordered in front by narrow diagonal black bar and crossed by another; sides and flanks dull grayish-brown; elsewhere below mainly white; bill and iris red; legs and feet dull red. *Young male in first winter plumage:* "In first plumage the young male resembles the adult female, but the crest is less, the bill much shorter, and the plumage of the upper parts more slaty and not nearly so brown, and the cheeks more red with less white. The ends of the tail are also worn. By the end of October young males are easily recognised by their superior size and bill. It is not until December that much change takes place. The red-brown crest is then abundant, and black feathers begin to appear on the sides of the crown and cheeks, chin, mantle, and scapulars. The tail and rump also begin to moult to blue-grey, and many vermiculated feathers mixed with slaty-brown ones come in on the thighs and flanks. By the end of March some white feathers appear on the scapulars and the first white broadly black-edged feathers come in on the sides of the breast overlapping the wings. These prominent feathers are, however, never complete as in the case of the adult males, but are always divided in colour, the lower halves being red and vermiculated with black from the broad black edge to the white above. The nape is now very dark brown edged with worn blue-grey, and not a clear rich red-brown as in the female. The long inner secondaries, similar to adult males, now also appear." [1] *Young male in eclipse plumage:* Similar to eclipse plumage of adult male except wing which is "brown and slate on all its upper parts." "The young male does not come into full dress until the end of November." (Millais). *Young female:* Similar to adult female but crest shorter; less black around eye; colors not so bright; feathers of upper plumage and tail worn and faded. *Downy young:* Above "hair brown," with "a large yellowish white spot on each side of rump and a whitish mark along hind border of each wing"; sides of head and neck rusty, a pale space before eye bordered by two dusky stripes; lower eyelid whitish; below whitish.

MEASUREMENTS. — Length 20.00 to 25.00 in.; spread 31.00 to 35.00; folded wing 8.50 to 9.50; tail 3.80 to 4.40; tarsus 1.60 to 1.90; bill 2.18 to 2.50. Weight 2 lbs. to 2 lbs. 8 oz. (Walter H. Rich). Female smaller than male.

MOLTS. — In young birds molt is most noticeable in male; in December partial molt occurs and change of plumage continues until end of March, after which tail is renewed; during May and June bird molts again and passes into eclipse similar to that of adult male, except wing; in August, September and October of second year complete molt occurs, succeeded by adult plumage; adult males begin to molt in March and seem to molt almost continuously and slowly until late in July; again they are molting from September to January; adult females have complete molt (August to February).

FIELD MARKS. — At a distance in flight (which is usually swift, noiseless and direct) males look black and white, females brown and white, both with white patches on wings, and white bellies; in flight their long, slim, outstretched necks, slim red bills and narrow heads distinguish them from Scoters, Golden-

---

[1] Millais, J. G.: British Diving Ducks, Vol. II, 1913, p. 101.

eyes or Old-squaws; head, neck and body in flight held in straight line; the "build" differentiates the rakish Sheldrake (Merganser) from the short, stout "chunky" Whistler (Golden-eye) almost as far as eye can see.   *Male (on water)*: Black head with long, thin double crest, slim bill, white neck and streaked reddish-brown breast; flying overhead, reddish band between white neck and white belly is conspicuous (male of larger Merganser or "Pond Sheldrake" has no markings on breast); white on wing very noticeable, but when compared with more extensive white on wing of Whistler, is a restricted space which has appearance of being *framed*.   *Female and young (on water)*: White in wing sometimes not evident; less contrast between color of head and back than in female and young of Merganser; the latter have bluish-gray backs while the backs of females and young of Red-breasted Merganser are browner.   (See also "Field Marks" under Merganser, pages 176–177.)

VOICE. — When alarmed, several low guttural croaks (D. G. Elliot); female with young, a low, distinct, husky *khā-khā-khā* (E. W. Nelson); nuptial "song," a loud, rough, purring, slightly double note (C. W. Townsend).

BREEDING. — Near lakes, rivers, small ponds, or even pools, often near sea-coast; usually near marsh or on island.   *Nest:* Hidden by grass or sheltered by bushes, bank, rock or trees; sometimes in thick growth of coniferous trees; of grass, weeds, seaweed, fibrous roots, etc., lined with gray down and white feathers from female.   *Eggs:* 6 to 12, sometimes as many as 16; 2.48 to 2.65 by 1.65 to 1.82 in.; elliptical; dull, creamy-buff, darker than those of Merganser.   *Dates:* In northern United States and Maritime Provinces eggs have been found from mid-May until late June.   *Incubation:* Period 26 to 28 days (Burns); 28 days (R. M. Strong); by female.   One brood yearly.

RANGE. — Northern parts of Northern Hemisphere.   In North America breeds from Arctic coast of Alaska, northern Mackenzie, Baffin Island and central Greenland south to southern Washington, central Alberta, Saskatchewan, southern Manitoba, Minnesota, northern Illinois, Michigan, southern Ontario, northern New York, Massachusetts (casually) and Maine; winters (mainly on coast) from southern British Columbia, northern United States, Great Lakes, Ontario and Maine south to Lower California, Florida and Gulf coast; casual in Bermuda, Cuba and Hawaii; in Eastern Hemisphere breeds commonly in northern Europe and northern Asia; winters in Europe and central Asia and from northern Africa to Japan.

DISTRIBUTION IN NEW ENGLAND. — Common to abundant migrant and winter resident coastwise; rare migrant in interior; breeds in Maine on offshore islands and sparingly on inland lakes in thinly settled regions; breeds very rarely on coast of Massachusetts; a few non-breeding birds summer off New England coast.

SEASON IN MASSACHUSETTS. — Rare, irregular, local summer resident, breeding on coasts of Essex, Plymouth and Barnstable counties; migrant and winter resident from September 23 to May 30.

HAUNTS AND HABITS.   The Red-breasted Merganser is one of the most abundant water-fowl that migrate along the coast of Massachusetts.   Nevertheless it is almost unknown to the inland people of southern New England.   On the Atlantic coast it breeds mainly about fresh-water ponds and streams near the sea and as soon as the young are able to fly (if not before), they seek salt water on which they spend the greater part of the year.   Sometimes in Maine several pairs breed on one of the sea-islands.   In the interior of that State this bird nests usually on islands in the lakes.   I am not aware that the nest of the Red-breasted Merganser has been found in Massachusetts, but along the south shore of Cape Cod small young have been seen occasionally for many years; also on the coast of Essex County where apparently one brood at least was hatched in 1922, as downy young were seen and one was caught by a dog.[1]

---

[1] See Townsend, C. W.: Memoirs of the Nuttall Ornithological Club, No. V, Supplement to the Birds of Essex County, Massachusetts, 1920, p. 49; and also Game Birds, Wild-Fowl and Shore Birds, Massachusetts State Board of Agriculture, 1916, p. 66.

As these cases of breeding occurred on the coast where many of the species are shot each year, it seems possible that one of the parents in each case may have been slightly crippled and so unable to fly farther north or east, and that its mate remained to breed with it.   Nevertheless one breeding bird that I had an opportunity to examine showed no old shot marks.   Cripples or non-breeders may be seen in summer on the coast as far south at least as North Carolina.

Along the New England coast this Merganser, unless driven inland by heavy gales, keeps largely to salt water.   It may be found in the open sea, in sounds, bays and estuaries.   It may seek shelter under the lee of islands or in ponds, but it seems to prefer sea water.   Like the loon it must be able to drink both salt and fresh water, for it breeds far in the interior in many northern lakes.

The Red-breasted Merganser is a skilful, rapid diver, at times using its half spread wings as well as its feet for progression under water when pursuing swift fish, but seems not to be able to swim quite so fast or so far in this manner as the larger and more powerful Merganser.   Often on coming to the surface it rises erect and flaps its wings as if to shake off the water.   It is wary and if wounded uses all manner of stratagems to escape from the gunner.   It dives and conceals itself in submerged water-plants, swims away with only the bill above water and sometimes clings with its bill to some object on the bottom. Mr. Stanley C. Jewett asserts that in May, 1915, at Netarts Bay, Oregon, a wounded bird of this species dived to a submerged root in about three feet of water and died while clinging there.   Several hours later when the tide had ebbed, the dead bird was found on the bare flat with its bill still fastened to the object that it had seized.   Mr. Allan Keniston, Superintendent of the State Reservation for the Heath Hen on Marthas Vineyard, tells me that "twenty years ago," while hunting the Red-breasted Merganser in a flat-bottomed boat, fourteen feet long, one of this species was shot which went to the bottom in three feet of water.   The water was clear and the bottom pure sand.   The boat passed completely over the bird which was seen lying motionless, flat on the bottom, with neck outstretched.   It stayed there until the boat had passed over when it "bobbed up like a cork," alive.

In mild days in March and early April the male Red-breasted Mergansers display their charms before the females.   All seek some quiet bay and there in the sunlight under the lee of the shore, the bright males in their best feather gather with the females and pay them court.   The male birds stretch up their heads showing their long, white necks, and then bob about with partially submerged breasts and widely opened beaks exhibiting their red bills and mouths to the best advantage.   They rush back and forth, splashing the water with their flying feet and dashing sparkling jets three or four feet behind them. A male swims toward a female, throws his head out, forward and upward, with bill elevated, working his feet rapidly and sometimes flapping his wings, until under the urge of wings and splashing feet he rises upright in the water with head held proudly high and bill drawn in, turned down and resting upon his neck.   The females often retreat and seem indifferent to their ardent lovers, but in time they grow more responsive and begin to bob and call in apparent excitement. This response often stirs up mad rivalry among the amorous males which rush at each other with open bills in mimic war and sometimes seize their rivals, but I have never seen any resultant bloodshed.

The female assumes the entire care of the young, while the male in his eclipse plumage either goes to sea or skulks amid rank water vegetation during the time when the flight feathers of the wings are growing and he is unable to fly. The mother is very devoted to her young, and often in case of danger takes them on her back to insure their safety.

In late August or September, on their chosen breeding-grounds, the young Red-breasted Mergansers gather into large flocks led by some old female, and in October the main southward migration begins. The birds that appear in early fall seem to be all females and young, but probably some of them are adult males in their eclipse plumage as usually they do not assume full adult winter plumage until November or later. By the second week in October this species usually is common locally on its chosen winter feeding-grounds either in shallow water near shore or over some outlying shoal. In October and November vast numbers pass along our shores. In December the numbers grow less but they are abundant locally all winter. Where they are much disturbed by gunners and power boats, they keep well offshore, where hundreds and sometimes thousands of them may be seen until midwinter, but usually they are found along the coast in small parties, often diving through the surf or feeding in secluded bays or estuaries.

Sometimes in the dead of winter the males of the species seem to predominate along the coast, but I am told by natives of Nantucket that most of the birds seen there in midwinter are females or young, and Mr. J. A. Farley informs me that at Plymouth, even in some of the coldest winters, the numbers of females and young are equal to those of the males, while old gunners on Marthas Vineyard have given him information to the same effect.

In spring there seems to be a double migration. In February and early March large numbers appear off Cape Cod while in April another great flight passes the Massachusetts coast. This flight, decreasing, continues into May.

Mr. J. A. Farley gives me the following notes on the feeding habits of this species in winter at Plymouth:

"The winter of 1912 was very cold in Plymouth County, especially from the last of January. Plymouth Inner Harbor was frozen 'tight as a drum' from January 7, and often the ocean itself was frozen from a quarter to half a mile out. This was often the case after a bitter night, but the waves would break the ice up in good season in the forenoon.

"The first two weeks of January were very cold and rough. Ducks were driven to Town Brook on account of the ice.

"Feb. 3d, 1912. Saw three Ducks in Town Brook. Watched them from the foundry bridge. They were only a little way off. There were two Red-breasted Mergansers (an old male and a brown bird) and a Whistler. The Mergansers were diving. The male got a young eel, probably 8 inches long. He slapped and twitched it. The brown Merganser swam very fast to the male and got the eel away from him and the male in turn got the eel, and so on, first one and then the other.   It was quite an exciting 'mix-up' for five minutes, but finally the brown bird gave up and swam away and left the male in possession of his catch.   While they were snatching the eel from each other, they made the water *boil*, and showed much swimming ability — both as to speed and power of turning quickly.   The male finally swallowed his eel and then went through the usual shaking and stretching of his neck.

"The Mergansers drink water after getting an eel down.

"Feb. 13.   After 4 P.M. watched the Ducks in Town Brook.   There were thirteen in all — two male Whistlers and at least four females; two male Red-breasted Mergansers (one, a fine fellow); several brown Mergansers; and one Scaup.   They were in the water or on the ice.   A male Merganser dived and came up with an eel, and a Herring Gull, which had been standing on the ice, flew, and in a trice got away with the eel.   It was done so quickly that I did not see the actual second of the robbery.   The Merganser swam very fast and there was another Merganser in the 'mix-up' but the Gull was off with the eel in a twinkling.   He went back on the ice and swallowed the eel without any ado.   A brown Merganser dived and got an eel (about one foot long, I should say) and another 'female' seized one end of the eel while the first bird kept the other, and how they *pulled!*   The eel seemed to *stretch* and how the water *boiled!*   They swam around; it was almost like 'Snap the whip'; but the captor kept the prize and the other bird gave up and swam off.   The captor seemed in a great hurry to swallow her eel before any more interference, and gulped it down quickly; but afterwards seemed to have quite a time with it, for she stretched and twitched her neck for some time.   The crests of the Mergansers after coming up would be so wet that only a wisp was left of the feathers.

"Feb. 15.   This A.M. watched for twenty minutes the Ducks in Town Brook.   There were Mergansers and Whistlers.   A male Merganser dived and came up with a small eel, and a Herring Gull which was on the watch flew at him but he immediately dived.   The Gull floated on the water, looking around coolly on all sides, and when the Merganser came up with the eel still in his bill, went for him again.   This was done twice again (making four times in all), a shorter and shorter interval elapsing between dives.   At the fourth time up, the Merganser dropped the eel, but the Gull got it quicker than a flash, although I think the eel had got under the water.

"These Mergansers were seen distinctly to swim under water and thrust their bills into the bank and pull out their prey."

The food of the Red-breasted Merganser appears to be similar to that of the Merganser, consisting largely of fish and other aquatic animal life, with a small percentage of shell-fish (periwinkles, etc.); but it takes a much larger toll of marine life than does the former species.   Also like the Merganser it appears to collect food of some kind from the surface of the water by swimming with the neck stretched along the surface and the bill opened and immersed.

ECONOMIC STATUS.   See page 174.

Lophódytes cucullátus (Linnæus). Hooded Merganser.

Other names: HOODED SHELDRAKE; WOOD SHELDRAKE; POND SHELDRAKE; PICKAXE SHELDRAKE; SPIKE-BILL; HAIRY-CROWN; HAIRY-HEAD; SAW-BILL DIVER; WATER PHEASANT; KOKUS SHELDRAKE.

Plate 11.

DESCRIPTION. — Bill shorter than head, nostrils in basal half; frontal feathers extending much beyond those on sides of bill; a high, compressed crest, in both sexes; male opens and shuts crest like a fan. *Adult male in nuptial plumage:* Head, neck and upper plumage mainly black, changing to dark brown on flight-feathers, rump and tail; broad, snow-white patch extending from back of eye backward each feather black-tipped, these tips forming a black border; this white patch when erected fanlike forms the greater part of the semicircular crest, when lowered becomes a narrow, white triangle, flattened and extended backward; two black crescentic bars extend from upper back before wing down sides of white breast; fore-wing gray; white wing-patch on outer secondaries and ends of greater coverts crossed by black bar; inner secondaries and tertials black, rayed with sharply-defined attenuated stripes of white; sides and flanks reddish-brown, finely cross-waved with black; below, neck to tail, including axillars and under wing-coverts, mainly white, sometimes tinged cream or salmon color; under tail-coverts brownish waved with dusky bars; bill black; iris yellow; legs and feet light yellowish-brown. *Adult male in eclipse plumage:* Strictly only a partial eclipse; head and neck mottled with brownish; breast and flanks similar to those of female. "The full plumage is assumed early in fall, much earlier than in young birds, and is usually complete in October" (A. C. Bent). *Immature male:* In March, head and neck light brown; more or less sprinkled with new black feathers; crest brownish-white with broad, brown margin; upper plumage dark brown, lighter feather-edges; upper breast dusky-gray; lower breast and abdomen white; in May and June these traces of winter feathers are lost and a semi-eclipse is assumed, similar to adult male (J. G. Millais). *Adult female:* Head and neck grayish-brown, darker on top; crest cinnamon, smaller than in male and more bushy; back dusky-brown; sides and flanks lighter dusky-brown or dark ashy-brown with lighter feather edges; throat paling toward whitish chin; lower neck and upper breast a mixture of brown and whitish, giving a grayish-brown effect; lower breast, belly and wing-patch white, latter crossed on its fore part by a dusky bar; white of wing (both patch and rays on secondaries and tertials) restricted or impure; bill dusky or black above, its edges and most or all of lower mandible yellow or orange; iris brown; feet brownish or dusky. *Young:* Similar to adult female but chin and throat whitish; crest smaller or wanting (especially in young female); back, sides and under tail-coverts browner; colors more subdued. *Downy young:* Above brown, paling to cinnamon or buff on cheeks, darkening on back and rump; small white spots in 3 pairs on back, hind edge of wings and rump; below from chin to tail white or dingy whitish except a brown or gray band across fore neck.

MEASUREMENTS. — Length 16.00 to 19.25 in.; spread about 24.00 to 26.50; folded wing 6.50 to 8.00; tail 3.50 to 4.00; bill along ridge 1.50 to 1.70; tarsus 1.15 to 1.90. Weight: 1 lb. to 1 lb. 7 oz. (Audubon). Female smaller than male.

MOLTS. — Young birds have slight partial molt in early spring and apparently partial summer molt, but there is no great change in appearance during first year; in November and December of second winter male begins to assume plumage resembling adult; in spring this is nearly complete but duller than in fully mature bird; partial eclipse plumage occurs in the following summer and apparently male assumes full adult dress in ensuing fall and winter when nearly two years and six months old; immature female apparently assumes adult plumage in November of second year or soon afterward when about 17 months old; adults (both sexes) have a summer molt as in other species but this has not been fully worked out; in early autumn adults begin another molt, which is succeeded by winter (nuptial) plumage.

FIELD MARKS. — *Male:* Smallest of Mergansers; smaller than Wood Duck; black and white; narrow, fan-shaped (when erected) white-patched head-crest; two black bars in front of wing, and brown sides; male Buffle-head has a white-patched head-crest but no black border like that of this species. *Female:* Much smaller than other Mergansers; breast darker; her short, slim, narrow, rounded bill separates her from other ducks.

VOICE. — A hoarse croak like a small edition of Red-breasted Merganser (D. G. Elliot); female surprised with young, a guttural, chattering cry (E. A. Samuels); a variety of guttural, chattering notes (J. H. Bowles); a rough grunt "resembling the syllables *croo crooh crooh*" (Audubon).

BREEDING. — In forests near water; often in wooded swamps. *Nest:* In hollow tree or stump; sometimes in nesting-box; often high above ground or water; very rarely on ground under tree roots; built of grasses, weeds, etc., lined with down from breast of female. *Eggs:* 5 to 12; 2.05 to 2.15 by 1.70 to 1.75 in.; nearly globular; ivory white. *Dates:* March 15 to August 10 in United States. *Incubation:* Period 31 days (W. Evans); by female. One brood yearly.

RANGE. — North America. Breeds locally in wooded regions from southeastern Alaska, central British Columbia, Great Slave Lake, Northern Manitoba, Ontario and New Brunswick (probably in central Ungava (northern Quebec), southern Labrador and Newfoundland) south to Oregon, northwestern Nevada, northern New Mexico, southern Louisiana, southern Tennessee, Alabama and central Florida; winters from southern British Columbia, Utah, Colorado, Nebraska, Illinois, Indiana, Pennsylvania and Massachusetts south to Lower California, southern Mexico, the Gulf states and Cuba; uncommon to rare in northeastern part of range. Recorded from St. Michael, Alaska, also Ireland, Wales and Bermuda.

DISTRIBUTION IN NEW ENGLAND. — Rare migrant and summer resident in Maine, New Hampshire and Vermont; uncommon migrant and rare winter resident in Massachusetts, Rhode Island and Connecticut; probably bred formerly in southern New England but not known to breed now.

SEASON IN MASSACHUSETTS. — March 18 to May 2 (August 11); September 28 to December 28; winters locally and irregularly from Boston southward.

HAUNTS AND HABITS. The cold and privations of winter have passed, and now in the solitude of small secluded pools, streams and ponds in swamp and forest the Hooded Mergansers disport themselves. Returning spring with its annual awakening kindles anew in their breasts the glowing fires of reproduction. The males, in all the splendor of their elegant spring plumage, seek and pay court to their prospective mates. Gallantly they dash back and forth, rippling the dark waters, expanding and contracting their flashing fan-shaped crests, now proudly rising erect on the water with bill pointed downward and head drawn back, now speeding in rapid rushes to and fro. The ardent males chase the females, pursuing them on the surface and even following them under water. I have lain prone amid grass and underbrush watching the kaleidoscopic changes of such a scene where several males, two of them in splendid nuptial plumage, were coursing over the dark water in full display before an appreciative group of the other sex.

The Hooded Merganser is not ordinarily, like the Merganser, a frequenter of swift waters but seems to prefer slow streams and quiet, shaded pools. Nevertheless when wintering in the north, it goes by necessity to fast running streams, river rapids or open spring-holes, and probably rarely seeks salt water, for I have never seen it in water more salt than brackish lagoons near the sea. It is not quite so wary as are the other mergansers and this lack of caution has led to its decimation. It is fond of decoy ducks which when employed by the gunner readily lead it to its doom. It is attracted readily to park ponds in which ducks are kept and may be seen occasionally in such ponds in Boston.

It was formerly a common bird throughout a large part of the American continent. Now it is uncommon or rare over considerable areas. It is a swift and almost noiseless flier and easily threads its way among the branches of trees in its swampy woodlands. Estimates of its flight-speed, however, running up to 90 or 100 miles an hour probably are excessive. It lives in haunts similar to those of the Wood Duck and as it also nests in hollow trees, it is known as the "Wood Duck" to many people on the Pacific coast. Mr. J. H. Bowles has sent to me two photographs showing nesting-boxes which he fastened on trees near Tacoma, Washington, and in which Hooded Mergansers have nested.

Its nesting cavities often are very high above the ground. In many cases the young climb out of the nest soon after they are hatched and jump, scramble, fall or flutter to the ground or water below. It is said that sometimes the mother takes them, one at a time, and flies with them to the nearest water. Spreadborough records a case where a pair nested for four years in an elm stub in Ontario. The "old bird," he says, "carried her young from the tree to the water in her bill." The nest was about thirty feet from the ground and the nesting tree was on the bank of the river.[1] Dr. Hatch states that while rowing on a lake with a lady, his companion saw what both supposed was a Wood Duck carrying her duckling by the neck. He says that, lying in wait with a field glass, they saw the bird "resume the loving task" and identified it as a female Hooded Merganser.[2]

In early September when the young are well grown and fledged, they gather in small companies, and soon their travels begin. In Massachusetts, particularly near the coast, the species in migration is most common in October. Very few adult males appear, but often the females and young are common locally at this season. In winter an occasional bird or two may be seen in favorable seasons in small ponds near the coast or on open water in the rivers of Massachusetts. In spring the main northward flight passes through Massachusetts in late March or April. During the seasons of migration they frequent the haunts of the Wood Duck and the Black Duck but do not often associate with them.

The Hooded Merganser is not at all dependent on fish, although, like its larger congeners, it eats them. It remains for considerable periods in ponds where there are no fish. It takes small frogs, tadpoles, insects, seeds and even the roots or bulbs of water plants, and has been known to eat corn. Its food is not well known but it appears to be a harmless bird. It should be protected sufficiently at least to allow it to increase in numbers. It is considered a table delicacy as compared to other mergansers, but it is too small to have great food value.

ECONOMIC STATUS. See page 174.

---

[1] Macoun, J., and Macoun, J. M.: Catalogue of Canadian Birds (Canada Department of Mines, Geological Survey Branch), 1909, p. 763.
[2] Hatch, P. L.: Notes on the Birds of Minnesota, Geological and Natural History Survey of Minnesota, 1892, p. 27,

SUBFAMILY **ANATINÆ**. RIVER DUCKS.

Number of species in North America 15; in Massachusetts 12.

Ducks other than the mergansers have rather broad, flat bills. They fall naturally into two groups — the fresh-water, surface-feeding ducks, and the diving or bay and sea ducks. River ducks differ from both mergansers and sea ducks in having no lobe

FOOT OF RIVER DUCK

or flap on the hind toe. River ducks get their food mainly in shallow water by tipping up, head downward, which enables them to reach bottom, or by dabbling along the margin. All of them, however, can dive in case of necessity and sometimes they do so, but not commonly. Most of these ducks have a note-worthy marking, a brightly colored, iridescent patch on the secondary feathers of each wing known as the speculum.

All male surface-feeding ducks of North America (and apparently females also) undergo a double molt beginning in the season of reproduction. After the first of these molts in summer the male has assumed an inconspicuous plumage (called the eclipse plumage — which is rather brief), usually very similar to that of the female, and after the second molt (out of the eclipse plumage) takes on the usual adult winter or nuptial plumage. In species where the male and female are alike and in females of most species the changed plumage of summer is so much like that of winter that it is not noticeable. During the entire year most of the feathers are shed twice, but "the long scapulars, wings and ventral feathers are renewed only once," being molted among the last of all; young males of the second year molt in a similar manner. The dates of these molts vary much according to the age of the birds or the latitude of the locality. The males usually begin to molt into eclipse plumage in May or June but do not shed all their flight feathers until August. They then are unable to fly. This is often (but perhaps not always) the case with females, though usually they are flightless (if at all) for a shorter period.

Ánas platyrhýncha LINNÆUS. Mallard.

Other names: GRAY MALLARD; GREENHEAD; GRAY DUCK (FEMALE); WILD DUCK; DOMESTIC DUCK; ENGLISH DUCK.

Plate 12.

DESCRIPTION. — *Adult male in winter and nuptial plumage:* Head and most of neck iridescent green with some purple gloss; a white ring almost entirely around neck, broken only behind; front and sides of lower neck, and breast chestnut; center of back brown (finely cross-waved with whitish), graying over shoulders, scapulars and tertials and blackening toward tail; wings mainly brownish-gray; wing-patch or speculum violet, bordered in front and behind with black and white; tail dark gray, outer feathers paler gray; outer webs of all tail feathers bordered white or whitish; upper and under tail-coverts black, glossed bluish-green; rest of under plumage silver-gray, finely cross-lined with darker, most heavily on sides (flanks end in white); axillars and under wing-coverts pale cream; a tuft of up-curled tail-coverts

PLATE 12

PLATE 12

MALLARD
Page 190
Winter (Nuptial) Plumage

Adult Female

Adult Male

BLACK DUCK
Page 195

RED-LEGGED BLACK DUCK
Page 194

GADWALL
Page 199
Winter (Nuptial) Plumage

Adult Male

Adult Female

All one-sixth natural size.

on tail near end; bill lemon-yellow, greenish-yellow or yellowish-green, tip (and sometimes ridge) black; legs and feet reddish-orange, brick-red or coral-red; iris dark brown or hazel. *Adult male in eclipse plumage:* Assumed for a short time in summer; variable; similar to female, usually darker and more uniform above, especially top of head, and upper breast darker; wing, which is molted but once each year, is that of winter and nuptial plumage, with speculum deeper and more blue than that of female, which is more greenish; male usually shows one or more long gray scapulars; no curled feathers above tail. In full eclipse when wing-feathers have been shed, male and female are much alike; when going into eclipse or coming out of it enough old or new feathers remain in wing to identify the male. *Adult female in winter and nuptial plumage:* Above dark brownish becoming blackish on lower back; feathers edged buff; throat buff, in some cases spotted and streaked dusky; wing similar to that of male; tail rather dark grayish-brown with pale buffy edges and markings; head and neck lighter than body and finely mottled and streaked darker; top of head dark (streaked blackish), also an inconspicuous dark line through eye to nape; speculum like male's but duller; breast brownish-buff marked with black spots and U-shaped marks; below buffy, spotted dusky; sides and flanks dark with buffy feather edges; bill orange or greenish-olive with dark nail and with more or less black elsewhere, very variable; legs and feet reddish-orange. *Young in juvenal plumage:* Similar to adult female; upper plumage usually darker; dusky mottlings and streaks duller, less clearly defined, those on breast wide shaft-streaks instead of horseshoe-shaped figures; legs and feet duller in color; tails of all young birds usually more ragged, worn and blunt at tips than those of adults; wing of young male generally brighter in color than that of young female and bill clear olive-green; young female smaller than adult. *Downy young:* Top and back of head brown or "brownish green" lightening on forehead; sides of head and sides of forehead yellowish-buff; dusky or dark brown stripe through eye and small dark spot in ear-region; other upper plumage brown, a trifle lighter than top of head; two pairs of yellowish spots, one spot on each side of base of tail and one spot near hind border of each wing; below yellowish-buff to yellow, sides grayer with some brown patches.

MEASUREMENTS. — Length 19.25 to 28.00 in.; spread 32.00 to 39.75; folded wing 10.00 to 12.00; tail 3.00 to 4.50; bill 1.55 to 2.40; tarsus 1.50 to 1.90. Weight, 2 lbs. to 3 lbs. 12 oz. Female smaller than male.

MOLTS. — Juvenal birds molt into first winter plumage, August to December or later; in this plumage both male and female resemble adults, but probably are not fully mature until another year; adults molt twice yearly though in some cases, in addition, the adult male has in spring a slight molt of body-feathers; his molt into the dull (protective) "eclipse" plumage begins in June (rarely in May) and involves all the contour feathers; the flight-feathers which are molted but once a year, are among the last to be shed "while the drake is in eclipse plumage in August" (Bent), but are quickly regained so that the duck is not flightless for long; males in changing plumage very variable; much time is occupied in two transitional molts — into and out of brief eclipse plumage; annual complete molt covers period from August to November (body-feathers (partially) and tail and tertials (all of the eclipse) being again shed and all flight-feathers being likewise renewed, thus making this molt complete), and the bird again takes on brighter colors of full plumage of following winter and spring; adult females molt into winter and nuptial plumage (October to March) losing in the process all body-feathers and sometimes tail-feathers as well; there is some molting in next April and May, but in following summer (July and August) all body- and tail-feathers are molted, following which most of the flight-feathers are shed and renewed.

FIELD MARKS. — Like domesticated Mallard, but smaller, slimmer; size of Black Duck; wing linings creamy-white in both sexes. *Male: Green head, narrow white ring around neck,* gray sides, *up-turned feathers on tail. Female:* Resembles Black Duck but lighter in color; wing patch or speculum bordered *both before and behind* by a *white bar* where Black Duck has none or only a mere white line; "at long range white under parts of the male show as a light area even in poor light . . . female bears super-ficial resemblance to female Baldpate . . . there is much more white in wing of Baldpate" (Ludlow Griscom).

VOICE. — Female: loud harsh *quack* like that of domestic duck. Male: a similar note but softer — *kwek-kwek-kwek-kwek* (Ludlow Griscom).

BREEDING. — Usually on prairie (wet or dry) or in marsh; sometimes on dry cultivated land, sometimes in tall timber. *Nest:* Commonly on ground near water but sometimes far from it; rarely in tree; commonly hidden by reeds, flags, leaves, low branches, etc.; built of reeds, flags, grasses, leaves, etc., warmly lined with down from female's breast. *Eggs:* 5 to 14; 2.06 to 2.55 by 1.40 to 1.80 in.; average 2.26 by 1.60; ovate; yellowish-white, yellowish-drab, pale greenish-white, pale greenish-buff, buffy-pea-green, or some similar shade, usually dirty or dingy. *Dates:* Last week in February to July 2 in various parts of United States. *Incubation:* Period said to vary from 23 to 29 days; most authorities say 26 or 27; by female. One brood yearly.

RANGE. — Northern Hemisphere. Breeds in North America from Aleutian and Pribilof Islands, northwestern Alaska, northern Mackenzie, northern Manitoba, west coast of Hudson Bay, eastern Ontario, New Brunswick and Nova Scotia (casually) south to northern Lower California, Arizona (probably), southern New Mexico, southern Texas (casually), southern Kansas, central Missouri, southeastern Illinois, southwestern Indiana, southern Ohio and northern Virginia; winters from Aleutian Islands, central Alaska, western Montana, southern Saskatchewan (casually), Nebraska, Minnesota, southern Wisconsin, northern Indiana, Ohio, Maryland, and Nova Scotia (casually) south to southern Mexico, Lesser Antilles and Panama; casual in Bermuda and Hawaii, Cuba, Jamaica and Grenada; breeds also in Eastern Hemisphere, in Iceland, through Europe south of the Arctic Circle, in the Azores and northern Africa, in Siberia and central Asia and from Turkestan to China; also in Japan, Chosen, Kurile and Commander Islands; it ranges in winter to Madeira, the Canary Islands, and in Africa south to Tropic of Cancer; also to India and Burmah and casually to Borneo; a distinct race of Mallards is found in Greenland.

DISTRIBUTION IN NEW ENGLAND. — Formerly a rare migrant in all the New England states; recorded in Maine, Massachusetts and Rhode Island as a winter resident; regular transient in small numbers in several ponds of southeastern Massachusetts and near the mouth of the Connecticut River; now probably breeding in all New England states, but rather uncommon or rare generally at all times in these states, though sometimes locally common.

SEASON IN MASSACHUSETTS. — Resident the entire year, but it is difficult to distinguish between wild, half tame and escaped birds; most common in fall from October to December; rather rare in late March and April; breeds irregularly and locally.

HAUNTS AND HABITS. Normally the Mallard is a rather rare duck in New England where its place is taken by the Black Duck. During the second decade of the twentieth century, however, it became more common here. This may be due to some extent to the greater protection recently accorded wild-fowl under state and national laws, but the increase in numbers of this handsome duck is due largely to recent propagation of the bird by park commissioners, game commissioners, sportsmen and gamekeepers. Many escaped or released birds are now mating with wild Mallards or other escaped birds, and their progeny continues to increase the stock of wild ducks native to New England. The Mallard will breed almost anywhere if unmolested. Its adaptability has made it the chief wild duck of the world. It readily adapts itself to civilization. It does not require a secluded island in an isolated lake in some vast northern wilderness; it will nest on a little islet in a small pond in a city park, on a marshy spot near a noisy boiler factory, under sage-brush near a small waterhole in a desert with no other water for miles around or under a bush in a hillside pasture. It feeds readily on land and requires very little water. Although like all ducks it welcomes an ample supply, it can be happy in a puddle.

Like all wild-fowl, however, it prefers an aquatic courtship and mating. The male in his wooing antics displays his beauties upon the surface of the water, rearing up proudly, bowing to his mate, pursuing her here and there until she responds by nodding in her turn which seems to signify her acceptance of his suit. The nest usually is well concealed. When incubation begins, the male, like those of most other ducks, when thus left to their own devices, deserts the female and seeks only his own comfort and pleasure, leaving the mother to care for the young. The ducklings leave the nest probably within twenty-four hours after they are hatched, and go to water, where they readily dive, and in case of danger hide either beneath the surface or amidst the water plants, with only the bill above water. If food conditions are not satisfactory where they are hatched, the mother leads them overland to other waters. By the latter part of August those that have survived are fully fledged, and in September the migration begins. The Mallard often mingles with other species of ducks, especially Pintails.

The Mallard is very adaptable in the matter of food. It eats many kinds of succulent water plants, seeds, acorns, insects, particularly grasshoppers, many small aquatic animals and probably all the grains grown within its range. It is very fond of corn, wheat and wild rice and in the season of ripening grain is one of the best water-fowls for the table.

ECONOMIC STATUS. Economically the Mallard is by far the most important duck in the world. Its great numbers and wide distribution in the wild state have placed it in the first rank of wild-fowl that for many centuries have provided food for aborigines and settlers in the Northern Hemisphere. In recent times it has become the chief wild duck in the markets of the world. As an object of sport because of its great numbers and wide distribution it transcends all other ducks. It comes well to decoys and is an excellent table bird. It is the principal wild duck of the game farm and game preserve and also the most important of decoy ducks. As a stock duck it is the progenitor of most of the domestic ducks the world over, most varieties being descended wholly or in part from the Mallard. The income or food value of its eggs and flesh used throughout the world equals millions of dollars annually and the capital invested in duck raising probably runs into many millions.

Mallards are very destructive to the larvæ of mosquitoes and appear to be much more effective than fish in clearing stagnant pools where mosquitoes breed. It is a well-known fact that these larvæ, hatched in stagnant water, live and develop there into the full-grown insects. Ducks feeding about such pools eat thousands of the larvæ and by stirring up the water drown thousands more. Dr. Samuel G. Dixon, Commissioner of Public Health of Pennsylvania, in 1914 introduced goldfish into a specially constructed pond as mosquito destroyers and twenty Mallards were turned into a similar pond for the same purpose. In the goldfish pond the larvæ continued to flourish while in the Mallard pond they disappeared. Ten Mallards were then turned into the goldfish pond. In forty-eight hours only a few larvæ survived.[1] See also page 174.

------

[1] Journal American Medical Association, Vol. LXIII, 1914, p. 1203.

Anas rúbripes rúbripes Brewster. Red-legged Black Duck.

Other names: RED-LEG; WINTER BLACK DUCK; CLAM DUCK.

Plate 12.

DESCRIPTION. — *Adults (sexes alike)*: Similar to Black Duck (see page 195) but averaging larger; feathers of top of head conspicuously edged with grayish or fulvous; *dark markings on fore neck and sides of head coarser, blacker, more sharply defined;* entire throat usually streaked or *spotted with blackish;* iris brown; legs and *toes bright coral red,* webs dusky; bill yellow, nail black; both sexes sometimes have bill olive-green or greenish-yellow; in female sometimes green and blackish. *Young:* Similar to adults; smaller, bill duller, sometimes bluish-gray, lower mandible pinkish and feet not so bright red. *Downy young:* Similar to those of Black Duck.

MEASUREMENTS. — Length 21.00 to 24.00 in.; spread 33.00 to 39.00; folded wing 10.47 to 12.00; tail 3.50 to 4.00; bill 1.95 to 2.30; tarsus 2.15 to 2.50. Weight 2 lbs. 9 oz. to nearly 4 lbs.; "heaviest male noted by myself, 3 lbs. 12 oz." (J. C. Phillips). Females smaller than males which are a little more richly colored.

MOLTS. — Probably molts are same as in Black Duck. (See page 196.)

FIELD MARKS. — (See under Black Duck, page 196.) This duck cannot be distinguished ordinarily in field from Black Duck as it is even more wary; when near enough in a good light and with a good glass the *coral red legs* or the *yellow bill* which distinguish typical Red-legs from typical Black Ducks may be seen, but there are many young birds or adults intermediate between the two races in which the colors of these parts vary.

Voice and Breeding are similar to those of Black Duck.

RANGE. — The range of this race as distinguished from that of the Black Duck is not definitely known; but the Red-leg appears to occupy a boreal region north of the range of the Black Duck. The range may be approximated as follows: Eastern Canada and northeastern United States. Breeds from central Keewatin, Hudson Bay, northern Ungava (Quebec) and northern Labrador south to the northern border of the Black Duck's range; winters largely in the coastal region from Nova Scotia south to northern South Carolina, Georgia, Florida, Alabama, Louisiana and Texas; in migration westward to northeastern North Dakota, southeastern Kansas and Arkansas.

DISTRIBUTION IN NEW ENGLAND. — Common spring and fall migrant, largely coastwise; common to abundant winter resident, mainly coastwise; probably rare or casual summer resident.

SEASON IN MASSACHUSETTS. — September 22 to May 5. Occasional in summer; may breed rarely.

HAUNTS AND HABITS. The Red-legged Black Duck appears to be a hardy northern race which was well known to Massachusetts gunners for many years before it was described in 1902 by my friend, the late William Brewster, the eminent ornithologist of Cambridge. Even then it was not generally recognized by ornithologists as a valid distinct race or subspecies and it is not listed in the third edition of the A. O. U. check list. Even now some ornithologists regard the Red-leg as merely the mature adult of the Black Duck, notwithstanding the fact that Mr. F. H. Kennard has taken a young bird with red legs (1913) and the further fact that Dr. C. W. Townsend has watched captive Black Ducks to and through the third year of their lives and found that their legs although growing more orange in color did not at any time assume the bright coral-red of the Red-leg.

I have examined many live birds taken in traps and also many skins and finally incline to the opinion that Mr. Brewster was right, but the variation in colors of legs, feet and bills and the many intermediates between the types make identification often difficult.

Further investigation and discussion by Messrs. Brewster, Dwight, Townsend and others apparently confirm the original decision although the form is not yet (1925) recognized by the American Ornithologists' Union Committee on Nomenclature. Probably individual variation is due largely to the fact that the two forms are merely subspecies, and in the area of transition all sorts of intermediates will naturally occur. The Red-legged Black Duck apparently is a virile bird, increasing its numbers and extending its range. If not already the principal wintering Black Duck of the Atlantic coast it soon will be at its present rate of increase. Its habits and food are similar to those of the Black Duck but it migrates later in autumn. While the Black Duck begins to move during the latter half of September, the Red-legs are rare then in Massachusetts. They come in larger numbers in late October and November and remain abundant all winter in suitable sheltered places such as the neighborhood of Plum Island off Newburyport and Ipswich, under the lee of Nahant beach, in Plymouth Harbor or Duxbury Bay. Some may be seen in open fresh-water ponds about Boston, especially where no shooting is allowed, but to see large numbers of these birds one must go to the salt water. This is a hardy race, many individuals of which remain in the North during the most severe winters. When the flats are frozen and they can get no food, they go to open springs to drink, and spend their days and nights mainly in sitting on the ice and slowly starving. In such winters many perish for want of food; or weakened by starvation they are killed and eaten by ravenous crows, gulls, eagles and foxes. Their habits and food are much the same as those of the Black Duck, but they are more addicted to salt water and tidal flats, are even more shy and do not come readily to live decoys. Black Ducks of both races get many small mussels and some very small clams after severe frosts come in the fall and early winter. Red-legged Black Ducks are very fond of such food. Clams found in their stomachs are often broken, but small shell-fish, with shells thick and strong, mussels, quahaugs and snails, are swallowed unbroken. No doubt these birds use their feet in working ("puddling") small clams out of the sand, but it is impossible to see the operation clearly as they are very shy, and usually work in the dusk of evening or at night by moonlight. They feed in very shallow water on the sand-flats or work in under the edge of the marsh, among the roots of the grass, and get only tiny clams which are not far below the surface.

ECONOMIC STATUS. The Red-legged Black Duck is quite as important economically as the Black Duck. It is a larger and hardier bird and therefore of more value for food and sport and in late autumn and winter its numbers in New England exceed those of the Black Duck.

Anas rubripes tristis BREWSTER. **Black Duck.**

Other names: DUSKY DUCK; DUSKY MALLARD; BLACK MALLARD; SUMMER BLACK DUCK.

Plate 12.

DESCRIPTION. — *Adults at all seasons (sexes alike)*: Resemble female Mallard but darker and with little or no white except linings of wings which are silvery-white; prevailing color dusky or blackish-brown somewhat lighter below and sometimes darkening to black on lower back and rump, feathers mostly edged pale brownish-gray or buffy; top of head and nape dark and usually very slightly marked with lighter color; sides of head and neck pale brownish-gray or buffy with fine dark streaking, a dark line along whole side of head through eye; throat and chin pale brownish-gray or buffy, usually unmarked; wing-coverts dusky-gray, the lesser with lighter edges, the greater tipped black, forming a black front edge to deep purplish-blue or violet speculum or wing-patch (changeable iridescence may show green and rusty-red) which is bordered both before and behind with black, sometimes with a narrow white hind border (probably in fully adult males); primaries and tail blackish; iris dark brown; bill and feet variable in color; bill usually olive, dusky-olive or olive-green in female and yellowish-green, greenish-yellow or "dusky-yellow" in male, often marked blackish (sometimes greenish-black on ridge); nail dark; legs and feet greenish or olivaceous-brown, varying to reddish-brown or orange-red (but not coral-red),

DOWNY YOUNG BLACK DUCK
About ½ natural size.

very variable. *Young:* Similar to adults, but bill and feet darker or duller in color, tail feathers worn at tips and under plumage having a more striped appearance. *Downy young:* Resembling young Mallard, but usually a little darker brown above; top of head dark brown to brownish-black with yellowish tinge on forehead; chin and throat brownish-white or pale yellowish-brown; stripe through eye dark brown to brownish-black above which runs a light stripe; variable; some young have a second dark stripe from gape to ear, others have large dark patch back of eye, others a dark patch in ear-region; hind border of wing, a spot on each side of back behind wing and another spot on each side of rump brownish-white; fore neck pale yellowish-brown; below usually yellowish or whitish, though sometimes darker or dusky.

MEASUREMENTS. — Length 21.00 to 23.50 in.; spread 32.00 to 36.50; folded wing 10.14 to 10.52; tail about 2.75; bill 1.93 to 2.05; tarsus 1.75 to 2.20. Weight, female about 2½ lbs., male reaching over 3 lbs.; average weight in December (possibly increased by artificial feeding), male "3.24 lbs.," female "2.66 lbs." (J. C. Phillips); largest male 3 lbs. 10 oz., largest female 2 lbs. 15 oz.

MOLTS. — In juvenal plumage young bird appears more striped below than adult but by midwinter its molt into winter plumage has been completed and it has assumed plumage very similar to that of adult; bill and feet change color in spring, bill of male becoming lighter greenish-yellow while that of female changes from blackish to dark olive-green; legs of male become more orange while those of female become yellowish; during summer both adults and young seem to be almost continually molting; probably adults have a double molt like other ducks, but since both male and female are alike there is no real eclipse plumage, and there is little color change throughout the year.

FIELD MARKS. — Size of average Mallard; like female Mallard but *darker;* has practically no white on borders of wing-patch or speculum where Mallard shows white; indistinguishable at a distance from Red-legged Black Duck by its (usually) darker bill and lighter red, brownish or dusky legs; known from most other ducks by its large size and rather uniform dark (but not black) tone, with no prominent markings; on salt water it almost never dives; in flight looks very dark with *silvery*-white wing-linings and long neck, lighter than body in color, stretching often a trifle downward.

VOICE. — Female, a loud quack somewhat like that of Mallard. Male, a lower and shorter quack.

BREEDING. — Usually in wooded regions, rarely among stunted trees, often in bushy or grassy fields or pastures, sometimes on islands in lakes or ponds, sometimes near brooks. *Nest:* On ground usually, but not always near water, rarely high in trees in an old nest of crow or hawk; of weeds, grass, flags, leaves, feathers, etc., well lined with down which often as in the case of other ducks is added to as incubation advances (fig. 23). *Eggs:* 6 to 12; ovate to elongate-ovate; 2.22 to 2.50 by 1.63 to 1.83 in.; average 2.41 by 1.72; grayish-white or creamy-white to greenish-buff; practically indistinguishable from those of Mallard. *Dates:* April 2 to May 24, New England. *Incubation:* Period 26 to 28 days (Barnes and H. H. Bailey); by female. One brood yearly.

RANGE. — Most of eastern United States and southeastern Canada; northern limit of breeding range in Canada not well determined. Breeds on Atlantic slope from Labrador, Quebec and Newfoundland south to eastern North Carolina and west to western Iowa, central Minnesota and Colorado (where very rare), also in Manitoba and on west coast of Hudson Bay; apparently extending its range westward; winters mainly along east coast of United States (and in certain inland localities where waters remain open) south to Florida and other Gulf states as far west as south-central Texas; rare west of Mississippi River; casual in Saskatchewan, Cuba and Jamaica; accidental in California and Bermuda.

DISTRIBUTION IN NEW ENGLAND. — Common to abundant migrant, and summer resident and less common winter resident, mainly coastwise; less common to rare in interior but breeding in suitable localities in all New England states and in mild seasons wintering in numbers in some inland waters.

SEASON IN MASSACHUSETTS. — Resident but most common in migration in March and in September and October.

HAUNTS AND HABITS. The Black Duck is the "wild duck" of New England. Here it fills the place occupied in the western States by the Mallard. It furnishes most of the duck shooting for gunners of the interior when the season opens in September and before the more hardy ducks have come down from the North. When the birds first come from inland waters and while they are feeding on wild rice and other vegetal food, their flesh is excellent, for it lacks the rank flavor acquired by Black Ducks and "Red-legs" later in the season when the ponds are locked in ice and the birds, perforce, must feed on the tide-flats. Early in the season before the young ducks have become acquainted with the gunner and his wiles, it is not very difficult to take them, but all that then escape the gunner soon acquire sufficient "education" to keep well out of gunshot as they pass by. The Black Duck is the wildest of them all, excepting only the "Red-leg," and he who would stalk these sagacious birds successfully must be as wily as a serpent. Few Black Ducks would be shot in New England were it not for the use of live decoy ducks and also for the fact that Black Ducks must have fresh water and must come to some "spring-hole" to drink when the ponds and rivers are frozen. There the gunner, lying concealed and taking advantage of their necessity, shoots them as they come in. Much has been spoken and written about the keenness of scent shown by these birds but I know by long experience that if a man can keep concealed and move *noiselessly*, he can approach Black Ducks down wind. However, the slightest sound will betray him. Their hearing is so much keener than ours that a favoring wind carries to their ears sounds that we would never notice.

The Black Duck is very much alive in every sense, and extremely active. It has many game qualities. It does not, like many ducks, drag itself slowly from the water into the air with laboring wings and splattering feet, but springs up at a bound. When it fears concealed danger from more than one quarter it often flies skyward; then, if not quickly shot down, it soon "towers" beyond the reach of the shotgun. It is so swift in flight that most "blunderers with a gun" will shoot far behind its tail. Although it does not ordinarily dive much for its food, when wounded it knows so well how to dive and hide under water that it often escapes to cover on shore where it hides away unnoticed.   When mortally wounded it will sometimes push under vegetation on the bottom, die there and remain entangled in the clinging water-weeds or grass.   Black Ducks are more or less nocturnal and when too much disturbed on their feeding-grounds in daylight, they fly out to sea or to the larger lakes to rest during the day and come into the smaller ponds and streams to feed at night, thus evading the gunner, but where not molested they feed during the day.   Like all ducks they are active on bright moonlit nights.

Dr. C. W. Townsend gives an excellent description of the courtship of these birds.[1] They begin by chasing one another about on the surface of the water.   Those chased dive with splashing wings.   The male often rises from the water in short flights and flies with body drooping a little and neck extended a trifle downward with bill open while he displays all his plumage, especially the white wing linings.   These flights are short and are ended by splashing down into the water near a female.   There is more or less bobbing of the head in the surface antics and often there is an extended pursuit of the female by the male.   They fly back and forth swiftly and close together, plunge into the water and race about on its surface for half an hour or more.

When the little ducklings are hatched they soon seek the water with their mother, and feed in shallow reaches of ponds among or near water plants where they can readily hide in case of danger.   There, however, they are exposed to attack from large frogs and snapping turtles which sometimes seize and devour them, and if they get into deep water they may be swallowed by large trout or pickerel.   In one way or another their enemies thin them out as the season advances.   By the last week in April or the first week in May in southeastern Massachusetts some of the ducklings are already swimming.   When the mother is suddenly surprised with her young she feigns to be wounded or helpless and so leads the intruder away.   On one such occasion on the island of No Man's Land, a dog scented or saw the mother with her brood among the water grass at the edge of a small pond.   As the brute ran into the water after them, the mother fluttered along just in front of his nose and while he followed the apparently disabled bird the young ones dived, swam along under water, came to the surface and dived again, keeping cunningly concealed amid the aquatic plants until the dog had been led far away by their devoted mother.   Then they swam ashore leaving the pond and creeping close to the ground through the short grass until they reached another small pond where they disappeared from our sight in the water-herbage.   The tiny things could not have been more than a day or two old.   They had our full sympathy.   We called the dog off and left the anxious mother circling round the spot.

During the summer until the young can fly they learn to keep well concealed whenever an intruder approaches.   By August they are on the wing and gather in small flocks in their favorite resorts.   In September they are ready for migration.   The Black Duck begins to migrate or work toward the salt water early in September.   Nearly all

---

[1] Townsend, C. W.: Auk, Vol. XXIII, 1916, pp. 13–15.

the flight-birds seen near our coast in September are of this race. Sometimes in migration they fly very high. The flight is more or less intermittent but continues all through the autumn and quite a number of the race winter in Massachusetts waters. In February, if the weather is mild, the northward flight begins, and in March as the ice breaks up the Black Ducks seek more and more the waters of the interior. While the ponds are still locked in ice, the birds seek open streams or "spring-holes" or even small rain-water pools in pasture hollows until their favorite grassy ponds and watery swamps are released from their fetters of ice. The Black Duck feeds in fresh ponds and salt marshes, but if in the latter it must go once or twice daily to fresh water to slake its thirst.

The food of the Black Duck has been carefully worked out by Mr. McAtee of the Biological Survey.[1] According to him substantially three-fourths of the food is vegetal and one-fourth animal. Fully one-half of the vegetal food is derived from pondweeds, eel-grass and wild celery. Grasses and their seeds form an important part, among them the grains, wild rice, also locally corn and wheat supplied to the ducks by gunners as "bait." Sedges are eaten and many seeds of weeds. In the viscera of one bird were found the enormous number of 36,300 seeds of smartweed. Considerable numbers of reed seeds are eaten. About half the animal food consisted of shell-fish, most of which are of no economic value, such as mussels, tiny clams and snails. Crustaceans, including barnacles, sand-fleas, shrimps and crawfish were eaten in appreciable numbers together with many insects. There was a very small proportion of fishes and their eggs. Mr. Allan Keniston tells me that during the first hard freeze in November, 1921, many young alewives were killed by the frost in Oyster Pond, Marthas Vineyard, and many more seemed to be partly paralyzed. Black Ducks fed on them for some time, probably mainly on the living, but disabled, ones. While feeding on these fish for at least a week these ducks, he says, were unfit to eat and their odor was disgusting.

ECONOMIC STATUS. As a game bird and food supply in the eastern United States the Black Duck has great economic value. The slight harm it may do by destroying small shell-fish and the eggs of fishes may be balanced by the destruction of insects, crawfishes and marine worms some of which destroy edible shell-fish.

Chaulelásmus stréperus (LINNÆUS). Gadwall.

Other names: GADWELL; GRAY DUCK; SPECKLE-BELLY; CREEK DUCK.

Plate 12.

DESCRIPTION. — Bill with many (about 50) lamellæ; distance from front border of nostril to tip of upper mandible more than three times that from same point to nearest loral feathers; tail-feathers 16. *Adult male in winter (nuptial) plumage*: Head and most of neck pale brownish, buffy-gray, or whitish, thickly speckled with grayish-brown or blackish, lightest on throat; top of head sometimes unspotted, but more often both top of head and hind neck darker than rest of head; lower neck and breast dark slaty-brown to black, broken up by crescentic bars of white so as to present a scale-like appearance; some of these feathers also have white centers; light upper neck contrasts abruptly with dark lower neck,

---

[1] McAtee, W. L.: United States Department of Agriculture, Bulletin No. 720, 1918, pp. 10–14.

rarely a more or less perfect black ring at juncture (this ring very seldom complete, if ever); back, scapulars, sides and flanks finely cross-lined with undulations of slaty-gray or slaty-brown and white, darkening through slaty-gray on rump to black on both upper and under tail-coverts; some scapulars gray, their edges broadly tinged pale yellowish-brown; tail-feathers and most of flight-feathers brownish-gray, tail-feathers faintly edged whitish; folded wing shades gradually from brownish-gray at bend to deep chestnut on middle coverts and black on greater coverts; a black frame incloses white wing-patch or speculum in front and below; lower breast and belly white, with faint dusky barring in region of vent; linings of wings and axillars white; bill above dull orange, along edges and below black or blackish; iris dark brown or hazel; legs and feet dull orange-yellow or bright ochre-yellow, webs dusky. *Adult male in eclipse plumage:* Similar to adult female in winter plumage but wings and tail similar to those of adult male in winter; top of head brownish-black; indistinct dark streak through eye as in female; rest of head and neck as in winter; back, rump and upper tail-coverts blackish-brown, each feather margined buffy; sides and flanks dark brown, the feathers marked and margined lighter rusty-brown; rest of under plumage dull white with blackish spot in center of many feathers. *Female:* Head and upper neck similar to that of male but a trifle more distinctly spotted; dark markings of upper neck usually grade insensibly into those of lower neck but black collar has been noted very rarely in this sex; dark shade or line from bill through eye to ear-region; no crescentic marks on breast, which is buffy, spotted blackish; wing-patch and wing-markings similar to those of male *but smaller* with less black and white and little or *no deep chestnut;* in autumn the speculum sometimes not white but gray; otherwise unlike male; colors largely brownish-dusky and very light brownish in irregular spots, bars and streaks; dusky predominates above and brownish or brownish-white below; lower part of breast and belly white; legs pale yellow; bill dusky-brown on and near ridge, below yellow or light orange, including edges of both mandibles. *Young:* Closely resemble adult female, but in winter plumage wing of young male generally lighter or more gray than that of female and in juvenal plumage he has light bars on upper back. *Downy young:* Resembles young of Mallard but paler and not so greenish; top of head and line from bill through eye dull bone-brown; above this line light stripe from upper mandible over eye to nape, narrowing behind; sides of head and neck dull creamy-buff; spot over ear dusky; upper surface of body dark brown growing darker toward tail; tip of tail brownish-white; paired brownish-white spots on hind margins of wings and sides of rump; throat and fore neck pale buff or creamy white; under surface of body mainly buffy-white or brownish-white; band across chest buff; young grow lighter in color as they grow older.

MEASUREMENTS. — Length 18.00 to 22.00 in.; spread 34.00 to 35.00; folded wing 9.62 to 11.00; tail about 4.50; bill along ridge 1.52 to 1.78; tarsus 1.42 to 1.70. Weight of male, 2 lbs. to 2 lbs. 6 oz. Female smaller than male.

MOLTS. — Young birds pass through usual fall and winter molts; the males (changing gradually with advance of winter) appear in March in practically adult plumage except for lower plumage, which is spotted, and wings; by June 1 bird resembles adult male except that its unmolted wings are duller; eclipse plumage is assumed early, usually by July; often in next November full adult winter plumage is complete; adult males molt earlier, assuming eclipse plumage in June or July and begin to change in August.

FIELD MARKS. — Smaller than Black Duck; slender, gray, with long, pointed wings and white speculum; adult male Baldpate has fore wing nearly all white, but this large *patch* is much farther forward, larger and more conspicuous than small white *speculum* of Gadwall; *Female:* Closely resembles female Baldpate but is darker on back and rump and has white speculum — the only female river duck so marked; otherwise female somewhat resembles female Mallard, but is considerably smaller, looks slimmer in flight, shows white below and beats its wings faster.

VOICE. — Male in flight, a curious croak somewhat resembling the cry of a raven (J. G. Millais); in flight an oft-repeated quack, higher pitched and weaker than that of Mallard (E. H. Eaton); call of female essentially that of Mallard (J. C. Phillips).

BREEDING. — In meadows or marshes; very often on islands in lakes. *Nest:* A hollow in dry ground, among grasses not far from water, padded with grasses and weed stems and lined with down. *Eggs:*

7 to 12; average about 2.09 by 1.57 in. (Ridgway); average 2.15 by 1.50 (E. A. Samuels); a trifle over 2.00 by about 1.55 (Coues); oval, creamy-white; very like Baldpate's eggs. *Dates:* April 16 to July 20, California; May 18 to July 16, North Dakota. *Incubation:* Period 28 days (H. K. Job). One brood yearly.

RANGE. — Northern Hemisphere mainly. Breeds in North America from southern British Columbia, central Alberta, northern Saskatchewan, northern Manitoba, and Anticosti Island (casually) south to southern California, northwestern New Mexico, Texas, Louisiana, southwestern Kansas, northern Iowa and Missouri (formerly); winters from southern British Columbia, Utah, Wyoming (casually), northeastern Colorado, northern Arkansas, southern Illinois and Maryland south to southern Lower California, central Mexico and Florida; accidental or casual in Alaska, Bermuda, Cuba, Jamaica and Hawaii; rare in migration in middle and northeastern states north to Newfoundland; breeds also in Iceland and temperate regions of Europe and Asia, southern Spain and northern Algeria; winters far into Africa and in southern Asia.

DISTRIBUTION IN NEW ENGLAND. — Rare migrant in all New England states; casual in winter in Rhode Island.

SEASON IN MASSACHUSETTS. — September 22 to November 1; March to April 15.

HAUNTS AND HABITS. The Gadwall is so rare in Massachusetts and New England generally that few gunners recognize it. Probably, however, it is not so rare as the general belief would indicate, as the females and young which are much more numerous than the adult males are likely to be mistaken for young or females of the Baldpate or Pintail or might pass for small female Mallards. Records of specimens taken in recent years are very scattering. I have only seven for Connecticut, but the species is reported occasionally in Massachusetts by accurate observers and should be looked for, particularly in the fall migration.

In 1904 two were shot in October near Newburyport, one in the same month at Wenham Lake and another November 1, also near Newburyport. In October of the same year six were taken in the lakes near Middleboro.[1]

Following the present increase in the number of wild-fowl under protective laws some increase of this species in New England may ensue. The Gadwall breeds mainly in western Canada and winters largely in Louisiana and Texas. Therefore it cannot be expected to occur in any great numbers in the New England states. It keeps mainly to fresh water and in autumn when it has been feeding on wild rice and succulent roots it is an excellent fowl for the table. Although it is one of the surface-feeding ducks and some ornithologists assert that it never dives for its food, it is in reality a skilful diver. Audubon says that it dives well on occasion, especially when wounded, and Dr. Hatch remarks that the Gadwall is an exceptionally good diver and rapid swimmer. The idea that any water-fowl never dives should be discarded. Individuals of all species of water-fowl dive. No one can be sure that all individuals of every species acquire the habit, but probably all dive more or less when very young, when courting, when wounded or when the wing-quills have been shed and the birds are unable to fly, and therefore must dive to escape their enemies. This applies not only to ducks and other small water-

---

[1] Townsend, C. W.: Memoirs of Nuttall Ornithological Club No. III, The Birds of Essex County, Massachusetts, 1905, p. 129.

fowl, but also to geese, brant and swans, for individuals of all such species have been seen to dive.

The Gadwall rests high and buoyantly upon the water and when in air flies rapidly in small, compact flocks. When alarmed it springs at once into the air, climbing upward as readily as a Black Duck.

Early in September a few Gadwalls start south from their breeding-grounds but the main flight begins in October. The spring flight may start in February and a few of these birds may be seen rarely in March and April in New England.

The Gadwall feeds on insects, snails, tadpoles, small fish, crawfish, mollusks, tender grasses, succulent aquatic plants, bulbs and roots, seeds, nuts, acorns and grains. The flavor of its flesh on the table depends largely upon the kind of food that predominates in its diet. It is perhaps more largely a vegetarian than any other American duck.

ECONOMIC STATUS. See page 174.

Maréca penélope (LINNÆUS). European Widgeon.

Other names: WIDGEON OR WIGEON; RED-HEADED WIDGEON.

Plate 13.

DESCRIPTION. — Distance from front edge of nostril to tip of bill less than three times distance from same point to nearest loral feathers; lamellæ much coarser than in Gadwall; less than 15 visible from outside; tail feathers 14; a tendency to variation — at least two color phases noted. *Adult male in winter (nuptial) plumage:* Forehead and fore part of crown (sometimes all of latter) creamy-buff or creamy-white; chin and throat narrowly black along middle; upper eyelid black, lower white; rest of head and upper neck cinnamon-red or reddish-brown, more or less flecked with very fine black or iridescent spots; back, sides and flanks white, barred with fine undulating lines of black, giving a rather light gray effect; base of rump grayish-brown; tail blackish above, ashy below; wing pattern and color similar to that of Baldpate *except for grayish axillars* (in Baldpate these are white); broad area

AXILLARS OF BALDPATE　　　　AXILLARS OF EUROPEAN WIDGEON

After Phillips.

on chest and breast, extending on sides to shoulder, pinkish-brown; ends of upper, and all of under tail-coverts black; under plumage mainly white; bill light grayish-blue, tip black; iris dark brown; legs and feet variable, light gray-blue to brown, webs dusky. *Adult male in eclipse plumage:* Head and neck as in adult female; other upper plumage excepting wings very dark ashy-gray; fore part of back with indistinct, whitish, undulating cross-lines, rest of back and scapulars edged tawny; wings and tail as in winter except that white on fore wing is changed to ashy-blue-gray, and middle coverts are darker, with slightly lighter edges; upper part of breast and flanks rusty-brown; below mainly white. *Adult female:* Head and upper neck pale rusty or yellowish-red, paler before eye and on cheeks, speckled with

PLATE 13

PLATE 13

EUROPEAN WIDGEON
Page 202
WINTER (NUPTIAL) PLUMAGE

MALE

FEMALE

GREEN-WINGED TEAL
Page 211
WINTER (NUPTIAL) PLUMAGE

FEMALE

MALE

EUROPEAN TEAL
Page 209
NUPTIAL PLUMAGE

MALE

BALDPATE
Page 205

WINTER (NUPTIAL) PLUMAGE

ADULT FEMALE

ADULT MALE

BLUE-WINGED TEAL
Page 214
NUPTIAL PLUMAGE

FEMALE

MALE

All one-sixth natural size.

dusky or greenish-black and barred same, especially on crown; dusky patch around eye; rest of upper plumage dusky-brown, feathers edged and more or less barred light brown, brownish-red or whitish; outer surface of closed wing mainly dusky-gray; white wing-coverts as seen in male indicated in female by dusky-gray with white or whitish tips; dark terminal bar on tips of greater secondary coverts is indicated; inner secondaries dark gray; speculum dull grayish; tail feathers brownish-gray with lighter edges; lower neck, upper breast, sides and flanks dull, light reddish, indistinctly barred grayish-brown or whitish; wing-linings and axillars white or whitish, with fine dusky mottling giving a gray effect; rest of under plumage mainly white or whitish, under tail-coverts barred dusky; very old females have been known to assume a plumage similar to that of male; bill slightly duller than in male; legs and feet as male. *Young in first winter plumage:* Resemble adults; may be distinguished by worn, blunted, juvenal tail and male by juvenal wing. *Young in juvenal plumage:* Closely resembles adult female; young male distinguished from young female by "one or two gray ribbed feathers" between thigh and tail and by a gray feather with ribbing on its edge at end of scapulars (J. G. Millais). *Downy young:* Top of head dark brown or brownish-black; forehead, sides of head and hind neck light cinnamon-brown; back brown; below dull straw-yellow; wash of light cinnamon on fore neck; some specimens have a pair of tawny or cinnamon-buff spots near base of tail, a spot on each side of back and another on hind border of each wing; distinguishable from other nestling ducks by unusually small body and large head and bill.

MEASUREMENTS. — Length 17.50 to 20.00 in.; spread 29.50 to 35.00; folded wing 9.25 to 11.00; tail 3.40 to 4.50; bill 1.34 to 1.60; tarsus 1.45 to 1.65. Weight 1 lb. 3 oz. to 2 lbs. Female smaller than male.

MOLTS. — There is the usual double molt and eclipse plumage as in Baldpate. Millais says that some young males assume in March what is practically the adult dress while others do not complete this change until this second November.

FIELD MARKS. — Size of Baldpate. *Male:* Usually seen with Baldpates; creamy forehead and crown not nearly so striking as the "staring white" forehead and crown of Baldpate; more gray on back, scapulars and flanks than in Baldpate. *Female and young:* Practically indistinguishable from Baldpate even when seen on water at close range under favorable conditions; head and neck of female and young Widgeon usually brownish or reddish where same parts of female and young Baldpate appear largely grayish.

VOICE. — A shrill whistling *Wheé-yŏŭ* (authors); female, a low purr or croak (H. Saunders); a low note like *kir-r-r* (F. M. Chapman).

BREEDING. — Usually in open country, moor or tundra near water, but sometimes far from it. *Nest:* On ground, of grasses and other plants. *Eggs:* 5 to 10; 2.13 to 2.50 by 1.40 to 1.53 in.; pointedly ovate; buffy-white. *Dates:* May 12 to June 21, Iceland. *Incubation:* Period 24 to 25 days (W. Evans); 24 days (H. K. Job); by female. One brood yearly.

RANGE. — Northern part of Eastern Hemisphere. Breeding range in America unknown; breeds in Europe and Asia; winters in the British Isles, southern Europe, northern Africa and southern Asia; occurs uncommonly or rarely in winter and in migration in Greenland, Dominion of Canada, Alaska and Pribilof Islands and in United States (mainly in states along Atlantic and Pacific coasts and in Mississippi Valley) south to California, Texas, Louisiana and Florida.

DISTRIBUTION IN NEW ENGLAND. — Seen or taken uncommonly or rarely to casually usually in autumn or winter in all states except Vermont.

SEASON IN MASSACHUSETTS. — October 17 to December 31 (January 16); March 4 to 23.

NOTE. The European Widgeon has been rated by ornithologists generally as an accidental wanderer from the Old World. In my "Game Birds, Wild-Fowl and Shore Birds" I expressed the opinion that this bird probably was a permanent resident in this country, but later found that many years earlier Mr. C. J. Maynard with his usual perspicacity had recorded a similar belief (Birds of Eastern North America, 1896, p. 84). This bird is by no means accidental in North America, and as the marks for its

identification become better known, more and more instances of its occurrence are reported.   In 1916 I
listed eleven authentic records of the species in Massachusetts.   Dr. John C. Phillips has records of
13 birds taken at Wenham, Massachusetts, as follows: 1903, two; 1904, two; 1912, one; 1914, two;
1916, four; 1920, one; 1921, one.   On March 4 and 8, 1919, Mr. Francis A. Foster reported two birds
of this species, apparently male and female, on Sengegontacket Pond, Marthas Vineyard, and on March
23, 1920, he saw two males there with a flock of Baldpates.   Mr. Charles B. Floyd records two birds seen
December 23, 28 and 31, 1913, in Jamaica Pond, Boston; two January 10 and 14, 1914, in Leverett
Pond; and two December 19, 1920, in Jamaica Pond.   On December 5, 1920, one was seen in Jamaica
Pond, Boston, and was reported there or in near-by ponds later by several careful observers.   During
the same period another or the same bird was seen several times in Belmont.   On December 12 and 15,
1920, Mr. Charles L. Whittle saw a female at Spy Pond, Arlington.

Not all the Massachusetts records of the species are given here but enough to show that the Widgeon
should not be considered a casual or accidental visitant, but rather a rare and irregular migrant, probably
less rare than the Gadwall.   Records are fewer in other New England states than in Massachusetts.
I have but one for Connecticut,[1] but lack of records may be accounted for by lack of interested trained
observers.

The bird is well known to some of the gunners at Currituck Sound and in the Mississippi Valley as
the Red-headed Widgeon, and were it as readily recognized by gunners generally as by ornithologists, it
would not be regarded as accidental.   As yet there is no conclusive evidence of its breeding in this
country.   A bird taken on Long Island was apparently breeding but it may have escaped from confinement.   A "mated pair" was seen March 7, 1923, at Branchport, New York, by Mr. Verdi Burtch
(Auk, Vol. XL, 1923, p. 65).

A specimen was taken in Alaska on May 27, which must have been near the beginning of the nesting
season.   Mr. Harrison F. Lewis saw without doubt four European Widgeons June 13, 1923, at Esquimaux Point, Canadian Labrador, Province of Quebec (Lewis *in litt.*).   It is hardly probable that
all the birds of this species now taken in the United States (together with very many more that are doubtless overlooked) came here either from Europe or from Asia.

HAUNTS AND HABITS.   The European Widgeon is very likely to visit ponds where
wild celery and some of its favorite pondweeds grow.   Any pond frequented by Scaups,
Redheads and Baldpates is a good place to look for the Widgeon, which probably has
visited most such ponds within its migration range in this country.   In the British Isles,
however, this species frequents salt-water bays and estuaries where it feeds largely on
eel-grass or seaweed (*Zostera marina*).   Like its American congener, the Baldpate, it can
dive, but whenever diving for food becomes necessary it prefers to profit by the labor of
others, and so it often accompanies the Brant for the purpose of stealing favorite food
which that longer-necked bird brings to the surface.   So far as I know, no one has yet
reported a similar habit of the European Widgeon in this country, but it has been seen
here in company with the Brant in salt water.   Sportsmen can readily recognize it when
in hand by its rich brown or reddish head and its gray axillars, for both sexes, old and
young, have these distinctive marks, while the Baldpate has a grayish head and white
axillars.   If sportsmen would examine carefully all specimens of Widgeons taken by them
and save any with gray axillars for the museums, we might get a better idea of the
distribution of this species in this country than we have today.   The habits of the
Widgeon are much like those of the Baldpate.   Its note, however, is quite different.

_____

[1] Bishop, L. B.: Auk, Vol. XXXVIII, 1921, p. 583.

Having watched the male and listened to his call at close range, my own impression of it differs from those of other authors. The note is given by the swimming bird, which raises its head high, but holds it horizontally, and appears to inhale a full breath and then expel it. The first note seems to come with the indrawn breath, the second with the exhalation. To me it sounds like *er-whew!;* the first note soft and low, the second high and shrill. In New England the Widgeon appears late in October or in November, and may winter rarely in Massachusetts or Rhode Island, by going to the salt water after the ponds freeze. There are few New England spring records, and most individuals of this species seem to pass up the Mississippi Valley in spring, where they are more rarely seen in fall.

Little is known of the food of the Widgeon in the United States. But Mr. Douglas C. Mabbott, of the Biological Survey, reported on the contents of five Widgeons' stomachs. One contained the foliage of widgeon grass (*Ruppia maritima*) and eel-grass (*Zostera marina*); another "only widgeon grass"; another "rootstocks" of pondweeds (*Potamogetons*), a few seeds of dodder (*Cuscuta sp.*) and seeds of bur-reed (*Sparganium sp.*); the fourth, leaves of eel-grass; while the fifth had only seeds of the salt marsh bulrush (*Scirpus robustus*).[1]

ECONOMIC STATUS. The bird is so uncommon in Massachusetts that it has no economic value here. It is one of the finest of table ducks and might be a valuable addition to our domesticated fowls.

Mareca americána (GMELIN). Baldpate.

Other names: AMERICAN WIDGEON; GREEN-HEADED WIDGEON; SOUTHERN WIDGEON; CALIFORNIA WIDGEON; WHITE-BELLY; BALD-HEAD; WHITE-FACE.

Plate 13.

DESCRIPTION. — Somewhat similar to European Widgeon; much individual variation, but axillars always white. *Adult male in winter (nuptial) plumage:* Forehead and top of head white (sometimes slightly tinged with buff); sides of head and neck less purely white or more buffy, thickly speckled with lusterless dusky-greenish; a broad glossy green patch extending from eye region to nape and sometimes down upper hind neck; lower hind neck and back mainly pale vinaceous-brown, finely penciled with waving, blackish cross-lines; rump darker, finely cross-waved with whitish, giving a gray effect and fading into whitish on central upper tail-coverts; outer upper tail-coverts mostly black; lesser wing-coverts gray; fore wing with a broad white patch (middle and greater coverts), bordered behind with a black band (the tipping of greater coverts), and a metallic green speculum, which darkens to black behind; chin, throat and upper fore neck usually black; lower fore neck, upper breast and sides light brownish-red or vinaceous; under tail-coverts black; rest of under plumage including axillars white (latter sometimes slightly speckled at tips); primaries (variable) and tail gray, tail-feathers white-edged; iris dark brown; bill grayish-blue, with black tip and a little black on outer edges and on extreme base; feet light bluish-gray, yellowish or brown, webs dusky or slate. *Adult male in eclipse plumage:* Resembles female but wing as in winter male. *Immature male:* Has crown not pure white and more or less spotted, lacks black on chin which is buff and has green on head much restricted or wanting. *Adult female:* Top of head blackish, more or less mottled whitish; rest of head and neck whitish, spotted dusky; back buff,

---

[1] United States Department of Agriculture, Bulletin 862, 1920, pp. 16, 17.

barred dusky; speculum mainly black; indications of white patch on fore wing, forming white or whitish bar; breast and sides reddish-brown, with dusky spots on breast; rest of under plumage white including *axillars* which are sometimes slightly speckled near bases and tips; bill and feet like male but duller; iris brown. *Young in juvenal plumage:* Similar to adult female, but colors of male more pronounced and better defined; by October some cross-waved feathers appear in male. *Downy young:* Above mainly "dark olive brown"; a spot of "greenish-buff" on hind border of each wing, one on each side of back and another on each side of rump; sides of head and neck, and under-down pale olive buff; a dark streak from bill through eye.

MEASUREMENTS. — Length 18.00 to 22.00 in.; spread 30.00 to 35.00; folded wing 9.00 to 11.00; tail 4.00 to 4.50; bill 1.30 to 1.50; tarsus 1.37 to 1.65. Weight, male, 2 lbs. to 2 lbs. 7 oz.; female 1 lb. 8 oz. to 2 lbs. (J. C. Phillips).

MOLTS. — Juvenal plumage is mottled and is complete in August; molt then begins; in September gray feathers appear on back of male, later breast also changes so that by December or January male resembles adult though wings still show gray mottling on lesser coverts such as is peculiar to young; in some individuals lesser coverts become almost pure white in spring but immature wing is usually carried into eclipse; molt into this plumage begins in June in both adults and young; in October or November eclipse plumage has been shed and then young are practically as adults; adult male has prolonged double molt of body-feathers in summer and autumn, going into eclipse in June or July and out of it in September and October, wings being molted in August; female molts similarly to male (A. C. Bent).

FIELD MARKS. — *Male:* No other duck has such a *staring white* crown, broad white forehead and white belly, and no other male river duck but European Widgeon has *large white patch on fore wing;* in flight, when white forehead is not conspicuous, white fore wing becomes so, and black lower tail-coverts contrast with white belly; distinguished from male European Widgeon by pure white upper head and large green patch (looking blackish at a distance) just below white, while European Widgeon has cream colored forehead and reddish-brown lower head and neck. *Female and young:* Practically indistinguishable in field from those of European Widgeon which are generally darker and browner or more ruddy, particularly on head and neck where Baldpate appears lighter and more grayish or buffy; female somewhat like female Mallard, but paler, smaller and with much more white in wing.

VOICE. — Soft whistled, *sweet,* male (Audubon); "mewing whistle" resembling the syllables *whew whew;* loud *kaow kaow,* female (E. H. Eaton); lisping throaty whistle repeated three times in quick succession, light in character for size of bird; low short chattering resembling note of Pintail but greatly reduced in volume (J. H. Bowles); *quaw-awk, quaw-awk* (A. Wetmore); shrill yet mellow whistle, like *hue, hue, hue,* with strong accent on second syllable (C. B. Nordhoff); also a soft quack.

BREEDING. — Commonly on islands in lakes or in sloughs, also in river valleys. *Nest:* Usually on dry ground, concealed or open, often rather distant from water; a slight hollow, lined with grasses and weeds and an abundance of gray down. *Eggs:* 6 to 12; 2.00 to 2.37 by 1.42 to 1.60 in.; "elliptical ovate"; varying from almost white to deep cream or dull pale buff. *Dates:* May 25 to July 13 in Dakotas. *Incubation:* By female. One brood yearly.

RANGE. — North America. Breeds from northwest Alaska, northern Mackenzie and northern Manitoba (Hudson Bay) south to northeastern California, northwestern Nevada, northern Utah, northern Colorado, northwestern New Mexico and northern Arizona (probably), northern Nebraska, Kansas, northern Illinois possibly, southern Wisconsin and northern Indiana; winters from southern British Columbia, southern Nevada, central Utah, Arizona, northeastern Colorado, southern Illinois, Maryland and (irregularly) Massachusetts and Rhode Island south to Pacific coast of Central America, Lesser Antilles and Costa Rica; rare in migration to northern Ontario, northern Quebec, Labrador, New Brunswick and Newfoundland; rare to casual on Near and Commander Islands; accidental in Hawaii (extremely rare migrant), Bermuda, the Azores, Europe and Japan.

DISTRIBUTION IN NEW ENGLAND. — Uncommon or rare migrant in three northern New England states, except along Maine seaboard where fairly well distributed in migration; generally uncommon or rare in interior of Massachusetts, Rhode Island and Connecticut; fairly common in eastern Massachusetts and sometimes locally numerous in southeastern sections, usually less so in spring than in fall; winters in mild seasons near coast of three southern New England states and perhaps regularly on Long Island Sound.

SEASON IN MASSACHUSETTS. — (August 31) September 6 to December 17; (winter); March 10 to April 17.

HAUNTS AND HABITS. There seems to be some misapprehension regarding the distribution of the Baldpate in southern New England. Professor W. W. Cooke lists it as "hardly more than a straggler" in New England; others give it as rare here. The truth is that while the species probably is not so common with us as it was in the early half of the last century, it is found here now in considerable, or even large, numbers in certain ponds and lakes where wild celery, widgeon-grass or its other favorite food-plants grow. Among the ponds or lakes in Massachusetts visited by the Baldpate are Wenham Lake in Wenham, Ponkapoag in Canton, Assawompsett in Middleboro and especially several ponds on Marthas Vineyard. On the ponds of Marthas Vineyard, as well as on some near-by salt-water ponds or inlets, the Baldpate may be found regularly and not rarely in autumn, either in considerable flocks or in small companies; and it may appear during migration on any suitable New England water. In the autumn of 1922 I saw possibly 1,000 of these birds on three ponds on Marthas Vineyard and a much larger number has been reported on a single pond on that island. Nevertheless, notwithstanding their abundance, comparatively few are killed by the gunners. In the far West the Baldpate decoys readily and is considered an easy dupe, but here in New England there are few shyer birds. Most New England gunners take very few in a lifetime. Perhaps more have been taken in recent years on Squibnocket Pond on Marthas Vineyard than on any other in New England for there special care has been taken not to disturb them too often. Where some protection has been afforded ducks about Boston, a few individuals of this species have come into park ponds and in mild seasons some even have wintered near the city. It is probable that the species has increased in recent years under the spring-protective and non-sale laws, and this may account in part for its more common occurrence here now. The increased number of observers and the use of powerful glasses has added much also to our knowledge of the local distribution of this species. A wider diffusion of ornithological lore among sportsmen and gunners, which would enable them to differentiate the many females or immature birds of several species now known generally as "widgeon" or "gray duck," would extend our knowledge of the distribution of this bird in New England.

As the season of reproduction approaches the male Baldpates begin their prolonged wooing. Dr. C. W. Townsend says of the male that "in his courting he continually emits gentle but eager whistling notes, and with neck extended, and head low, bill wide open and wings elevated behind so that the tips are pointed up at an angle of forty-five degrees, he swims rapidly over the water behind or beside the duck. Occasionally he pecks playfully at the side of her head, and now and then jumps clear of the water and flies for two or three yards." The male often begins by bowing and whistling. Two rival males with assiduous attentions often force the female to fly and then pursue her through the air. Where males are numerous, the females are harassed for weeks by the persistent attentions of their ardent wooers.

Most of the Baldpates have mated before they reach their breeding-grounds. In southern waters where Canvas-backs, Scaups and Redheads, all excellent divers, are numerous and are diving continually on the feeding grounds, bringing up succulent roots, bulbs and other parts of submerged water-plants, the active Baldpate waxes fat by stealing tidbits from the hard-working diving ducks. The moment a bird comes to the surface, one or more Baldpates dash in, and sometimes one may succeed in snatching the morsel from the bill of the industrious diver. Probably in some localities they subsist to a considerable extent on the foliage of plants rooted up by the diving ducks which may content themselves with eating the roots or bulbs, discarding the leaves. In examinations of the stomach contents of Baldpates the foliage of wild celery was the principal part of the plant found. This habit of obtaining sustenance through the labor of other fowls has been so commonly observed that some of the earlier ornithologists have regarded the Baldpate as primarily a parasite on the diving ducks and have asserted its inability to dive under any circumstances. This belief has been perpetuated by many writers, but the Baldpate is not always a poacher. Dr. C. W. Townsend, an accurate observer and chronicler of the habits and behavior of ducks, writes as follows regarding this habit : "I have seen a flock of five Baldpates eagerly following half a dozen American Coots that were frequently diving in a pond and bringing up weeds from the bottom. The Baldpates gathered about the Coots as soon as they emerged on the surface and helped themselves to the spoils, tipping up occasionally to catch some sinking weed. They seemed even to be able to perceive the Coot coming up through the water, for they would begin to swim towards the spot just before the Coot emerged. The Coots appeared to take the pilfering as a matter of course ; in fact they pilfered from each other, and continued to work for themselves and the poachers." [1]

This experience might well justify Dr. Townsend in his expressed belief that the Baldpate is unable to dive.

Apparently the Baldpate is not a skilful nor a very deep diver, but it can and does dive for food when necessity requires. Professor Lynds Jones writes that he has "seen Baldpates dive for food in water that was too deep for the tip-up method"; Mr. Ludlow Griscom says that in mixed flocks of Baldpates and Redheads most of the former robbed the diving Redheads; a few, however, tried to dive. They could get down but could not stay down. Mr. Charles E. Clarke writes that at Jamaica Pond, Boston, he saw two Baldpates diving, but that they did not remain long under water. Mr. W. M. Pierce of Claremont, California, asserts that the Baldpate will dive when wounded. Dr. A. K. Fisher says that he has seen ducks of this species dive while feeding, while frolicking and when wounded. Mr. Francis H. Allen informs me that on October 24, 1915, he saw a

    [1] Townsend, C. W.: Memoirs Nuttall Ornithological Club, No. III, The Birds of Essex County, Massachusetts, 1905, p. 130.

female Baldpate in Jamaica Pond, Boston, diving in company with some Black Ducks in shallow water and bringing up weeds. The wings were closed as the bird dipped but were opened immediately, their tips making an audible splash. The Baldpate, he says, was not poaching on the Black Ducks. The Coot, like the Canvas-back and other diving ducks, can go to the bottom and secure the roots of the wild celery. The Baldpate probably dives deep enough to dislodge the leaves or parts of eel-grass and wild celery but possibly cannot dig up either plant from the bottom. All surface feeding ducks perforce must dive when, flightless in summer, they are pursued by hawks or eagles. If any individual is unable to dive, its doom is sealed.

As Baldpates breed mainly in the western half of the Continent, they must migrate east or southeast to reach New England. Therefore they are not so abundant here in spring, fall or winter as in the South Atlantic and Gulf states. They usually begin to reach Massachusetts from their northern homes in September although most of them come much later. Wherever their favorite foods may be had, they remain, if unmolested, so long as the foods last or until ice closes the waters. During many winters some numbers have remained until spring on Marthas Vineyard. Late in February the northward movement begins. The majority of the birds that pass over Massachusetts leave us during late March or early April. Early in May the vanguard of the species has reached the mouth of the Yukon River in Alaska.

The Baldpate feeds mainly on vegetal matter; therefore its flesh is excellent food. In the fields it eats grass. Mr. Mabbott recorded the results of the examination of the stomach contents of 229 birds. He found that pondweeds composed 42.82 per cent. of the food; grasses 13.9; algæ 7.71; sedges 7.41; frogbit family 5.75. Various other plants make up smaller percentages. Animal food amounted to but 6.77 per cent. of the stomach contents and most of this consisted of mollusks with a small quantity of crustaceans. Insects constituted only 0.42 per cent.; but if the birds had been taken through the summer and if the stomachs of ducklings had been examined, a much larger proportion of insect food might have been expected.[1]

ECONOMIC STATUS. This duck seems not to injure any crop appreciably. At times it feeds largely on insects and probably helps to regulate the increase of locusts, grasshoppers, beetles and crickets; its food value is high and it is an important game bird.

Néttion crécca (LINNÆUS). European Teal.

Other names: TEAL; EUROPEAN GREEN-WINGED TEAL.

Plate 13.

DESCRIPTION. — *Adult male:* Very similar to Green-winged Teal (see page 211) but *no white bar or crescent* on side of breast before wing; green band in chestnut on side of head bordered with whitish; barring or vermiculation of sides and upper plumage coarser; long scapulars largely white or creamy white, outer webs bordered black; "legs and toes gray, greenish or brownish with webs nearly black"

---

[1] Mabbott, Douglas C.: United States Department of Agriculture, Bulletin No. 862, 1920, pp. 11–16.

(J. C. Phillips). *Female and young:* So closely resemble female and young of Green-winged Teal that competent ornithologists have failed to distinguish them; anterior buff wing-bar usually paler (especially at outer end) in both sexes and at all ages; sometimes pure white toward end; "they seem to be browner and less finely variegated than the American bird" (E. H. Eaton).

MEASUREMENTS. — Length 12.50 to 15.00 in.; folded wing 6.25 to 7.40; bill 1.40 to 1.60; tarsus 1.10 to 1.25. Weight 8 to 14 ounces. Female smaller than male.

MOLTS. — When 5 or 6 weeks old young female assumes juvenal plumage and by end of November or earlier has molted again into first winter plumage; in early spring partial molt is followed by renewal of some scapulars and flank feathers and bird appears in first nuptial plumage; in summer flight-feathers are shed and bird appears in plumage like that of first winter; in next spring when two years old bird becomes as adult; young male has only trace of molt into first winter plumage and soon begins to show signs of maturity; some individuals show signs of nuptial plumage even in September, others not until November; in July of the next year male goes into eclipse plumage, in which there is great variation; male in first winter and summer "not to be distinguished with certainty from adult male unless some juvenile feathers are retained"; young female resembles adult female (Practical Handbook of British Birds); adults have one incomplete and one complete annual molt (E. L. Schioler).

FIELD MARKS. — *Adult male:* Like Green-winged Teal but no *white streak* on scapulars *above fore wing;* white bar before wing. *Female and young:* Indistinguishable from those of Green-winged Teal.

VOICE. — Similar to that of Green-winged Teal. Male, a soft single or double whistle. Female, a weak, high-sounding quack (J. C. Phillips).

BREEDING. — In marsh, bog, field, heath or woods; close to water or at some distance from it; sometimes at considerable elevations. *Nest:* On ground, of grasses, weeds and seeds, lined with down. *Eggs:* 8 to 16; about 1.75 by 1.30 in.; oval; yellowish-white; indistinguishable from those of Green-winged Teal. *Dates:* May 3 to June 14, England. *Incubation:* Period 22 days (W. Evans); 28 days (H. S. Gladstone); by female. One brood yearly.

RANGE. — Northern part of Northern Hemisphere. Common in many parts of Europe and Asia but generally rare to casual in North America; recorded on Pacific coast from Pribilof and Aleutian Islands and California and on Atlantic coast locally from Greenland to Virginia; breeds in Aleutian Islands; in Old World breeds north to Iceland and in northern Europe and Asia from 70° north latitude south to the Azores, the Mediterranean, Persia, Afghanistan, Manchuria, Corea, China, Japan and the Maldive Islands; winters south to Canary Islands, northern Africa and southern Asia; casual in Greenland and Spitzbergen.

DISTRIBUTION IN NEW ENGLAND. — *Maine:* Casco Bay, adult male in full plumage taken April 6, 1903, in collection of Dr. H. H. Brock;[1] Scarborough, male in good plumage, taken about March 26, 1910, also in the possession of Dr. Brock.[2] *Massachusetts:* Specimen killed about 1855, sent to E. A. Samuels;[3] Muskeget Island, adult male taken March 19, 1890, went to the Brewster collection;[4] Sagamore, adult male trapped about February 20, 1896, by Rev. E. A. Phillips, also to Brewster collection.[5] *Connecticut:* East Hartford, adult male taken November 14, 1889, now in collection of J. H. Sage.[6]

SEASON IN MASSACHUSETTS. — November to April.

NOTE. The European Teal has been considered for many years as a mere casual or accidental visitor to this country. When, however, in 1911 Mr. A. C. Bent visited the Aleutian Islands and found this species breeding commonly on the western and central islands, it was necessary to revise the breeding range of the species.[7] Some collectors who had made prior visits to these islands had mistaken European Teal for Green-winged Teal. Two males from the Aleutian Islands previously deposited and mislabeled in the National Museum were found to be referable to the European species. Mr. Bent failed to

[1] Knight, Ora W.: Birds of Maine, 1908, p. 87.   [2] Norton, Arthur H.: Auk, Vol. XXVIII, 1911, p. 255.
[3] Bryant, Henry: Proceedings of the Boston Society of Natural History, Vol. V, April 18, 1855, p. 195.
[4] Mackay, George H.: Auk, Vol. VII, 1890, p. 294.   [5] Brewster, Wm.: Auk, Vol. XVIII, 1901, p. 135.
[6] Treat, Willard E.: Auk, Vol. VIII, 1891, p. 112.   [7] Smithsonian Miscellaneous Collections, Vol. LVI, No. 32, 1912, pp. 11, 12.

find the Green-winged Teal breeding on the Aleutian Islands and every full-plumaged male teal taken there by his party proved to be a so-called European bird. It is not improbable that the species may breed elsewhere in Alaska. It is less rare in North America than the records would indicate as there is little likelihood that the females or young (which are in the great majority in winter when the birds migrate southward) will ever be recognized, and it is only when a full plumaged male is seen at close range or taken that there is a probability of an authentic report. All specimens of the Green-winged Teal taken should be carefully examined.

HAUNTS AND HABITS. The European Teal resembles the Green-winged Teal closely not only in form and plumage but also in habits. It frequents the same shallow fresh waters, and estuaries and marshes near the sea. Wherever the Green-wing is found the European Teal may be looked for along either coast of North America. In time it may be found to be only a very rare visitor in some American regions where it is now regarded as accidental.

The European Teal is chiefly vegetarian. It feeds more on the seeds of many plants than on their leaves or stalks. In spring it eats old waste grain; but snails, worms, slugs and insect larvæ form a considerable part of its food (J. C. Phillips).

ECONOMIC STATUS. See page 174.

Nettion carolinénse (GMELIN). Green-winged Teal.

Other names: GREEN-WING; MUD TEAL.

Plate 13.

DESCRIPTION. — Bill nearly as long as head, longer than tarsus, narrow and parallel-sided. *Adult male:* Head sub-crested; head and upper neck chiefly chestnut; chin black; a broad patch from just before eye to hind head metallic green, running into black below on its lower edge (bordered below and sometimes in front by a narrow buff line which may extend to bill) ending in a black tuft on nape and hind neck; rest of hind neck, sides of breast, upper back, scapulars, sides and flanks very light brownish-gray, finely cross-waved with black lines; some long outer scapulars widely edged outwardly with black; a white bar before wing (sometimes wanting); lower back, rump and upper tail-coverts brownish-gray; some black on outer upper tail-coverts; wings grayish-brown or gray; speculum or wing-patch metallic-green, edged in front light chestnut, below black and behind white; upper breast reddish-buff, with roundish black spots; rest of lower plumage whitish, sometimes tinged brown; under tail-coverts black, a triangular creamy patch on each side; bill black; iris dark brown; legs and toes dark bluish-gray or olive-gray, webs brownish-black. *Adult male in eclipse plumage:* Similar to female, but quite variable; older males are likely to have fewer and more distinct spots below and some cross-lined or vermiculated scapulars and to be more uniformly colored above with few light edges; older females commonly more mottled below. *Adult female:* Top of head and back dusky-brownish, feathers of back and scapulars edged buff, ashy or whitish; chin and throat light buffy or whitish; wing much like that of male, but wing-bar before speculum sometimes white; breast buff, spotted blackish; sides and flanks heavily marked dusky and buffy; rest of under plumage largely whitish; iris, bill, legs and feet much as in male, bill not so dark. *Young in juvenal plumage (sexes practically alike):* Similar to female but tail feathers more blunt at tips; largely white below with more spotting on belly of female than in adult female; young female has colors of wing a trifle duller than male; young male has concealed black spots on breast (J. C. Phillips); "the anterior buff wing-bar is usually of a richer color" in Green-winged Teal, at all ages and in both sexes, than in European Teal (J. C. Phillips). *Downy young:* Above grayish-brown; top of head, line through eye, spot on ear-region, and back of neck dark brown; sides of head yellowish; back with four spots (paired) of straw-yellow, two on either side above wing and two near tail; "below dull light buff" or yellowish.

MEASUREMENTS. — Length 12.50 to 15.75 in.; spread 22.00 to 24.00; folded wing 6.25 to 7.50; tail 2.61 to 3.60; bill 1.35 to 1.60; tarsus 1.07 to 1.25. Weight 10 to 14 oz. Female slightly smaller than male.

MOLTS. — Bent states that the young male becomes lighter below and that "the red plumage of the head appears in October"; also that in December the bird is practically indistinguishable from adult male; young male, however, is not as perfect in plumage as adult; adult male begins molting in June or July, shedding all contour-feathers and scapulars, and in August is in full eclipse plumage; flight-feathers are shed and renewed in August, and in next three months another molt of body-feathers is followed by adult winter or nuptial plumage; adult female has similar double molt.

FIELD MARKS. — Smallest of our River Ducks; *Adult male in winter or spring:* Chestnut head, green patch on side of head and (usually) *white bar in front of wing. Female and young:* Readily distinguished from Black Duck or other large ducks by small size; from Blue-winged Teal by *absence* of blue *fore-wing;* most of wing, however, including green wing-patch or speculum, of Green-wing is often covered by body-plumage, but shows in flight or when wing is flapped; in early fall both this and the Blue-winged Teal are in a similar dull plumage with exception of green and blue of wing, respectively.

VOICE. — Peculiar chirping, almost twittering, as they fly (E. T. Seton). Male, short mellow whistle; "a sound like the low soft whine of a little puppy" (A. F. Warren); a low rolling whistle (Allan Brooks). Female, a quack like Black Duck but fainter, high-pitched and more often repeated (E. H. Eaton); "when surprised *kup-kup-kup,* when curious *ek-ek-ek*" (F. Harper).

BREEDING. — On dry ground in or near marsh, near water, or on higher land at considerable distance from water; often in edge of bushy timber. *Nest:* Of grass, sedges, weeds, feathers and much down, usually in hollow, in dense growth of grass or other vegetation or under bushes. *Eggs:* 7 to 12 or even more; 1.60 to 1.90 by 1.20 to 1.36 in.; bluntly ovate; pale olive-greenish buff or pale dull buff. *Dates:* May 28, North Dakota; May 20, northern Ontario. *Incubation:* Period 21 to 23 days (H. K. Job); by female. One brood yearly.

RANGE. — North America. Breeds from northwestern Alaska, northwestern Mackenzie, Great Slave Lake, northern Manitoba, northern Ontario, northern Quebec, Labrador and Newfoundland south to south-central California, northwestern Nevada, northwestern Utah, northern New Mexico, southern Colorado, northern Nebraska, southern Minnesota, central western Iowa, Wisconsin (formerly), northeastern Illinois, northeastern Michigan, southern Ontario, casually, western New York and Pennsylvania, southern Quebec, New Brunswick and the Gulf of St. Lawrence; winters from southeastern Alaska, British Columbia, central Montana, northern Nebraska, southern Iowa, the Great Lakes (irregularly), central Illinois, northern Indiana, Ohio, western New York (irregularly) and Massachusetts and Nova Scotia (both casually) south to southern Lower California, Lesser Antilles and Honduras; occasional in Bermuda; accidental in Hawaii (extremely rare migrant), Japan, Greenland, Great Britain, and Bermuda, and occurs in Marshall Islands.

DISTRIBUTION IN NEW ENGLAND. — Generally an uncommon migrant, perhaps more common in Maine and Vermont than in other New England states (may breed in northern Vermont); winters casually or irregularly on coasts of Massachusetts, Rhode Island and Connecticut.

SEASON IN MASSACHUSETTS. — (August 30); September 3 to December 13 (has been observed about Boston all winter); March 23 to April 23.

HAUNTS AND HABITS. The lovely little Green-winged Teal is one of the swiftest fliers among game-birds. Its speed has been estimated at 160 miles an hour, but to reach this rate it would have to be borne on the wings of a hurricane. It often flies in compact flocks, its line of flight either definite and direct or else vacillating, with quick turns in exact concert. In the water it is a buoyant swimmer and an excellent diver but does not ordinarily dive except to escape some enemy. Mr. T. Gilbert Pearson relates an instance which shows how the teal may even attach itself to objects on the bottom when wounded and attempting to escape. A fine male teal had been shot from a passing flock and had fallen and disappeared beneath the water of a pond thickly grown with vegetation. Mr. Pearson says: "It was easy to determine the exact spot so I waded out and looking down into the water saw it holding to the stem of a submerged plant, its tail pointing toward the surface. Lifting it in my hands, the plant came up, still tightly clasped in the bird's beak." [1] Mr. Charles B. Morss of Bradford tells me that he has known two Green-winged Teals to cling to objects on the bottom until death.[2] Much of the food of this teal is procured in very shallow water or on land. It is fond of wading and "puddling" in a few inches of water in muddy places or on bare mud flats, in company with the sandpipers. It is particularly active on its feet, walks and runs well and often travels on foot for some distance on land either in search of food or in passing from pool to pool. When alarmed by the hunter, it springs direct from the water into the air and is soon out of danger; but if some members of a flock are shot down, the rest are likely to circle about and return and may even alight among their dead or dying comrades. This habit and that of gathering in close companies have given the market hunter his opportunity. Skilful gunners often have destroyed a whole flock. Teals come readily to decoys in compact flocks but "flare" and scatter when the gunner rises to shoot. The Green-wing is naturally tame and unsuspicious, and old people on Cape Cod have related often how the teal formerly fed with the barnyard ducks.

The natural tameness of this species has been its undoing. Excellent as a table bird it was in great demand in the market, and now in New England where formerly it was common and even abundant at times in migration, it has become uncommon or rare.

The Green-winged Teal begins to leave its northern breeding-grounds in October (although a few stragglers move southward in September), and until late in November it may be seen in its favorite waters in New England. It frequents the fresh water by preference; but if the ponds and rivers freeze, it goes to salt water estuaries until the fresh waters are freed from ice. In New England the species goes north earlier and south later, although it is an early autumnal migrant in the west.

The Green-winged Teal like other surface-feeding ducks often feeds in shallow water by thrusting its head down to the bottom. Mr. T. Gilbert Pearson found by experiment with a small flock of these birds that when seven heads were under water and only four pairs of eyes were watching, a sudden motion on his part started all the ducks into the air "with the quickness of thought." How is it possible for birds with heads under water and tails in the air to sense the alarm and spring up as quickly as those with heads in the air? This is one of the wonders of bird life.

The food of this teal includes flies, dipterous larvæ, grasshoppers, locusts and many other land and aquatic insects, but these seem to form less than 5% of its normal food. Mollusks including snails, also crustaceans and other animal food, bring the total animal

[1] Bird-Lore, Vol. XXIV, 1922, p. 181.　　[2] Massachusetts Department of Agriculture, Bulletin No. 8, 1922, p. 46.

quota up to 9.33%. The rest of the food is of a vegetal nature and is largely composed of seeds of water plants such as pondweeds and bulrushes or sedges, smartweeds and grasses. It feeds on the succulent parts of these plants, also on duckweeds and many other water plants, wild rice, wild oats and some grain — mostly scattered waste grain.[1] At times it takes chestnuts, acorns, wild grapes and berries, and when driven in winter to the salt water it feeds on marine life. At such times its flesh, ordinarily a delectable viand for the epicure, becomes rank and unsavory. This is often the case in British Columbia where the bird gorges itself on putrid salmon.[2]

ECONOMIC STATUS. See page 174.

Querquédula díscors (LINNÆUS). Blue-winged Teal.

Other names: BLUE-WING; SUMMER TEAL.

Plate 13.

DESCRIPTION. — *Adult male in winter and nuptial plumage:* Head and upper neck dusky-leaden-gray, more or less tinged with faint gloss of purplish or lavender; chin and top of head from bill to nape black or blackish; a large white, black-edged crescent in front of eye, extending down to throat; upper plumage mainly dark brown, feathers more or less edged or otherwise marked buff or light rusty-brown; outer surface of fore wing light blue, this color extending over some of outer long scapulars, blue fore wing with posterior border of white separating it from glossy green speculum, which also is posteriorly (but very narrowly) edged white and bordered above and below by black; flight-feathers dark brown; most of linings of wings and axillars and a spot on each side at base of tail white; under plumage and sides light brown or buff, spotted black, except that lower flanks are sometimes barred in curved lines; under tail-coverts brownish-black, under side of tail ashy; bill bluish-gray or bluish-black, black on ridge; iris dark brown or hazel; legs and toes dull yellow to yellow orange with dark webs. *Male in eclipse plumage:* Similar to female but retains some trace of white face patch, and wing is much as in winter plumage, with blue larger and brighter and speculum brighter than in female. *Adult female in winter and nuptial plumage:* Top of head dusky, throat whitish, an indistinct dusky stripe before and behind eye; rest of head and neck pale brownish or brownish-white streaked dusky; back, wings, rump and upper tail-coverts dusky, with V- or U-shaped buff edgings on back; breast, sides and flanks pinkish-buff or grayish-white, marked blackish; flanks with dusky V-shaped marks; belly whitish-gray, with obscure mottling; wing much as in male, but with less blue, no black, little white and speculum duller; bill greenish-black; legs and feet duller or darker than in male; iris hazel. *Young in juvenal plumage:* Like female, but lighter below, often with nearly immaculate white belly and gray speculum; young female more uniformly gray on back; "feet very pale or flesh tinted" (Coues); young male has speculum more prominent and richer than young female. *Downy young:* Top of head and upper plumage brown, darkest on top of head and rump; a buff or yellowish spot in front of each wing, one across each wing and another at each side of rump; forehead, stripe to eye, and under surface of body and neck pale buff or corn-yellow with local shadings of deeper tints; sides of head, and hind neck "ochraceous-buff"; dark line through eye, and in some cases another below it.

MEASUREMENTS. — Length 14.50 to 16.00 in.; spread 24.00 to 31.25; folded wing 7.00 to 7.50; tail about 3.50; bill 1.40 to 1.65; tarsus 1.16 to 1.30. Weight 10½ oz. to 1 lb. Female smaller than male.

MOLTS. — In August young have acquired juvenal plumage; during fall, winter and early spring more or less molting takes place until first nuptial plumage is assumed, which is much like that of adult

---

[1] Mabbott, D. C.: U. S. Department of Agriculture, Bulletin No. 862, 1920, pp. 17–22.
[2] Millais, J. G.: The Natural History of British Surface-feeding Ducks, 1902, p. 90.

but somewhat duller and without long blue-edged scapulars; first eclipse plumage is assumed in summer, and after autumnal molt birds appear in adult plumage. Autumnal molt in adults seems very variable in time, some assume nuptial plumage in winter and others not until spring. They have the usual double molt beginning in July.

FIELD MARKS. — *Adult male:* Sky-blue fore wing and broad white crescent in front of eye; in flight, blue of wing is conspicuous in both sexes and all ages. *Female and young:* May be distinguished from blue-winged female Shoveller by smaller size and shorter, narrower bill; female and young of Cinnamon Teal closely resemble those of this species but have never been recorded in New England. (See Field Marks under Green-winged Teal, page 212.)

VOICE. — Male, whistling peep repeated five or six times; "call-note of male a high-pitched *tseef, tseef, tseef*, entirely different from notes of other male teal with which I am familiar" (Alex. Wetmore). Female, quack similar to that of Green-winged Teal (E. H. Eaton).

BREEDING. — In open prairie, marsh or field not far from water, or on a small island. *Nest:* Usually on dry ground in or near meadow or marsh; sometimes on a muskrat house; usually concealed by over-arching grass, and eggs covered with a blanket of down when female is off the nest; a hollow lined with grass and dark-brown, mottled down larger and lighter-colored than Green-winged Teal's; the typical nest neat and basket-like, set either into rank grass or the ground. *Eggs:* 6 to 15, commonly 10, 11, 12; 1.71 to 1.93 by 1.25 to 1.40 in.; bluntly ovate; pale olive-buff or buffy-white, averaging slightly lighter than those of Green-winged Teal. *Dates:* June 3, North Dakota; June 13 to July 9, Saskatchewan. *Incubation:* Period 21 to 23 days (H. K. Job); by female. One brood yearly.

RANGE. — Western Hemisphere. Breeds from central British Columbia, southern Mackenzie, northern Saskatchewan, Manitoba, Ontario, probably Quebec and casually Labrador and Magdalen Islands south to central Oregon, northern Nevada, central Utah, northern New Mexico, Oklahoma, central Kansas, Missouri, southern Illinois, southern Indiana, Ohio, West Virginia, western New York, Rhode Island (formerly) and casually Maine; reported as breeding in Texas, Louisiana, South Carolina, New Jersey, Long Island, Iceland, the Antilles and Honduras; winters from southern California, Arizona, southern Illinois, southern Indiana, Maryland, Delaware and casually Rhode Island south to Bahamas, Antilles, Brazil, Ecuador, Peru and Chile; recorded on Clipperton, Cocos and Galapagos Islands; accidental in Bermuda and western Europe.

DISTRIBUTION IN NEW ENGLAND. — Common to rare migrant; much rarer in spring than in autumn in three southern New England states; "very rare in spring but occurs regularly in fall migration in Maine" (A. H. Norton); bred formerly (Boardman) and may breed still, in Washington County, Maine; bred formerly in Rhode Island and possibly in Massachusetts (Arlington Heights and Marthas Vineyard).

SEASON IN MASSACHUSETTS. — (July 27) August 15 to November 26; (March 21); April 9 to May 31 (June).

HAUNTS AND HABITS. Fleeing first of all wild ducks from the frost king and following the retiring sun toward the equator come the Blue-winged Teals. In the waning summer or with the full September moon they come; and swinging low out of the northern sky they sweep along the sedgy banks of some marshy river where wild rice and pickerel weed grow. Borne on swift whistling pinions, careering swiftly back and forth, they turn and return, and, as they swing and shift, show alternately light breasts and dark backs with flashing azure wings. Back and forth they rush reconnoitering the landfall until, suspicions allayed, and satisfied at last, they check their speed with wings, feet and tail and alight all together on some still, marsh-bordered pool, the haunt of rails, muskrats, tortoises and frogs, where blackbirds tunefully emit their throaty notes and swallows flit on still summer evenings until the bats come out.

The Blue-winged Teal is fond of still waters and slow currents. It frequents small ponds and pools where it dabbles among the lily pads or the marshy borders of slow-running streams. Its flight, like that of the Green-winged Teal, is remarkably swift. It comes readily to decoys, particularly if live birds are used, and is normally tame and unsuspicious. "Quite curiously it is often associated singly with one or two Black Ducks" (J. C. Phillips). In wet seasons it often alights in pools of rain-water. Formerly its flights were immense. As it flew and swam in close flocks, it offered an excellent target for the "scatter gun." Audubon tells of a gunner who reported that he had killed 120 at one discharge. Audubon himself records that he saw 94 killed by the simultaneous discharge of both barrels of a double gun.

In the first half of the nineteenth century this teal was abundant in migration in New England but its numbers gradually lessened until it became rare. Now under protective laws it seems to be slowly increasing. It is one of the most prolific of all ducks and is said sometimes to hatch 15 to 17 young. If given reasonable protection its increase may continue.

Though this teal migrates southward very early and does not linger here long, a few sometimes may be seen in October and November in Massachusetts and rarely a bird or two may be recorded in winter. Miss Elizabeth Dickens informs me that a pair spent the greater part of one winter at Block Island, Rhode Island. I have never seen the species in spring in Massachusetts, and at that season it probably passes rapidly through the state, having learned by sad experience during the winter that a closely settled country is unsafe. As it is more often seen in spring in the wilder parts of northern New England, perhaps it remains there longer while waiting for the ice to leave more northern waters. It is most likely to appear here on its way north in late March or early April.

In reporting on the food of this teal, Mr. Douglas C. Mabbott found that 10.41% of its stomach contents consisted of insects chiefly caddis-flies, beetles, dragon-flies, other flies and bugs. The larval forms of these insects chiefly were taken. There were also soldier-flies and midges and other miscellaneous insects, grasshoppers, locusts, moths and a few ants. Insects' eggs are eaten. About seven-tenths of the Blue-winged Teal's food is vegetal matter, including sedges, pondweeds, grasses, smartweeds, algæ, water-lilies, rice, corn, water milfoils, reeds, etc.* A few small crustaceans, such as shrimps and sand-fleas, are taken by this bird; also some snails.[1]

ECONOMIC STATUS. See page 174.

---

*Mabbott, Douglas C.: U. S. Department of Agriculture, Bulletin No. 862, Bureau of Biological Survey, 1920, pp. 23–28.
[1] Whether shell-fish form a part of the diet is doubtful, but a bird of this species was caught in Ware with a fresh-water clam attached to its foot.

Fig. 22. — Sheld Duck

From a specimen in the Museum of Comparative Zoölogy

Fig. 23. — Nest of Black Duck.   Page 196

Tadórna tadorna (LINNÆUS). Sheld Duck.

Fig. 22.

DESCRIPTION. — Both sexes with rounded carpal spur, most prominent in adult male; tail of 14 feathers, nearly even at end; bill broader toward tip than at base, considerably upturned. *Adult male in winter and nuptial plumage:* (A high knob above base of upper mandible appears only in breeding season and not then on non-breeding male); head and upper neck dark green with some tinge of amethyst, small white mark below eye, point of chin sometimes white; lower neck encircled by wide collar of white, below which a light chestnut or tawny band surrounds base of neck, upper back and breast; rest of back white; scapulars, part of secondaries, and primaries mainly black; wing-patch or speculum green; rest of upper plumage, including part of scapulars, wing-coverts and tail mainly white, latter rather broadly tipped black; upper tail-coverts sometimes tipped blackish; a broad band, black or dark brown in middle and in its upper part merging into tawny belt on each side, runs down center of breast and belly and widens toward vent; under tail-coverts "cinnamon-rufous"; other under plumage white; bill, including basal knob, bright red ("carmine or blood red"), nail dusky; legs and feet flesh colored. *Adult male in eclipse plumage:* Much like adult female. Head largely blackish, feathers faintly edged dusky-brown, tipped greenish, and showing whitish mottling on face and throat; lower neck white, but white feathers on back of neck next body tipped blackish; back tawny with broad blackish feather-tips; scapulars mainly dull black with faint white tips, some partly white and some white with wavy black cross-lines; feathers of sides and flanks white, but more or less speckled and suffused with tawny; black line in center of breast more or less broken up by tawny feather-tips; wings and tail as in winter; bill paler than in spring. *Adult female in nuptial plumage:* Similar to male but head and neck usually (not always) duller; some show more or less white in face and forehead; tawny breast band narrower and black of breast and belly duller than in male; bill as in male, but duller; legs and feet about as in male. *Young in first winter plumage: Male:* As adult, but green of head and upper neck usually duller; lower scapulars gray instead of white as in adult; tawny band on breast and black area in its center narrower; wing still largely as in juvenal; easily distinguished by white tips to inner primaries and secondaries. *Female:* Similar to adult female, but feathers of head largely tipped dusky-brown; wing much as in male at this stage; breast and under plumage show signs of immaturity. *Young in juvenal plumage:* No tawny nor black coloration; general appearance ashy-brown and white above, white below; forehead, chin and face about to eyes white; top of head blackish, feathers with buffy-brown tips; nape, cheeks and sides of neck blackish, feathers with narrow white tips; upper back generally dark brown, more or less mottled or edged white; some scapulars brownish-gray; lower back, rump and upper tail-coverts white, latter in part tipped blackish and in part cross-waved with brownish-gray; tail blackish-brown, edged and tipped whitish, outer feathers more or less white; wing as in adult, but primaries narrowly edged white, and some tipped broadly same; speculum less brilliant than in adult; inner secondaries gray with chestnut outer webs; greater coverts gray, and median coverts white tipped gray; bill grayish-pink; iris brown; legs and feet pale grayish-white. *Downy young:* Forehead and face including cheeks white; elsewhere above mainly sooty or chocolate-brown; small patch on center of upper back and streak on sides of back and rump white; below white.

MEASUREMENTS. — Length 19.00 to 22.00 in.; folded wing 11.25 to 13.50; tail 3.75 to 5.60; bill 1.87 to 2.40; tarsus 1.85 to 2.16.

MOLTS. — In August young birds begin to molt juvenal body-feathers and tail and sometimes some of wing-coverts; this molt may last until March and sometimes is much prolonged and incomplete; some birds retain many juvenal feathers in spring while some young males have black band on breast and belly as fully developed as adult; in July and August most of under plumage and part of upper plumage is molted, followed by wings and tail as bird goes into eclipse; in autumn young birds molt again and either in winter or following spring most of them become as adults; adults molt in July and

August when wings, tail and much body-plumage is shed, and again in autumn (August or September to December) when body plumage is renewed.

FIELD MARKS. — Size of Mallard or Black Duck; at a distance looks black and white and poses like a goose; near at hand red bill, white neck and tawny or chestnut breast-band are conspicuous.

VOICE. — Male: Deep *korr korr;* in spring, whistles a low, clear *wh'chee-you.* Female, loud harsh quack.

BREEDING. — Mainly along sea-coast and about estuaries. *Nest:* Usually in a rabbit hole or other deep burrow. *Eggs:* 8 to 15, but many more have been found, due to two or more females; 2.80 by 1.80 to 2.46 by 1.20 in.; white. *Incubation:* Period variously given as 24 to 26 and 28 to 30 days; chiefly by female. One brood yearly.

RANGE. — Europe, Asia and northern Africa. "Breeds in British Isles and in northern Europe from about latitude 70° in Norway and 51° in Ural Mountains to France and Spain and on salt lakes of southern Siberia and central Asia; also in eastern Asia"; migrates south to Mediterranean and northern Africa, northern India, Burmah, China, Formosa and Japan; casual in Iceland and Faroe Islands; accidental in Massachusetts.

DISTRIBUTION IN NEW ENGLAND. — A female in first winter plumage was brought to me in the flesh by Deputy Carl E. Grant of the Division of Fisheries and Game of the Massachusetts Department of Conservation. This bird was shot October 5, 1921, near the mouth of the Essex River in Ipswich Bay, Essex County, Massachusetts, by Capt. Howard H. Tobey of Gloucester. The bird was shot over decoys about one-half mile from shore and was very shy. Its plumage, beak and feet were in excellent condition showing that it had not been recently in captivity, and it was apparently a wild bird. This is the first and only record for the species thus far in North America. The specimen is now in the Peabody Museum at Salem. This seems to be a wanderer from Europe. Its occurrence was recorded by Mr. Albert P. Morse [1] and by myself. [2]

HAUNTS AND HABITS. This species frequents mainly the shores and estuaries of the sea and salt lakes but is often found at some distance in the interior. It feeds largely on mollusks and crustaceans and also to some extent on vegetal matter such as algæ and fragments of *gramineæ* and occasionally eats some insects. Its occurrence on the western side of the Atlantic is purely accidental.

Spátula clypeáta (LINNÆUS). Shoveller.

Other names: SPOONBILL; BROADBILL.

Plate 14.

DESCRIPTION. — "Bill much longer than head or tarsus, twice as wide at end as at base, broadly rounded at end; nail narrow and prominent, laminæ very numerous and protrusive; tail of 14 acute feathers" (Coues). *Adult male in winter and nuptial plumage:* Head and most of neck dark, glossy, metallic-green, with some violet and purple reflections, dullest on top of head, on throat and around base of bill, where it becomes brownish or blackish; lower neck all round and whole breast white except a narrow dark line down back of neck to back (some adult males have black or dark semicircular markings on breast, probably feathers retained from eclipse plumage); middle of back mainly slaty-black, feathers edged light brown or whitish; rump and upper tail-coverts slightly darker with some metallic-green luster; tail centrally blackish, its outer edges white; fore part of wing including all coverts, except tips of greater coverts, light blue, most scapulars white, longer ones light blue — a continuation of the blue of fore wing but streaked white and blackish toward tips; speculum brilliant metallic-green bordered in front by

---

[1] Bulletin of the Essex County Ornithological Club of Massachusetts, 1921, p. 68. [2] Auk, Vol. XXXIX, 1922, p. 104.

PLATE 14

PLATE 14

WOOD DUCK
Page 225
WINTER (NUPTIAL) PLUMAGE
MALE

FEMALE

AMERICAN PINTAIL
Page 222
WINTER (NUPTIAL) PLUMAGE

FEMALE   MALE

SHOVELLER
Page 218
WINTER (NUPTIAL) PLUMAGE

MALE   FEMALE

All one-sixth natural size.

white tips of greater coverts, above by black, and behind by a very narrow white line; inner secondaries black with a metallic light greenish tinge and streaked narrowly white toward ends; rest of flight-feathers dusky with slight greenish reflections; abdomen "purplish chestnut" or "rich cinnamon"; sides and flanks lighter along upper edges than abdomen, flanks finely vermiculated with blackish; a white patch on each side of base of tail; vermiculation of black and white behind vent; under tail-coverts greenish-black and under surface of tail white or whitish; axillars and wing-linings mainly white; bill black or bluish-black, paler below; iris orange or yellow; legs and feet orange-red or "vermilion." *Molting male (as seen on Atlantic coast in autumn or early winter)*: Similar but very variable; dark head and neck finely spotted white; white and dark markings on breast and back; dull brownish tint on abdomen; adult males are barred on white upper breast where young birds are spotted. *Male in eclipse plumage*: Similar to adult female but under plumage largely brown, also some white may remain on breast, and wing markings are brighter than those of female and much as in nuptial plumage. *Adult female*: Above mainly warm brown, feathers on head, neck, back, rump and upper tail-coverts edged with ashy or light pinkish-buff; head and neck usually somewhat grayer than other upper plumage, finely streaked (except chin and sometimes throat) with dusky; wing with little if any black, with much duller blue than in male and much less greenish luster on speculum, which is bounded before and behind by narrow white bar; flight-feathers lighter than in male; scapulars with large U-shaped buff marks; tail edged white or whitish; sides and flanks lighter or grayer than back; under surface of body varying from buff to whitish, often mottled more or less; bill variable in color — "olive gray," "olive brown," "yellowish, shading to greenish at tip" or greenish-brown; edges of mandibles orange, upper finely spotted with black which disappears after death, under orange; iris hazel; legs and feet orange, paler than in male. *Young in juvenal plumage: Male*: Similar to adult female but of a lighter shade; breast with tinge of chestnut; belly pale chestnut. *Female*: Similar but fore wing dull slate and speculum dusky, with little metallic-green. *Downy young*: Above mainly brown; whole top and back of head dark brown; dark stripe through eye and a pale brown stripe above it; narrow dark mark under eye and another over ear; spot on each side of back, stripe on each wing and spot on each side of rump whitish; below mainly grayish-white, breast tinged brown, and chin and throat buff; bill not very noticeably different from that of other ducklings at first but develops as young grow.

MEASUREMENTS. — Length 17.00 to 21.00 in.; spread 29.50 to 35.00; folded wing 9.00 to 10.00; tail 3.00 to 3.50; bill 2.50 to 2.80; tarsus 1.33 to 1.50. Weight 1 lb. 1 oz. to 1 lb. 10 oz., rarely 2 lbs. Female smaller than male.

MOLTS. — *Young female;* molts juvenal plumage and acquires during late autumn and first winter months a first winter plumage in which head, body and tail-feathers are renewed, but not wings; in spring another molt occurs followed by new feathers on top of head, upper body, scapulars, innermost secondaries and some tail-feathers — the first nuptial plumage; like male, female molts again after breeding season. *Young male;* begins a series of similar molts, in early autumn, but feathers of first winter plumage have no more than reached maturity when those of first nuptial plumage begin to appear; this molt lasts until spring when first nuptial plumage has been assumed, showing, as a rule, but not always, less glossy green head than adults and some dark horse-shoe markings on white fore-neck and breast; first nuptial plumage is followed by eclipse (when wings are molted the first time) and this by second nuptial [or winter] plumage (E. Lehn Schiöler); there seems to be nearly a continuous molt and feather change from the time young male sheds the down until it goes into first eclipse; Millais says that young male gains in 17 months "a plumage dull and incomplete, yet resembling that of the adult male"; also he says: "His plumage, so far as my experience goes, is never absolutely perfect until the third season"; apparently no American river duck is more variable in color pattern than the male of this species in its progress to maturity; adult male begins molting into eclipse plumage (late May to July) and before end of August has undergone an extensive but incomplete molt; another molt (out of the eclipse) (apparently complete with exception of wings which are molted in August) occurs in autumn and winter; adult female has similar molts.

FIELD MARKS. — Hardly as large as Wood Duck, but its rather slender neck, long bill and large, long, pointed wings give it in flight a deceptively large appearance. *Male:* Unmistakable; seen from below at a distance head and neck seem black; from neck to front of wing, bird is white; chestnut lower body coming next seems dark and is separated from black under tail-coverts by narrow belt of white; thus five alternating areas, dark-white-dark-white-dark. *Female and young:* Might be mistaken for Blue-winged Teal (though somewhat larger) except for length and shape of bill — this so long that in flight wings seem to be set too far back; Shoveller also usually flies less swiftly and in a more hesitating desultory manner than Teal.

VOICE. — Usually silent except when a startled flock rises; male in breeding season a low, guttural *woh woh woh,* or *took took took;* female, a few feeble quacks (A. C. Bent).

BREEDING. — In open grassy or bushy lands as marshes, meadows, prairies or on islands in lakes. *Nest:* A hollow in dry or moist ground, near or far from water, usually hidden in grass or under bushes, lined with grasses, rimmed with down, eggs often covered (as incubation advances) with it. *Eggs:* 6 to 14; 2.00 to 2.38 by 1.38 to 1.50 in.; nearly "elliptical ovate"; indistinguishable from Mallard's in color but smaller. *Dates:* May 9 to July 3, Minnesota and North Dakota (A. C. Bent). *Incubation:* Period 21 to 23 days; by female. One brood yearly.

RANGE. — Northern Hemisphere, in temperate regions and northern parts of Southern Hemisphere. Breeds in North America from northwestern Alaska, northwestern Mackenzie, and eastern Manitoba, south to southern California, central Arizona, northwestern New Mexico, northern Texas, Kansas, northeastern Missouri, northern Illinois, northern Indiana and casually west central New York; winters from southern British Columbia, Arizona, New Mexico, southern Texas, southern Missouri, southern Illinois, northwestern Indiana, Maryland and eastern Virginia south to Antilles, Colombia and Hawaii; occasional in migration north to Prince Edward Island; accidental in Bermuda and Labrador; in Eastern Hemisphere breeds from Great Britain and European and Asiatic regions near Arctic Circle south to southern Europe and central Asia; winters south to Canary Islands, Senegambia, Arabia, the Philippine Islands and Australia.

DISTRIBUTION IN NEW ENGLAND. — Rare migrant growing rarer in eastern Maine; seen mostly about fresh water or in brackish ponds near coast; recorded principally from seaboard; formerly less rare.

SEASON IN MASSACHUSETTS. — March 20 to April 23; September 3 to November 20 (Winter).

HAUNTS AND HABITS. The Shoveller stands alone. No other duck in North America carries about such a long, broad, extremely specialized spatulate bill, and no other exhibits in the full plumage of the handsome male so peculiar an arrangement of striking colors. It bears no close resemblance to any other bird. It may be looked for occasionally anywhere in these states where muddy ponds and pools are found, especially near the sea-coast, where it is rarely seen in salt water. Its bill with its many comblike processes is used to dabble in the mud from which the bird sifts out much of its food, and for this reason it frequents the small ponds or shallow mudholes which supply it with its favorite food.

The Shoveller is one of the first ducks to flee before the coming of winter, and the first severe frost will usually send it southward; but as its chief American breeding-grounds are in the western part of the continent, comparatively few ever reach New England. It comes singly, in pairs or in small companies and seeks the society of other ducks, such as Blue-winged Teal, Baldpate and Lesser Scaup. It should be looked for among other wild-fowl in September and early October. Those seen later than the latter date are usually cripples or belated stragglers.   By December the vanguard has reached South America.   (A young bird of this species remained about Boston through December, 1924, and January, 1925, but such occurrences are rare.)   They are a little later than most of the ducks on the return trip, for I find no Massachusetts records before early April; and this seems to be about the average time of their arrival near the northern border of the United States, though there are some March records.

The Shoveller is regarded as a rather "slow" bird, comparatively unsuspicious and easily taken.   It comes well to decoys and often seems slow and vacillating in flight, but in reality when aroused or frightened it is one of the most active and swift of water-fowl.   When startled it springs quickly from the water with an audible flapping of its long wings and goes away with a rush.   Its speed when alarmed and under full headway is difficult to estimate.   The only full plumaged adult male that I have taken passed by me in full flight riding high on a strong wind.   Swinging the muzzle of my gun far ahead I killed him instantly at perhaps 50 yards, but the impetus of his headlong, hurtling flight carried him on and he fell 90 paces from the place where I stood.

I have enjoyed watching the feeding habits of the Shoveller.   At times there are no ducks more active on land or water.   They dart about in pursuit of insects, splash in play and chase each other round and round.   The great, peculiar bill is an excellent trap for both land and water insects and more than any other duck, the Shoveller uses the long comb-like pectinations of the spoon-shaped member to sift from water or ooze the food it most desires.   I have watched many surface-feeding ducks swimming low in the water with head and neck extended and bill partially immersed.   In this way they often drink but perhaps still more often secure food which is retained by the sensitive tongue or the lamellated mandibles while the water and inedible residue passes out on either side; but no species that it has been my good fortune to observe practises this so often and so continuously as the Shoveller.   Three or four Shovellers will form in line following one after the other and then the leader will swing round in an ellipse, turning and following the hindmost, each one apparently straining through its bill the water stirred by the paddling feet of the one before it.   Thus round and round they go with chattering bills, each one apparently enjoying the guttering exercise and getting some sustenance from the disturbed and turgid element.   The male and female also circle about in this manner during courtship.

A bird so highly specialized as the Shoveller might be expected to subsist to some extent on certain minute objects not so readily separated from the ooze by ducks with ordinary bills unprovided with so fine a straining apparatus.   An examination of the food of the Shoveller tends to confirm this theory.   It is well known that some ducks under certain circumstances, as when starving in winter, swallow considerable mud and that many, by straining mud and water through the lamellated edges of their bills, are able to separate from the elements thus strained certain animal and vegetal foods.   At times the Shoveller's feeding exemplifies this process.

Mr. W. L. McAtee has published the most authoritative account of the food of the

Shoveller.[1] It is based on examinations of the stomach contents of 70 birds collected in 12 states. These contained 65.76% of animal food and 34.24% of vegetal food. The largest animal items consisted of fresh-water snails; aquatic insects were next in quantity; while small fishes made up 3%. Evidently most of the animal food is taken from mud and water. Among the crustaceans found were crawfish and eight species of ostracods. Large numbers of these tiny creatures, also copepods and diatoms (the last vegetal), were taken no doubt as a result of the thorough straining of the "bottom ooze" through the specialized bill of the birds. Much debris of a vegetable origin is taken also from the mud. The leading items of the vegetal food are not dissimilar to those taken by other fresh-water ducks, for sedges, pondweeds, grasses, algæ, water-lilies, duckweeds and smartweeds are given among the stomach contents.

The Shoveller is especially fond of widgeon grass (*Ruppia maritima*) and for this reason it may be that the bird is found most commonly in ponds near the coast where this plant grows. It eats the seeds and other parts of many land and aquatic plants, also small frogs, tadpoles, leeches and many land insects.

Prof. Aughey obtained in May a specimen in Nebraska which had in its stomach 37 locusts, 22 other insects, some small, fresh-water mollusks and some seeds.

Economic Status. Mr. McAtee finds that so far as known the Shoveller damages no crop nor feeds on animals of pronounced value to man. It devours various enemies of fish such as dragon-fly nymphs, giant water bugs, water scorpions, water-tigers, back-swimmers and crawfish, the last of which are also destructive to crops, dikes and levees. If we add to this the fact that the bird feeds to some extent on grasshoppers and locusts and recall that it is one of the best ducks for the table, when feeding on vegetal food, it would seem that the Shoveller is a bird to protect and preserve.

Dáfila acúta tzitzihóa (Vieillot). American Pintail.

Other names: sprig tail; pheasant duck; gray duck; picket-tail; sea widgeon.

Plate 14.

Description. — Neck unusually long and slender; form more slender than that of most ducks; tail of 16 feathers; adult male has middle feathers much longer than the rest and slightly upturned at ends; tail tapering and pointed at end; female and young have tail short, tapering and pointed without elongation of middle feathers. *Adult male in winter and nuptial plumage:* Head, chin and throat, including upper fore neck, dark rich olive-brown with green and purplish gloss, top of head darkest; hind neck (narrowly) black or blackish, graying toward its juncture with back, and separated from brown of upper neck and throat on each side by a long, white stripe extending upward from neck to back part of ear-region; under plumage mainly white; fore part of folded wing gray; primaries darker; a light rusty-brown or cinnamon bar on tips of greater wing-coverts precedes the iridescent speculum or wing patch which is changeable metallic-green to bronzy-purple, crossed by a narrow subterminal bar of velvety black and tipped white, a stripe of black frames its upper edge; inner secondaries, tertials and long pointed scapulars striped lengthwise with sharply contrasting black and silver-gray or whitish, the latter color largely marginal; a conspicuous wide black scapular stripe reaching back above speculum; rump and

---

[1] Auk, Vol. XXXIX, 1922, pp. 380–386.

upper tail-coverts mainly gray or grayish; outer tail-coverts largely blackish, their inner edges whitish; tail-feathers dark brown above, edged whitish, pale gray below, two long middle feathers black or blackish with iridescent reflections; lower neck, upper back, sides and flanks narrowly cross-waved or vermiculated with blackish and white or whitish, producing a gray effect; on flanks gray changes into white or yellowish-white toward tail, contrasting sharply with deep black of under tail-coverts, outermost of which have outer edges white; wing-linings and under surface of wings grayish-brown, axillars very variable, gray, edged whitish or dull white with some dark shaft-streaks and more or less finely mottled dusky; bill blackish-gray on ridge and nail, lead color or bluish-gray on sides of upper mandible; iris brown or hazel; feet olive-gray, joints dusky (Grinnell, Bryant and Storer), "legs and toes pale bluish-slate (about color of sides of upper mandible), with dark dusky or blackish webbing" (J. A. Farley). *Adult male in eclipse plumage:* Somewhat similar to plumage of female but back browner, tail darker brown and generally darker above; fore wing and speculum much as in winter male; variable, some birds broadly barred above, others coarsely or finely vermiculated above and mottled below. *Adult female in winter and nuptial plumage:* Top of head reddish-brown, heavily marked blackish; sides of head and neck all round lighter brown, more buffy and more finely streaked blackish; chin and throat lighter or less streaked; other upper plumage and sides dark brown, each feather with U-shaped marks or irregular bars of light reddish-brown or whitish; upper tail-coverts widely edged white; tail dark brown or dusky narrowly barred light brown or whitish, each feather edged whitish; wing not nearly so bright as in male, with no black marks, speculum much lighter and duller, brown or brownish-gray with faint greenish and purplish reflections, tertials and scapulars not much striped; below dingy-white but feathers of lower neck usually show U-shaped brown markings; other under plumage slightly mottled, with some grayish feather centers; under wing-coverts fuscous, edged whitish; axillars barred or mottled with black; iris dark brown; bill blackish, feet grayish-blue (Coues); bill and feet similar to those of male (Ridgway); "bill dark bluish-slate, tarsus and toes light slate, webs darker" (J. A. Mann). *Adult female in eclipse plumage:* Much like adult female in winter except lower plumage is not white but spotted much like that of juvenal plumage. *Young in juvenal plumage:* Closely resemble winter female though much more streaked with gray or dusky below; later young male becomes larger and grayer than young female and by December resembles adult male more or less, long middle tail-feathers being about the last to appear. *Downy young:* "Grayer and browner than other young surface-feeding ducks and thus easily recognized" (A. C. Bent); above grayish-olive or brown, darker on top of head and on rump; dull white spot or stripe on each side of back; white space across end of wing; sides of head variable, but usually whitish stripe over eye, brown stripe behind eye running to hind head and spot or stripe of brown in ear-region; lower part of cheeks, sides of neck and all under plumage white or grayish-white, darker on lower fore neck, with yellowish or brownish tinge on under surface of body.

MEASUREMENTS. — *Male:* Very variable; length 26.00 to 30.00 in.; spread 33.00 to 36.00; folded wing 9.80 to 11.20; tail 5.00 to 9.50; bill 1.85 to 2.25; tarsus 1.55 to 2.15. *Female:* Much smaller; length 20.00 to 24.00 in.; spread about 24.00; folded wing 9.60 to 10.42; tail 3.80 to 5.00; bill 1.75 to 2.10; tarsus 1.56 to 1.70. Weight 1 lb. 2 oz. to 2 lbs. 12 oz.

MOLTS. — Young female acquires juvenal plumage after natal down, and first winter plumage succeeds partial postjuvenal molt; this molting sometimes continues until February or even March and is followed by partial spring molt and an incomplete first nuptial plumage (still consisting in part of first winter plumage) in which new inner secondaries are acquired; this plumage becomes much worn and abraded during summer and is replaced in late summer or early autumn by first postnuptial plumage which is grayer than that of adult female; adult nuptial plumage is acquired after a molt in following spring when bird is about 22 months old; molts of young male similar, except that there seems to be only trace of first winter plumage, feathers of which are soon lost and are succeeded before spring by a nuptial plumage which resembles that of adult male though showing signs of immaturity; in summer young male goes into first eclipse plumage (molting in August, as usual flight-feathers) which begins to disappear in September and October but "not completed usually until November or December"

(A. C. Bent), after which bird assumes its second winter or nuptial plumage — that of adult male; there seems to be considerable variation in the molting period and in the time required to reach maturity, and some birds may not become fully adult until the third year; there are two adult molts annually, one (in summer) incomplete, the other (in autumn and winter) complete except wings, which were molted previously (in August).

FIELD MARKS. — Size of Black Duck. *Male:* Readily recognized when close at hand by its gray coloring, long, pointed, cocked-up tail and long white streak running up from white neck and breast into dark sides of neck and head; at a distance long, slender tail-feathers are invisible but if bird is flying, its long, thin neck, white under plumage and general slenderness are conspicuous. *Females and young:* Readily mistaken for female Mallards, Baldpates or Gadwalls, but more slender in shape and sitting high on water; at close range and when speculum can be seen with a good glass (often it is covered by feathers of sides), Pintail shows but one narrow white bar in wing where Mallard has two; unlike Gadwall, Pintail has no white speculum and it has a light buffy bar before speculum where Mallard has a white one and Baldpate a dark one; in flight the long, slender neck is as noticeable as in male, also long, narrow, pointed wings.

VOICE. — A loud quack, a mellow whistle and a harsh rolling note (E. W. Nelson); quack usually attributed to female and whistle to male, but Mr. Benjamin F. Howell relates that he heard a male on the wing utter two syllables *qua qua* resembling a quack but not so loud as that uttered by Mallard; in spring males have low, soft notes "that seem to flow from deep down in the throat" (E. H. Eaton).

BREEDING. — On islands, prairies or tundra; usually in the open. *Nest:* Sometimes but seldom in marsh land, more often on dry ground, sometimes a mile from water; usually in grass or under a bush, often near water but not always, a slight hollow in ground lined with rushes, straw, grass or stubble and dark down. *Eggs:* 5 to 12; average 2.00 by 1.51 in.; closely resemble those of Mallard in shape and color but slightly smaller; covered with down when bird leaves nest. *Dates:* Breeds early. April 28 to July 16, California to Alaska (A. C. Bent). *Incubation:* Period "22 or 23 days" (A. C. Bent); by female. One brood yearly.

RANGE. — North America. Breeds on coast of Bering Sea and on Arctic coast from Alaska to Kee-watin, along west coast of Hudson Bay, on both coasts of James Bay, rarely east of Lake Michigan, as in Ontario and New Brunswick south to southern California, northern Utah, northern Colorado, west central Nebraska, western Missouri (possibly), central Iowa, northern Illinois (now or formerly) and New Jersey casually (1908); winters from southeastern Alaska, British Columbia, northeastern Colorado, southern Kansas, central Missouri, southern Illinois, southern Indiana, southern Ohio, Pennsylvania, Connecticut (rarely), New Jersey and Massachusetts (casually), south to Porto Rico and Panama, and in Hawaii; said to winter casually in southeastern Nebraska; in migration occasional on Atlantic coast to Labrador and northern Ungava and on Pacific side to Marshall Islands; casual in Greenland and Bermuda. The Old World form completes the distribution of the species over the Northern Hemisphere.

DISTRIBUTION IN NEW ENGLAND. — Rare migrant, perhaps less rare in southern New England than in northern part; occasionally common locally; winters casually in Massachusetts and in Maine (at least a part of winter); rarely in Connecticut.

SEASON IN MASSACHUSETTS. — September 11 to December 21 (winter); February 22 to April 3.

HAUNTS AND HABITS. The Pintail is one of the finest and most widely distributed water-fowl of the world. Elegant in form, beautiful in plumage, fleet, intelligent, cautious, and excellent upon the table, it has all the desirable qualities of a game bird. It is so suspicious and swift, and when alarmed gets away so quickly that it taxes the skill of the sportsman to the uttermost. Any unusual object or the slightest motion of the hunter is enough to cause it to disappear instantly on the wings of the wind.

It is regrettable that this splendid bird is not more common in New England. If seen at all here it is generally alone, in pairs or in small parties, although in occasional seasons it appears in greater numbers. It is normally a fresh-water bird frequenting rivers, lakes and ponds, but it often feeds on flooded salt-marshes. Along the coast when much pursued it will go to sea to rest during daylight but returns to its favorite inland feeding grounds when night has fallen. Occasionally during mild winters the very few Pintails wintering in the ponds near Boston will be driven to the salt water when the ponds are closed with ice. Even in the hard winter of 1922–23 one bird was reported in the neighborhood of the city practically all winter; it left the fresh water only when no open spot could be found. This is one of the earliest of the water-fowl to appear in spring. Even in late February while the rivers are still locked in ice, it may be seen sometimes in rain-water pools and unfrozen spring-holes, and usually it is here in March while floating ice still blocks the streams. We see little of its courting here.

In safe retreats it seems to delight in leaving the water during the warm hours of the day and resting and dressing its plumage on some bar or open strand. When on the water it rides buoyantly and gracefully, its long tail held high, and when alarmed it springs into the air as readily as a Black Duck. There is no dragging or pattering along the surface with the active, clipper-built Pintail. Although a surface-feeding duck it can dive and swim readily under water, and like several other species it has been known when wounded to cling fast to some object on the bottom.

The Pintail is one of the earliest of the ducks to return southward in autumn and sometimes comes along with the Blue-winged Teal, the first of the early ducks.

This bird is fond of pondweeds and the seeds of sedges and grasses including the cultivated grains, especially rice, but it seems to get little but waste grain. It takes the seeds of common weeds, especially many of those growing near the water, and eats various succulent parts of many water-plants. It also destroys small mollusks and crustaceans and many insects such as beetles, flies, grasshoppers, dragon-flies, mosquitoes, water-bugs, etc.[1]

ECONOMIC STATUS. Possibly this bird might rank close to the Mallard as one of the most beneficial ducks. Its size, beauty and adaptability are such that it is a wonder that it has not long ago been commonly domesticated. Apparently it would make a great addition to our domestic poultry as it is a native of those temperate regions best suited to the great civilized races of mankind.

Aix spónsa (LINNÆUS). **Wood Duck.**

Other names: SUMMER DUCK; WOOD WIDGEON; ACORN DUCK; TREE DUCK.

Plate 14.

DESCRIPTION. — Head full-crested; bill shorter than head, very high at base, few lamellæ, nostrils large, oval, set well back near feathers of head; nail large, long, decurved, occupying whole end of bill. *Adult male in winter and nuptial plumage:* Head metallic-green and blue on upper part with a long profuse crest of purple, and marked with two lines of narrow white feathers; sides of head deepening to purplish-

---

[1] See Bulletin 862, United States Department of Agriculture, Contribution from the Bureau of Biological Survey, by Douglas C. Mabbott, 1920, pp. 32–36.

black below eye; throat white, the white running a spur up side of head and another across side of upper neck; upper body rich greenish-brown, bronze-green and purple; closed wings show velvety black, purple and white, with a purplish, steel-blue speculum succeeded by a white bar; exposed inner webs of primaries steel-blue; outer webs silvery-gray toward tips; tail long and dark with bronzy green reflections; upper breast rich reddish-chestnut, with small white markings, a white bar or crescent edged with black before bend of wing; flanks light buffy-brown, finely cross-lined, and bordered above and behind by black and white; rest of under plumage white, except under tail-coverts, which are dusky; bill pinkish-white, red and black with a yellow basal line; iris and eyelids red; feet orange. *Adult male in eclipse plumage:* Similar to female in summer plumage but like juvenal male has white side markings on head similar to those of male in nuptial plumage; wing much brighter than in female. *Adult female:* Less crest; head grayish; chin, throat, line about base of bill, ring around eye and patch behind it white; rest of upper plumage brownish, dark or grayish-brown with greenish-bronzy reflections on upper tail-coverts and tail; wings somewhat as in male; neck, upper breast and flanks streaked and mottled with gray or brown and buff, breast spotted with whitish, flanks with white; belly white, with here and there a dusky spot; bill dusky or "dark lead color" with large white spot on each side; legs and feet yellowish-brown. *Young in juvenal plumage:* Similar to female but much mottled on belly. *Downy young:* Colors variable; above dark brown, darker on top of head and tail; bar on back edge of each wing and spot on each side of rump whitish or pale yellowish; side of head generally yellowish-buff, often varied with cream or yellow; a wide blackish-brown stripe from back of eye to back of head; below whitish or dingy white, becoming brownish on sides and crossed on flanks by a whitish bar.

DOWNY YOUNG WOOD DUCK
About ½ natural size.

MEASUREMENTS. — Length 17.00 to 20.50 in.; spread about 28.00 to 29.00; folded wing 8.35 to 9.50; tail about 4.50; bill 1.10 to 1.40; tarsus 1.25 to 1.44. Weight 1 to 1½ lbs. Female smaller than male.

MOLTS. — Young begin to molt juvenal plumage by September; abdomen of young male now grows white; in October head resembles that of adult and in November bird appears much like adult, but its plumage is not perfect until following year; in early summer molt into eclipse plumage begins and in July or August flight-feathers are molted; in August and September bird molts again and assumes winter (nuptial) plumage which is usually complete before winter sets in; adults molt into the eclipse plumage in summer, lose flight-feathers in July or August, and complete the molt in autumn.

FIELD MARKS. — Smaller than Black Duck (which is the common New England duck in summer); in flight overhead Wood Ducks show a white or whitish belly where Black Ducks are dark; in migrating flocks, among other ducks in flight, it would be difficult to pick out a female or young Wood Duck from a female or young of Baldpate or Pintail; but where markings can be seen at close range, the crested male with its unmistakable marks and the female with her white eye-ring and the white patch or line behind eye are recognizable.

VOICE. — A frightened plaintive whistle, *oo-eek, oo-eek* (Chapman). A note of the drake is *pcet, peet,* uttered at intervals; the duck when startled, *cr-r-e-ek, cr-r-e-ek, cr-r-e-ek* (Eaton). The shrill little whistle of the male is very distinct from the louder and comparatively hoarse quack of the female (Wright and Harper).

BREEDING. — Usually near water but sometimes far from it. *Nest:* In hollow trunk or limb from 3 feet to 50 feet from ground or water, rarely on ground or in a building, also in nesting boxes, of grayish-white down (sometimes profuse) on punky wood of hole (normally). *Eggs:* 8 to 15, variable in number; (the largest set of which I have record is the nest of 19 eggs found in Rochester by Mr. J. A. Farley); 1.98 to 2.20 by 1.45 to 1.61 in.; "short elliptical"; pale buff, buffy-white or creamy-white. *Dates:* Late February and March, Florida; April 1 to 25, South Carolina; April 20 to June 14, Massachusetts; May 14 to July 2, Connecticut; May 10, Rhode Island. *Incubation:* Period 28 to 30 days (H. K. Job); by female; young remain in nest from 24 to 30 hours (Dixon). One brood yearly.

RANGE. — Temperate North America. Breeds from southern British Columbia, northwestern Montana, Great Slave Lake (rarely), southern Manitoba, southeastern Ontario and Labrador south to southern California (probably Nevada and Utah), southwestern Colorado (very rare), south central Texas, Florida and Cuba; winters (chiefly in United States) from southern British Columbia, Kansas, Missouri, Illinois, Indiana, Michigan (casually), Pennsylvania, New Jersey, New York, Connecticut and Massachusetts (very rarely) south to southern California, central Mexico and Gulf of Mexico; accidental in Bermuda and Jamaica.

DISTRIBUTION IN NEW ENGLAND. — Uncommon migrant and summer resident on fresh water during the first twenty years of the 20th century in most parts of New England, rare as a summer resident in Connecticut and very rare in summer in Rhode Island; now increasing in numbers and a rather common breeder in some of the well-watered woods of northern New England, especially in Maine, and sometimes locally abundant in migration in Maine, New Hampshire, Massachusetts and Connecticut; rare on salt water.

SEASON IN MASSACHUSETTS. — March 1 to November 30 (winter — a number of scattered records).

HAUNTS AND HABITS. Loveliest of all water-fowl the Wood Duck stands supreme. Deep flooded swamps where ancient mossy trees overhang the dark still waters, secluded pools amid the scattered pines where water-lilies lift their snowy heads and turtles bask in the sun, purling brooks flowing through dense woodlands where light and shade fleck the splashing waters, slow flowing creeks and marshy ponds — these are the haunts of the Wood Duck. See that mating pair on the dark and shaded flood of a little woodland river; they seem to float as lightly as the drifting leaves. The male glides along proudly, his head ruffled and his crest distended, his scapular feathers raised and lowered at will, while his plumes flash with metallic luster wherever the sun's rays sifting through the foliage intercept his course. She coyly retires; he daintily follows, exhibiting all his graces, the darkling colors of his plumage relieved by the pure white markings of head and breast and the bright reds of feet and bill and large lustrous eye. What a picture they make, as, intent on one another, they glide along close together, she clothed in modest hues, he glowing and resplendent. He nods and calls in low sweet tender tones and thus, she leading, he pursuing, they disappear into the shadows where the stream turns upon another course. I have lain concealed beneath the foliage, and watched a flock of these exquisite creatures disporting themselves upon a woodland pool. Such a picture no pen can adequately describe. The changing colors of the water reflecting sun, sky and foliage, all are reproduced in the plumage of the active birds as they pass, turn and repass upon their favorite element.

The Wood Duck is a part of Nature's heritage vouchsafed to the American people. It lives and migrates mainly within the United States. It breeds more generally throughout the land than any other duck. How have we kept that heritage? Once this beautiful bird was common to abundant throughout New England, wherever there were wooded river valleys and swamps, along all the water-courses, about the margins of lakes and ponds and all over our well-watered terrain. In heavily timbered regions they were even more abundant than the Black Duck. Within fifty years they were so numerous that at sunset in the season of migration they came by hundreds into some of their favorite wooded swamps in northern Worcester County. Their former abundance in suitable regions in the northern United States is thus described by Dr. Hatch who wrote about 1887: "Arriving simultaneously with the other earlier species, none other braves the last rigors of the departing winter in the closing days of a Minnesota March with greater spirit, and when they come, like the rains of the tropics, they pour in until every pool in the woodlands is deluged with them." This should have been written in the past tense as Dr. Hatch was writing then of experiences of earlier years — years when the Wood Ducks were as familiar to the country people as were robins and blackbirds. These ducks often built their nests in the hollow trees of the orchard or in the shade trees that overhung the farmhouse. Spring shooting which went on merrily even after the ducks had laid their eggs brought the species nearly to extinction in the early part of the twentieth century. At that time there were said to be more Wood Ducks in Belgium than in the United States. The Belgian pigeon and poultry fanciers, recognizing the value of the Wood Duck's peerless beauty and the danger of its extinction, imported them and reared them artificially in large numbers, and the time came when Americans who desired live Wood Ducks were forced to buy them from the Belgians at exorbitant prices.

State and National laws were passed protecting the bird at all times and now at last its numbers are beginning to increase. Nevertheless many are shot by mistake. A New England sportsman awaiting ducks in his blind need not mistake the Wood Duck for any other bird. It is the only white-bellied river duck in New England except the Baldpate, which it does not otherwise resemble. The wing action of the Wood Duck is unlike that of any other duck. Mr. A. J. T. Grant tells how to recognize it as it comes in over decoys: ". . . it *never* careens to face the wind in alighting as is so often noted in other water-fowl. He comes *rolling* from afar, little change in style of flight, and never hits the water without giving that weakish, peeping call for many rods before preparing to alight. Though he may be with other ducks, they will sight the decoys and give warning, then take to their queer antics before settling, but never the Wood Duck — he comes direct, sure, and peeping to the water." [1]

No doubt lumbering had something to do with the decrease of this duck, as it nests normally in the hollows of forest trees or in holes made by Pileated Woodpeckers. These great woodpeckers decreased with the cutting away of the primeval forest and the increase of hunters. The destruction of old hollow trees also greatly reduced the nesting places for Wood Ducks. In their search for domiciles the females have been entrapped in chimneys and stovepipes; they have even been known, where suitable trees were lacking, to nest upon the ground. Many years ago such a nest was found in Carver, always a

---

[1] The Michigan Sportsman: September, 1919, pp. 32 and 33.

famous Wood Duck town, near a pond where the trees were mainly scrub oaks and small pines, and there is more than one case on record (elsewhere as well as in Carver) where a female has entered a barn through a hole in the boarding and made her nest in a haymow; in Carver also a Wood Duck once laid her eggs in a vacant hen-house. The Wood Duck may become as abundant as in the past only by perpetual protection and by supplying it with artificial tree nesting-boxes simulating the hollow limbs of the forest.

Young Wood Ducks when hatched are well equipped for climbing as they are provided with exceedingly sharp, pin-pointed, hooked claws and with hooked nails at the ends of their bills; so expert are they that in many cases when confined in a box or keg, they have been known to climb out, going up the perpendicular sides like flies walking on a wall. When the eggs begin hatching, the young remain quiescent in the nest for a day or two; but when the female alights on the ground or water and calls them, they quickly climb out of the nest. If the trunk of the tree leans, they may scramble down the bark backward or roll and tumble to the ground. If not, they fall fluttering lightly to the ground without suffering any serious injury, and the mother leads her brood proudly to the nearest water. As is the case with most ducks, the male leaves the female when the duties of incubation begin, but occasionally a male has been seen with his family before or after it has reached the water. The evident fitness of the ducklings for going to water as above described, and the fact that in zoölogical parks in Europe they get to the water in the same way, have inclined certain European ornithologists to the belief that the parent bird never carries them. There is incontestable evidence, however, that the young often are conveyed to the water by the parent not only when the nest is at a considerable distance from water but sometimes when the tree almost overhangs it. When the Wood Duck was in danger of extinction, I endeavored to secure for the benefit of posterity the statements of eye-witnesses in many parts of the United States who had seen how this was accomplished in the days when these ducks were abundant. Since the recent increase of the species I have been able to learn of such observations, made within the past few years. Some of these already have been published, and others will be, but the lack of space precludes their appearance here. The many accounts of these occurrences now in my possession indicate that the rules laid down by Audubon for the behavior of the ducklings and their parents on these occasions are more honored in the breach than in the observance. He asserts that if the nest is situated directly over the water, the young scramble to the mouth of the hole and with feet and wings spread drop "into their favorite element; and when the nest is thirty or forty yards from the water, the mother allows them to fall on the ground and leads them to it, but whenever their birthplace" was at some distance, the mother carries them to the water in her bill. Three observers who have reported to me from different parts of the United States assert that while in an excellent position to watch, they saw the mother bird carry the young *on her back*. In each case the nest was almost directly over the water, and in each case the bird flew downward, and the young fell from her back either before she reached the water or as she alighted. In other reported cases nests were either near or far from the water, in one case two miles from the lake to which year after year the duck flew carrying her young, one at a time. In nearly all these cases the young were carried in the bill. Two observers could not see how the young were carried, but saw them placed in the water; while two believe that they were carried in some way between the legs. On the other hand several observers report that they have seen the mother leading her young over long distances to water. It seems therefore that we can lay down no rule for the behavior of the mother bird, nor can we describe the circumstances under which she will invariably proceed in a certain way. We must allow something for individuality. But at least we must admit that the Wood Duck at times carries her young from nest to water. In three cases the bird was seen to carry more than one young at a time. In one case the nest was in a tree on the bank of the Penobscot River in Maine and the bird flew down with the young clinging to her in some way. As she struck the water, several ducklings fell off into the stream. In support of this tale told by an accurate observer (and corroborated by others), may be cited the fact that young Wood Ducks reared by bantam hens seem often to take delight in mounting the hen's back and riding on her. The sharp claws and hooked bill which assist the ducklings in climbing out of the nest may be equally effective in mounting the mother's back and clinging there. The young birds thrive in shallow water along the edges of sloughs, weedy ponds and slow running streams. They are especially fond of the larvæ of mosquitoes of which surface-feeding ducks destroy great quantities. Many of the ducklings are killed and eaten by snapping turtles and large frogs and no doubt the fishes and hawks take their toll, but usually a good part of the brood is safely reared.

In September the migration of the Wood Ducks begins. They move at first in small flocks or family groups and during late September or October quite large companies may be seen in favorite swamps and ponds or along the larger rivers of New England. After October their numbers decrease and a winter Wood Duck in southern New England is a rarity. In spring when the ice has left the ponds and streams and when the chorus of the wood frogs and hylas is heard in the land, the main flight of Wood Ducks appears. They continue to pass northward through late March and early April.

The late Douglas C. Mabbott (1920) gave the following summary of the food of the Wood Duck:

"More than nine-tenths (90.19 per cent) of the food of the Wood Duck consists of vegetable matter. This high proportion of vegetable food is very similar to that taken by the mallard. With the Wood Duck it is quite evenly distributed among a large number of small items, chief among which are the following: Duckweeds, 10.35 per cent; cypress cones and galls, 9.25; sedge seeds and tubers, 9.14; grasses and grass seeds, 8.17; pondweeds and their seeds, 6.53; acorns and beechnuts, 6.28; seeds of water-lilies and leaves of water shield, 5.95; seeds of water elm and its allies, 4.75; of smartweeds and docks, 4.74; of coontail, 2.86; of arrow-arum and skunk cabbage, 2.42; of bur marigold and other composites, 2.38; of buttonbush and allied plants, 2.25; of bur reed, 1.96; wild celery and frogbit, 1.31; nuts of bitter pecan, 0.91; grape seeds, 0.82; and seeds of swamp privet and ash, 0.72 per cent. The remaining 9.4 per cent was made up of a large number of minor items. . . .

"The Wood Duck's animal food, which amounted to 9.81 per cent of the total consisted chiefly of the following items: Dragonflies and damselflies and their nymphs, 2.54 per cent; bugs, 1.56; beetles, 1.02; grasshoppers and crickets, 0.23; flies and ants, bees and wasps, 0.07; miscellaneous insects, 0.97; spiders and mites, 0.63; crustaceans, 0.08; and miscellaneous animal matter, 2.71 per cent. Thus nearly two-thirds of the animal food consisted of insects." [1]

ECONOMIC STATUS. The Wood Duck is a harmless bird, a destroyer of pernicious insects, a splendid game bird and in every way desirable — a bird to be protected and fostered.

SUBFAMILY FULIGULINÆ. SEA DUCKS.

Number of species in North America 22; in Massachusetts 17.

Ducks of this subfamily have the hind toe free and lobed. The large flap on this toe at once distinguishes ducks of this group from the Anatinæ which have no such lobe. Also the feet of the sea ducks are larger and placed farther back and the tarsi are shorter, and therefore these birds are better fitted for diving and less so for walking or running than are the river ducks. Like the mergansers, the sea ducks are all diving birds and get most of their food by diving to the bottom or to plants or animals that grow or live beneath the surface — in contradistinction from the river ducks which do not habitually dive for their food. Most birds of this subfamily along the Atlantic coast are regarded as sea-fowl by the gunners, although several species are known to breed far in the interior of North America. Of the sixteen species regularly seen on the coast of New England, all but two, the Ruddy Duck and the Lesser Scaup, habitually winter here. The latter are mainly transients, although they may be seen sometimes in winter.

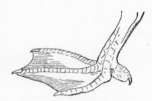

FOOT OF SEA DUCK

Maríla americána (EYTON). Redhead.

Other names: AMERICAN POCHARD; RED-HEADED RAFT DUCK.

Plate 15.

DESCRIPTION. — Greatest width of bill much over one-third its length: *profile of its ridge concave; forehead bold and comparatively high; head fluffy.* *Adult male in winter and nuptial plumage:* Head and upper neck reddish-chestnut with purplish gloss; rest of neck, breast, fore part of back, upper and under tail-coverts and tail all black or blackish, tail paling toward tip; most of upper surface of body (including scapulars), sides and flanks barred with fine wavy black and white lines of nearly equal width, giving a gray effect; wing-coverts leaden-gray, speculum pale bluish-gray bordered narrowly by white behind, with lines of black on outer edges of three upper feathers; flight-feathers pale slaty-gray, dusky

[1] United States Department of Agriculture, Bulletin 862, 1920, pp. 166, 167.

at tips; axillars white, wing linings gray; fore part of abdomen white, hind part with wavy white and blackish bars as on scapulars; bill dull grayish-blue or slaty, tip of upper mandible black; whole bill sometimes "black" (A. Wilson); iris lemon-yellow; legs and feet bluish-gray or "dark ash," webs blackish. *Adult male in eclipse plumage:* This is a partial eclipse in which head and neck become browner, breast and under plumage mottled as in breeding female; many brown feathers appear in back "and the crissum is veiled with light edgings" (A. C. Bent). *Adult female in winter and nuptial plumage:* Head and upper neck pale "grayish-brown," "reddish-brown" or "brownish-gray" darkening on crown and lightening to grayish-buff or whitish about base of bill and on chin and contiguous parts of throat; upper plumage, lower neck and upper breast, sides and flanks mainly brown, with light feather edgings, which are most conspicuous on lower neck, sides and flanks; wings much as in male; lower breast and belly mainly white, shading into brownish-gray behind; bill and feet similar to those of male but duller; iris brown (some authorities say yellow). "There is a very frequent tendency to albinism in the female redhead, not in the male"; head and back of neck sprinkled with white feathers; head of some birds almost white and under down on lower surface of body the same (Allan Brooks). *Adult female in eclipse plumage:* Becomes more mottled both above and below. *Young in juvenal plumage:* Somewhat similar to adult female; head reddish-brown; scapulars and back gray, edged brownish; belly mottled brown and white (A. C. Bent); a slight, very narrow, white border both before and behind speculum. *Downy young:* Above olive-brown; spot back of base of each wing (sometimes one on hind border of each), and one on each side of rump, yellow; below deep buffy-yellow, paler behind; no distinct markings on side of head; "color of downy young exactly the same in both birds" [*i.e.*, Ring-necked Duck and Redhead] (Allan Brooks).

MEASUREMENTS. — Length 17.00 to 23.00 in.; spread 30.00 to 33.00; folded wing 8.50 to 10.00; tail 2.50 to 3.00; bill 1.70 to 2.25; tarsus 1.50 to 1.60. Weight 1 lb. 12 oz. to 3 lbs. Female smaller than male.

MOLTS. — Apparently the Redhead shows little if any trace of first winter plumage; by November young male shows signs of first nuptial plumage, when black, brown-tipped feathers appear in breast and neck and by mid-winter plumage resembles that of adult male, but probably never acquires full perfection until a year later; adults molt in summer as well as in autumn, assuming partial eclipse plumage in breeding season, with renewal of much body plumage.

FIELD MARKS. — *Male:* With *high forehead*, black lower neck and gray back should never be mistaken for male Canvas-back (although with similarly colored head) with *low forehead*, brown neck and whitish back; nor for brown-headed female Golden-eye with whitish ring on neck just below head; in flight Redhead looks darker and shorter than Canvas-back. *Female:* Is more like female Canvas-back but low forehead and long bill of latter are as distinctive as in male; Redhead closely resembles the smaller female Ring-necked Duck; also females of these two species may be indistinguishable in the field.

VOICE. — A hoarse, guttural, rolling sound (D. G. Elliot); a hollow rapid croaking (F. M. Chapman); male, a deep-toned *me-ow* like the "voice of a large cat" (J. H. Langille); a peculiar *qua quaa* (E. H. Eaton); female, "sounds like a growl . . . r-r-r-r-wha, r-r-r-r-wha, given rather deliberately in pairs" (Ludlow Griscom); a loud, clear *squak* higher than that of Mallard or Black Duck (Langille).

BREEDING. — Near shallow, marsh-bordered lakes, in sloughs or cattail swamps. *Nest:* Usually deep, well made, of reeds or flags, lined with whitish down, often found covered with a downy blanket; often canopied with rushes bent over by bird. *Eggs:* 6 to 22, usually 10 to 15; 2.64 by 1.79 to 2.47 by 1.70 in. (sometimes smaller); hard and glossy; "pale olive buff to cream buff." *Dates:* May 18 to June 28, Minnesota and North Dakota. *Incubation:* Period 22 to 24 days (A. C. Bent); by female. One brood yearly.

RANGE. — North America. Breeds from central British Columbia, central Alberta, Great Slave Lake, central Saskatchewan, southern Manitoba, southern Minnesota, southern Wisconsin, southeastern Michigan, Maine (formerly) and Newfoundland (probably) south to southern California, central Nevada, northwestern New Mexico, southwestern Utah, southern Colorado and central western Nebraska;

PLATE 15

PLATE 15

CANVAS–BACK

Page 234

WINTER (NUPTIAL) PLUMAGE

ADULT MALE   ADULT FEMALE

REDHEAD

Page 231

WINTER (NUPTIAL) PLUMAGE

ADULT FEMALE

ADULT MALE

LESSER SCAUP DUCK

Page 241

WINTER (NUPTIAL) PLUMAGE

ADULT MALE

ADULT FEMALE

SCAUP DUCK

Page 237

WINTER (NUPTIAL) PLUMAGE

ADULT FEMALE

ADULT MALE

RING–NECKED DUCK

Page 243

WINTER (NUPTIAL) PLUMAGE

ADULT FEMALE   ADULT MALE

All one-sixth natural size.

winters from southern British Columbia, southeastern Arizona, northeastern Colorado, northern Arkansas, Illinois, Lakes Erie and Ontario, Maryland, Delaware and Massachusetts south to central Mexico, Florida, the Bahamas, Cuba and Jamaica; in migration casual in Alaska and Labrador, regular on Atlantic coast north to the Gulf of St. Lawrence.

DISTRIBUTION IN NEW ENGLAND. — Generally an uncommon to rare and local migrant but sometimes locally common, particularly near Maine coast (bred formerly near Calais (Boardman)); irregularly common to abundant locally in the cold months in southeastern Massachusetts; common winter visitor in Rhode Island.

SEASON IN MASSACHUSETTS. — March 6 to April 3; September 21 to December 27; wintering irregularly about Marthas Vineyard; one noted in a Boston pond, winter of 1909–10.

HAUNTS AND HABITS.　There is no place in New England where Redheads can be seen during the fall, winter and early spring in such abundance as in some of the larger ponds on the south side of Marthas Vineyard where wild celery and pondweeds attract them. There in October and November hundreds may be seen in company with Blue-bills riding the white-capped wavelets driven by the strong sea wind. Along the low, sandy lee shores of the pond rows of white froth gleam. The sun shines brightly on the sparkling waves; fleecy clouds race across the blue sky; gulls wheel and call over the beach ridge which divides the pond from the sea; and the long rafts of ducks lend added interest to the animated scene. Some are diving, some preening their feathers, others resting with heads on their backs. Occasionally one rises erect in the water with flapping wings.

In New England Redheads vary much in numbers from time to time. On Marthas Vineyard they were abundant for a long series of years; then they suddenly became much less numerous for a few years; and now (1922) they are again abundant. On Nantucket they are comparatively scarce.

Redheads in flight may not be known by any definite flock formation. Although they sometimes move in wide V-shaped flocks, they are quite as likely to fly bunched in dense flocks or in irregular formations. Like most ducks they like to swing about and reconnoiter before alighting; they then set their wings and sail down to the water, or, as Doctor D. G. Elliot says, they sometimes fall rapidly from the sky in a zigzag course.

Dr. Alexander Wetmore well describes the mating display of the Redhead.[1] The female jerked her head up and down or bowed to the male. The male extended his neck, holding his head erect or throwing it back until it touched his back while he gave his peculiar groaning or mewing call or "sank down with his head drawn in while the female bowed before him."

On Marthas Vineyard some of the market hunters of the old days were adepts in the art of "wafeing." The concealed hunter waved a red cloth in a way which attracted numbers of Redheads and Scaups within easy gunshot. Ordinarily these birds keep well away from the shore but their curiosity is great and they come in readily to the sportsmen's decoys. They feed largely at night and rest much during the day, though they often fly about in flocks from pond to pond especially early in the morning and late in the afternoon.

---

[1] Auk: Vol. XXXVII, 1920, p. 243.

From what we know of the Redhead's migration, it seems probable that the birds of this species that reach southern New England come from the northwest by way of the Great Lakes on a line of flight running a little south of east.   We shall know more about this when a few thousands of these birds have been marked on their breeding grounds with the aluminum bands furnished by the Biological Survey at Washington.   Redheads usually arrive in Massachusetts in October, are abundant in November and stay as long as the ponds are open.   There are many winters during which they can remain on Marthas Vineyard with its relatively mild climate, but a severe cold wave that covers ponds and flats with solid ice will send them southward.   In spring a few begin to move toward their summer homes before the ponds of the interior are clear of ice and often by the middle of March the movement becomes general.

As the Redhead is an excellent diver, its food is obtained largely beneath the surface and well away from shore, though it sometimes dabbles in very shallow water near the margin.   Evidently it prefers to feed in fresh water where it dives to obtain the foliage, bulbs and roots of aquatic plants.   Its vegetal food consists largely of wild celery, pondweeds and in fact the succulent shoots of almost any nutritious aquatic vegetation. It also includes some seeds and according to Audubon beech nuts and acorns.   Its animal food is almost equal in variety but less in quantity.   It eats fresh-water clams, snails, leeches, small fish, tadpoles, frogs, lizards and insects.

ECONOMIC STATUS.   As a table duck, the Redhead ranks second to none.   In autumn, when fatted on wild celery and other vegetal food, it may equal in flavor the famous Canvas-back and formerly it was sold in the markets under that name.   Though it can no longer be disposed of legally for cash, its importance as an object of food and sport is very considerable.

Marila valisinéria (WILSON).   Canvas-back.

Other names: CAN; WHITE-BACK.

Plate 15.

DESCRIPTION. — Bill longer than head, narrow (sometimes barely widened toward end), and high at base, *in profile almost wedge-shaped;* forehead sloping gradually backward in line with outline of ridge of upper mandible; head feathers short; eye very small; tail very short and pointed, of 14 feathers; feet very wide and large. *Adult male in winter and nuptial plumage:* Head and neck chiefly dark reddish-chestnut, darkening to blackish around base of bill and on top of head (rarely a small triangular white spot on extreme feathers of chin); base of neck encircled by wide black collar, which extends on fore part of body in front of wings; upper surface of body, sides, flanks and belly mainly white, with very fine wavy cross-lines of dusky; slightly thus marked (penciled) below, cross-lines increasing toward vent; wing-coverts gray with many small blackish spots; rump dusky or black; upper tail-coverts same, tail blackish-slate; speculum grayish or pale bluish-gray bordered behind by white, its uppermost feather-edged black; region about vent and under tail-coverts black; flight-feathers mainly slaty-brown; wing linings light gray, axillars white; bill blackish or greenish-black; iris carmine; legs and feet "grayish-blue" or "pale ash," webs dusky. *Adult male in eclipse plumage:* This plumage is only partial; head and neck more or less mottled and obscured with dusky and dull brownish feathers; black of breast more or less obscured by brown and gray, and belly somewhat mottled. *Adult female in winter and nuptial plumage:* Head, neck and breast dull dark reddish-brown, darkening on top of head and lightening to nearly white on chin, upper throat and in a rather indefinite stripe behind eye; back generally light slaty-brown with traces of fine, wavy white barring; rump blackish; upper and under tail-coverts and tail dusky-brownish; closed wing mainly slate-gray; flight-feathers, speculum and under surface of wing including axillars, much as in male; sides and flanks somewhat lighter than back, with some wavy white and dusky bars; under plumage mainly whitish, mottled with grayish-brown; bill shaped as in male, blackish; iris hazel; legs and feet much as in male. *Young in first winter plumage:* Male somewhat resembles adult male, but back, wings and sides still show many brown feathers; female similar to adult female. *Young in juvenal plumage:* Resembles adult female. *Downy young:* Above (top of head, hind neck and most of back) varying from "greenish-brown" or "sepia" to "buffy-olive"; sides of head "deep straw-yellow marked with dusky"; yellow spots in pairs — on hind edge of wing, behind wing and at base of tail, latter inconspicuous; sides of neck and under plumage "deep yellow."

MEASUREMENTS. — Length 20.00 to 24.00 in.; spread 34.00 to 36.00; folded wing 8.50 to 9.50; tail 2.35 to 3.40; bill 2.10 to 2.75; tarsus 1.60 to 1.81. Weight, male about 3 lbs.; female about 2 lbs. to 2 lbs. 6 oz.

MOLTS. — Young birds begin to molt from down into juvenal plumage when hardly half size, but flight-feathers do not appear until young are well grown and about 10 or 12 weeks old; young male then begins to assume reddish head and upper neck, and continuing to molt the juvenal plumage during fall and early winter, assumes in spring nearly adult dress; in late July or early August the young duck molts partially, assuming in late August an incomplete eclipse; in early October another molt is in progress, as a result of which young bird acquires adult winter plumage; adults have usual partial summer molt in late July and August, followed by molt of wing- and tail-quills, and an autumnal molt of the rest of the plumage in October.

FIELD MARKS. — *Adult male:* May be distinguished always by reddish-brown head and neck and canvas-colored body, whiter (as a whole) than that of any other native duck; large size, large head, low forehead and long, wedge-shaped bill, at once distinguish either sex from Redhead or female Golden-eye or Scaups, all of which have high foreheads (see also field marks under Redhead); in flight Canvas-back, with its long, slender neck and bill all carried with a slight downward curve, gives impression of wings placed far back, something not so apparent in either Scaups or Redheads; flocks fly in lines or V's like geese.

VOICE. — A harsh, guttural croak (D. G. Elliot); "a peeping or a growling note"; female, a quack or a screaming *currow* (E. H. Eaton); while mating a low *cooo*, a rather sharp high-pitched *ick ick* (A. A. Allen).

BREEDING. — Usually among reeds or flags in prairie sloughs; rarely on open prairie near water. *Nest:* On bed of dead reeds, in clump of marsh vegetation, surrounded by water, built of surrounding vegetation and lined with gray down. *Eggs:* 7 to 15; "greenish-drab" or grayish-olive, usually less buffy and darker than those of Redhead and averaging about same in size or a trifle larger; as in case of other slough-nesting ducks, eggs of other species (Redhead, Ruddy Duck, etc.) sometimes found in nest with those of Canvas-back. *Dates:* May 9 to June 25, Minnesota and North Dakota (A. C. Bent). *Incubation:* Period 28 days; by female. One brood yearly.

RANGE. — North America. Breeds from central Alaska (infrequently), northern Mackenzie, Saskatchewan and western Manitoba south to central Oregon, western Nevada, northern Utah, northern New Mexico, central western Nebraska, southern Minnesota and southern Wisconsin (casually); winters from southern British Columbia, northern Montana, northern Colorado, northeastern Arkansas, southern Illinois, southeastern Michigan, western New York, eastern Maryland and Massachusetts south to central Mexico, Gulf coast and Florida; in winter more or less abundant in Maryland, Virginia and North Carolina; casual in Pribilof Islands, West Indies, Bermuda and Guatemala; in migration north rarely to New Brunswick and Nova Scotia.*

---

* Numbers of Canvas-backs are said to pass the Marshall Islands northeast of New Guinea both spring and fall. These islands lie over 2200 miles southwest of the Hawaiian Islands (Phillips, J. C.: Auk, Vol. XXXIII, 1916, p. 22).

DISTRIBUTION IN NEW ENGLAND. — Considered a rare migrant in three northern New England states; occurs in Vermont on Lake Champlain but not recorded from New Hampshire; less rare in three southern New England states and growing more common (since 1904) in southeastern Massachusetts and southern New England generally where sometimes locally common; winters rarely in Massachusetts.

SEASON IN MASSACHUSETTS. — October 19 to December 18 (winter); March 11 to 31 (April 22).

HAUNTS AND HABITS. On March 19, 1919, a southerly storm swept the south coast of Marthas Vineyard. Through all the preceding night the surf beat upon the sands with a sound like distant rolling thunder. In the morning the wind shifted to the northward while the sound of the surf lowered to a sullen rushing roar which filled all the air, and the sea was obscured by drifting mist. Gulls wheeled along the shore, wildfowl flew singly or in pairs across the misty sky, while the rain fell in great drops or drove in sheets and clouds like spray before sharp gusts from off the land. The sea had thrown upon the beach a windrow of sea-moss, kelp, rock-weed, sponges and all the flotsam of the tide. A flock of sheep attracted by the sea-wrack nuzzled along the beach. Toward night as the wind swung to the northwest, the sky began to clear and the westering sun threw his slant rays over the tumultuous waters. All along down toward Squibnocket the great rollers charged the shore, each like some great sea-monster boring in toward the beach, its high mane of white sea-foam towering at its forefront and its spray streaming backward like white smoke. The scene was magnificent as, lighted by the setting sun, Niagaras of foam were poured upon the beach.

On Watcha Pond hundreds of ducks, with heads to the wind, rode the waves in security. They were largely Scaups and Redheads, but here and there was a lordly male Canvas-back, his great white body standing out conspicuously among his darker and lesser companions.

Here if anywhere in Massachusetts we shall find the Canvas-backs. In the ponds of southeastern Massachusetts they appear more generally in fall than in spring; and in some winters may be seen in Waquoit Bay, rarely on Nantucket, and occasionally in Boston, Plymouth and other harbors, and in the ponds about Boston.

The Canvas-back was formerly considered a very rare straggler in Massachusetts but early in the present century its numbers apparently increased, as recorded by Mr. S. Prescott Fay.[1] Although its numbers fluctuate from year to year, it is no longer a great rarity in Massachusetts but is locally common at times, especially on Marthas Vineyard. However, it may again become rare as it has in the past in some other regions, and as it usually does wherever its favorite food gives out.

I have never seen any signs of its courtship antics here but the males are said to throw the head over on the back as Golden-eyes and other ducks do at such times. Dr. A. A. Allen has described some of this behavior in Mr. Bent's Life Histories of North American Wildfowl.[2]

The Canvas-back with its very large feet and large wide webs is a powerful swimmer and an excellent diver. It goes to the bottom and there grubs up roots and shoots of

---

[1] The Canvas-back in Massachusetts, Auk, Vol. XXVII, 1910, pp. 369–381.
[2] Smithsonian Institution, United States National Museum, Bulletin 126, p. 190.

aquatic plants. It is the most celebrated of American ducks for the epicure and is supposed to acquire delectable flavor from feeding on the "eel-grass" known as wild celery (*Vallisneria spiralis*). It is now well known that Great Pond and Watcha Pond on Marthas Vineyard, where the Canvas-back is most commonly seen and taken, are fresh-water ponds which support much wild celery and succulent pondweeds. Nevertheless, the Canvas-back is said to have its best flavor when it first comes to the Atlantic coast from the West where it is supposed to feed to some extent on grain, of which it is very fond, and also on quite a variety of vegetal and animal food. On the Pacific coast it sometimes feeds on dead decaying salmon and so becomes unfit for human food. It is by no means a superior table bird except when feeding on its choicest vegetal aliments. The Redhead, Shoveller and some other ducks are in some circumstances fully its equal on the table.

ECONOMIC STATUS. This is one of the most important American ducks because of the fact that very large sums of money change hands during its pursuit. When marketing of wild-fowl was legal in this country, the Canvas-back brought high prices in the market, as it was considered by epicures the finest table duck that the world has produced. See also page 174.

Marila marila (LINNÆUS). Scaup Duck.

Other names: GREATER SCAUP; BLUE-BILL; BLUE-BILL WIDGEON; BROAD-BILL; RAFT DUCK; BIG BLACK-HEAD; TROOP FOWL; GREEN-HEAD.

Plate 15.

DESCRIPTION. — Bill as long as outer toe with claw, broad, and wider at end than at base. *Adult male in winter and nuptial plumage:* Head, neck, breast, shoulders, a little of upper back, lower back, rump, all tail-coverts, tail and ventral region black or blackish; most of head and upper neck with iridescent green gloss; (some individuals have a brownish ring around neck, and rarely a small triangular white spot on chin); scapulars and middle back, together with most of under plumage, white; scapulars, most of upper back, sides, flanks and lower belly cross-waved with fine, zigzag lines of blackish, giving a light gray effect (sides and flanks whiter and only faintly waved); greater and middle wing-coverts much darker but similarly though more finely and obscurely marked, blackish predominating; three or four outer primaries, and tips of all, chiefly brownish-black, *inner primaries showing a strong tendency to white on parts of both webs;* tertials blackish and greater wing-coverts tipped with same which frames front border of white speculum or wing-patch formed by secondaries; this white extends across secondaries but their ends are more or less black; axillars and most under wing-coverts mainly white, marginal wing-coverts with more or less dark gray mottling; bill pale grayish-blue, "dull blue" or lead color with black nail; iris yellow; feet "leaden gray" or "dark slate" with blackish webs. *Adult male in eclipse plumage:* Variable; head and neck dull brownish-black, with a few white feathers near base of bill, grayish cheeks and more or less whitish mottling on face and throat; nape and upper body darker than in nuptial plumage and sprinkled with gray feathers cross-waved with black; breast dark with white feather edgings; wings, scapulars and tail as in winter; flanks brownish-gray; white of under plumage somewhat obscured by brownish mottling. *Adult female in winter and nuptial plumage:* Head dusky or dark brown, which color replaces black and grayish elsewhere of male; region around base of bill, including chin, white, sharply contrasted with dark head; black and white cross-waving or vermiculation either wanting or faintly indicated; general plumage more obscure than in male; wings much as in male; bill dull blue or bluish-gray with black nail; iris dark yellow; feet lead color with blackish webs. *Adult female in eclipse or breeding plumage:* Variable; head much lighter than in winter and plumage generally lighter or more faded above and on breast, sides and flanks. *Young in juvenal plumage:* Similar to adult female in winter; but young male's wing more like adult male's and its head darker than female's. *Downy young:* Above deep, rich, dark brown which lightens on sides of head, and shades gradually on neck and sides into light brown, yellowish-white or buff of throat and fore neck; some indistinct dark shading on sides of head; belly, light brown, dull yellowish or cream-buff; dull dark band encircles lower neck and fore breast; scapulars and rump lack light-colored spots.

MEASUREMENTS. — Length 17.00 to 20.75 in.; spread 29.00 to 35.00; folded wing 8.00 to 9.00; tail 2.80 to 3.00; bill 1.64 to 2.20; breadth of bill 1.00; tarsus 1.30 to 1.57. Weight 2 lbs. to 2 lbs. 12 oz. Female smaller than male.

MOLTS. — Duckling becomes duller as it grows older, and is nearly full grown before the faded down disappears wholly from its neck; wings develop last, and the flightless stage continues through August and part of September while adults also are flightless; in September young resemble adult female, but lack white forehead and white face is mottled; grayish-white vermiculation of lesser wing-coverts usually distinguishes male from female at this age; in October young begin to resemble adults which resemblance progresses through winter and spring; in October first greenish-black appears on head and neck of male, gray vermiculation begins to replace brown on back, while black and white waving appears on scapulars; in November black adult feathers begin to show on breast and by February the head is practically as adult; before summer rest of plumage is much like that of adult; young Scaups apparently do not breed in the spring after their first winter but flock by themselves while completing molt; both adults and young molt in July or August but eclipse plumage is not complete; following this summer molt adults and young are practically indistinguishable, but another year is needed for young to acquire fully adult dress; in October nuptial plumage begins to show and while some birds (probably oldest) are in full plumage practically by November or December, this plumage may not be attained by others until April.

FIELD MARKS. — *Male:* Dark head, neck and breast, *blue* bill, pure white speculum, together with light gray back and white belly which last, contrasting sharply with black breast, may be seen in flight, easily distinguish male Scaup from almost any other duck except Lesser Scaup; (young scoters sometimes resemble scaups when seen from below); the two scaups resemble each other so closely that under usual conditions they cannot be distinguished readily, if at all, in the field, where greater size of the present species is rarely noticeable; metallic-green of head in male Scaup is usually replaced by purplish on head of male Lesser Scaup; "white flanks of male scaups make them appear almost as white as Canvas-backs but from above their darker backs quickly dispel the illusion" (A. A. Allen). *Female:* Differs from any other American duck (except Lesser and in some cases Ring-necked Scaups) in having a distinct white area around base of bill (but much less sharply defined in Ring-neck); seen *through a good glass* this white face is conspicuous in the field even at a distance; females of Scaup and Lesser Scaup are separable only by size, but both differ from female of Ring-neck in having speculum white, while latter's is gray; but this "difference is too slight when bird is moving to be reliable" (Ludlow Griscom).

VOICE. — A harsh, loud, discordant "scaup"; rarely heard by a flock in chorus; a soft purring whistle when excited or calling to their mates (E. H. Eaton).

BREEDING. — In grassy sloughs or near marshy ponds. *Nest:* Above water level, as on a hummock; often more or less hidden in clumps or tufts of grass or flags; built of grass stems, broken flags, rushes, etc., with lining of fine grass usually, and down; no down generally in new nest with eggs, but mixed in as incubation advances; down soft and compact, dark brown or gray, with obscurely paler centers; some small breast-feathers white or grayish, mixed with down. *Eggs:* 5 to 22, usually 7 to 10; largest sets are probably laid by two females; 2.50 to 2.70 by 1.68 to 1.75 in.; elliptical-ovate; greenish-gray or greenish-brown, "deep olive-buff" or "olive-buff" to "yellowish-glaucous" — "a much darker olive-buff than in other ducks' eggs" (A. C. Bent). *Dates:* June 14 to July 5, Alaska and Arctic America; May

25 to July 6, Manitoba, Saskatchewan and Alberta; May 30 to July 10, Iceland. *Incubation:* Period 3 to 4 weeks; by female. One brood yearly.

RANGE. — Northern parts of Northern Hemisphere; practically circumpolar. In North America breeds from Aleutian Islands and northern Alaska, along Arctic coasts of Canada, in southwestern Ungava (central western Quebec) and casually east to northern New Brunswick and Gulf of St. Lawrence south to central British Columbia (rarely), central and eastern Alberta, southern Manitoba (probably), Minnesota and North Dakota (formerly, but rarely now if at all), northern Iowa (formerly) and southeastern Michigan (casually); has bred casually in northern New Jersey; rare east and south in its breeding range; winters mainly on coasts of United States — on Atlantic side from Maine to Florida, chiefly from southern New England and Long Island to North Carolina; on Gulf coast — Louisiana and Texas — almost to Mexico; on Pacific side from Aleutian Islands to southern California; fewer winter in interior — Great Lakes and Southwest (Colorado, Utah, Nevada, Arizona and New Mexico); rare in migration in Newfoundland, eastern Labrador and Greenland; in Europe, breeds in Iceland and Faroe Islands, and in northern Europe and Asia, from Scotland to Bering Sea, southward from about 70°; winters south to the Mediterranean; northern Africa, Black and Caspian seas, Persian Gulf, northern India (rarely), China, Japan and Formosa.

DISTRIBUTION IN NEW ENGLAND. — Common to abundant migrant along coast, becoming more abundant south of Cape Cod, in Narragansett Bay, Long Island Sound and lower Connecticut and Housatonic rivers; less common or uncommon in interior where it visits the larger lakes; winters occasionally in Maine and in numbers at certain points on coast, as Boston and Lynn harbors, — and especially south of Cape Cod and along coasts of Rhode Island and Connecticut where it appears locally in numbers in late winter and early spring.

SEASON IN MASSACHUSETTS. — September 18 to May 12.

HAUNTS AND HABITS. The Scaup is known to most of the gunners of New England as the Blue-bill or Broad-bill. It is generally regarded as one of the uncommon ducks of these states, but nevertheless through the cold months it is often common and even abundant locally in Massachusetts. It is often numerous in Boston Harbor and still more so in Nantucket and Marthas Vineyard waters and at other points on the coasts of the three southern New England states. It frequents salt-water ponds, bays, estuaries and large harbors as well as brackish or fresh-water ponds near the sea. Like the Redhead and the Canvas-back it is an excellent diver, and is attracted particularly by wild celery and certain pondweeds; therefore it may be found in places where these plants grow. The habits of the bird are much like those of the Redhead, with which species it may be often found in flocks. It feeds mainly by diving in deep or shallow water at some distance from the shore, though it sometimes dabbles along the margin. In diving it usually keeps the wings close to the body, though if wounded and pursued, it may at times use them to accelerate its speed beneath the surface. In its anxiety to escape it has been known to seize with its bill vegetation under water and hold on tenaciously until death (or even after death), an act which as a last resort is common to many waterfowl.

In courtship the male lifts his head very high, and points the bill upward at an acute angle. When the female becomes responsive, she bows repeatedly. The Scaup is normally an unsuspicious duck, possessed of great curiosity, and can be tolled close to the shore by one who is skilled in the process; but the birds learn by experience and soon become gun-shy. Nevertheless they usually come well to decoys. Scaups are gregarious birds. On the water they flock close together; and if only two are seen at one time, they will usually approach each other so that the concealed gunner who has patience can secure both with one shot. In rising they do not spring into the air like a Black Duck but must tread considerable water with many wing-flappings before they leave it. They fly usually in a compact flock, although if the flock is excessively large, it may string out to great lengths, bunching in places. There is no regular formation, though occasionally a small flock may assume the shape of a wedge. When set in their course, they fly direct and fast and occasionally turn from side to side.

In Massachusetts Scaups arrive in some numbers from the north during October, especially in the latter half, though a few may appear even in September. Their numbers increase until November, but decrease much in hard winters when many go south, while others starve and freeze. In spring the species seems to push up early from the South along the coast to Massachusetts, while the lakes and rivers are still frozen; and therefore the birds often seem more abundant in early spring than in autumn on the southern coasts of New England. From these coasts, however, many apparently turn toward the interior, and they are much less numerous in northern New England than in the three southern states. In the latter part of March or by April most of them usually disappear from the New England coast.

The Greater Scaup feeds much at night, and at about sunset on winter evenings the flocks may be seen leaving their resting places in harbors and estuaries and passing out over the sea to their feeding places on the mussel-beds where they eat small mollusks and crustaceans. In summer they take some insects. Among their food materials while with us are wild celery and eel-grass and its seeds. Mr. Bent says that Mr. Arthur H. Norton found the stomach of a Scaup Duck killed in winter on the coast of Maine well filled with the shells of *Macoma balthica*, and that Dr. J. C. Phillips reported that the stomachs of Scaup Ducks killed in autumn in Wenham Lake held bur-reed, pondweed and bivalves (*Gemma gemma*). He also quotes Dr. Henry F. Yorke as having identified among the food materials of this duck plants of the genera *Lymnobium, Zizania, Piper, Elymus, Iris, Nuphar, Nymphæa, Myriophyllum, Callitriche* and *Utricularia*.

Economic Status. As an article of food the Scaup is not equal to the celery-fed Canvas-back, but people who are accustomed to the taste of scoters and sheldrakes find the Scaup palatable even in winter when it feeds largely on "fishy" bivalves. When feeding much on vegetation, wild celery especially, it is regarded as a good table bird; and owing to its great numbers it is an important object of food and sport over a large part of the United States.

Appearing as the Scaup does, often in large numbers, in Narragansett Bay and Long Island Sound and in some of the estuaries contiguous to those waters, it is, in the estimation of the sportsman, one of the chief waterfowls of Rhode Island and Connecticut. In the latter state especially, many gunners engage in the pursuit of the "Broad-bill," as it is known, along that coast.

Marila affinis (EYTON). Lesser Scaup Duck.

Other names: LITTLE BLACK-HEAD; LITTLE BLUE-BILL; RAFT DUCK; CREEK BROAD-BILL; RIVER BLUE-BILL; COVE BLUE-BILL; BLUE-BILL COOT.

Plate 15.

DESCRIPTION. — Similar to Scaup Duck but smaller, averaging nearly 2 inches shorter and proportionately less throughout; width of bill of Lesser Scaup ranges from .80 to .95 inch (average .89), while that of Greater Scaup ranges from .85 to 1.05 inch (average .97); bill relatively narrower at base and wider at widest part (toward tip) than that of Greater Scaup. The two species (except adult males) must be carefully examined to distinguish them. The females can be separated only by the relative width and shape of bill and by size, but *M. affinis* sometimes measures up to the minimum measurements of *M. marila*. *Adult male in winter and nuptial plumage:* Head usually with a purplish gloss (which may appear greenish when viewed from the front) instead of a greenish gloss as in *marila;* also sides and flanks usually more strongly waved with blackish than in *marila;* in some individuals a dull brownish ring, *not chestnut* as in Ring-necked Duck, around neck; *no white on outer webs of inner primaries.* *Adult male in eclipse plumage:* This plumage is partial and resembles that of female, but head is darker, with little or no white about face, and back and scapulars are grayer. *Adult female in winter and nuptial plumage:* Exactly like female of Scaup. *Adult female in breeding (eclipse?) plumage:* "... a distinct breeding plumage which is much browner than the winter plumage and in which the white face wholly or partially disappears" (A. C. Bent).

A female in this plumage, from the collection of Allan Brooks, taken June 21, 1901, on the nest at Cariboo, B. C., is generally lighter and browner above than female in winter, with scarcely a trace of gray vermiculation on back, scapulars or interscapulars; white of under plumage less extensive than in winter and mottled with brown; head lighter and browner; throat whitish, thickly mottled with brown; a little whitish on face and chin (so mottled with brown as almost to conceal or veil it) and no white on forehead; light brownish and grayish feather-edgings on upper plumage, sides and flanks. Major Brooks notes on label: "Bill dark gray, iris brownish-yellow." Some breeding birds have under parts lighter than this specimen.* *Young in juvenal plumage:* Young male and female are much alike and resemble superficially the adult female. *Downy young:* Above dark rich brown, lightest on shoulders, darkest and most lustrous on lower back; dark color above fades into dusky band around lower neck and encroaches on region about vent; below buffy, brightest on cheeks and breast; head markings indistinct usually, but dusky stripes on buffy sides of head; yellowish spot usually on each shoulder region. As the young duck grows older it becomes duller and lighter.

MEASUREMENTS. — Length 15.00 to 18.00 in.; spread under 30.00; folded wing 7.50 to 8.25; tail 1.90 to 2.70; bill 1.55 to 1.90; tarsus 1.27 to 1.50. Weight 1 lb. 12 oz. to 2 lbs. Female smaller than male.

MOLTS. — Apparently the sequence of plumages to maturity and seasonal molts of adults are substantially the same in both species of scaups. Like the Scaups, young Lesser Scaups do not breed in their first spring. Following their first complete summer molt (when they are a few months over one year old) they become practically adult in plumage.

FIELD MARKS. — Female and young of the two species of scaups are very much alike. They are often confused, as they vary much in size. (See Field Marks of Scaup Duck.)

VOICE. — Similar to that of the Scaup Duck.

BREEDING. — About shallow lakes or ponds or in swamps; sometimes on sea-islands near fresh-water ponds. *Nest:* Usually on dry ground though not far from water; concealed (more or less) in

---

* Major Brooks says, however (Auk, Vol. XXXVII, 1920, p. 355), that adult breeding females are very variable in color and that in some the head is very dark brown with a conspicuous white patch on face; these dark birds often have the back speckled with white.

grass or reeds, etc., in a depression or hollow; of dry grass stems and lined (more or less) with very dark down, "'clove brown' or 'bone brown,' in color with inconspicuous lighter centers" (A. C. Bent); some small white or grayish breast feathers mixed in occasionally. *Eggs:* 6 to 15, commonly 9 to 12; 1.97 to 2.38 by 1.40 to 1.62 in.; elliptical-ovate to nearly oval; shell smooth and a little glossy; like Scaup's eggs in color, but "decidedly smaller" (A. C. Bent). *Dates:* June 17 to July 18, Alaska and Arctic America; May 20 to July 14, Manitoba, Saskatchewan and Alberta; May 1 to July 10, Minnesota and North Dakota (A. C. Bent). *Incubation:* Period probably 3 to 4 weeks; by female. One brood yearly.

RANGE. — North America. Breeds from central Alaska and northern limit of trees in northern Canada (Mackenzie and Anderson River regions), as far east as west shore of Hudson Bay, and southeastern Ontario south to northern Ohio, northern Illinois, southeastern Iowa, northern Nebraska (possibly), northeastern Colorado (not commonly), northwestern Montana, southern British Columbia and southern Alaskan coast; has bred casually near San Francisco, in southern Louisiana and North Carolina; winters from southern British Columbia, southeastern Arizona, northeastern Colorado, northeastern Arkansas, southeastern Michigan, Illinois, Massachusetts (irregularly) and Long Island Sound south to the Bahamas, Lesser Antilles, Panama and Pacific coast of Central America; winters in large numbers in South Atlantic and Gulf states; accidental in Bermuda and Greenland; rare in migration in Newfoundland and Nova Scotia.

DISTRIBUTION IN NEW ENGLAND. — Rather uncommon migrant in Maine; generally rather rare in New Hampshire and Vermont; common autumnal transient in the three southern New England states, October and November; rarer in spring; very rare in winter in Maine, less rare in Massachusetts but not uncommon in Connecticut (or on Long Island Sound); more common migrant in interior than Scaup, but less often seen in migration in salt water.

SEASON IN MASSACHUSETTS. — March 2 to April 21 (May 5); October 8 to December 6; (winter).

HAUNTS AND HABITS. The Lesser Scaup is so like the Scaup that in the field it is difficult to distinguish one from the other. In some cases even their measurements overlap, and the usual difference in the shade of the gloss on the head of the male is not always evident. Possibly the two may interbreed. The Lesser Scaup, however, is an American bird, while the Scaup (if we disregard the recent separation of the American bird from that of the Old World) has a much wider distribution. In winter the Scaup frequents mainly the larger unfrozen lakes and the sea-coasts, while the Lesser Scaup is at all seasons more distinctly a fresh-water bird. Nevertheless at times both species may be seen together on salt, brackish or fresh water. The Lesser Scaup being more southerly in its winter range is the most numerous duck in winter on many of the lagoons and lakes of the Gulf states, where it is often called the "raft duck," because of its habit of collecting in enormous dense flocks or "rafts" on such waters. In the winter of 1877–78 in Florida I saw one such "raft" that extended a mile in length. When a boat approached such a gathering, only those nearest rose and flew over the "raft" and settled on its farther side. The approach of any craft was followed by a continual thunderous roar of wings as the birds successively shifted their position to a place of greater safety. At night these great flocks were sometimes drifted by the wind to one shore or another which gave the crafty fox or the sneaking lynx an unusual opportunity. Gunners also after such a night crept to the shore in the early morning light to take advantage of such a chance for a raking shot.

The flight of the Lesser Scaup is swift and often very erratic. It is an excellent swimmer and diver, diving usually with closed wings. When wounded, it employs every artifice to conceal itself, keeping mostly under water and in some cases forcing itself under aquatic vegetation where it sometimes becomes entangled and drowns; or if all else fails, it may even seize some under-water plant with its bill, and as a last resort hold on until death ensues in its anxiety to escape its pursuer.[1]

On its autumnal migration the Lesser Scaup arrives in small numbers in Massachusetts usually during the second week in October, though in the ponds of the interior it is more common than the Scaup; and there during its stay it is sometimes second only in numbers to the Black Duck. In November most individuals of the species pass on to the southward. Returning in March in much fewer numbers they pass northward, and in April and May reach their northern breeding-grounds.

The Lesser Scaup feeds on water insects, fish-fry, tadpoles and other small aquatic animals, including crustaceans, on snails and mollusks, such as mussels, also on pondweeds and the seeds of many water plants.

ECONOMIC STATUS. This species is not less important as an object of sport or as food than the Scaup; although a smaller bird, its numbers apparently exceed those of the Greater Scaup in America.

Marila colláris (DONOVAN). Ring-necked Duck.

Other names: RING-NECKED SCAUP; RING-NECKED BLACKHEAD; RING-BILLED BLACKHEAD; RING-BILL.

Plate 15.

DESCRIPTION. — Feathers of top of head elongated to form a dense, more or less erect, crest. *Adult male in winter and nuptial plumage:* Head and upper neck above ring or collar lustrous black, with green, purple and violet gloss; chin white (a small triangular patch); inconspicuous ring around neck rich chestnut or orange-brown; lower neck, chest, upper plumage and under tail-coverts mainly black or blackish; scapulars and parts of back slightly waved or finely dotted with grayish, sometimes minutely sprinkled with white; a white crescentic bar, an extension of white of under plumage, runs upward on each side in front of wing into the black upper plumage; below mostly white, including axillars and most of lining of wings; ventral region black; sides, flanks and lower belly finely vermiculated with dusky and white (a gray effect); white of breast contrasts sharply with black of chest but passes gradually behind through wavy marks into black of ventral region; under wing-coverts mixed white and gray; wings sooty; speculum or wing-patch bluish-gray, formed by outer webs of some secondaries which are either uniform or a little darker at ends where sometimes tipped narrowly white; primaries dark gray except for blackish on outer webs and tips; tail blackish; bill dark slate with black end, base, edges (narrowly) and wide band near end of upper mandible, white in life, pale blue after death; iris yellow; legs and feet grayish-blue, with dusky or black webs, but variable, "greenish-ash, bluish-ash, or pale yellow-ochre dashed with black" (G. Ord). *Adult male in eclipse plumage:* Plumage of a male taken September 27, by Maj. Allan Brooks at Okanagan, B. C., indicates that in eclipse it resembled winter female but was darker; much grayish-brown or brownish-gray on head, neck, breast, sides and flanks and some on

[1] Samuels, E. A.: Birds of New England, 1870, p. 506. Elliot, D. G.: Wild Fowl of North America, 1898, p. 166. Todd, W. E. Clyde: "The Birds of Erie and Presque Isle, Erie County, Pennsylvania," Annals Carnegie Museum, Vol. II, No. 3, Feb., 1904, p. 521.

scapulars and interscapulars; no indication of white about face except on chin; ring about neck identical in color with rest of neck but showing light grayish feather-tips; back, wings and tail as in winter male and under surface of body resembling same plumage but ventral region grayer. *"Adult male* (taken from captives on Dr. A. A. Allen's pond at Ithaca, N. Y., September 15, 1923) *when bird had come into full eclipse:* Head, dark umber on crown and malar regions, shading off to light brownish-gray on throat and neck; area at the sides of base of the bill and large chin-area white; a few darker feathers scattered through throat region, but not as much so as is usual in adult females; hind neck and upper back region uniform fuscous, or dark, grayish-brown, lacking the rich ochraceous color of these parts in female; breast feathers tipped with ashy, but otherwise like the neck and upper back feathers, flanks and region at the front of bend of wing brownish-gray, all the feathers with many fine white flecks; the black back and scapular feathers show fine white specks over distal third of feathers, but not as much so as in breeding plumage; bill is blackish in eclipse, except for the light gray or nearly plumbeous subterminal ring which persists. In breeding plumage tip of bill is black, the two rings china white and the intermediate area plumbeous. (Another male in eclipse at the present time is nearly identical but has perhaps a little less white at base of bill.)

"The plain brown flanks of young male and his unflecked back seem to be characters that will tell him from an adult in eclipse plumage. An eclipse male is much grayer than female and lacks the ochraceous-brown of back, breast and sides of the female; light head markings of the female are more abrupt and conspicuous than in male (eclipse) and have more blackish feathers scattered through face and throat regions." (Miles D. Pirnie.) *Adult female in winter and nuptial plumage:* Wing and speculum much as in male; no collar; head, neck, most of breast and upper plumage generally dark brown where male is black (feathers light-edged), darker on crown and back of neck, and paling gradually to grayish or soiled white about base of bill; cheeks and throat mottled grayish-brown and whitish; a narrow white ring around eye; lower back and rump black; outer webs of outer tertials metallic-green; upper tail-coverts and tail pale brown, feathers tipped yellowish-brown; white below less extensive than in male and less pure, with none of fine vermiculation of male; a space only on breast and belly white or whitish; upper breast, sides, flanks and lower belly and region about vent grayish-brown with a rusty tint; under tail-coverts white speckled with brown; bill blackish, with obscure markings similar in shape to those of male (usually with indistinct cross-bar of light blue or whitish near tip); iris brown; feet variable as in male. *Adult female in breeding plumage (June):* Top of head lighter and more rusty than in winter; *no white face* but chin and throat *much whiter* than in winter; under plumage *much* more mottled with brownish; "iris brown or yellowish-brown" (Allan Brooks); otherwise much as in winter. *Young in juvenal plumage:* Young male and female in early fall much alike; above dull dark brown or blackish-brown, with lighter edgings; below mottled with dull, light brown and whitish; wings like those of adult female; speculum dull gray and secondaries dusky near ends and very narrowly, if at all, tipped white; sides of neck and head mottled with brown and whitish; crown dark brownish-black, brown-mottled; chin broadly white (A. C. Bent). *Downy young:* Forehead, sides of head and neck and under-plumage yellowish or dingy buff, darkening to brownish on flanks and lower belly; a dusky, narrow streak or spot behind eye; top and back of head and upper plumage warm grayish-brown; a short, narrow streak in middle line of upper back, two shoulder patches, two rump patches and two narrow wing stripes, cream-buff or "pale straw-yellow"; iris hazel; bill lead color above, flesh color below; feet lead color, toes tinged yellowish; young in down very light colored, resembling young of Canvas-back and Redhead, and quite different from dusky, unspotted young of Lesser Scaup (Allan Brooks, Auk, Vol. XX, 1903, p. 277).

MEASUREMENTS. — Length 15.50 to 18.00 in.; spread 25.00 to 30.00; folded wing 7.00 to 8.50; tail 2.75 to 3.40; bill 1.75 to 2.00; tarsus 1.25 to 1.45. Female smaller than male.

MOLTS. — In autumn young (male and female, molting) differentiate rapidly so that by last of December young male often is nearly full plumaged, though chestnut neck-ring is scarcely in evidence, wings are still immature and all colors dull; during winter and spring further advance toward maturity is made; after new wings are acquired, at next complete molt, young becomes as adult. Adults have usual double molt and eclipse plumage.

FIELD MARKS. — Rather like Lesser Scaup with which species it is often seen, but head more puffy or crested and speculum bluish-gray instead of white. *Male:* Back blackish instead of grayish as in Scaup; white "crescent" in front of wing continuous with white of under surface (upper part of this white bar between black of breast and of wing, lower part between black of breast and barring of side); close at hand, narrow dark bill of male with light or white band near tip may be seen; chestnut collar is of no value as field mark as it can be made out only at close range when neck is stretched up. *Female:* Less easily recognized; resembles closely larger female Redhead but has browner body; if near enough ringing of Ring-neck's bill, together with white eye-ring and light cheeks, may be seen; both species have bluish-gray speculum — hence, in case of female or immature plumage, size only can be relied upon to distinguish the two species at any distance in field; amount of white feathering at base of bill in female or immature plumage varies greatly in both species, some having almost none; in female Ring-neck white is less sharply defined than in Lesser Scaup; chin and throat of Ring-neck are often continuously whitish.

VOICE. — Said to resemble that of Greater Scaup (Grinnell, Bryant and Storer); in courtship this species emits "a note resembling the sounds produced by a person blowing through a tube" (Audubon).

BREEDING. — In wet places usually such as marshy borders of shallow lakes or wet meadows. *Nest:* In marsh grass or rushes (often a clump) over or near water; of grass, finer inside, with lining (sometimes thick) of dark gray down; breast feathers mixed with down, white or grayish, tipped white. *Eggs:* 8 to 12; like Lesser Scaup's in shape, size, texture and color. *Dates:* May 31 to July 6, Manitoba, Saskatchewan and Alberta; June 1 to 18, Minnesota and North Dakota. *Incubation:* By female.

RANGE. — North America. Breeds in interior from south central British Columbia, central Mackenzie Valley, northern Alberta, northern Saskatchewan and northwestern Ontario south to south central Oregon and northeastern California (one record), northern Utah, northern Nebraska, northern Iowa, southeastern Wisconsin and northern Illinois; said to have bred near Calais, Maine; winters from southern British Columbia, Nevada (probably), New Mexico, northern Texas, northeastern Arkansas, southern Illinois, Chesapeake Bay, southeastern Massachusetts (rarely), south to Porto Rico and through Mexico to Guatemala; in southern United States chiefly along Gulf coast from Texas to Florida; east to Bahamas; accidental in Bermuda and Nova Scotia (Sable Island).

DISTRIBUTION IN NEW ENGLAND. — A very rare migrant along coast of Maine and New Hampshire, most rare in spring; Vermont, one record, a bird shot November 9, 1908, at North Ferrisburg, Lake Champlain, by George L. Kirk; rare winter visitant or winter resident on coasts of southern Massachusetts and southern New England but chiefly a migrant in fall or winter.

SEASON IN MASSACHUSETTS. — Late March and April; October 4 to November 30; casual in winter north to Boston; rare winter resident or visitant in parts of Barnstable and Dukes counties.

HAUNTS AND HABITS. The Ring-neck is one of the rarest ducks of the Northeast. Though not so rare as the Gadwall or the Shoveller, it seems to occur less often than the European Widgeon. However it may be less rare than the general belief would indicate. The males may easily escape notice in a flock of scaups; while the females and young resemble female scaups or Redheads, and so may be overlooked or mistaken for one or the other.

The Ring-neck is usually classed with the scaups, which it superficially resembles, but its affinity with the Tufted Duck of the Old World seems to be closer. Like the Lesser Scaup it appears to prefer fresh to salt water, and is much more abundant in the interior of the country than on either the Atlantic or the Pacific coast. It commonly haunts rivers and small shallow waters in preference to the open water of large lakes.

Its flight is extremely swift and like that of the Scaup is accompanied by more or less whistling of the wings. The Ring-neck flies in small and rather scattered flocks or parties and in feeding does not mass in great companies on the water as do the scaups. Like *affinis*, "when diving, the tail is always spread, and is deflexed as the head is dipped under water."[1] In its migrations in New England the Ring-neck is most likely to appear in October. On its nesting-ground it takes many aquatic insects, tadpoles, small frogs and snails and the seeds, roots and tender shoots of aquatic plants.

ECONOMIC STATUS. See page 174.

Glaucionétta clángula americána (BONAPARTE). Golden-eye.

Other names: WHISTLER; AMERICAN GOLDEN-EYE; BRASS-EYE; GREAT-HEAD; GARROT; QUANDY (FEMALE).

Plate 16.

DESCRIPTION. — Height of upper mandible at base less than distance from front edge of loral feathers to front edge of nostril and usually little or no greater than distance from nostril to tip of bill; head moderately puffy. *Adult male in winter and nuptial plumage:* Head and upper neck black with green gloss or very dark metallic-green with violet reflections in life, appearing black at a distance; a good-sized, rounded, white spot before eye — at base of bill near gape; lower neck all around (in strong contrast to dark head), under plumage, middle and greater wing-coverts, nearly all secondaries and some scapulars (largely), white; greater wing-coverts with dark bases; axillars and lining of wings mainly dusky or sooty brown; under greater wing-coverts "leaden gray"; some dusky mottling about vent and sides of belly; scapulars (in part), inner and outer secondaries, edge of wing, primaries and their coverts and back, black; flank-feathers edged sharply with black; tail, ashy-gray; bill black, "bluish-black" or "greenish-dusky"; iris bright golden-yellow; legs and feet orange or yellow with black claws and dusky webs. *Adult male in eclipse plumage:* Variable; similar to adult female in winter but no white collar; much more white in wing (coverts); head and upper neck paler brown, darkening between eye and bill and on nape; belly as in adult male in winter; some specimens show indications of the white spot near bill. *Adult female in winter and nuptial plumage:* Variable; head less puffy than in male, plain snuff or cinnamon-brown; no white spot before eye; fore neck white, with faint gray tinge, making incomplete collar; in general, brownish, grayish-brown or bluish-gray where male is black; upper back-feathers edged bluish-gray; upper tail-coverts with brownish tips; white of wing not so extensive nor so complete as in male; scapulars not white as in male but color of back; speculum and under plumage white, former sometimes crossed by a dark bar; chest, flanks and sides grayish or brownish; axillars and under surface of wing dark brown; iris dull or pale to bright yellow; feet orange or brownish-yellow, webs chiefly blackish; bill dusky, usually with "dull orange," yellow or yellowish-olive band near end in spring, nail black. *Adult female in eclipse plumage:* Similar but without ring or collar on neck and no white in scapulars; nail and tip of lower mandible more or less black (later entire bill becomes dark). *Young in first winter plumage:* Similar to adult female (see progress under molts). *Young in juvenal plumage:* Also like adult female but male larger than female and usually has larger light patch on wing-coverts; iris — male, bright yellow, female, dull yellow; eyes of "4 nearly fully-fledged young still unable to fly" were "gray-blue and inconspicuous" (C. W. Townsend); bill olive or dusky-olive; feet duller than in adult. *Downy young:* Head and hind neck dark brown; throat and cheeks white; back and sides dark sooty-brown with white spots in pairs; below white; fore neck shaded with light brown; bill blackish, tip of lower mandible flesh colored; iris brownish; feet olive.

---

[1] Smyth, Ellison A., Jr.: Auk, Vol. XXIX, 1912, p. 512.

PLATE 16

PLATE 16

BUFFLE-HEAD
Page 252
Nuptial Plumage

Adult Female

Adult Male

GOLDEN-EYE
Page 246
Nuptial Plumage

Adult Female

Adult Male

BARROW'S GOLDEN-EYE
Page 250

Adult Male in Winter
(Nuptial) Plumage

OLD-SQUAW
Page 255

Adult Male in Summer or
Breeding Plumage

Adult Male in Winter
Plumage

Adult Female
in Winter
Plumage

All one-sixth natural size.

MEASUREMENTS. — Length 16.50 to 23.00 in.; spread 27.00 to 32.00; folded wing 7.30 to 9.30; tail 3.00 to 4.50; bill 1.28 to 1.65 (*circ.*); tarsus 1.23 to 1.75. Weight averages about 2 lbs. (Wilson); from 1 lb. 8 oz. to 2 lbs. 5 oz. Female smaller than male.

MOLTS. — Young birds molt out of juvenal plumage apparently in September and October; this seems to be only a partial body molt; late in winter or in March most young birds are molting again; young males in March or April begin to show black feathers on head and some indication of white spot between eye and bill and white collar, more or less broken, on back of neck; as the season advances upper breast becomes whiter, more dark feathers appear on back, sides and flanks, and more white on scapulars; in July young birds molt into eclipse plumage similar to that of their parents, and in their second winter most of them become as adults; adults have a double molt, going into eclipse in July and August, after an incomplete molt; then they shed their flight-feathers and tails, and acquire their winter plumage by a complete molt of body feathers from September to December.

FIELD MARKS. — Both sexes have short neck and large rounded head; male black and white, female gray with brown head. *Male:* A medium-sized, stocky duck (appearing large) with contrasting black and white (largely white) plumage — unlike any other duck except Buffle-head and mergansers; but former is much smaller and its puffy head has large triangular white patch behind eye, while latter are much longer and more rakish in build; seen at close range round white spot between bill and the *yellow* eye make bird unmistakable; extensive white of male when seen at a distance, seems to give it almost a continuous white side (and body), as white flank-feathers cover much of wings; but in flight (particularly when bird is rising or is below the observer) black of back and of wings appears. *Female:* With same chunky body, is as easily distinguished as male; though lacking white spot at base of bill, it has yellow eye, *white* speculum and white collar (more or less), latter contrasting with brown head; female and immature Golden-eye bear a slight superficial resemblance to Redhead which, however, has a *gray* speculum; female and immature difficult, if not impossible, to distinguish in field from those of Barrow's Golden-eye, but males of these two species when floating on the water are separated easily; male Golden-eye has wing apparently chiefly white, while Barrow's has wing chiefly black and more black on back and scapulars; rounded white spot between bill and eye of Golden-eye is replaced by triangular or crescentic white spot in same place in Barrow's — also there is a row of large white spots on black scapulars of Barrow's; bills of both male and female Golden-eye are usually noticeably longer and proportionately lower at base than those of Barrow's whose female in spring (if adult) usually has bill largely yellow; but these distinctions are visible only at close range and do not always hold; Golden-eye rises up rapidly from the water but with some splashing and pattering of feet; "the flock never strings out but lifts in a cluster" (A. A. Allen); when flying directly away show dark bodies and great white patches in wings.

VOICE. — Love note of male, a flat, vibrant, short *paaap* (Wm. Brewster); a harsh, rasping double note, *zzzee-at*, vibratory and searching in character; female utters loud harsh croaks which appear to be alarm notes when there are downy young (C. W. Townsend); a low-pitched quack to call their young (O. W. Knight); duck when startled or lost calls out a sharp *cur-r-rew* (E. H. Eaton).

BREEDING. — In forested country, usually about lakes or rivers in woods. *Nest:* Hole in large tree trunk, at height ranging from 6 or 8 to 50 or 60 feet; usually over or near water; lined with very light gray down, each feather with a paler center; nest may be on level with and scarcely back from hole, or at the bottom of hollow, 6, 10, 15 feet or even more below entrance, which may vary from 15 inches to diameter so small as scarcely to admit bird; has bred in nesting-box; bird lines nest with her down after all eggs are deposited.* *Eggs:* 5 or 6, 8 or 10, oftenest 12 or 15, and even 19 "all of which almost certainly belonged to one bird" (Wm. Brewster); 2.25 to 2.58 by 1.52 to 1.78 in.; rounded-oval; ashy-green, glossy; "from a clear pale malachite green . . . to a more olivaceous or pale chromium green . . ." (A. C. Bent); closely packed eggs usually cover bottom of hole and are often piled in two layers. *Dates:*

---

* Golden-eyes have bred in a blind brick chimney in Camrose, Alberta. When the young leave, they roll down the roof to the ground whence they are taken in human hands to the waiting mother in the water.

May 29, Maine; May 30, North Dakota. *Incubation:* Period 20 days in confinement (H. F. Witherby); by female. One brood yearly.

RANGE. — North America. Breeds from central Alaska, southern Mackenzie, northeastern Manitoba, coast of northern Labrador and Newfoundland south to southern British Columbia, northwestern Montana, North Dakota, northern Minnesota, northern Michigan, northern New York and northwestern and northern New England; winters from Commander and Aleutian Islands, British Columbia, northwestern Montana, Nebraska, Minnesota, Iowa, the Great Lakes, Gulf of St. Lawrence and Maine south to southern California, central western Mexico, Gulf States and South Carolina; occurs in Pribilof Islands and Bermuda; has been recorded in Bahamas, Cuba and Barbados.

DISTRIBUTION IN NEW ENGLAND. — Fall and spring migrant and winter resident; general along coast; occurs occasionally inland in winter where water is open; breeds locally in northern New England (particularly in central northern and eastern Maine), "in limited numbers" to "abundantly."

SEASON IN MASSACHUSETTS. — September 20 to May 2; most abundant from November to April; (June 1); (July 26).

HAUNTS AND HABITS. The Golden-eye comes with the biting frost. No bird is more typical of winter on the New England coast. In days of brief winter sunshine when harbors are filled with floating ice, at daybreak keen and cold when hoar frost clusters on trees along our icy coast — then we may hear the clear, melodious whistle of the Golden-eye's fast-beating wings. At evening when the clouds reflect in evanescent tints the glory of a sun already sunk behind the western hills — then we may see his fleeting form speeding afar over the sea, tracing the pathway of the "illimitable air."

The species is well and widely known as "Whistler" by the gunners of New England, while the female is known to many as "Quandy." The bird is one of the hardiest of ducks, and may be seen in winter usually well outside the breakers, continually diving in pursuit of its favorite food. No other wild duck except the Merganser shows so much white as the male Whistler. He rides the waves lightly, with the white feathers of sides and flanks thrown up in such a way as to cover most of the wing, and his white sides flash continually in the sunlight. The much darker, brown-headed females and young are often seen in company with the males, and do not appear to ride quite so high in the water. All dive usually with closed wings, and tails widely spread, but sometimes, perhaps when in haste, they open the wings and use them under water. I saw once two of these ducks which were floating close together, raise their wings as they dived. The tips struck the water with a splash, exactly at the same angle as the wings of the diving Old-squaw. As these two birds dived at the same instant and evidently in great haste, I supposed that they had seen some small, swift-moving fish or other aquatic animal, and had started together in pursuit, using the wings to accelerate their speed.

In late winter on our waters the hardy Golden-eye begins its courtship. The male swims about the female, often with head lowered and neck stretched along the water, but his most characteristic motion is that of raising his head upward and backward until with the bill pointing toward the zenith he utters his harsh note. Sometimes the head is thrown over until it almost touches the back. Often the bird dashes forward while the orange-colored feet strike backward and upward with such force as to throw strong jets of water into the air and at the same time display the brilliant coloring. Dr. C. W. Townsend has given an excellent account of the courtship of this species.[1]

As the Golden-eye in northern Maine nests in hollow trees like the Wood Duck, its manner of getting the young to the water has attracted some attention. The young birds have been seen to tumble out of the nesting-tree and flutter down to the water.[2] On the other hand other observers claim to have seen them carried from the nest to the water on the back of the parent; while others still report that the young are conveyed in the bill of the mother, or in some way between her feet.[3]

Mr. William H. Moore of Scotch Lake, New Brunswick, sends some interesting notes on the habits of this species, of which extracts follow:

"This species is most wonderfully shy during day time, and it is really difficult to approach on foot to within a couple of hundred yards of them, but as evening comes on and the light is rather dusky they lose their sense of fear to a great extent, and they may be approached in a boat to within a few yards, if no noise is made. . . .

"During the period of incubation the male is ever on the alert to lure enemies away from his mate and her treasures. I recall a case when one spring-time I was walking along a ridge of one of the Keswick Islands, when along came an old male, talking, fluttering and doing his best to draw my attention, and he did. He fluttered along much after the manner of a nesting night-hawk or grouse and I followed, at the same time keeping watch to note where the female and nest might be. After following for some distance, he got up and flew away, having, as he thought, lured me away from his home. Upon my return to where he first came to me, he returned and again went through his antics. I followed but did not bother him any more as I had seen how attached he was to his duties."

The Golden-eye is largely a fresh-water bird and many remain all winter in the lakes and rivers of the interior, so long as the fresh waters are unfrozen; but when severe frosts close most inland waters, Golden-eyes flock to the coast. Some flocks are seen in November on the New England coast, but the greatest number appear coastwise in winter after most of the inland waters are locked in ice. Like the Scaups, Golden-eyes push northward early in spring. They move as fast as the ice breaks in the rivers, and in early May reach their most northerly breeding-grounds near the Arctic Circle.

The food of the Golden-eye is not very well known, but it is believed to feed to some extent on aquatic and other plants that grow near the water, both in the interior and on the sea-coast. It feeds on eel-grass or "sea-grass." Mr. W. L. McAtee found in the stomach of a bird of this species taken in Massachusetts, "seeds of pondweed, water-lily, bayberry and bur-reed, buds and roots of wild celery, and bits of water boatmen, and dragonfly nymphs."[4] In our waters much of its food consists of mussels or other mollusks and crustaceans which it seeks in both salt and fresh water. Small fish and crayfish are

[1] Auk, Vol. XXVII, 1910, pp. 177–178.
[2] Brewster, William: Auk, Vol. XVIII, 1900, pp. 207–216.
[3] Bailey, F. M.: Condor, Vol. XVII, 1916, p. 55. Boardman, Forest and Stream, Vol. LII, 1899, Jan.–June, p. 346.
[4] Phillips, John C.: Auk, Vol. XXVIII, 1911, p. 200.

included in its regimen, also brine shrimps and alkali fly larvæ and pupæ of the salt and alkaline lakes of the west.

ECONOMIC STATUS.   On the New England coast the Golden-eye is considered a rather better article of food than the scoters or "coots," and so is appreciated as a game bird. Many gunners consider the "Whistler" an important bird both as food and as an object of sport.   In Massachusetts the "Whistler" is able to maintain itself well in severe winter weather and to keep in fairly good condition.   When other ducks grow thin and fishy, by comparison it becomes palatable.   It does not come readily to decoys, but many nevertheless are shot over the wooden ducks.   Some of our hardy New England coast-gunners lie out among shore-ledges in tiny gunning "floats" in freezing December weather surrounded by flocks of wooden ducks.   The crafts are dressed with seaweed so that the whole arrangement, gunner included, resembles a seal lying on a rock with a flock of ducks resting near it on the water.   So long as the gunner remains quiescent, notwithstanding his slowly congealing feet, his chances of deceiving the wary "Whistlers" are good, and many are thus killed and used for food whenever severe frosts drive them in numbers to our shores.

Glaucionetta islándica (GMELIN).   Barrow's Golden-eye.

Other name: ROCKY MOUNTAIN GARROT.

Plate 16.

DESCRIPTION. — Similar to Golden-eye but differing in shape of bill. *Adult male in winter and nuptial plumage:* Head large, very dark or black, glossed chiefly purple and violet, puffy with slight crest-like lengthening of upper and hinder feathers; *large somewhat wedge-shaped crescent or triangle of white before eye* extending upward along lateral whole base of upper mandible and above it; body generally with more black and less white than Golden-eye; *outer surface of closed wing mainly black,* except middle and greater coverts and exposed parts (terminal half) of 5th and 6th inner secondaries, which are white; white of wing divided more or less completely by a black bar formed of black bases of greater coverts; scapulars black and white, *the white (in life) forming a row of white spots running above the wing;* bill bluish-black; iris yellow; feet and legs yellow, webs black; "iris chrome-yellow; feet orange-yellow; bill black" (May 7, 1910, Cariboo, British Columbia, Allan Brooks). *Adult male in eclipse plumage:* Similar to adult female in winter but bill dark and some slight indications of white patch near its base; wing, lower back, rump and upper tail-coverts as in winter adult male. *Adult female in winter and nuptial plumage:* Similar to female Golden-eye; head slightly darker (but variable), its color running farther down on neck, particularly in front, thus *narrowing the white collar;* head somewhat more *puffy and with longer feathers behind;* some blackish spots on ends of greater wing-coverts; bill (in spring) usually nearly all orange or yellow instead of the yellow band near tip as in female Golden-eye, but this is not a sure distinction as some Golden-eyes may have bill largely yellow (in late summer, autumn and early winter entire bill may be dark); the dark bar across white of wing is not always present and not surely distinctive, as some female Golden-eyes have it; bill usually deeper at base and wider in proportion to its length than in Golden-eye; its nail also longer, more curved and usually wider; iris yellow, lighter in spring; legs and feet yellow with dark webs; "iris pea-green; bill dirty orange, dusky on base and tip; feet ochre, webs and posterior surface black" (June 21, 1901, Cariboo, British Columbia, Allan Brooks). *Young in first winter and juvenal plumages:* Similar to adult female; juvenal and first winter males have median and lesser coverts darker than in Golden-eye, sometimes a few median coverts with gray or grayish-white tips, but apparently never tipped white as in many Golden-eyes; "young females have an olive brownish or blackish bill, no yellow" (Allan Brooks). *Downy young:* Top and sides of head down to level of bill, and hind neck, "uniform dark chocolate brown" or "seal brown"; throat white; upper plumage and sides dark brown; large paired white spots on hind margin of each wing, on flanks behind wings and at base of tail; below white with light brown or brownish-gray band across lower fore neck; iris brownish; bill and feet olive-ochre.

MEASUREMENTS. — Length 20.00 to 23.00 in.; spread usually 30.00 or more; folded wing 7.80 to 10.00; tail 2.95 to 3.91; bill 1.10 to 1.37; tarsus 1.37 to 1.60.

MOLTS. — Apparently the molts and sequences of plumage of this species are the same as those of Golden-eye; and young bird's plumage becomes indistinguishable from that of adult in second autumn or winter.

FIELD MARKS. — Male readily distinguished from male Golden-eye as far off as a duck can be identified by much greater amount of black on sides of body; *outer surface of closed wing chiefly black*; row of white spots on black scapulars and angular white spot on head may be made out *with a good glass* at 200 yards; head purplish instead of greenish black as in Golden-eye; usually females and young cannot be positively identified in the field. (See Field Marks under Golden-eye.)

VOICE. — A hoarse croak (Allan Brooks).

BREEDING. — *Nest:* Like that of Golden-eye; in hollow tree and lined with white down; in Iceland where trees are extremely few and local, holes in the ground are utilized. *Eggs:* 6 to 10; average about 2.48 by 1.74 in.; bluish-green, sea-green or dark, grayish-pea-green; indistinguishable from those of *G. c. americana. Dates:* May 19 to June 30, Iceland; May 12 to 31, British Columbia; May 28 to 30, Alberta. *Incubation:* Period 4 weeks (Hantzsch); by female.

RANGE. — Northwestern Europe and North America. In North America breeds (mainly in Rocky Mountain region) from south central Alaska, northwestern Mackenzie, Great Slave Lake, northern Quebec (Ungava), northern Labrador (probably) and Greenland south to southern Oregon, southwestern Colorado (uncommon) and central Quebec; winters from southeastern Alaska, southern British Columbia, northern Montana, the Great Lakes (rarely) and Gulf of St. Lawrence south to central California, Utah, southern Colorado, eastern Kansas, southeastern Iowa, Illinois, Indiana, Maine and Massachusetts (regularly) and North Carolina (rarely); breeds commonly in Iceland; casual in British Isles and Spain.

DISTRIBUTION IN NEW ENGLAND. — Rare winter visitor mainly coastwise. *Vermont:* Two or more birds were shot November 17, 1917, at Bridport on Lake Champlain.[1]

SEASON IN MASSACHUSETTS. — November to April 16.

HAUNTS AND HABITS. Probably this dark and handsome duck is not so rare in New England as it has been regarded. When hunted it is one of the shyest of "sea-fowl"; therefore very few are found in the hands of gunners. The females and young which undoubtedly are more numerous than the males, so closely resemble the females and young of the Golden-eye that the most expert ornithologist cannot always be sure of recognizing them in the field, and some have mistaken their identity even when in hand. The males are easily recognized, and often in winter I have seen from two to four males with five to twelve others which appeared to be females and young of the same species feeding on the mussel beds off Red Rock at Lynn beach. South of Cape Cod the bird seems rarer and I have seen it there only once — in Vineyard Sound.

Courtship antics of these hardy vigorous birds may be seen on pleasant March days. There is more or less bowing or bobbing. The male swims rapidly about the female, erects the loose feathers of the head and now and then throws it backward until it nearly

---

[1] George L. Kirk *in litt.*; also Vermont Botanical and Bird Clubs, Joint Bulletins Nos. 4 and 5, April, 1919, p. 30.

touches the back, when with the bill slightly opened and pointing to the sky the bird presumably utters its love note. Owing to distance and the sound of the breaking surf I have never heard a vocal sound from these birds. Barrow's Golden-eye is a strong swimmer, a powerful diver and swift in flight. With us it seems to feed chiefly on mussels, as it frequents mussel beds, and, no doubt, like other diving ducks swallows these bivalves whole while under water, as it never seems to bring anything to the surface.

This bird appears to be a late migrant in autumn, as Prof. Cooke gives October 23 as the date of the earliest arrivals in Montreal, while very few are seen before December in southern New England. Since the above was written, Mr. W. F. Lisk of Enfield has given me an inland Massachusetts record of this species — an immature male taken February 28, 1910, at Greenwich.

ECONOMIC STATUS. This bird is of little importance in the East because of its shyness and rarity. In the West, it is common enough to be important as an object of sport; also it is said there to be an excellent table fowl.

Charitonétta albéola (LINNÆUS). Buffle-head.

Other names: BUTTER-BALL; DIPPER DUCK; SPIRIT DUCK; DIPPER; DAPPER.

Plate 16.

DESCRIPTION. — Head and upper neck exceedingly puffy, feathers lengthened especially on back and sides of head, giving it a large appearance; tail slightly pointed. *Adult male in winter and nuptial plumage:* Head and a little of upper neck very dark, rich green, with purple, violet, amethyst, orange-yellowish and bronzy reflections, appearing black at a distance; a large, nearly triangular white patch from below eye widening to and over nape; neck (except a little next head), some secondaries, outer scapulars, upper wing-coverts (largely), sides, flanks and under plumage generally white, graying on belly; axillars brown marked with white; under wing-coverts variable gray and white, some white scapulars and feathers of sides narrowly edged black, back mainly black or blackish, graying behind from rump to tail; primaries and outer secondaries very dark brown or brownish-black; tail gray; bill dull leaden-blue, edge of upper mandible yellowish and nail dusky; iris dark brown; legs and feet pale pink, yellowish-pink or "light flesh color with a lavender tinge" (Gurdon Trumbull). *Adult male in eclipse plumage:* Resembles a similar stage in Golden-eye (J. G. Millais); similar to adult female in winter except for increased amount of white in wing (which resembles that of male in nuptial plumage) and more white on sides of head. *Adult female in winter and nuptial plumage:* Head less puffy than in male, slightly iridescent on top; head, neck and upper plumage generally grayish-brown or sooty-brown; spring birds have (more or less) light feather-edgings on shoulders, sides of breast and upper back; an elongated white patch on side of head much smaller than in male, passing from below eye nearly to nape; head and wings slightly darker than other upper plumage; white wing-patch on secondaries, and often some white on greater wing-coverts; sides, flanks, upper breast, lower belly and under tail-coverts ashy or brownish-gray; rest of under plumage white; wing-linings and tail much as in male; iris very dark brown; feet pinkish-gray or bluish-gray, usually tinged pink; bill dark lead color; some specimens have more or less whitish on throat. *Young in first winter plumage:* Similar to adult female but young males are larger with usually a larger white patch on side of head. *Young in juvenal plumage:* Female closely resembles adult female, but head lighter in front and on sides and throat; white head patch smaller; male is larger, with usually a larger white head patch or indication of it. *Downy young:* Above, including head to below eye, dark brown, darkest on top of head and on rump; bar across wing, and three pairs of spots on sides of back and rump, whitish; "lower cheeks, sides of neck, chin and throat white; upper breast, sides of body, under tail-coverts and more or less of thighs grayish-brown or dusky-brown"; other under plumage grayish-white.

MEASUREMENTS. — Length 12.26 to 15.00 in.; spread 22.00 to 25.00; folded wing 5.90 to 7.00; tail 2.31 to 3.12; bill about 1.00; tarsus 1.10 to 1.24. Weight 8 oz. to 1 lb. Female much smaller than male.

MOLTS. — Young male molts in February or early spring and gradually assumes a plumage similar to that of adult male, taking on in spring rather more than half of adult plumage; in February, March and April white feathers appear in nape, lower neck and upper breast become white and white shows on sides and flanks; there is a partial eclipse in July and a complete molt in August and September; young male does not assume full adult plumage until its second winter; young female apparently becomes earlier indistinguishable from adult; adults have the usual double molt.

FIELD MARKS. — Smaller than Blue-winged Teal. *Male:* At a distance looks black and white, with large head and large triangular white patch running from below eye over back of head; Hooded Merganser has a similar patch but it does not extend around back of head, its bill is slim while that of Buffle-head is stubby, and lower neck of this Merganser is mainly black. *Female:* A little dusky brownish bird with large head and white patch back of eye; white wing-patch may not be visible as bird swims but shows in flight; wing-beats are exceedingly rapid; white patch on side of head distinguishes it from female Ruddy Duck; at a distance, in flight, resembles a Golden-eye, but usually flies nearer the water, with wings beating faster.

VOICE. — A guttural croak (F. M. Chapman); resembles croak of Golden-eye, but feebler (T. M. Brewer); a short quack (Wilson); female has low grating note (J. G. Millais).

BREEDING. — About wooded lakes, rivers and swamps. *Nest:* In hollow of tree, usually in nesting hole of flicker or other woodpecker, rarely in burrow in ground; composed of light gray down and a few white feathers. *Eggs:* 6 to 8, sometimes 10 to 14, rarely only 2 or 3; "ellipsoidal, about 2.00 by 1.50 in., in tint buffy-drab (between grayish-olive and rich creamy-white)" (Coues); smooth and cream color or "old ivory" (Allan Brooks). *Dates:* May 6, Saskatchewan; May 25, Mackenzie. *Incubation:* By female. One brood yearly.

RANGE. — North America. Breeds from west central Alaska, lower Mackenzie River, Great Slave Lake, west coast of Hudson Bay, James Bay and probably Quebec south to British Columbia (casually northeastern California), northern Montana, Ontario (formerly Wyoming, North Dakota, Minnesota, Wisconsin and Iowa), New Brunswick (probably) and Maine (formerly); winters from Aleutian and Commander Islands, Alaska Peninsula, British Columbia, northwestern Montana, the Great Lakes, western New York and Maine south to northern Lower California, central Mexico, the Gulf coast and Florida; recorded from Hawaii, Greenland, Newfoundland, Nova Scotia, Pribilof Islands, Bermuda, Cuba, Porto Rico and Great Britain.

DISTRIBUTION IN NEW ENGLAND. — Migrant frequenting both salt and fresh waters; in general not very common, although "abundant on Narragansett Bay"; more common in autumn than in spring; winters locally coastwise, usually in small numbers, but occasionally in flocks of 50 to 100; a flock of nine Buffle-heads was seen in July, 1921, in Daisy Pond, near Mt. Katahdin, Maine, by Dr. Walter G. Fanning of Danvers; breeds, or formerly bred, in Washington County, Maine.

SEASON IN MASSACHUSETTS. — (September) October 9 to December 23; March 11 to May 2; winters locally coastwise.

HAUNTS AND HABITS. After a winter storm at Nahant the handsome, hardy, vivacious little Buffle-head may be seen at its best. The sea still rages, and the white-topped surges pound and roar upon the seaworn ledges, tossing the spouting, snow-white spray high in the sunlit air. A piercing northwest wind cuts the spindrift from the rollers and carries it seaward in sheets. The western sun lights up the heaving sea and the acres of foaming white water that now at low tide rush upon the shallows of the beach. Most of the ducks have flown to the harbor or to the creeks in the salt marsh, but a few hardy White-winged Scoters and Old-squaws lie out on the open sea; close in-shore, in shoal water and in the very boiling of the surf, groups of little Buffle-heads ride easily, swimming and diving as unconcernedly as if on some calm, untroubled pool. Now and then the surf seems to break directly over a bird; but at the instant when the towering crest seems to fall on its uplifted head, the head is no longer there. The little duck has dived either to the bottom for food or to reappear as before riding easily on the farther slope of the wave. The Buffle-heads play in the white-topped surf. They are perfectly at home and not in the least inconvenienced by foaming surge, raging wind or stinging cold. They seem cheerful, happy and contented, intent only on a supply of food that will enable them to withstand the cold and stress of winter on a wave-beaten coast.

On our shores Buffle-heads usually keep by themselves in small flocks on favorite feeding grounds. They float lightly when undisturbed with puffed-out heads drawn down between their shoulders, while the white feathers of the sides and flanks of the males are thrown up over the wings which seemingly are held close to the sides as the birds dive.

The courtship of the Buffle-head is rarely observed in our latitude. Dr. C. W. Townsend says that the male "spreads and cocks his tail, puffs out the feathers of his head and cheeks, extends his bill straight out in front close to the water and every now and then throws it back with a bob in a sort of reversed bow." A male alights beside a female, "sliding along on his tail, his breast and head elevated to their utmost extent." There is much excitement, with diving, splashing and flapping.[1] Mr. J. A. Munro of Okanagan Landing, British Columbia, states that he watched a pair of Buffle-heads and a single drake which "would sink below the surface and swim under water toward the other drake, putting his head out once or twice to get the correct line, and then rise directly under the second drake, half lifting him from the water." Flying a few yards he repeated the performance.[2]

The bird's nesting habits are well-known, but apparently there is no definite information regarding how the young reach the water. Like other tree-nesting ducks, this species is said occasionally to carry its ducklings from the home-tree to the water, but I have been unable to find even one observer who has seen this.

In migration Buffle-heads commonly appear late in October or in November in Massachusetts and in March or early April return north in smaller numbers. In interior waters they are seen more frequently in autumn than in spring; they rarely occur in winter in the interior.

The food of the Buffle-head while on our coast consists largely of small marine forms of life. In the interior it takes small bivalves and minnows and on its breeding-grounds eats many insects and snails.

---

[1] Auk, Vol. XXXIII, 1916, p. 17.　　　　[2] Oölogist, Vol. XXXV, 1918, p. 120.

ECONOMIC STATUS. Sometimes in autumn the Buffle-head is considered a savory morsel, but it becomes fishy when feeding in salt water. It is not large enough nor in numbers enough to possess much value in an economic sense, but its presence is an added attraction to our winter sea-shore.

Clángula hyemális (LINNÆUS). Old-squaw.

Other names: OLD INJUN; OLD WIFE; SCOLDER; SCOLDENORE; SOUTH-SOUTHERLY; COCKAWEE.

Plate 16.

DESCRIPTION. — Unique in having different nuptial and winter plumages; bill shorter than head or tarsus, high at base, sides nearly parallel to rounded end, nail broad, nostrils high in basal half; scapulars long, slender, pointed and drooping; tail pointed, of 14 feathers; male with middle tail-feathers very long, slender and slightly curved both upward and outward. *Adult male in winter plumage:* Sides of head mainly light smoke-gray; a large brownish-dusky patch on each side of neck reaching the gray on sides of head; rest of head, including narrow ring round eye, rest of neck and a little of upper breast and upper back, white (latter sometimes pale gray); rest of breast and upper back blackish tinged with chocolate, this or a deeper tinge extending down middle of back and rump and over long central feathers of tail and closed wings; scapulars mostly pallid gray, lower ones blackish-brown; wing linings and axillars dusky; sides and flanks pallid gray; below from breast to tail white; tail-feathers shading gradually from blackish-brown on middle feathers through pallid gray to white on several outer feathers; basal half of bill black (on sides), rest light rose-pink or pinkish-orange, nail bluish-gray or black; iris apparently variable, bright carmine, reddish-hazel, light brown, straw or white; legs and feet light bluish-gray or slate, webs dusky. (The foregoing describes the usual plumage, but Millais asserts that there is also a dark phase. This I have not seen.) *Adult male in summer or nuptial plumage:* Sides of head largely grayish as in winter; eyelids and large space behind and over eye white; rest of head and neck and upper plumage chiefly very dark sooty-brown which sharply frames the gray and white sides of head; feathers of upper back, upper scapulars and long scapulars edged broadly russet; rest of plumage as in winter; iris reddish-hazel; bill, basal half black, light part "salmon pink" or "rose pink," nail dark; legs and feet pale bluish or slate, webs dusky. *Adult male in eclipse plumage:* This is but a partial eclipse, similar to summer plumage, but upper back darker; scapulars brownish or sooty-brown, some (particularly the longer) shaded and broadly edged buffy-brown; sides and flanks drab; otherwise as in summer plumage. *Adult female in winter plumage:* Head, neck, under plumage and sides of rump chiefly white, a dusky-brown patch on side of neck; top of head and back of neck (forehead to back) shading from dusky brown on forehead to blackish-brown; upper back blackish-brown, the feathers and those of scapulars with russet or cinnamon-buff edges; lower back, rump and upper tail-coverts still darker, but latter sometimes shaded with cinnamon-buff and tipped grayish-white; upper breast ashy-brown with tinge of cinnamon-buff on feather tips; lower breast ashy-brown, feathers fringed white; flanks sometimes very pale gray; central tail feathers (not long as in male) blackish-brown edged faintly white; others more or less dusky, edged white, outer ones chiefly white; wing much as in winter male; bill grayish-black, olive-gray or "dusky green" (Audubon); iris yellow, light gray or white; legs and feet greenish-gray, webs dusky. *Adult female in summer plumage:* Head somewhat as in winter but less white and more dusky or blackish-brown; a large blackish-brown or dusky patch extending over cheeks and sides of neck, nearly surrounded by white of face and neck; whole tone of upper plumage darker and a little duller than in winter; scapulars appear browner; breast hair-brown, "feathers fringed yellowish white or light grayish olive"; "rest of body, tail and wings as in winter"; bill "dusky olive gray" (variable but probably always dark or blackish); iris yellow; legs and feet bluish-gray (D. G. Elliot). *Male in second winter and summer plumage:* As adult, but long pair of central tail-feathers considerably shorter. *Male in first summer plumage:* Great individual variation; some birds retain much or all of winter plumage; some vigorous advanced birds have head and neck much as in summer adult male but long tail-feathers not developed; also new feathers of upper body and breast not so extensively blackish-brown as in adult; sides as in first winter; under plumage as in juvenal. *Male in first winter plumage:* Resembles adult winter male in a certain amount of gray plumage; crown, nape and interscapulars as in adult winter male, but all intermixed with worn juvenal feathers; worn juvenal wing and tail retained; long scapulars shorter and sometimes much darker than in adult; some dusky-brown feathers in the white or gray on sides of head and often some in white throat; some blackish feathers on breast; new flank feathers as adult but rest of under plumage as juvenal. *Female in first summer plumage:* Distinguished from adult summer female by juvenal body feathers retained; like first winter plumage but nape and sides of neck, throat and lower neck intermixed with blackish-brown feathers with whitish bases. *Female in first winter plumage:* Similar to juvenal bird, but distinguished by broad gray edges of scapulars; head and neck much as adult winter female but head pattern imperfect; new feathers at sides of upper breast with paler dusky centers and pale gray tips, those of rest of upper breast white; upper mandible, dusky, becoming leaden-blue toward base; lower mandible leaden-blue, tip dusky; iris very dark brown; legs and toes pale bluish-gray, back of legs, bottoms of feet, and webs blackish. *Young in juvenal plumage:* Like adult female but more uniform coloring above; back and rump have no russet edgings; scapulars dark, shading to buffy-brown at edges; cheek, side of upper neck, chin, throat and fore neck "drab brown"; tail-feathers broader than in adult and with blunt rather than pointed tips; bill blue-gray; iris brown; legs and toes pale gray, webs nearly black. *Downy young:* Above, including cheeks and sides of body, blackish-brown with light golden-brown tips; cream colored spot in front of eye; small white patch below and sometimes above eye, and narrow white streak from it toward nape (not always present); upper breast dusky-brown; rest of under plumage grayish-white.

MEASUREMENTS. — *Male:* Length variable, 20.75 to 23.50 in.; spread about 29.00 to 30.00; folded wing 8.40 to 9.50; tail — lateral feathers 2.50 to 3.50, middle feathers 8.00 to 10.00, pair next to middle pair 3.30 to 6.30; bill 1.04 to 1.14; tarsus 1.25 to 1.48. *Female:* Length 15.00 to 18.00 in.; spread about 26.00 to 28.00; folded wing 7.90 to 9.00; tail about 2.50; bill .92 to 1.04; tarsus 1.20 to 1.38. Weight, male about 2 lbs. to 2 lbs. 8 oz., female about 1 lb. 12 oz.

MOLTS. — After juvenal plumage is shed, there is much individual variation in time of molting and probably in length of molt; amount of first winter plumage varies considerably individually; birds occur in February still in full juvenal plumage with no sign of molt (A. C. Jackson); usually part of feathers of head and body are molted in autumn and winter; in spring another molt (partial) commonly takes place in which some feathers of head, neck, scapulars, interscapulars (in some cases back and rump), upper tail-coverts, upper breast, sides and flanks are shed; in some cases very little molt or change takes place at this season; immature birds probably have a partial molt in the ensuing summer after which wings and tail are shed, but I have not seen a specimen in this plumage; in autumn and winter another molt occurs after which young birds become nearly indistinguishable from adults; but elongated central tail-feathers of male are shorter than in fully adult birds, and probably they never assume full length before third winter or following spring; adults normally have a fall and a spring molt; there is a body molt (August or September to November), a molt of head and a partial body molt (February to June) and apparently a partial molt of head and body feathers and a complete molt of wings and tail (July and August); but there is much individual variation in time and amount of molt. Mr. Walter H. Rich says: "Some birds are found carrying the winter dress through the summer or vice versa." [1] Mr. Winthrop S. Brooks, who was on St. Lawrence Island and the Chukchi Peninsula in June, 1913, states that throughout the month "the males could be found in every stage of plumage change"; of two males taken June 22, one was in full summer plumage; the other in "winter dress but little changed." [2] Dr. E. W. Nelson says the winter plumage is frequently retained through the nesting season. [3] The various changes in

---

[1] Feathered Game of the Northeast, 1907, p. 364.
[2] Bulletin of the Museum of Comparative Zoölogy, Vol. LIX, 1915, p. 392.
[3] Report on Natural History Collections made in Alaska between 1877 and 1881, 1887, p. 73.

plumage during the prolonged erratic molting periods of this species defy description. Some birds appear late in March or in April in nearly full nuptial plumage.

FIELD MARKS. — *Adult male:* Unmistakable close at hand when its long tail can be seen; when seen in winter where White-winged Scoters, Red-breasted Mergansers and Golden-eyes are common, it is known also by white dark-sided head, dark pointed wing with no white speculum, its blackish breast and the great quantity of white on its body; in flight Old-squaws show dark brown and white in patches; these marks, with dark wings, give Old-squaws a queer spotted or pied appearance; in flight, their wings seem to be carried low, show well below body and are directed backward; flocks either bunchy or scattering, seldom fly in line formation; in winter (both sexes) a dark patch on side of white or light neck; male seen from below appears white with dark wings and black band across breast. *Juvenal birds:* Sometimes seen in autumn are very dark.

VOICE. — Most noisy of sea ducks; how much imagination goes into our rendition of bird-notes may be seen by the way the calls of this bird are translated by various persons. Resemble syllables "south south southerly" or "old south southerly" (D. G. Elliot); *o-onc-o-onc-ough-egh-ough-egh* (G. H. Mackay); the Scotch call it "coal an' can'le licht"; while Dr. C. W. Townsend renders it *ung-ung-a-ung hic* and *a-ou a-ou a-oudlic;* spring note of male *a-lĕ′ĕdle-â a-lĕ′ĕdle-â* frequently repeated in deep reed-like tone (E. W. Nelson); note "aptly imitated by Eskimos Ar-hī′-lŏŏk" (J. Grinnell); *cā-cā-coralwee* (Millais); *ah-ah ah-er-lit* (C. J. Maynard); *er-lit ah-er-lit, ca-câ-we, honk-â-link, ogh, ogh, ogh, ough, egh, ogh, ou egh* (Nuttall). Indian renditions vary as much as those of whites. Loquacious birds like talkative people are likely to be often misquoted.

BREEDING. — On the tundra, usually not far from water or on an islet. *Nest:* Sheltered by low vegetation, in hollow of moss or grass, lined with small, dark, light-centered down-feathers. *Eggs:* 6 to 10; 2.36 by 1.54 to 1.96 by 1.42 in.; "greenish-gray" or light grayish-olive. *Dates:* May 18 to June 27. *Incubation:* Period said to be from 24 to 25 days; by female. One brood yearly.

RANGE. — Northern Hemisphere. In North America breeds from islands of Bering Sea, Arctic coast of Alaska, Melville Island, Wellington Channel, Grinnell Land, northern Greenland and probably on most Arctic lands south to Aleutian and Commander islands, east central Mackenzie, northern Hudson Bay, Ungava Bay, and northeastern Labrador; winters from Aleutian Islands south to Washington and southern California (rarely), in southern Greenland, and from Gulf of St. Lawrence and Great Lakes south to North Carolina and infrequently in Montana, Colorado, Texas, Nebraska, Alabama, Louisiana and Florida; in Old World breeds in Iceland, Faroe Islands, Spitzbergen, northern Scandinavia, northern Russia and northern Asia; winters south to Italy and Black and Caspian seas and to Lake Baikal, Japan and China; casual in Azores, Madeira and Switzerland.

DISTRIBUTION IN NEW ENGLAND. — Mainly an abundant fall and spring migrant and common winter resident coastwise; a few non-breeding birds summer in Maine and casually on the Massachusetts and Connecticut coasts; in Vermont a rare migrant, chiefly on Lake Champlain and in Connecticut valley.

SEASON IN MASSACHUSETTS. — October 10; May 22; (June 17) (summer). Most abundant in November and in March and April.

NOTE. In the summer of 1921 Old-squaws with young were reported about Monomoy by a fisherman. On July 18th of that year as I sailed into the little harbor on the outer point, three Old-squaws were seen sitting on the beach within 20 feet of the boat. They sprang into the water, swam a few yards, dived and came up beyond gunshot. Later I crept within 30 yards of them where they floated on the water in full sunlight and studied them with 8-power binoculars. They were an adult male and female in summer plumage and a smaller bird apparently in juvenal plumage. A search of two days did not reveal any more birds of this species. Probably Old-squaws seen here in summer are mostly crippled birds.

HAUNTS AND HABITS. As the autumn sun retreats southward and leaves the Arctic sea in cold and darkness, the hardy Old-squaws follow the retiring orb and so reach the shores of New England.   Clothed in a thick coat of down and feathers they easily withstand the winter's cold.   After a February storm when a northwest gale clears the sky and lashes the surface of the sea into white-capped breaking waves, hundreds of these birds seek the lee of our headlands.   While crossing on such a day from Woods Hole to Naushon Island we saw hosts of Old-squaws and many White-winged Scoters riding the waves.   As our boat with close-reefed sail leaped and plunged over the choppy seas, the piercing wind continually dashed chilling showers of spray over us until deck, sail and rigging were encased with a heavy coating of ice.   But the happy birds swarming into the air in flight before us or diving and playing on either hand showed not a trace of ice upon their plumage.   The sea is their element and they seem to joy in riding crested surges.   After such a winter storm on our coast while the bellowing surf still beats madly on the rocks, one may see the vigorous Old-squaws riding on the face of a towering wave and diving in time to avoid the white and toppling crest — perfectly at home on the wintry sea.   This species is full of life and vigor.   It is one of the swiftest ducks that flies.   When alarmed its flight is often so erratic that it shows its back and then its breast as it turns and wheels.   I have seen an Old-squaw that was shot in the back as it flew overhead.   When shot at in flight, it will sometimes turn and plunge downward into the sea and swim away under water.   In alighting it occasionally turns to check its impetus, but almost always plumps into the water with a great splash and often shoots straight ahead for some distance along the surface before its momentum is checked. It is a powerful diver, and as it goes under always, so far as I have observed, spreads its wings somewhat.   It is said to use them in under-water swimming.[1]   With the aid of its powerful wings it can dive to great depths.   Professor Jones says that it has been taken in nets at 5 fathoms.[2]   Professor Barrows avers that a fisherman at St. Joseph asserted positively that he had seen it caught repeatedly in nets set at a depth of 30 fathoms (180 feet).[3]   He also quotes A. W. Butler who says (Birds of Indiana, 1897, p. 626) that Old-squaws are caught off Michigan City in gill nets in 20 to 30 fathoms of water.   Professor E. H. Eaton says that on the Great Lakes this species is frequently taken in nets set at 15 fathoms and sometimes at 27 fathoms (162 feet).   Former Governor W. D. Hoard of Wisconsin assured me that the lake fishermen take ducks in nets set at 50 to 100 feet in depth.   Probably few species of diving birds reach such depths in pursuit of food.

While it may be possible that the Old-squaw actually dives and obtains food in fresh water at some of these extreme depths, it seems very improbable that it is able to go down so far in salt water which has a greater density.   Millais says that in the Baltic when forced to resort to deeper water, they can obtain food to a depth of 30 feet, but they soon become thin.[4]   Mackay writes that in 1888, when one could stand on the highlands of Nantucket and see only ice as far as the horizon on the sea surrounding the island,

[1] Hull, Edwin D.: Wilson Bulletin, Vol. XXVI, 1914, p. 120.
[2] Dawson, W. L., and Jones, Lynds: The Birds of Ohio, 1903, p. 613.
[3] Barrows, Walter B.: Michigan Bird Life, 1912, p. 103.
[4] Millais, J. G.: British Diving Ducks, Vol. I, 1913, p. 123.

Old-squaws were reduced to skin and bones and some apparently starved to death.[1] This indicates that they were unable to secure food by diving in deep water outside the ice.

The courtship of the Old-squaw is characterized by an act that I have never seen so prominently displayed by any other duck. As the male swims about the female, his tail is sometimes raised high and wagged horizontally, widely and rapidly like the tail of a dog; occasionally the wagging tail is only a trifle lifted. The male pursues the female both when she dives and when she flies, as told by Nelson. The male commonly throws the head over until it touches the back, and often both sexes stretch the neck out along the water.

Old-squaws are perhaps our most loquacious ducks. Their resounding cries have been likened to the music of a pack of hounds. The "towering" of these birds is well described by Mr. George H. Mackay as follows: "These ducks have a habit of towering both in the spring and in the autumn, usually in the afternoon, collecting in mild weather in large flocks if undisturbed, and going up in circles so high as to be scarcely discernible, often coming down with a rush and great velocity, a portion of the flock scattering and coming down in a zigzag course similar to the scoters when whistled down. The noise of their wings can be heard for a great distance under such conditions."[2]

Old-squaws while in New England feed mainly in salt water but they occasionally frequent some pond near the sea where they find suitable food. Small mollusks, small crabs, shrimps and other small crustaceans together with small fish make up a great part of their winter food. They are said to feed also on pondweeds; while in summer in the fresh-water lakes where they breed, they devour the seeds, buds, shoots and roots of aquatic plants and also "insects and worms" (Millais).

ECONOMIC STATUS. Old-squaws are commonly considered too fishy for human consumption, and therefore many that are shot are left where they fall or thrown away. If properly prepared, however, they are both palatable and nutritious.

Histriónicus histrionicus histrionicus (LINNÆUS). Harlequin Duck.

Other names: ROCK DUCK; LORD AND LADY; SQUEALER; SEA MOUSE.

Plate 17.

DESCRIPTION. — Bill very small, shorter than head, higher than wide at base, tapering to rounded end which is covered by a large fused nail; nostrils in basal half, their front margins about halfway from nearest feathers to tip of bill; wings and tail short, tail pointed; the only New England sea-duck having a glossy metallic speculum. *Adult male in winter and nuptial plumage:* Prevailing color mainly dark leaden blue, with some purplish gloss, becoming black about edges of most white markings and blue-black or blackish on chin, throat, top of head, lower rump, tail-coverts and tail; peculiar, somewhat crescentic, white patch before eye, covering large part of front face from chin to forehead and crown and extending narrowly alongside latter toward back of head; white spot near ear, white stripe extending from a little back of this down side of neck; narrow white collar around lower neck (sometimes interrupted before and behind); white bar across side of breast to shoulder; scapulars (mostly), spot on wing-coverts,

---

[1] Mackay, George H.: Auk, Vol. IX, 1892, pp. 334-335.   [2] Auk, Vol. IX, 1892, p. 331.

bar across ends of greater coverts, webs of two inner secondaries and longest tertial (partially) and spot on each side at base of tail, white; a reddish-cinnamon or chestnut streak bordering below the white near top of head and running from above eye to nape; wing mainly dark brown; three secondaries with outer webs steel-blue, glossy and changeable, in some lights violet-purple (speculum); axillars and under wing-coverts mainly hair-brown; sides of belly and flanks chestnut; feathers of lower breast, belly and vent hair-brown, more or less edged dark leaden-blue; bill bluish-gray, bluish-black or olive, its nail lighter or horn color; iris reddish-brown; legs and feet pale bluish-gray or brown, webs dusky. *Adult male in eclipse plumage:* Similar to adult female but head darker; white markings of head absent or more or less obscured by dusky tips but white ear-spot retained in part at least; white markings of neck, breast and shoulder wanting; chin mottled whitish and dusky; throat and fore neck sooty-brown or blackish; speculum or wing-patch dull, dusky, brownish-gray with little gloss; sides, flanks and under tail-coverts grayish-brown or sooty-brown, some feathers of body and flanks sometimes tipped olive-brown and cross-waved blackish-brown; other under plumage hair-brown, sometimes more or less tipped with blackish lead color, sometimes "grayish-white spotted grayish-brown." *Adult female in winter and nuptial plumage:* A small, obscure duck differing widely from male; prevailing color grayish-brown; head and upper plumage darkest, approaching clove-brown, darkest on top of head and rump, lightest on chin and throat; whitish patch on cheek below eye, another on ear and a little whitish before eye extending toward forehead (sometimes meeting the cheek patch); wings and tail mainly glossy blackish-brown; under plumage more grayish, passing into whitish on belly, usually somewhat mottled; bill paler than in male; iris, legs and feet similar to those of male but duller. *Male in first winter plumage:* Some, retaining much juvenal plumage, resemble adult female; others, more advanced, somewhat resemble adult male but markings less well defined; scapulars dark as in adult but without white; sides and flanks with much dark leaden-bluish, some flank-feathers suffused with chestnut toward tips; speculum dull, very little white in this plumage. *Female in first winter plumage:* Like adult female but upper plumage browner with less dark sheen and lighter below; tail lighter, more worn at ends. *Young in juvenal plumage:* Like female but lighter and more olive-brown; whitish patch above eye and another below it (which usually does not extend toward bill) and another near ear; "chest, flanks and under tail-coverts decidedly brownish" (Ridgway). *Downy young:* Head to below eye and all upper plumage, sides and flanks blackish-brown; small patch from forehead to front of eye, another near base of upper mandible and another below eye, white; a rather indistinct spot on wing, another on side of back behind wing and one on either side of center of back, white, latter sometimes ill-defined; below, mainly white, tinged grayish on throat and sides.

MEASUREMENTS. — Length 15.00 to 17.75 in.; spread 23.75 to 27.00; folded wing 7.00 to 8.27; tail 3.00 to 4.00; bill .90 to 1.14; tarsus 1.30 to 1.52. Weight 1 lb. 4 oz. to 1 lb. 8 oz. Female smaller than male.

MOLTS. — Following natal down, juvenal plumage is assumed in late summer; autumnal molt appears to affect but small part of head- and body-feathers but from October more or less molting goes on until most feathers of head and neck, some of scapulars, upper tail-coverts, breast, sides and flanks and all or part of tail are shed; in following summer there is a molt into first eclipse plumage, including body-feathers, and later wings and tail; this molt may last almost continuously from July to December or longer; immature males during their molts show much variation and many stages of plumage, but probably most of them and the females as well during their second winter become as adults; adults have a double molt; the molts into and out of eclipse plumage seem to be more or less continuous (July to December).

FIELD MARKS. — *Adult male:* Harlequin in full plumage is unmistakable when seen close at hand; at a distance where the white markings do not show, it looks black. *Female:* Smaller and so entirely unlike her mate that at a distance she might be mistaken for female Buffle-head, Ruddy Duck or even for one of the scoters; near at hand her small size and small bill will separate her from the latter, and the two or three white patches on head (two of them on fore part of face) will distinguish her from Buffle-

PLATE 17

PLATE 17

KING EIDER
Page 268
Nuptial Plumage
Male

Female

NORTHERN EIDER
Page 263
Nuptial Plumage
Male

EIDER
Page 264
Nuptial Plumage
Male

Female

HARLEQUIN DUCK
Page 259
Winter (Nuptial) Plumage
Male

Female

All one-sixth natural size.

Louis Agassiz Fuertes.

head which has but *one* and that one *behind* eye; young Old-squaw with large light patch around eye is most like her in color and at a distance, where details of head markings are not clear, might be mistaken for her; when swimming in flocks Harlequins crowd close together in regular formation, floating high and buoyantly, and often carry their tails cocked up.

VOICE. — In flock, sometimes a chorus of gabbling and chattering sounds (E. W. Nelson); when mated, low notes that "might remind one of the conversational tones of the coot"; call of male, "a loud, clear *qua qua qua* uttered in rapid succession" (C. W. and E. Michael); males have a "low piping whistle" — probably the note that gives bird name of Squealer or Sea Mouse by which it is often known on Maine coast where gunners say they "squeak like mice" (A. H. Norton).

BREEDING. — Largely in interior; on mountain streams; on islands in rivers. *Nest:* In holes in rocks, under rocks or logs or in hollow stumps or trees. *Eggs:* 5 to 10; roundish oval; about 2.35 by 1.57 to 2.30 by 1.62 in.; greenish-yellow or yellowish-buff. *Dates:* Mid-June to mid-July, Iceland. *Incubation:* Period 24 to 25 days; by female. One brood yearly.

RANGE. — Northeastern North America, eastern Asia * and Iceland. Breeds from southern Greenland south to northern Ungava (northern Quebec) and Newfoundland (formerly to Bay of Fundy); also in northeastern Asia, the Ural Mountains and Iceland; winters on the coast from Gulf of St. Lawrence regularly to Maine, rarely to New Jersey and accidentally to Florida; resident in Iceland; rare to casual in Scandinavia, parts of Russia, Germany, Great Britain, Switzerland and Italy.

DISTRIBUTION IN NEW ENGLAND. — Formerly winter resident common coastwise locally in Maine, now not common there; rare winter visitor coastwise in New Hampshire, Massachusetts and Rhode Island; two records in Connecticut; no record for Vermont; Audubon called the Harlequin a common bird from Boston eastward, but now it is becoming rare even on the eastern part of the Maine coast.

SEASON IN MASSACHUSETTS. — Winter visitor; November 1 to April.

HAUNTS AND HABITS. Harlequin! Rightly named, fantastically decorated, but nevertheless in beauty second only to the Wood Duck. The bird is so elegant that the people of the north coasts have well named its little companies the "Lords and Ladies" of the sea. Unfortunately for New Englanders, however, the beauty of these birds is reserved mainly for the far North, for mountain wildernesses or the wintry Atlantic where the waves dash on isolated, lonely offshore ledges.

It has never been my good fortune to see this rare and lovely duck alive in New England, but in summer I have watched by the hour many flocks of Pacific Harlequins on the west coast near the Straits of Fuca. While suspicious of the slightest motion, this duck seems not to notice a motionless figure on the shore. While sitting once in a little cove I watched a flock of Harlequins at their play until they swam within a few feet of me. At my first motion, however, they churned the water into foam in their frantic flight. They are very playful birds and chase one another like children at a game of tag.

The Harlequin is equally at home on the quiet waters of some sheltered bay, on a rushing mountain torrent or amid the tumult of the crested seas that break in winter on our coast. The downy young soon reach their favorite element in some mountain stream where they dive and bob about in rushing waters and among the rocks, as much at home as are their parents on the restless sea. Charles W. Michael and Enid Michael have made a notable contribution to the life history of the Harlequin in their paper

---

* Pacific birds have been separated from the eastern form.

entitled "An Adventure with a Pair of Harlequin Ducks in the Yosemite Valley." [1] Though they did not find the nest, they had an excellent opportunity to watch, feed and photograph a mated pair in the Merced River. These ducks ate pieces of bread thrown into the water or left in a floating feeding tray. The female also ate macaroni, cooked potatoes and raisins. This may indicate that Harlequins feed to a considerable extent on vegetation, although the particular pair observed were not seen to eat any other vegetal food. In mating these ducks swam close together with much bobbing of the head. They fed in water, where either they could wade about or swim in any depth, from the shallows where they could "tip up" in the manner of surface-feeding ducks to water six feet deep. Always when diving they went down on a gravelly bottom and sometimes they chose the swiftest ripples. In diving they used their wiry tails as a spring for making the plunge, while in going down both wings and feet were used for propulsion. In rising they floated to the surface without motion of the wings or feet. They swam and dived facing the current, and walked on the bottom with ease by keeping the head down, with body and neck slanting at an angle. In a current of a certain speed, the birds could stand still on the bottom, for the pressure and weight of the water passing backward up their slanting backs seemed to hold them down. To keep on bottom in a slower current they were obliged to move forward against it.

As appears from the foregoing, the Harlequin is an excellent diver, swimming and diving with ease in rough water. If wounded and pursued, it seeks concealment below the surface. Mr. G. Dallas Hanna informed me that at the Pribilof Islands, he sought a wounded duck of this species that dived and failed to reappear. He found it dead, clinging with its bill to kelp near the bottom where the water was about 8 feet deep.[2]

The last of the Harlequins are leaving their breeding-grounds in Greenland when in early November the species first appears on the Massachusetts coast. Once they came in small flocks; now rarely more than a few individuals are observed together. They may be seen well off shore, along the rocky islands and ledges of the North Shore or even about Marthas Vineyard or Nantucket where a few sometimes spend part of the winter. A few winter occasionally at No Man's Land, where, so Mr. J. W. Blythe assures me, they stay until April.

The food of the Harlequin in salt water consists largely of mussels and other mollusks and crustaceans (with some small fish) and is obtained mainly by diving. Sometimes a large mussel is said to retaliate by catching the duck's bill in its shell and holding on until the cessation of the bird's struggles indicates that life is extinct (D. G. Elliot). In its fresh-water breeding-places this duck feeds to some extent on insects.

ECONOMIC STATUS. When feeding in salt water the Harlequin is of inferior quality as food and it is now so rare in New England as to be of no economic importance. It should be protected at all times by law for its beauty alone.

---

[1] Auk, Vol. XXXIX, 1922, pp. 14–23.
[2] Department Bulletin No. 8, Massachusetts Department of Agriculture, 1922, p. 41.

Somatéria mollíssima boreális (BREHM). Northern Eider.

Other name: GREENLAND EIDER.

Plate 17.

DESCRIPTION. — Similar to American Eider (*S. mollissima dresseri*) (see page 264) but membranous processes extending from base of bill on either side of forehead *narrower and more nearly pointed ;* greenish wash on sides of head of male *not extending forward below black cap almost to bill* as in American Eider ; bill of male in spring "bright orange yellow" ; practically indistinguishable in all plumages from American Eider except by characters noted above.

MEASUREMENTS. — *Adult male:* Length about 24.00 in. ; spread about 40.00 ; folded wing 10.00 to 11.50 ; tail 2.75 to 4.00 ; bill from apex of feathered forehead to tip 1.80 to 2.00 ; from apex of frontal process to tip 2.40 to 2.75 ; tarsus 1.70 to 1.95. Weight of male 3 to over 5 lbs. Female smaller than male.

MOLTS. — In all respects similar to those of American Eider.

FIELD MARKS. — Ordinarily indistinguishable in field from American Eider. (See under that species.)

VOICE. — Similar to that of American Eider.

BREEDING. — Breeding habits, nest, eggs and incubation period similar to those of American Eider ; but eggs often found in old nests of Brant and Glaucous Gull (D. B. MacMillan). *Dates:* From June 10 to July.

RANGE. — Northeastern North America and possibly Iceland. Breeds from Ellesmere Island and both coasts of Greenland south to northwestern Hudson Bay, southern Ungava (central Quebec) and Labrador ; winters in southern Greenland and south to Massachusetts rarely.

DISTRIBUTION IN NEW ENGLAND. — A few stragglers reach the coast of Maine ; one taken in Casco Bay, April 6, 1903 (John A. Lord) ; another taken in Sagadahoc County (H. L. Spinney) ;[1] reported in Massachusetts in winter coastwise and three taken November 9, 1909, at Furnace Pond, Pembroke (John C. Phillips) ;[2] a female was taken by George H. Mackay on Muskeget Island, March 15, 1890, now in collection of Boston Society of Natural History ; doubtfully reported from Rhode Island.

BILLS OF EIDERS (REDUCED), VIEWED FROM ABOVE AND IN PROFILE.

Upper right and middle figures Eider ; others Northern Eider.

HAUNTS AND HABITS. I have never knowingly seen the Northern Eider alive. Its haunts and habits are much the same as those of the American Eider except that it is more northern in distribution. The records of its occurrence in Massachusetts are few, but if all eiders taken here could be examined by ornithologists, probably the number of records of this subspecies would be increased. Field observation cannot be depended upon to distinguish two races that so closely resemble one another.

ECONOMIC STATUS. This Eider, being a far northern bird, is not so prominent economically as the more southern race, but as a producer of eider-down its possibilities are great. See American Eider, p. 267.

---

[1] Knight, O. W.: Birds of Maine, 1908, p. 107. [2] Auk, Vol. XXVIII, 1911, p. 195.

Somateria mollissima drésseri SHARPE. Eider.

Other names: AMERICAN EIDER; SHOAL DUCK; BLACK AND WHITE COOT; SEA-DUCK; WAMP.

Plate 17.

DESCRIPTION. — Bill with two frontal processes, *each with broad rounded ends* and extending backward on each side of forehead between short pointed feathering of forehead and much longer extensions of feathering on sides of upper mandible; in both sexes feathering of head (at lores) extends forward to below hind end of nostril; nail fused with bill, forming entire tip of upper mandible. *Adult male in winter,* as seen here: Chiefly black and white; long pointed scapulars and inner secondaries or tertials curved outward and downward, drooping over other secondaries and primaries; top of head glossy bluish-black with iridescent lavender tints, divided in center of crown by a creamy-white streak which blends into sea-green wash of back of head, nape, upper neck and ear-region (black of head bordered below by this green for nearly its entire length); cheeks, chin, throat, neck, lesser and median wing-coverts, conspicuous patch on either side of rump, back and scapulars white; white scapulars, together with lesser wing-coverts and drooping inner secondaries or tertials (and sometimes neck and upper breast), slightly tinged yellow or cream; center of rump, upper and under tail-coverts, greater wing-coverts, all secondaries but inner, sides, flanks, lower breast and belly black or brownish-black; primaries brown; axillars and wing linings largely white; two inner secondaries in part white; some birds have small black or dusky V on throat; bill *in spring* orange-yellow, varying at other times from gray to green; nail pale horn; feet and legs yellow or green, webs dusky; "iris brown. Feet and legs dark green. . . . Frontal processes a rich yellowish-green or orange" (Walter Rich). *Adult male in eclipse plumage:* Not resembling either adult male or female winter plumage; mainly brownish-black or blackish above with mixture of sooty-brown and white on back, with much white on wing-coverts and long scapulars; irregular whitish line through eye and black streak before it; chin, throat and neck largely a mixture of sooty-brown and white but mostly dark, feathers showing more or less ill-concealed whitish bases; a band of more or less white across breast, variable; some feathers of upper breast with buff tips and barred blackish; rump, tail-coverts, sides, flanks, lower breast, wings and tail much as in nuptial plumage except where lighter or duller. *Adult female in winter and nuptial plumage:* Chiefly brown or deep tan; feathers of head and neck largely edged pinkish-cinnamon or cinnamon-buff and streaked finely with blackish; body and wing-coverts generally barred or spotted in cross rows so as to give impression of irregular barring with dusky or black and broad brown or buffy feather-tips; black usually predominates on back; tail and primaries lighter or browner than in male; secondaries lighter on inner webs, outer webs tipped white or whitish; innermost secondaries edged tawny or brown; inner greater wing-coverts tipped white or whitish (bird thus has two short light wing-bars); belly sooty-brown or drab-brown with indistinct markings; bill olive-green above (sometimes yellowish) shading gradually into blue-gray below and in front of nostril, nail "bone yellow." *Young in juvenal plumage: Male:* Somewhat similar to adult female in winter but darker above; feathers with narrower buff edges; below hair-brown with narrow buff feather-tips. *Female:* Like juvenal male but secondaries lighter; innermost secondaries shorter, less sickle-shaped; back and rump often with broader buff feather-edgings; legs and feet bluish-gray. (*Immature plumages:* Succeeding juvenal plumage of male comes a long series of molts with continual changes toward maturity until third year; impossible in limited space to describe the many plumage changes.) *Downy young:* Above plain, dark, grayish-brown, long downy filaments in some specimens slightly buffy-brown at tips; below paler grayish-brown, lightening on throat or chin and belly; dark stripe running from bill to beneath eye contrasting with lighter color above and beneath.

MEASUREMENTS. — Length 20.00 to 26.00 in.; spread 39.00 to 42.00; folded wing 10.50 to 12.00; tail 3.42 to 4.50; bill from apex of feathered forehead to tip about 1.83 to 2.45; from apex of frontal process to tip 2.23 to 3.39; from posterior end of nostril 1.35 to 1.48; from anterior extremity of loral feathering 1.75 to 2.00, its width across middle not less than .45; tarsus 1.78 to 1.90. Weight "3 lbs. 12 oz. to 5 lbs. 5½ oz." (Audubon). Female smaller than male.

MOLTS. — From September onward young male by partial molt of feathers of head, neck and body grows lighter on head and browner above, with a streak of light buff or whitish through eye; the molt is more or less continuous through winter and spring; in next summer plumage, cheeks, sides of chin, throat, neck and upper breast show more or less white, and some green sometimes appears on sides of neck; there is a first eclipse plumage much like that of adult male, but juvenal wings and under plumage are retained until late August or September when wings are shed; in the autumn upper body-feathers and some of under plumage are molted from September onward; in second winter and next summer immature male resembles adult, but usually shows signs of immaturity in blackish tips to many white feathers of head, neck and other plumage, but some birds retain eclipse plumage through second winter; in second eclipse, some body-feathers are molted from June to August; in eclipse most of these feathers, together with those of tail and wings, are renewed, and bird next begins to assume its third winter plumage in which it becomes practically adult; young female goes through a similar process of molting and becomes practically as adult female in third winter; adult male molts in April and May and from late summer to midwinter; before assuming winter plumage he molts many body-feathers, beginning in June, when he starts to molt into eclipse plumage, following which rest of body-feathers, wings and tail are renewed. Female molts similarly but is darker above in eclipse plumage than in winter; she may assume winter plumage later than male.

FIELD MARKS. — Flight rather sluggish, usually not very high, often just clears waves; head carried rather low; frequently alternates flapping with sailing; maritime, frequenting mainly rocky sea-coasts and islands. *Male:* Very large; heavily built; black under plumage, tail and top of head contrast strongly with white of breast and upper plumage; greenish wash on head and upper neck. *Female:* Ruddy brown, black-barred, of a much warmer brown than female scoters and larger than any of them except White-wing, but not to be distinguished in field from females of Northern Eider or King Eider.

VOICE. — Male: a raucous, moaning voice, *he ho, ha ho* or *a-o-wah-a-o-wah*; his love notes *aah-ou* or *ah-ee-ou* (C. W. Townsend). Female: a quack like that of domestic duck; when flying from nest *kuk, kuk, kuk* (O. W. Knight).

BREEDING. — Usually in communities on rocky islands in sea or lake or on shore of some river or estuary near sea, rarely using nest of Herring Gull. *Nest:* On ground, usually sheltered by rocks, trees or undergrowth or grasses; of mosses, seaweed, sticks or grass, lined with down. *Eggs:* 3 to 10, very rarely 12; 3.16 by 2.08 to 2.99 by 2.07 in.; pale greenish-olive. *Dates:* June 5, Labrador (F. M. Chapman). *Incubation:* Period 25 to 26 days (J. Beetz); by female. One brood yearly.

RANGE. — Northeastern North America. Breeds about the southern half of shores of Hudson Bay and James Bay, in southern Labrador, and from north shore of Gulf of St. Lawrence and Newfoundland south to coast of eastern Maine; winters from Newfoundland and Gulf of St. Lawrence south on Atlantic coast commonly to Massachusetts, rarely to Delaware; in interior occasionally on Great Lakes; rare in migration or in winter in Maryland and Virginia.

DISTRIBUTION IN NEW ENGLAND. — Common to abundant migrant and local winter resident coastwise from Maine to Massachusetts; rather common migrant and winter resident coastwise in Rhode Island; rare winter resident in Connecticut; breeds on certain Maine islands, where it formerly summered in considerable numbers; "the Eider Duck bred in 1921 in Maine as far west as Jericho Bay (Isle au Haut)" (A. H. Norton); few pairs now breeding within limits of United States.

SEASON IN MASSACHUSETTS. — (September 20); November 5 to April 19; (May 3).

NOTE. In his recent annual reports as Field Agent for Maine of the National Association of Audubon Societies, Mr. Arthur H. Norton speaks encouragingly of the possibility that the Eider Duck is coming back to some of its old Maine haunts or taking up new breeding-places. In his report for 1922, published in Bird-Lore (Vol. XXIV, pp. 410–411), he says: "Eider Ducks are lingering at many places along the coast where they have not been known in summer for years, and it is probable that some are soon to be, or now are, breeding at new points." And in his 1923 report of his 200-mile trip of inspection along the Maine coast from April 13 to May 2 (Bird-Lore, Vol. XXV, p. 460), he further says: "Eider Ducks were seen in rather large numbers at several places, but not migrating."

HAUNTS AND HABITS. The great, sturdy, handsome Eider Duck passes by the outer points along the New England coast, and thousands feed in winter on the shoals off Marthas Vineyard and Nantucket. Nevertheless, this species is not often seen from the mainland, as it chiefly keeps to the sea. In migration, however (and often in winter), its flocks may be seen on or near outlying rocks and ledges such as those off the Maine coast, the Salvages off Rockport, Milk Island off Cape Ann, the rocks south of Squibnocket, Marthas Vineyard, those off Cohasset and those off Sakonnet Point, Rhode Island. Eiders are sometimes abundant in early April off Chatham.

Dr. C. W. Townsend, who has given excellent descriptions of the courtship behavior of ducks, says that the male American Eider in courtship frequently repeats his love notes, which have so much volume that they "can be heard at a considerable distance over water" and that the tones vary, much as do those of the human voice. Sometimes the head of the bird is drawn down with the bill on the breast and then raised until it is vertical; then the head is jerked stiffly backward and returned to its usual position. The eager bird frequently displays his black belly by rising almost upright on the water. At times he throws back his head and flaps his wings. The female may seem indifferent to this display or may show her appreciation by facing him and "throwing up her head a little." [1]

At low tide Eiders may be seen in small companies sitting on wave-washed rocks that rise above the surface or floating on the water near them. Mr. George H. Mackay has given an excellent account of the Eiders on their wintering grounds off the Nantucket coast.[2] He says that on the shoals adjacent to Marthas Vineyard, Nantucket and Muskeget, their favorite haunts lie about the sunken rocks where they chiefly find their food, and that at night they leave the neighborhood of these rocks in flocks and fly out to sea. Apparently they become scattered during the night, as at daybreak they return to their feeding grounds from points covering sixty-five degrees. They are slow ordinarily and heavy but if frightened they are agile and swift. Being expert divers, they are difficult to capture if wounded. Mr. Mackay says that he has seen a flock at forty-five yards go under water at the flash of the gun, before shot could reach them. In diving they open their wings, and sometimes, if not always, use them for progression under water. When a shot is fired at Eiders on the surface, those under water near-by come up with their wings moving and apparently fly directly from the depths into the air.

In the autumnal migration Eiders appear off the Massachusetts coast early in November and less commonly in October. In spring all but a few stragglers have left by the latter part of April, at which time some may have appeared already in Canadian Labrador. When about to begin their northward migration they land upon sand-bars and

---

[1] Auk, Vol. XXVII, 1910, pp. 180–181. 　　　　　　　　　　[2] Auk, Vol. VII, 1890, pp. 315–319.

(as the gunners say) "take in sand ballast," after which they may be seen flying north in long lines.

Eiders have many enemies. At sea they must be on the watch for sharks and other large predatory fishes and seals, and in the Pacific they are pursued by the Killer Whale, *Orca gladiator*. On land they are preyed upon by Arctic foxes, wolves, skuas and falcons.

Their food is obtained mainly by diving from a point usually just outside the breaking wave. They detach mussels from the rocks and come up again outside the breaker. I have seen a male Eider lying on the surface of the sea in calm weather at low tide, and taking mussels off a rock, sometimes at the surface and sometimes by submerging head and neck, but this must be unusual. In our waters they feed largely on mollusks and crustaceans. Mussels, small sea clams and scallops are commonly eaten, also sea-urchins, starfish and crabs. Rarely the mussel catches the duck. Mr. George H. Mackay gave me on Jan. 3, 1923, the head of a female Eider that had been found dying on Nantucket with a large mussel in its mouth. The mussel had closed its shell on the bird's tongue. The bird was unable to rid itself of the mollusk and so starved. The mussel was still alive and holding on with a death grip. On their breeding-grounds Eiders are said to eat many small fish. Little is known about the vegetal food of the Eiders, but Johan Beetz asserts that the young birds eat "prawns and much herbage" during their first 18 months;[1] and Selous remarks that he has seen the common Eider apparently eating seaweed. Eiders are quick to find a source of food supply. In 1893 and 1894 American Eiders appeared in large numbers at Woods Hole and fed between that point and Naushon Island. Specimens dissected had fed on mussels and the spawn of sculpins.[2]

ECONOMIC STATUS. While many Eiders have been shot and eaten by gunners and sportsmen, young birds only are said to be fit for food. Nevertheless, the Eider is an important bird from an economic point of view because of the value of its eggs for food and of its down for pillows and coverlets. Our Canadian neighbors might reap a rich harvest by conserving these birds after the manner of the Scandinavians and Icelanders who kill no Eider Ducks, but take the down and some of the eggs from the nests, securing thereby much good food and a yearly revenue. The following extract from a letter written from a friend in Iceland to Mr. Aaron C. Bagg gives the modern method of conserving Eiders for profit in Iceland:

"Everything possible is done by land-owners to coax these ducks to nest in a region where they are in the habit of coming each spring, and there is quite a bit of rivalry in this respect, for the down belongs to the man on whose land the ducks nest. Even bright colors are hung up and musical bells rung when the ducks are coming.

"Much is done also to protect the nesting ducks. Small sheltering hills are built to shield the nests from storms, and ravens or gulls which have been shot are hung on poles to frighten away birds of prey. All shooting about the nesting ground is strictly for-

---

[1] Townsend, C. W.: Auk, Vol. XXXIII, 1916, p. 291.   [2] Mackay, George H.: Auk, Vol. XI, 1894, pp. 223–224.

bidden under penalty of a heavy fine. When the eggs are hatched, the mother duck takes the ducklings to the nearest water for their lessons in swimming. So many of the more feeble ones have perished from the rough or stormy water in the past that small ponds are built near-by where there is less danger. The eiderdown is collected when the old duck has abandoned the nest with her brood, so as not to frighten her while sitting on the eggs. Usually two gatherings are made, first when the ducks leave the nest; and second, from what are called the 'laggers.' I suppose by that is meant those ducks that for some reason or other have been delayed. Eggs are taken only when there are so many in a nest as to make it uncertain or difficult for all to be hatched. Only the owners are allowed then to take them, and sale of these eggs is absolutely prohibited. Eiderdown is valuable only when it is rightly and thoroughly cleaned. When taken from the nest, it is mixed with filth, grass, mosses and other undesirable particles. All this must be cleaned away— which makes a considerable problem. There are small machines especially adapted for this work, and the air is filled with dust and dirt when these machines are in operation. The process of cleansing takes considerable time and handling before the down is perfectly pure and ready for the market.''

Somateria spectábilis (LINNÆUS). King Eider.

Other names: WAMP'S COUSIN; KING BIRD.

Plate 17.

DESCRIPTION. — Bill and adjacent feathering quite different from those of other eiders and varying much not only between the sexes but in males at different seasons; base of bill becoming enlarged in February but much less evident in immature birds; fully adult males show modification of the two outer tertials; their shafts curve downward and the barbs of their outer webs are greatly enlarged, the outer edges of outer two being deeply notched which produces a peculiar tuft on each wing somewhat like that on wing of American Eider. *Adult male in winter*, as seen here: Top of head pearl-gray deepening on nape and sides of upper neck; emerald-green patch on cheek, and white line (usually) over eye extending to sides of upper neck; glossy-black line bordering forehead and inclosing base of upper mandible, the frontal processes of which are much enlarged, bulging high above rest of bill; a spot surrounding eye extending slightly beneath it and a large V-shaped mark on throat black; rest of head, neck, sides of upper back and shoulders creamy white; breast creamy pinkish-buff; scapulars, inner secondaries, lower back, center of rump, tail-coverts, sides and under plumage black; large patch on side of rump white with some black-tipped feathers; wings and tail mainly dark brown or blackish-brown; large white patch on fore wing but amount of white here variable; usually 2 narrow white wing-bars; drooping tertials purplish-black; axillars white; under wing-coverts mostly white; bill flesh-colored, sides of upper mandible orange, its high base reddish-orange and tip white; iris bright yellow or brown; feet dull orange-yellow or bluish-gray tinged yellow, webs dusky.* *Adult male in eclipse plumage:* Similar to that of American Eider but scapulars brownish-black with no white markings; upper plumage nearly all dusky-brown except a few white feathers in upper back and whitish lesser wing-coverts; abdomen as in winter but more faded and browner; chin and throat dusky-white with many ashy-brown feather tips; feathers of upper breast mainly sooty-brown with rounded, elongated white markings toward tips which are dark or buff, with a few white-tipped feathers among them; some

---

* In the Auk (Vol. XVII, 1900, p. 17) Mr. Arthur H. Norton gives a technical description of the perfected plumage of a superb male King Eider which was shot in April, 1899, off the coast of Maine.

birds have buffy or whitish upper breasts, barred with blackish-brown. *Adult female in winter and nuptial plumage:* Much like female of American Eider but top of head and nape more narrowly streaked, feathers edged more reddish-tawny; chin and throat paler; upper plumage generally with redder (or sometimes paler) feather-edgings; bill pale greenish-gray or yellowish, nail bluish-gray with yellow tinge; iris dull yellow; legs and feet dull greenish-gray; distinguished from female of American Eider by smaller size, head and bill proportionately shorter and deeper, and less ruddy coloring; feathers of upper back and scapulars not square-tipped but somewhat rounded or pointed; feathering of forehead extends almost to nostrils, but feathers on sides of head (loral) extend only about half-way. *Immature plumages:* Male during first winter differs rather slightly from female but shows toward spring a black inverted V more or less distinct on throat; from that time onward male shows more and more of black and white plumage like that of adult in winter and spring, while female becomes indistinguishable from adult female. Impossible in limited space to describe the many changes and variations of immature birds. *Young in juvenal plumage:* Similar to juvenal American Eider, but upper plumage and wing-coverts more broadly edged with deeper buff. *Downy young:* Much like young of American Eider but lighter above; below still lighter, lightening to ashy-white on lower breast and belly.

MEASUREMENTS. — Length 20.75 to 24.00 in.; spread about 28.00; tarsus 1.70 to 1.86; folded wing 10.50 to 11.25; tail 2.95 to 3.75; bill 1.20 to 1.30. Weight 4 to 5 lbs. Female smaller than male.

MOLTS. — Sequence of molts in this species seems to be same as in American Eider and it appears to reach maturity at about same age.

FIELD MARKS. — Adult males may be distinguished from those of American Eider by smaller size and pearl gray top of head where American Eider is black and green and by black scapulars where American Eider has white; "in the King Eider the wing is black with a white patch; in the American Eider the fore part of the wing is white, the terminal half black" (Ludlow Griscom); female usually has two narrow white wing-bars but these seldom can be seen in field; adult female is usually lighter, more rusty or buffy-brown than female of American Eider which commonly appears more sooty-brown; however, immature birds and females are as a rule indistinguishable in our waters from those of other eiders; as immature males approach maturity they become darker on back and scapulars than other eiders.

VOICE. — A croaking, guttural note similar to that of Pacific Eider (W. Sprague Brooks); its only note a single cooing sound, heard especially at night (A. T. Hagerup).

BREEDING. — Occasionally in colonies of other eiders but more often scattered over the tundra. *Nest:* Usually more or less concealed by overgrown vegetation and near water; lined with down. *Eggs:* 4 to 10; like those of American Eider but smaller; "2.77 inches to 3.08 by 1.88 to 2.07" (Grinnell, Bryant and Storer). *Dates:* Last half June and first half July. *Incubation:* By female. One brood yearly.

RANGE. — Northern part of Northern Hemisphere. Breeds in Bering Sea (St. Lawrence and St. Matthew Islands) and on Arctic coast of America from Icy Cape to Melville Island, Wellington Channel, northern Hudson Bay, Baffin Island, and Greenland south to northern Quebec (Ungava) and northern Labrador; winters on Pacific coast of North America from Pribilof Islands to Kadiak and Shumagin Islands; in interior to Michigan, Illinois, Great Lakes, Ontario and New York; and on Atlantic coast from southern Greenland and Gulf of St. Lawrence south regularly to Long Island; rare in New Jersey and Pennsylvania; accidental in California, Alberta, Minnesota, Missouri, Virginia, Georgia and Iowa; in Old World breeds on coast of Arctic Ocean in Spitzbergen, Novaya Zemlia and Siberia and winters in northern Europe and Asia; rare in British Isles and Iceland; casual in France and Italy.

DISTRIBUTION IN NEW ENGLAND. — Generally a rare winter visitor, mainly coastwise; a summer inland record from Maine — immature male and three females, June 13, 1918, Duck Lake, Penobscot County;[1] sometimes not uncommon locally in winter in Maine and not always very rare in migration on coasts of Bristol County (formerly at least) and of Rhode Island and Connecticut; a record from Vermont (Ferrisburg, Lake Champlain, two females seen and one shot November 29, 1904, by George L.

---

[1] Kennard, Frederic H.: Auk, Vol. XL, 1923, p. 120.

Kirk); probably occurs rarely on Lake Champlain; four specimens seen and three of them taken in lakes of eastern Massachusetts.[1]

SEASON IN MASSACHUSETTS. — October 21 to April 12.

HAUNTS AND HABITS. The King Eider, the handsomest of the eider ducks, is not so rare in Massachusetts as it has been reported. It has (or formerly had) a local stopping place off the coast of Bristol County where the gunners of Dartmouth and Westport who know the American Eider by the name of "Wamp" commonly refer to the King Eider as the "Wamp's Cousin." The bird is well known to them, whereas most of the gunners on the south side of Marthas Vineyard and on Nantucket and Muskeget would hardly recognize it. Probably this species in migration crosses Cape Cod at the head of Buzzards Bay and makes the south coast of Bristol County a stopping place on the way to the east end of Long Island where some numbers spend the winter. Possibly a few may remain through the entire winter off our coast at that point, but generally elsewhere they are considered very rare and there are but few records of specimens actually taken. This may be because they dive in rather deeper water than the other eiders and so keep farther off shore. Eaton says that this bird is able to procure its food in water more than 150 feet in depth and is occasionally caught in the deep water gill-nets of lake fishermen.[2] This may be a possibility in fresh water but perhaps not in salt water, where, however, it goes to considerable depths. Mr. W. Sprague Brooks who observed this species in Alaska gives the following account of its courtship: "On June 14 when approaching a small lagoon but still unable to see it owing to a slight elevation of the tundra before me, I heard a strange sound on the other side of the elevation. This peculiar noise came in series of three 'Urrr-URRR-*URRR*,' the last being the loudest, a sort of drumming call as when one expels air forcibly through the mouth with the tongue lightly pressed against the palate. I heard this noise once before during the winter made by an Eskimo and used with indifferent results for encouraging his dog team. I thought this call was an invention of his own at the time, but when in sight of the lagoon I found that the disturbance came from a small flock of King Eiders, three females and five males. They were on the beach and three males were squatted in a triangle about a female, each about a yard from her. They did much neck-stretching as many male ducks do in the spring, and frequently bowed the head forward. The males constantly uttered the above drumming note. During this time the female was very indifferent to the attentions of her suitors doing nothing more than occasionally extending her head towards one of them. After a brief period of these tactics, one or more of the males would enter the water and bathe vigorously with much bowing of heads and stretching of necks, to return to the beach in a few moments and repeat the foregoing performance." [3]

The King Eider winters about as far north as open water can be found and moves southward when driven by the ice, not usually arriving until November in Massachusetts.

[1] Bent, A. C.: Auk, Vol. XIX, 1902, p. 196. Brewster, William: Birds of the Cambridge Region, 1906, p. 122.
[2] Eaton, E. H.: Birds of New York, 1910, p. 220.
[3] Bulletin of the Museum of Comparative Zoölogy, Vol. LIX, 1915, p. 396.

In spring the vanguard of migration has been known to reach Greenland early in February, and only stragglers or cripples remain in early April off the Massachusetts coast.

The food of this species consists largely of mussels and other mollusks, crabs, sand fleas and other marine or fresh-water animals. Mr. Arthur H. Norton found by dissection that the favorite food of some King Eiders killed in Maine was young *Holothurians* (*Pentacta frondosa*).[1]

ECONOMIC STATUS. The King Eider because of the nature of its food is not highly valued by the epicure. It is so rare as to be of little account in New England, but its down is valuable and it has furnished a part of the eider-down of commerce.

Oidémia americána SWAINSON. Scoter.

Other names: AMERICAN SCOTER; COOT; BLACK COOT; BLACK BUTTERBILL; BLACK COOT BUTTERBILL; BUTTERNOSE; COPPERBILL; COPPER-NOSE; YELLOW-NOSE; YELLOW-BILL; PUNKIN-BLOSSOM-COOT; WHISTLING COOT; (for female and immature), LITTLE GRAY COOT; SMUTTY COOT; SMUTTY.

Plate 18.

DESCRIPTION. — Nail of bill narrowed toward end, more distinctly convex, and a little more decidedly hooked at tip than in our other scoters; feathering of head advanced nearly as far on sides as on forehead, which is not feathered to near nostrils, as in our other scoters; tail normally of 14 feathers. *Adult male in winter and nuptial plumage:* Generally black above; less glossy and a trifle lighter below; inner webs of flight feathers grayish; bill black, except a little more than basal half of upper mandible which is greatly swollen and variable in color, but in spring usually orange or nearing vermilion on sides, changing to yellow above and in front; iris brown; feet brownish-black; webs black. *Adult male in summer plumage:* Some Scoters seem to have a partial molt in summer and all (both sexes) shed quills of wings and tail in late summer and fall; during late summer and fall parts of head and body become duller in color and bird becomes lighter and browner below, but some of this change must be due to fading and wear; this has been called a partial eclipse plumage, but habits of male scoters are such that no real eclipse plumage is necessary; Dr. Jonathan Dwight has not found any real eclipse plumage in scoters. *Adult female in winter and nuptial plumage:* Top of head down to and around eye dark brown, rest of head, including chin, throat and upper fore neck grayish or light grayish, more or less indistinctly mottled brownish; rest of plumage generally sooty-grayish-brown, somewhat lighter on under surface from breast to near vent, often with paler tips on upper plumage, sides and flanks; bill, without basal bulge so conspicuous in male, black or blackish, sometimes streaked yellow; iris and feet as in male. *Young in first winter plumage: Male:* Gradually becomes black above and on breast, sides and flanks, but retains many brown feathers in upper plumage and whitish juvenal tint below; bill begins to show shape and color somewhat like that of adult before end of first winter. *Female:* Becomes more like adult female but abdomen, chin and throat generally lighter. *Young in juvenal plumage:* Similar to adult female; dark brown above with dark cap, but *much lighter below;* chin, throat, sides of head, and front and sides of neck chiefly brownish-white; lower fore neck and upper breast, sides and flanks approaching dark grayish-brown like upper plumage; elsewhere below whitish, with faint dark brownish spots or bars, mostly beneath surface, some exposed. *Downy young:* Above dark sooty-brown, with extension of same across fore neck; throat whitish; rest of under plumage grayish-brown.

MEASUREMENTS. — Length 17.00 to 21.50 in.; spread 30.00 to 35.00; folded wing 8.00 to 10.00; tail 3.00 to 4.30; bill 1.45 to 1.89; tarsus 1.64 to 2.00. Female smaller than male.

----

[1] Auk, Vol. XVII, 1900, p. 18.

MOLTS. — Juvenal dress is not always molted in September, but "may be worn for several months before the partial postjuvenal molt sets in" (Jonathan Dwight); dates of molting in scoters vary so that individual birds may be in molt in every month of year; Dr. Dwight, who is considered the chief American authority on molts of birds, says that he is convinced that young "males that are well advanced by January undergo a prenuptial molt in April or May"; but it is difficult to tell whether individuals taken then are in their postjuvenal or prenuptial molt; lack of summer specimens leaves the question of summer molt doubtful, but in September immature birds also exhibit the emarginate 1st primary, which shows that they have passed through a complete postnuptial molt, as young birds of the first year do not have this primary thus cut away; in the resulting plumage young male becomes black, and bill assumes color similar to that of adult male, but bird is somewhat lighter below; both male and female are now practically adult, but may show some signs of immaturity; molt in early spring precedes second nuptial plumage in which some male birds apparently are lighter below than some adults, which may be a sign of immaturity; adults have partial prenuptial molt in early spring and complete postnuptial molt (August and September).

FIELD MARKS. — *Male:* Unlike our other scoters, *black with no white marks;* close at hand with a good glass orange or yellow base of bill may be seen. *Female and young:* Can be distinguished from other scoters *only at close range* by light color of side head below black cap and absence of two whitish patches, one before eye and other behind it, which usually show at close range on head of female and young White-winged and Surf Scoters.

VOICE. — "A musical whistle of one prolonged note" (George H. Mackay); "their plaintive 'cour-loo' is the most musical of duck-cries, very different from the croaking notes of most diving ducks" (Allan Brooks).

BREEDING. — About marshes of salt- and fresh-water ponds. *Nest:* Sometimes hidden away in hollows of cliffs or banks, usually in grass well concealed, lined with grass, leaves, down (dark and white mixed) and feathers, and usually covered with down, grass and moss when female leaves it. *Eggs:* 6 to 10; 2.25 to 2.68 by 1.60 to 1.81 in.; averaging about 2.53 by 1.70; ovate to elliptical-ovate; pale ivory-yellow. *Dates:* Early June to July, Alaska. *Incubation:* Period unknown, probably about 28 to 30 days, like that of *Oidemia nigra,* the similar Old World species; by female. One brood yearly.

RANGE. — Northern North America and northeastern Asia. Breeds in northeastern Asia and from Kotzebue Sound to Aleutian Islands, including Near Islands, in northern Alaska, northern Mackenzie, on west coast of Hudson Bay, in Ungava (northern Quebec), Labrador and Newfoundland south to the interior of Canada and shore of Gulf of St. Lawrence; winters on Asiatic coast to Japan and from islands of Bering Sea south rarely to southern California; in interior not rare on Great Lakes but rare inland in contiguous states; on Atlantic coast common to abundant from Newfoundland and Maine south to New Jersey; rare in South Atlantic States; accidental or casual in Florida, Missouri, Louisiana, Nebraska, Colorado and Wyoming.

DISTRIBUTION IN NEW ENGLAND. — Common migrant and winter resident coastwise, but least common in Connecticut waters; a few non-breeding birds summer off coasts of Maine, New Hampshire and Massachusetts; less common on inland waters, but small flocks occasionally occur in rivers and lakes, particularly near coast, and in larger waters (Lake Champlain and Merrimac and Connecticut rivers).

SEASON IN MASSACHUSETTS. — August 28 to May 24 (summer).

HAUNTS AND HABITS. Instead of being known as a coot, the American Scoter should be called the "Black Duck," for the male is the only American duck with entirely black plumage. On the New England coast it is the least abundant of the three scoters, but is common enough to be observed by all who seek the sea ducks. Like all scoters it is tough, hardy, a quick and excellent diver, hard to kill and difficult to secure when wounded. It can swim a long distance under water and uses both wings and feet at

PLATE 18

PLATE 18

WHITE-WINGED SCOTER
Page 274
Winter (Nuptial) Plumage
Adult Male

Adult Female

SCOTER
Page 271
Winter (Nuptial) Plumage
Adult Female

Adult Male

SURF SCOTER
Page 277
Winter (Nuptial) Plumage   Adult Male

Adult Female

RUDDY DUCK
Page 280
Adult Female

Adult Male in
Winter Plumage

Adult Male in Nuptial
Plumage

All one-sixth natural size.

Louis Agassiz Fuertes.

need for under-water progression. Elliot says that it will commit suicide by drowning rather than permit itself to be captured.[1] Mr. George H. Mackay makes a similar statement regarding all three scoters and relates an instance where in clear water he saw a wounded one clinging with its bill to rockweed on the bottom, from which he dislodged it with an oar.[2] In such cases, however, there seems to have been no absolute certainty that the birds died from drowning. Gunshot wounds may have been the cause of death; so it is questionable whether they actually commit suicide.

As there are always some scoters in summer off the coasts of Maine and Nova Scotia, this species or either of the other two may be driven in on the Massachusetts coast at that season by a severe easterly gale; otherwise a very few non-breeding or crippled birds are seen here in summer, but the species is most abundant in fall and spring. Occasionally by the first of September a few small flocks pass along our coast, but usually no important movement occurs until the latter half of the month. Mr. Laurence B. Fletcher tells me that at this season at Cohasset, they are usually seen flying along shore on days of light easterly winds. Such days appear to be favorable for their migrations. Strong westerly winds drive them offshore and strong easterly gales are likely to drive them into harbors and estuaries; on windy days they fly low in a long line, often headed by an old male. In calm weather they frequently fly quite high and not very far outside the beach. Cape Ann, Cohasset, Manomet (Plymouth) and Centreville on Cape Cod are excellent places to observe this flight. In October they continue to pass and are common, but in winter much less so. The greater part of the spring flight northward along our coasts takes place in April and early May. By the latter part of May many scoters arrive on their breeding-grounds in the far North.

All the scoters feed very largely on mussels which they can bring up from a depth of about 40 feet in salt water. The principal food of the Scoter seems to be mussels but other bivalves, such as small sea-clams, short razor-shells and small scallops, are taken in considerable quantity. In inland ponds or lakes which they sometimes frequent they take fresh-water clams.

ECONOMIC STATUS. All authorities agree that the three species of scoters are unpalatable and unfit for the table. Nevertheless, if properly prepared they are eatable, though not equal to the celery-fed Canvas-back. If the entrails are drawn at once when the bird is shot, most of the offensive fishy taste is removed. The longer they remain in the bird the sadder the result. Properly prepared and stuffed with onions a young scoter is no mean dish. This and the other two species of scoters are killed and eaten by people living along the coast, where the women know well how to prepare them for the table. All the species thus have considerable economic importance because of their abundance. The destruction of small, unmarketable, edible shellfish by scoters may at times be a detriment to the fisheries, but usually this probably results merely in a necessary thinning.

---

[1] Elliot, D. G.: The Wild Fowl of North America, 1898, pp. 207–208.   [2] Auk, Vol. VIII, 1891, pp. 282–283.

Oidemia deglándi deglandi Bonaparte. White-winged Scoter.

Other names: BLACK WHITE-WING; BULL WHITE-WING; MAY WHITE-WING; EASTERN WHITE-WING; GRAY WHITE-WING; PIED-WINGED COOT; SEA BRANT; WHITE-EYED COOT; HALF-MOON-EYE.

Plate 18.

DESCRIPTION. — Frontal feathers encroach on bill nearly or quite to nostrils, and in most cases reach farther forward than loral feathering; tail normally of 14 feathers. *Adult male in winter and nuptial plumage:* Black, slightly brownish on sides, flanks and belly; a crescentic spot running backward from below eye, and conspicuous wing-patch (secondaries and ends of greater coverts) white; wing linings dark brown anteriorly, passing into brownish-gray and whitish behind; prominent knob at base of upper mandible and edges of both mandibles black; sides of upper mandible pinkish-purple or wine-purple turning to orange next to basal black, nail reddish-orange, ridge from nail to knob white; lower mandible reddish-orange at end, white from this to base, more or less of which is black; iris white; outer sides of legs and feet light wine-purple or purplish-pink, inner sides coral-red or orange-vermilion; joints and webs blackish. *Adult female in winter and nuptial plumage:* Head brownish-black more or less inconspicuously marked or flecked with whitish on sides; adult females are quite sooty above and in fresh plumage are devoid of white about head, but as feather-tips wear away, exposing white basal portions of feathers, more or less distinct white patches appear on sides of head, especially at site of posterior juvenal spot (Jonathan Dwight); plumage lighter or grayish-brown below; feathers on lower throat, front of neck, scapular region and sides more or less tipped grayish; wing-patch pure white as in male but smaller; linings of wings mixed brown, gray and white; bill blackish, more or less mixed with whitish on upper mandible, sometimes with patch of deep rose-pink on either side and striped on nail with brownish-yellow; "iris deep brown; feet, outer side vinaceous, inner side vinaceous-rufous" (G. Trumbull). *Young in first winter plumage:* Similar to juvenal plumage, but head of male usually darker, light patches more or less obscured by dark feathers; more or less of brown body plumage replaced by black and a dark brown band beginning to develop on sides and flanks; color of bill beginning to approximate that of adult, but no white crescent behind eye; in late winter or spring young male has blackish head and neck and light gray under plumage. *Young in juvenal plumage:* Somewhat variable; similar to adult female but breast and other under plumage usually lighter, sometimes whitish, and obscurely mottled; as this plumage wears, young birds become more or less whitish on under body and locally on side of head which commonly shows two whitish patches, one near base of bill, the other on cheek. *Downy young:* Dusky-brown above, dull white below, whitish under eye and white patch on wing.

MEASUREMENTS. — Length 19.50 to 23.00 in.; spread 33.50 to 41.50; folded wing 10.40 to 12.12; tail about 3.50; bill 1.35 to 1.70; tarsus 1.78 to 2.08. Weight male 3 lbs. 8 oz. to 4 lbs. 9 oz.; female 2 lbs. 12 oz. to 3 lbs. 7 oz. (Trumbull).

MOLTS. — Juvenal plumage is acquired by a complete post-natal molt, usually in summer; but some birds seem to remain in this throughout winter or most of it; in others partial molt into partial first winter plumage comes early; others molt body-feathers early in winter and the male soon gets some black plumage; in spring bird appears in its first nuptial plumage; in July there may be a partial molt followed by a so-called partial eclipse plumage, in which some feathers of head and neck are renewed and plumage generally becomes lighter and duller, followed by molt of wings and tail in August; this is succeeded by second winter plumage in which young male becomes blacker and much like adult, having white eye-patch, white wing-patch and eye changing from brown through yellow to white; young female now becomes as adult; second nuptial plumage, assumed in next spring, is colored like second winter plumage and is acquired by a partial prenuptial molt completed in late May or June; males browner below than the darkest are supposed to be in this plumage and to become as adult in third winter plumage; an immature male with a knob on its bill probably is at least about a year and a half old, and those with largest knobs two years or more; adults have practically same molts as immature birds.

FIELD MARKS. — Larger than Mallard; approaching Brant; stocky, robust and thick-necked black or sooty birds with large white wing-patch placed well back; no other New England scoter has this; sometimes it is covered by flank-feathers and so cannot be seen when bird is on water but is very conspicuous when bird rises and flies; Black Guillemot (only other black water-bird with white on wing) is very much smaller with white wing-patch farther forward; at close range small white eye-patch of male can be seen with a good glass.

VOICE. — Said to utter a low quack (G. H. Mackay) but I have never heard it utter a vocal sound.

BREEDING. — Near small lake or stream, often on tundra. *Nest:* On ground under bushes or other concealing vegetation; a depression lined with twigs, rubbish, feathers and down. *Eggs:* 6 to 14; 2.60 to 2.86 by 1.69 to 1.85 in.; ovate; pale salmon-buff or flesh color, varying to cream. *Dates:* Latter half of June, North Dakota to Mackenzie. *Incubation:* By female. One brood yearly.

RANGE. — North America and eastern Asia. Breeds from coast of northeastern Siberia, northern Alaska, northern Mackenzie, northern Ungava (northern Quebec) and Labrador (Newfoundland rarely) south to northeastern Washington, Alberta, Saskatchewan, central North Dakota and southern Quebec; winters on Asiatic coast to Bering Island, Japan and China, and in North America from Aleutian and Pribilof Islands south to Lower California, Great Lakes and their contiguous states (casually to Colorado, Nebraska and Louisiana), and on Atlantic coast from Gulf of St. Lawrence south to South Carolina (rarely Florida); non-breeding birds occur in summer south to Southern California, Long Island and (casually) Florida. (The western subspecies *dixoni* occurs in winter about the Pribilof Islands. Its status is doubtful.)

DISTRIBUTION IN NEW ENGLAND. — A common to abundant migrant and winter resident coastwise in maritime states; a few non-breeding birds summer offshore; in Vermont a rare migrant usually, but not uncommon locally at times on Lakes Champlain and Bomoseen and Connecticut River.

SEASON IN MASSACHUSETTS. — August 10 to May 25 (a few in June and July).

HAUNTS AND HABITS. In the Auk for 1891 (pp. 279–290) Mr. George H. Mackay in an excellent account of the scoters on the New England coast expressed the opinion that the Surf Scoter was then the most numerous of the three species. Today the White-winged Scoter seems to be most abundant. For this change in relative numbers no single definite reason can be given. As our birds winter on the Atlantic coast and breed in the far North or in the Interior, making long journeys over land and sea, we cannot know all the circumstances and conditions which govern their increase and decrease. Shooting the birds in fall, winter and spring, and the destruction of their nests and eggs by man have had some effect in reducing numbers and these causes may have worked unevenly with the different species. On the New England coast it has been the custom of gunners to mark some of the most favorable points at which to intercept these birds on their migrations, and to anchor their boats in line, at suitable distances from one another, in such a way that the flight, keeping steadily on, must pass by or over some of the boats. In this way great numbers of birds were killed formerly on the New England coast, and many are thus taken still. In early years the species was one of the least shy and suspicious of the water-fowl. It seemed to be so stupid as to be attracted by almost any kind of a black wooden block or anything resembling a duck, and seemed to consider itself safe in the company of the most grotesque and clumsy and unnatural of wooden decoys. It flew low down, passing close by the gunner's boat, and about all the gunner had to do was to "lead" the bird enough with the muzzle of the gun to be sure to put the charge into its head or neck, for the White-wing is swift on the wing. In recent years, however, the coots have been "hammered" so much along our coasts that they have learned a little caution. They fly higher over the boats, and judge better the distance called gun-shot range. This species, however, is as unsuspicious as any. Sometimes when a flock flies between the gunner's boat and the shore a high-pitched yell from the boat will cause the flock to turn away from the shore toward the boat — a stratagem that is not likely to have a similar effect with the American Scoter. A flock flying over a boat too high to be within range is sometimes brought down near the water by a shout or a gun-shot. The shaking of a gun-case or the throwing up of a hat may have a similar effect. I have often been asked the reason of this, but refuse to hazard guesses in regard to the psychology of the coot. The explanation seems simple but may not be so.

Writing of a tame bird of this species in the Journal of the Maine Ornithological Society, Vol. VIII, 1906, pp. 69, 71, Mr. Walter H. Rich says: "No fresh-water duck that I have ever seen in action could compare with him for speed or quickness in the water, but ashore he was the clumsiest of waddlers."

In autumnal migration the White-wings begin usually to pass Cape Ann a little later than the first of the American Scoters, but soon after the middle of September the flight is likely to be moving in force and reaches its height in October. Multitudes of this species spend the winter on the shoals and in the sounds off Nantucket, Muskeget and Marthas Vineyard. In April large flights pass northward and eastward, their move-ments, as always, being intermittent, and depending on conditions of wind and weather. Southwest winds seem to be favorable, but not absolutely necessary for these flights. In some years the birds dribble along steadily in small numbers; in other years great flights pass on a few favorable days. A part of the spring flight crosses Cape Cod and goes up the South Shore of Massachusetts; another part goes around outside of Cape Cod. Later in May there is a great flight to the west and northwest. Mr. George H. Mackay describes this well.[1] The flight consists mainly if not entirely of mated adult birds ready for breeding, among which are a few of the other scoters. It passes west-ward late in the afternoon and at evening along Long Island Sound, sometimes in part by Woods Hole, and over the coast of Dartmouth, Westport and the contiguous shores of Rhode Island. The flight is erratic, changing more or less in location and direction from time to time and from year to year, but all tend generally to keep the same ap-proximate course. On the Connecticut coast it turns overland toward the Connecticut and Hudson valleys, crossing the land mainly at night and probably passing to the Great Lakes and from there to the inland breeding-grounds of the great Northwest, perhaps going on even to the shores of the Arctic. Formerly many rested for a time on the Hud-son River. Now, according to Griscom, they are rare on the lower Hudson except near Ossining.[2] Possibly most of them fly from Long Island Sound to Lake Erie. Mr. J. H. Quincy in personal letter reports how the flight of 1923 passed Marthas Vineyard. May 20th he wrote: "This flight, while pursuing a general westerly course from Nantucket

[1] Auk, Vol. VIII, 1891, pp. 285–286.   [2] Griscom, Ludlow: Birds of the New York City Region, 1923, p. 115.

Shoals, varies from year to year in its route according to weather conditions or the vagaries of the birds.''

The food of this Scoter is similar to that of the American Scoter and includes small percentages of quahogs, amphipods, sea-urchins and other small forms of animal life. Dr. T. S. Palmer writes to me that Mr. W. L. McAtee finds that the common mussel (*Mytilus edulis*) comprises 72.9 per cent. of the food of Massachusetts scoters examined by him.

ECONOMIC STATUS. The economic importance of this species is greater than that of the American Scoter because of its much greater numbers.

Oidemia perspicilláta (LINNÆUS). Surf Scoter.

Other names: SKUNK-HEAD; SKUNK-TOP; SKUNK-BILL; BALD-HEADED COOT; BUTTER-BOAT-BILL; GOGGLENOSE; HORSE-HEAD; KING COOT; MUSSEL-BILL; PATCH-HEAD; SURF DUCK; SURF COOT; SURFER; PATCH-POLLED COOT; PISHAUG; PLASTER-BILL; BLACK DUCK.

Plate 18.

DESCRIPTION. — In both sexes frontal feathers encroach on ridge of bill, in male extending in a long, narrow point about halfway to tip of bill and nearly or quite to nostrils; no encroachment of feathers on sides of bill; tail normally of 14 feathers. *Adult male in winter and nuptial plumage:* Small triangular or heart-shaped patch on forehead and long triangular patch extending from back of head down nape, narrowing to a point at lower end, white; patch on nape sometimes absent; rest of plumage of neck black with more or less reddish-violet reflections; rest of plumage black or brownish-black, usually lighter or slightly mottled lighter below; iris white; base of upper mandible much expanded and ridge elevated to beyond nostrils; elevated part of upper mandible carmine-red or dull crimson shading into rich yellow-ish-orange or light scarlet from nostrils to tip, which is somewhat paler, sides of mandible from nail to below nostrils orange, from this point to base chiefly lustrous pearly white, basal half mainly occupied by large squarish black spot bounded above by orange or orange-yellow, behind by carmine-red or crimson and elsewhere by white; under mandible white from base to near end where it is orange or flesh color, nail yellow or mixture of white and orange; legs and feet outside mainly deep red or crimson, inner sides of legs and toes yellowish-orange deepening in part to orange-vermilion and blotched some-what with black; webs black. *Adult female in winter and nuptial plumage:* Forehead and top of head down to eye blackish; two irregular white patches on sides of head below level of eye, one on ear region, other near base of bill (some specimens have white patch on nape like male); rest of upper plumage chiefly dusky or sooty-brown; some black tips to feathers of rump and upper tail-coverts; abdomen silvery-gray or dusky, mottled; bill greenish-black, black spot on lateral base sometimes slightly indi-cated; iris brown; legs and feet "yellow orange"; webs dusky. *Young in first winter and first nuptial plumage: Male:* During first winter, protuberance and lateral bulge of basal half of bill begin to develop; more or less black in upper plumage, sides and flanks; head, neck and upper breast largely black; nape with white triangular patch; under plumage from breast to tail largely as juvenal, pale grayish, somewhat resembling male Scaup when seen from below. *Female:* More or less upper plumage as in adult female; under plumage much as juvenal. *Young in juvenal plumage:* nasal protuberance and lateral bulge in bill not yet developed; like adult female but never a white patch on nape; two white patches on side of head variable, sometimes merging, often ill-defined; young lighter in tone both above and below than adult female, browner above, approaching white on middle of lower surface; tail-feathers rather square at tip, shaft projecting; legs and feet dull orange and blackish; iris brown.* *Downy young:*

* "Iris is brown in young males, becoming yellow and finally white when the bird is about a year old" (Dwight).

Top of head and back of neck dark sooty-brown extending down on side of head below eye; rest of upper plumage sooty-brown lightening on sides and flanks; below pale gray or whitish, somewhat mottled with sooty-brown.

MEASUREMENTS. — Length 18.00 to 22.00 in.; spread 30.00 to 36.00; folded wing 9.00 to 10.00; tail 2.49 to 3.51; bill along gape 2.25 to 2.50, along ridge 1.30 to 1.63; tarsus 1.61 to 1.81. Weight 2 lbs. to 2 lbs. 6 oz. Female smaller than male.

MOLTS. — After juvenal plumage, acquired in late summer, there is a partial molt varying in time from September to winter; a few black feathers near mouth and bill may show in October; in some birds, perhaps many, there is a partial prenuptial molt, after which first nuptial plumage is assumed, and a late complete postnuptial molt (some individuals in early September still retain juvenal wings and tail which are eventually molted) when second winter plumage is assumed; in this plumage young birds are practically indistinguishable from adults; in spring (March, April and May) adult has a partial prenuptial molt confined chiefly to head and sides (Jonathan Dwight); in August and September it has a complete postnuptial molt during which, as usual, wings and tail are shed; Dr. Dwight believes that scoters have no eclipse plumage, while several European authorities have described a slight partial eclipse of some species; more summer specimens than are now in American museums are needed to settle this question.

FIELD MARKS. — Size nearly that of White-winged Scoter; male readily distinguished by white markings on forehead and nape ("In some changing or molting plumages this latter [hind crown white patch] is lost wholly or in part"), black plumage and absence of white speculum; female may be told from female White-wing by lack of white in wing (if seen in flight) and often by white patch on nape (not always present) but may be confused with female American Scoter; female and young Surf Scoters usually may be separated from those of American Scoter by two white patches on side of head; female and young American Scoters have rather uniform light side head; at a distance the two are indistinguishable; young males in spring are very pale gray or whitish beneath, in contrast to black upper breast, neck and head, and so resemble scaups when seen in flight from below, but *sides and flanks are dark, not white* or light as in scaups.

VOICE. — A low guttural croak like clucking of a hen (G. H. Mackay); in mating season a clear whistle (E. W. Nelson); in courtship males utter "a curious low, liquid note, like water dropping in a cavern" (Allan Brooks, Auk, Vol. XXXVII, 1920, p. 367).

BREEDING. — On ground near water, often on islands. *Nest:* Under bush on grassy tussock in marsh. *Eggs:* Usually 5 to 7, rarely 9; 2.25 to 2.50 by 1.60 to 1.75 in. (Coues); pale buff to creamy. *Dates:* June and July. *Incubation:* Period unknown; by female. One brood yearly.

RANGE. — North America and northeastern Siberia. Breeds in extreme northeast Siberia (Palmén) and in North America on Pacific coast from Kotzebue Sound south to Sitka, on Yukon River, and from northwestern Mackenzie and Hudson Strait south to northern Alberta, northern Saskatchewan, northern Manitoba, James Bay, southern Labrador and Newfoundland; non-breeding birds occur in summer in northeastern Siberia, south on Pacific coast to Lower California in Greenland (where it may breed), and south on Atlantic coast to Long Island; winters on Pacific coast from Aleutian Islands to San Quentin Bay, Lower California, and on Atlantic coast from Nova Scotia to Florida; common in migration and in winter on Great Lakes; occurs in interior in southern British Columbia, Montana, Wyoming, Colorado, Nebraska, Kansas, Missouri, Illinois, Iowa and Louisiana; has occurred occasionally in British Isles, Faroes, Lapland, Finland, Scandinavia, Belgium and France; casual in Bermudas.

DISTRIBUTION IN NEW ENGLAND. — Common to abundant coastwise in migration, less so generally in winter; usually rare in interior waters, but occasionally in flocks; a few non-breeding birds or cripples summer off coast.

SEASON IN MASSACHUSETTS. — (August 15); September 4 to June 4 (summer).

HAUNTS AND HABITS. The name of the Surf Scoter is descriptive. In New England it is mainly a bird of the sea-coast. It feeds much along the shore outside the breakers and often "scoots" through a great wave as its crest breaks into foam, bobbing up like a cork on its farther side or, avoiding the breaking wave in another way, dives to the bottom to feed. It is not so common as the White-winged Scoter on the shoals at long distances from the shore and is usually rare in our interior waters, though sometimes driven to them by stress of weather, during migration. It has all the swimming and diving powers of the other scoters and uses both wings and feet for progression under water as occasion requires. Mr. Frank M. Woodruff of the Chicago Academy of Sciences writes that he has collected eiders and scoters on both Atlantic and Pacific coasts and that in "sailing down" the birds he has frequently stood by the mast where he could watch the progress of one of them under water. As the water was very clear he could observe its motions, the action being "as clear and plain as if the bird were out of water." The wings were held about one-third spread and perfectly rigid. Used as planes or rudders they held the bird under water and on its course while the feet drove it onward. Both feet were used at once with powerful strokes, and he says: "I could plainly see the body rise slightly as the forward stroke was taken." Others assert that they have seen wounded scoters use their wings directly for propulsion under water. Mr. George H. Mackay asserts that in his experience wounded scoters when pursued and diving always use the wings as well as the feet.

Probably in the fall migration, which usually begins toward the middle of September and is at its height before the middle of October, continuing into November, most of the Surf Scoters pass outside Cape Cod. Nevertheless, many fly along the Plymouth coast and across the arm of the Cape at different points. The adults are the first to arrive; the young usually are much later. Late in March or early in April the return migration begins to pass our shores. This species and the American Scoter are likely to be on their way north before the White-wings begin to move, but after the middle of May there is a large movement of Surf Scoters. Part of these pass outside Cape Cod, but a large number, together with some American Scoters, swing into Buzzards Bay and fly toward its head and cross to Massachusetts Bay near the Cape Cod Canal.

This species and the White-winged Scoter are affected with parasitic (intestinal) diseases and many die from this cause.[1]

The food of the Surf Scoter is similar to that of the other scoters.

ECONOMIC STATUS. This scoter is quite as important economically as the White-wing, as it is perhaps equally abundant over its entire range and in migration extends rather farther south, thus covering more inhabited country. As sportsmen usually do not consider it fit to eat, it may be well to say here that, in my experiences, the younger birds have been found quite palatable, if skinned and dressed at once. If allowed to hang long with the viscera unremoved, they become vile. I recall a case where a lady cooked such a bird, thereby driving everybody out of the house. She had to throw away both bird and kettle.

---

[1] Brooks, Allan: Auk, Vol. XXXVII, 1920, p. 367.

Erismatúra jamaicénsis (Gmelin). Ruddy Duck.

Other names: BUTTER-BALL; BLACK-JACK; BLUE-BILL; BROAD-BILL; DAUB DUCK; DIPPER; DAPPER; DOPPER; BROAD-BILL DIPPER; CREEK COOT; POND COOT; DUMB BIRD; GOOSE WIDGEON; STIFF-TAILED WIDGEON; WIDGEON COOT; HARD-HEAD; TOUGH-HEAD; STEEL-HEAD; SLEEPY-HEAD; HARD-HEADED BROAD-BILL; BOOBY; MURRE; PINTAIL; SPOON-BILL; GRAY TEAL; BUMBLE-BEE COOT; SALT-WATER TEAL; SHOT POUCH; SPIKE-TAIL.

Plate 18.

DESCRIPTION. — Bill broad, deep at base, its ridge concave and running high on forehead, nail small, narrow, drooping and slightly turned under end of bill; neck thick and short; legs placed far back, feet uncommonly large; tail normally 18 feathers, exposed to base by shortness of tail-coverts; tail-feathers stiffened, narrow, pointed, shafts enlarged and channeled beneath, somewhat resembling tail of a cormorant. *Adult male in nuptial plumage:* Top and sides of head to just below eye glossy black; chin, and patch joining it on either side extending down from black cap to throat over chin, and back from base of bill below eye past ear-region white; neck, sides of breast, entire upper surface of body, except wings and rump, rich reddish-chestnut; outer surface of wing dark brown, secondaries sometimes tipped whitish, coverts sometimes finely sprinkled with grayish or light brown; rump dusky-brown; tail blackish-brown; sides and flanks rich chestnut; linings of wings and axillars variegated with white and grayish-brown; breast sometimes tinged pale rusty-brown; under tail-coverts white; under plumage otherwise silvery-white, more or less waved dusky-gray; bill and eyelids slaty-blue; iris reddish-brown or hazel; feet bluish-gray, webs dusky. *Adult male in autumn and winter plumage:* Cap to below eye blackish-brown; nape and back of neck blackish-brown, finely sprinkled ashy-brown; sides of head white as in nuptial plumage; elsewhere above dark brown, finely sprinkled ashy-gray; tail, wings and lower surface of body as in nuptial plumage except throat and broad collar on neck which are ashy-brown; wings and tail may become pale by wear; bill and feet darker than in nuptial plumage. *Adult female:* Similar to adult male in winter, but cap narrowly barred reddish-brown, sides of head grayish-white, with mottled dark stripe running across cheek from corner of mouth to below ear, paralleling lower margin of cap; upper surface of body similar to that of winter adult male and marked with ashy or buffy-brown; fore neck grayish-brown; breast indistinctly barred blackish and yellow-brown; below mainly silvery-ash, sometimes barred brownish; under tail-coverts whitish; bill dusky or duller than in male. *Young in juvenal plumage:* Similar to adult female, but cheeks and throat dull white, more or less mottled with dusky, feathers of crown tipped "brownish-buff" and breast feathers broadly tipped buff. *Downy young:* Upper down with "long hairlike filaments"; fore neck, upper breast, sides and flanks blackish-brown, darkening on top of head and lightening on fore neck; stripe from bill below eye to ear, lower cheeks, chin and throat, breast, belly and patch on each side of rump, whitish; indistinct band of drab on lower neck.

MEASUREMENTS. — Length 13.50 to 17.00 in.; spread 20.00 to 24.00; folded wing 5.50 to 6.10; tail 2.49 to 2.75; bill 1.44 to 1.72; tarsus 1.17 to 1.50. Weight, male 1 lb. 8 oz. to 1 lb. 12 oz. Female smaller than male.

MOLTS. — Apparently juvenal plumage is retained through first winter, with little change except that produced by wear and fading; prenuptial molt in spring apparently is followed by adult plumage excepting wings which are not molted; probably the young becomes indistinguishable from adult after the complete postnuptial molt when it goes into winter plumage; adults have a prenuptial molt (March to May) including body plumage and tail; and a complete postnuptial molt (July to October) which is succeeded by winter plumage. Apparently this species has no eclipse plumage.

FIELD MARKS. — Small size like teal; squatty, dumpy, blocky appearance; large thick neck; no white or other contrasting color on wing; large upturned blue bill; sides of head white or whitish; tail sometimes spread and erected; has habit of sinking down without diving but dives at need; male in bright red spring plumage (not often seen in Massachusetts) with white cheeks and black cap is unmistakable; females and young have dark cap to below eye like American Scoter, but show a dark stripe in light cheek; in flight the short *broad-tipped* wings are beaten very rapidly.

VOICE. — "A weak *squak*" (J. H. Langille). "I observed [at Lake Majeau] three Ruddies, two drakes and a female, a short distance out in the open water. The drakes were evidently courting the female and gave their love note repeatedly. As near as I can render it, it is *chica, chica, chica, chica, quak*. It is given with a feeble utterance, especially the *chica* sounds; the final *quack* is louder. This call is very rapidly uttered by the drakes while the head is quickly jerked up and down, the bill striking the water at the end of each word sound. The only note uttered by the female was a feeble quack. Afterwards I often heard the Ruddies near my home . . . , where at least three pairs were breeding in a bed of tules. . . . At a distance of about one hundred yards, the *chica* sounds were not audible, but the final *quack* or *quowk* was quite distinct . . ." (A. D. Henderson).[1]

BREEDING. — Usually near fresh-water sloughs, marshes or marshy rivers or lakes. *Nest:* Near water, in reeds (often basket-like), or floating on water, rarely in cavity of floating log; sometimes on ground; the canopying rushes often bent over by the bird; built of dry stems of water plants, lined often profusely with "dull whitish down." *Eggs:* 5 to 15; *very large for size of bird*, about 2.50 by 1.80 in.; short to elongate-ovate; shell decidedly rough; grayish-white to buffy-white. *Dates:* April 20, California; June, Maine; late June, North Dakota; June and early July, Ontario. *Incubation:* Period probably not far from 30 days (A. C. Bent); by female. One brood yearly, possibly two in the south.

RANGE. — North America; breeds from central British Columbia, Great Slave Lake, Alberta, Saskatchewan, northern Manitoba and northern Ungava (northern Quebec), south to northern Lower California, central Arizona, northern New Mexico, south central Texas, southern Minnesota, northern Iowa, southern Wisconsin (formerly northern Missouri), southeastern Michigan, Illinois, probably Ohio, formerly southern Ontario and Maine; also in Cuba, Porto Rico, Carriacou Island (where resident), the Grenadines, etc.; and rarely and locally in southern Lower California, Valley of Mexico, Massachusetts, Rhode Island, central New York and Guatemala; winters from southern British Columbia, Arizona, New Mexico, southern Illinois, Pennsylvania, Massachusetts and probably Maine (casually) south to Lesser Antilles and Costa Rica; rare in migration to Newfoundland and Bermuda; accidental in Alaska.

DISTRIBUTION IN NEW ENGLAND. — Formerly a common migrant both coastwise and in interior; has been found breeding in Maine, Massachusetts and Rhode Island; now rather rare, irregular and apparently diminishing.

SEASON IN MASSACHUSETTS. — March 11 to May 15; summer (very rare) two young taken out of a small flock, Aug. 11, 1890, at Provincetown;[2] (September 5); September 20 to December 8; winter casually.

HAUNTS AND HABITS. The following account of the haunts and habits of this species is taken in part, though slightly altered, from my own writing in the first volume of the Birds of America, published by the University Society as a part of the Nature Lovers' Library.

"The sprightly, comical little Ruddy Duck is a distinctly North American species and is distributed widely over the continent. It is perfectly at home on or under water and dislikes to leave it, often preferring to attempt escape by diving rather than by flying. This makes it easy game for the gunner, as a flock will sometimes remain in a salt pond so small that any part of it may be reached from the shore with a shotgun, diving at every shot until those left alive essay to fly and most of them pay the penalty

---

[1] Condor, Vol. XXVI, 1924, p. 32.   [2] Miller, G. S., Jr.: Auk, Vol. VIII, 1891, p. 117.

of their simplicity with their lives. They can dive so quickly that they often escape unharmed. Like the grebes they possess the power of sinking slowly down backward out of sight, but like them also they rise from the water with some labor and difficulty. They are extremely tough, hardy little birds and gunners know them by such names as Tough-head, Hard-head, Steel-head, etc. Other local names, such as Booby, Noddy, and Fool Duck, indicate a lack of respect for the birds' perspicacity.

"When the famous Canvas-back first showed signs of scarcity on the Atlantic coast, a price was put upon the head of the Ruddy Duck to meet the market demand. Unfortunately for its safety it feeds upon delicate grasses and other vegetable aliment in preference to sea food. Therefore, its flesh is a passable substitute for that of the Canvas-back. So the market gunners have pursued it until its numbers are no longer legion and its chances for extinction are good.

"The male is a handsome bird in the breeding season but presents rather a ridiculous appearance in mating time, as he swims pompously about with his head lifted proudly and drawn away back toward the spread tail, which is raised and thrown forward as if to meet it.

"This Duck nests in prairie sloughs, where the broods remain until after all the other breeding Ducks have departed. Old and young are regular gourmands and, according to Gurdon Trumbull, gunners near the mouth of the Maumee River told of finding them floundering helplessly fat on the water and in some seasons floating about dead or dying in numbers. But this was before the days of the market demand for their flesh. They do not have so much time to get fat now." [1]

In rising from the water the Ruddy Duck flutters and splatters along the surface. In flight it looks short and dumpy and usually flies low, but its fast beating wings drive it along at only medium speed. Its diving for food is usually done in shallow water and it goes down not vertically but diagonally. It is an excellent diver, however, and its large feet and strong wings used together propel it to considerable depths.

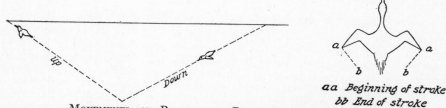

aa Beginning of stroke
bb End of stroke

MOVEMENTS AND POSITIONS OF RUDDY DUCK UNDER WATER

Mr. George F. Morse, Jr., Director of the Chicago Zoölogical Society, has sent me the following notes regarding the diving activities of a Ruddy Duck in Lake Michigan: "Last Saturday (March 17, 1923) I went out on the Municipal Pier which extends one-half mile into the lake. I was on the upper deck about sixty feet above the water.

---

[1] Birds of America, Nature Lovers' Library, Vol. I, 1917, pp. 153, 154.

A Ruddy Duck was swimming about immediately below me. The water was still. There was no one about. The duck was unaware of my presence. It kept diving to the bottom, which is about twenty-five feet deep. I could see it plainly to a depth of twelve or fifteen feet. It went down at a slant like this: [see cut]. I saw it go down and come up fourteen times. Every time in going down it used its wings under water to propel it, making eight to nine strokes until out of sight; coming up it made four to five strokes while visible. . . . While swimming under water it used its wings extended about two-thirds and made short quick strokes at the rate of one per second. The stroke started at a right angle to the body and finished at about a 40° angle. Most of the power of the stroke seemed to come at the primary joint." Mr. A. C. Bent quotes Mr. Wm. G. Smith, who says that he has seen a wounded Ruddy "dive down (in clear water), grasp a weed and remain in this position for twenty minutes."

This duck when swimming on the surface rides so low in the water as to seem partly submerged and it never has far to go to get below the surface. Being remarkably quick on land or water it "gets under" like a flash when a gun is fired at it and it often escapes with its life.

In the autumnal migration the Ruddy Duck begins to move southward in late August or early September, flying largely at night. It becomes most common in Massachusetts from the middle of October to November. It is exceedingly rare in winter, is usually most common in April on its return, and arrives in May on its northern breeding-grounds.

The Ruddy Duck feeds on a great variety of vegetal food — buds, wild celery, seeds of bur-reed, pondweeds, bulrush, etc. It also takes many insects and their larvæ. Dr. Yorke says that it eats small flies, slugs, snails, mussels, fish spawn, worms and "creeping insects." [1] Small crustaceans such as the smaller crabs are taken also.

ECONOMIC STATUS. Formerly an important and abundant bird in our markets, but nearly extirpated here within the past 40 years on account of the demand. They were shot in large numbers in the Middle States and sold as squab Canvas-backs. Now (1924) so rare as to be unimportant in New England.

Nomónyx domínicus (LINNÆUS). Masked Duck.

Figs. 10 and 11.

DESCRIPTION. — Shape much like Ruddy Duck, feet large, tail of stiff quills but nail of upper mandible *not turned under and axillars always white*. *Adult male:* Head from bill to ear-region black all round (some birds have white spot on chin); rest of head and neck dark rusty-cinnamon; upper back, scapulars and upper tail-coverts same color with conspicuous dusky or black feather centers, giving a striped effect; lower back and rump dark brown marked with black, some feathers edged white; wings brown, a long conspicuous white patch on their greater coverts; axillars white; wing linings rather deep brownish-gray with some light edges and tips; tail blackish; sides, flanks and under plumage generally rusty-cinnamon or brown, marked black, with some pale reddish-buff on breast; bill "pale blue", ridge, nail and bare skin of chin black, lower mandible whitish, tipped black; eyelids pale blue, iris dark brown; outer side of tarsus and two outer toes dark brown or black; inner side of tarsus, inner toe and webs

[1] Yorke, Henry F.: Our Ducks, 1899, p. 72.

pale brown spotted with black (Gundlach). *Adult female:* Similar, but no black mask, only top of head and two stripes on its side, one through eye and one from gape, black or blackish; rusty tone paler, sometimes dull yellowish, and *spotted* with less intense black; belly dull yellowish-white; white wing-patch smaller, wing-feathers tipped yellowish-white. *Young in juvenal plumage:* Resembles adult female; young male in first winter (?) resembles adult male but sides of head mottled with whitish or with two black and chestnut bars; under sides of body whitish.

MEASUREMENTS. — Length 12.00 to 14.50 in.; folded wing, 5.50 to 5.75; tail about 4.00; bill 1.30 to 1.40; tarsus about 1.00.

FIELD MARKS. — Smaller than teal. *Male:* Black mask over face; white wing-patch and generally rusty appearance with black spots or stripes. *Female and young:* Like those of Ruddy Duck, but smaller and with *two dark stripes* on each side of head.

RANGE. — Tropical America. Breeds in West Indies and mainly in eastern South America to central Argentina; occurs rarely and locally from lower Rio Grande in Texas south to Mexico, Guatemala and western South America; recorded from Wisconsin, Massachusetts, Vermont and Maryland (A. O. U. Check-list, 1910).

DISTRIBUTION IN NEW ENGLAND. — There is but one authentic record, an adult male taken in Malden, August 27, 1889, and now in the Field Columbian Museum, Chicago.[1] The specimen taken in 1858 in Vermont and deposited in the collection of the Boston Society of Natural History evidently escaped from captivity, as one wing was clipped.[2]

HAUNTS AND HABITS. This little black-faced duck is a mere straggler in temperate North America, coming from tropical or semi-tropical regions. Like the Ruddy Duck, it swims deeply, dives well and far and flies swiftly. It often frequents shallow ponds and in seeking concealment from its enemies prefers to dive or hide in the water-grass rather than to fly.

SUBFAMILY **ANSERINÆ**. GEESE.

Number of species in North America 13; in Massachusetts 8.

Geese form the natural connecting link between ducks and swans, the length of neck and usually the size being intermediate between the two (though there are some very small species of geese). Geese, unlike swans, have lores completely feathered, body raised and not so much flattened as in ducks, tarsi reticulated and legs slightly farther forward. Unlike most ducks they have no double molt in summer and autumn but molt completely once each year. This autumnal and winter molt is sometimes followed in young birds by a partial molt in early spring, but it is difficult to determine whether or not this is a mere continuation of the annual molt. They have no iridescent wing-patch or speculum. As a rule they walk better than ducks and feed more upon land and on vegetal food. They have long, broad wings and great powers of flight. In most species the sexes are alike. They have been divided into nine or ten genera and about forty species.

ECONOMIC STATUS. Geese are even more valuable in an economic sense than ducks, as they average much larger, and feeding largely as they do on vegetal food, are of excellent flavor. Their pursuit results in great expenditure of money among the country folk; but they do considerable injury in the grain fields of the western United States. Many geese are domesticated.

[1] Cory, Charles B.: Auk, Vol. VI, 1889, p. 336.   [2] Howe, Reginald Heber: Auk, Vol. XIX, 1902, p. 196.

PLATE 19

PLATE 19

GREATER SNOW GOOSE

Page 286

ADULT

YOUNG IN JUVENAL PLUMAGE

BLUE GOOSE

Page 288

YOUNG   ADULT

WHITE-FRONTED GOOSE

Page 290

YOUNG IN FIRST WINTER PLUMAGE

ADULT

All one-eighth natural size.

Chen hyperbóreus hyperboreus (PALLAS). Snow Goose.

Other names: WHITE GOOSE; LESSER SNOW GOOSE; WHITE BRANT.

See Greater Snow Goose, Plate 19.

DESCRIPTION. — *Adults (sexes alike)* : Plumage mainly white (sometimes more or less stained rusty on head, fore parts and under plumage) ; primaries gray at base, black at ends ; bill "light purplish-red," " salmon-pink," or pale rose-red, edges black, nail whitish ; iris dark brown ; legs and feet dusky-red or "deep purplish-red." *Young in juvenal plumage:* Head, neck, back and scapulars pale gray with brownish feather-edgings ; secondaries mottled drab, margined white ; rump, upper tail coverts and under plumage white ; primaries as in adult ; tail-feathers white and ashy-brown (variable) ; eyelids, bill and feet darkish. *Downy young:* "A very slightly cream yellow color, similar to but lighter than that of the young of Canada Goose" (R. M. Barnes).

MEASUREMENTS. — The following measurements furnished by Mr. F. H. Kennard are based on 36 adult males and 39 adult females. Mr. Kennard's measurements as given in millimeters are here reduced to inches. *Adult male:* Length 28.55 to 30.55 in.; spread 59.61 to 60.83; folded wing 15.50 to 18.11; tail 4.53 to 6.50; bill (exposed culmen) 2.13 to 2.40; tarsus 3.07 to 3.50. Weight 4 lbs. 8 oz. to 6 lbs. *Adult female:* Length 26.69 to 29.50 in.; spread 55.71 to 58.43; folded wing 15.18 to 17.32; tail 4.53 to 6.50; bill (exposed culmen) 1.97 to 2.40; tarsus 2.95 to 3.50. Weight about 4 to 6 lbs.

MOLTS. — The young of this species apparently retains some brownish plumage throughout the first winter and possibly in some cases through the second winter; apparently they have a partial spring molt. Adults have an annual complete molt in late summer and autumn.

FIELD MARKS. — Large size, approaching that of Canada Goose; long neck and short bill distinguish this bird from Gannet which also has black wing-tips; young Snow Goose, gray above, seems white from below or at a distance; indistinguishable from Greater Snow Goose in field.

VOICE. — In flight, a shrill *honk* (T. M. Brewer); occasionally a solitary note like a softened *honk* (D. G. Elliot).

BREEDING. — On barren grounds, usually near water. *Nest:* A hollow scratched in sand and built to some height by means of grass, moss and other vegetation, lined with down. *Eggs:* 5 to 8; 3.47 by 2.19 to 3.00 by 2.09 in.; ovate; white with slight yellowish tinge. *Dates:* June 9 to July 6, Arctic Canada (A. C. Bent). *Incubation:* Period 28 to 29 days (Heinroth); by female. One brood yearly.

RANGE. — North America and northeastern Asia. Breeds from coast of northern Alaska east to (probably Coronation Gulf, and Victoria and Melville Islands) Southampton Island, Hudson Bay, Baffin Island and probably on other Arctic lands north of the North American continent; occurs on Arctic coast of northeastern Asia where probably breeds; winters from southern British Columbia, Nevada, Utah, southern Colorado, southern Illinois, Virginia and (casually) Rhode Island and southern Connecticut south to northern Lower California, central Mexico and Gulf coast; on Asiatic coast winters to Japan; rare in migration in eastern United States and eastern Canada north to Cumberland Sound; casual in Cuba, Jamaica, Porto Rico and Hawaii; accidental in northern Europe.

DISTRIBUTION IN NEW ENGLAND. — Rare migrant or straggler in all the states, chiefly in autumn. Snow Geese are now reported nearly every year in New England, and a few are killed, but rarely identified. The majority of those positively identified have been of this subspecies.

SEASON IN MASSACHUSETTS. — October 15 to November 21; February 18; April 13.

HAUNTS AND HABITS. As the Snow Goose migrates southward along the Pacific coasts of Asia and North America and through the Mississippi Valley region, probably it has been always a rare migrant or straggler in New England. Nevertheless because of the extreme rarity now of the Greater Snow Goose in this region it has seemed safe to assign to the present race most of the few small flocks of white geese seen almost yearly in New England. Such stragglers may appear anywhere but most of the reports have come from coastal regions.

In migration Snow Geese are usually seen very high, flying in a wide diagonal or curved line, in an irregular flock or in an angular V-shaped formation like Canada Geese. They are not always so noisy in migration as Canada Geese and frequently pass without a sound; yet often they are very vociferous. When seen close at hand the young are readily distinguished by their gray or soiled appearance. This species feeds largely in marshes or fields and takes mainly vegetal food. In the fields it takes grass and grain and in the far north insects are added to its bill of fare.

ECONOMIC STATUS. The Snow Goose is not ranked highly as a table bird, although many of the species are eaten. In the wheat-growing states it is said to do considerable damage to the growing crops.

Chen hyperboreus nivális (J. R. FORSTER). Greater Snow Goose.

Other names: WHITE GOOSE; WHITE BRANT.

Plate 19.

DESCRIPTION. — Like Snow Goose but averaging larger; head often stained rusty; bill usually longer; iris, bill and feet similar in color to Snow Goose.

MEASUREMENTS. — The following measurements furnished by Mr. F. H. Kennard are based on 19 adult males and 9 adult females. Mr. Kennard's measurements as given in millimeters are here reduced to inches. *Adult male:* Length 30.12 to 32.48 in.; spread 58.07 to 62.80; folded wing 16.93 to 18.70; tail 4.92 to 6.30; bill (exposed culmen) 2.32 to 2.80; tarsus 3.03 to 3.82. Weight 5 lbs. 7 oz. to 10 lbs. 7 oz. *Adult female:* Length 29.53 to 31.52 in.; spread 53.15 to 62.80; folded wing 16.73 to 18.70; tail 5.12 to 5.91; bill (exposed culmen) 2.24 to 2.68; tarsus 3.15 to 3.54. Weight 6 lbs. 4 oz. to 7 lbs.

MOLTS. — Similar to those of Snow Goose.

FIELD MARKS. — Not distinguishable in field from Snow Goose (see Field Marks under Snow Goose).

VOICE. — Sharp cackling cries when alarmed, much less musical than those of Canada Goose (G. B. Grinnell); a high-pitched *honk-honk* (W. Elmer Ekblaw).

BREEDING. — On grassy Arctic flats and swales. *Nest:* In a depression among tussocks, built up with mud, grass and decaying vegetation, lined with grasses, white feathers and down. *Eggs:* The following measurements from a set of 4 eggs are furnished by Mr. R. M. Barnes; 3.11 to 3.24 by 2.10 to 2.20; white. *Dates:* June, northern Greenland.

RANGE. — Eastern North America. Breeding range little known; includes northern Greenland and probably Ellesmere Island and Grinnell Land; winters chiefly on coasts of Virginia and North Carolina; casual in West Indies; rare in migration west to Colorado and Montana and east to New England and Newfoundland. This is the Atlantic form of the Snow Goose.

DISTRIBUTION IN NEW ENGLAND. — Abundant migrant coastwise during settlement of the country; now very rare straggler. Since the beginning of the twentieth century there are few authentic records: *Maine:* Georgetown, male taken April 25, 1903, at Back River;[1] Lubec, bird taken April 30, 1906, by George Wallace;[2] Great Chebeague Island, Casco Bay, bird taken April 5, 1913.[3] *Massachusetts:*

---

[1] Spinney, Herbert L.: Journal Maine Ornithological Society, Vol. VI, 1904, p. 69.
[2] Clark, C. H.: Journal Maine Ornithological Society, Vol. VIII, 1906, p. 48.
[3] Norton, Arthur H.: Auk, Vol. XXX, 1913, p. 575.

Stoughton, adult caught alive May 7, 1917, preserved in collection of Boston Society of Natural History;[1] Westfield, immature bird taken November 24, 1921, recorded by Aaron C. Bagg, preserved in Museum of Natural History at Springfield;[2] Marthas Vineyard, young bird shot in November (between 15th and 20th), 1922, by Matthew H. Mayhew, mounted by Llewellyn Cleveland and now in collection of Boston Society of Natural History.[3] *Connecticut:* Westport, bird shot December 8, 1913, by Robert McCool, measured and mounted by the late Frank Sturges, a deputy game warden, of Westport, and given to William Disbrow of West Haven, who has the mounted specimen; a bird shot on the Great Marsh, December 8, 1919, and wings measured and preserved by Frank Sturges (this was one of two birds seen about one mile from Cockeno Island where Frank Novak, now warden of Birdcraft Sanctuary at Fairfield, saw on December 6 two Snow Geese, presumably the same birds; there are other reports of Snow Geese seen at about this time in Connecticut); South Glastonbury, bird shot November 24, 1921, and one wing preserved by the gunner, F. W. Taylor, and identified as that of a Greater Snow Goose by John H. Sage. Two Snow Geese also were shot on the same day (November 24) at Glastonbury by Julius C. Goodale. One of these was an adult, and its wings which were saved were found to "correspond perfectly" with the wing of Mr. Taylor's bird. The South Glastonbury bird was certainly identified as a Greater Snow Goose.

Other unidentified Snow Geese were shot on the same date in the same town by other gunners; some of these birds were secured in the Connecticut River. Still another Snow Goose was shot on the 24th out of a small flock by Foster Hyde in Ellington, which is about twenty miles from the South Glastonbury locality where Mr. Taylor secured his bird and where a flock of ten were seen.[*] A flock supposed to number one hundred birds was also seen at about 10 A.M. in the Connecticut River at East Windsor Hill, which is about twenty miles from Ellington and about eighteen miles from South Glastonbury.[4]

It appears from the Bagg and the Vibert correspondence that many Snow Geese (some at least presumably the greater variety) were diffused on or about November 24, 1921, in the valley of the Connecticut River in the adjacent parts of Massachusetts and Connecticut, the area covered being rather large. Mr. Bagg speaks about a flock estimated at "over one hundred birds" in Southwick Pond not far from Westfield; while Mr. Vibert, speaking of the Glastonbury section of Connecticut, reports that "Mr. Goodale, with others, estimated that the two flocks seen numbered between two hundred fifty and three hundred birds."

HAUNTS AND HABITS. As Dawson remarks in The Birds of Ohio, "snow banks of geese" in the Hudson Bay regions are rapidly melting before the "incessant flashings of the white man's gun." In Hearne's time (1795) Snow Geese were the most numerous birds during migrations on the shores of Hudson Bay. They passed along both coasts in enormous flocks and according to the early chroniclers they were exceedingly abundant from Maine to the Carolinas when New England was first settled.

William Wood, writing of New England (1629–34) speaks of a white goose almost as big as an "English tame goose" that was here in great flocks of two or three thousand, staying in the fall for five or six weeks and appearing again in March.

A few of the white geese seen in recent years may be of this subspecies but the only undoubted Massachusetts records are those of W. Sprague Brooks and of A. C. Bagg (given above); in the latter case two more birds (one adult and one immature) were taken

---

[1] Brooks, W. Sprague: Auk, Vol. XXXV, 1918, p. 234.

[2] Bagg, Aaron C.: Auk, Vol. XXXIX, 1922, p. 251.

[3] Brooks, W. Sprague: *in litt.*

[*] The measurements of the bird taken by Mr. Hyde and forwarded to me by Miss Alice Hyde are those of a large Greater Snow Goose (E. H. F.).

[4] Vibert, C. W.: *in litt.*

but not preserved. Mr. Willard E. Treat writes me that at least nine white geese were killed November 24 and 25, 1921, in small ponds between Hartford and Portland, Connecticut; but unfortunately as no ornithologist saw these birds and they were used for food, their identity is uncertain. Apparently this race which regularly winters in North Carolina comes down from Hudson Bay in small numbers through the Champlain-Hudson Valley and down the coast of the Middle States. Now and then stragglers reach the Connecticut Valley and the Atlantic coast of New England.

The haunts and habits of this bird and the smaller form are practically the same. It feeds largely on the roots and other parts of reeds and water-plants as well as on land grasses, seeds and grains.

ECONOMIC STATUS. The Greater Snow Goose formerly was used as a staple food among the people of the Hudson Bay region where geese were taken in large numbers and salted down in barrels for winter use. Since the decrease of the geese the Indians along the west coast of Hudson Bay are said to have been reduced often to the point of starvation. The Greater Snow Goose is generally considered superior to the Snow Goose from the point of view of the epicure.

Chen cæruléscens (LINNÆUS). Blue Goose.

Other names: BLUE SNOW GOOSE; BLUE-WINGED GOOSE; BLUE WAVEY.

Plate 19.

DESCRIPTION. — Nostrils in basal part of bill; tarsus as long as or longer than middle toe and claw. *Adults in nuptial plumage (sexes alike):* Head, much of neck, edges and tip of tail (sometimes lower back and rump and much of lower surface of body) white or whitish; amount of white on neck, lower back, rump, upper tail-coverts and under plumage very variable; some individuals have only a little of upper neck white, sometimes a blackish-brown line from top of head along hind neck; head and belly sometimes stained rusty, especially the head; elsewhere chiefly grayish-brown or sooty-brown; rounded feather tips lighter brownish or grayish-white, giving scaly effect; lower back, rump (usually), upper tail-coverts and wing-coverts bluish-gray; greater wing-coverts and tertials blackish along centers, fading outwardly to brownish or gray, edged whitish; primaries and secondaries blackish-brown to slaty-black, lightening to bluish-gray basally, shafts mainly white; wing-linings and axillars mostly bluish-gray; white-breasted birds have white axillars; belly and under tail-coverts usually light bluish-gray; iris dark brown; bill variable, pale pink to orange, nail pale pink or whitish, edges of both mandibles black; legs and feet purplish-red or pale rose-red changing to orange more or less in winter. *Young in first winter plumage:* Similar to juvenal plumage, but more or less white on head and neck; ("immature female shot . . . Oct. 21, 1916 — the upper and lower mandibles of this specimen were black, becoming flesh-purple at base, commissure dusky-black; legs and feet dark lead-gray (plumbeous), webs dusky"; this bird and another immature bird (Nov. 6, 1916) "were in dark gray plumage." J. H. Fleming in Auk, Vol. XXXVII, 1920, p. 432.) *Young in juvenal plumage:* Similar to adult, but head and neck dark grayish-brown or sooty-brown except chin which is white; no pure white anywhere except on chin and sometimes upper throat; bill, legs and feet duller than in adult; bill with flesh-colored base. *Downy young:* "Deep smoky or slaty bluish color" (R. M. Barnes).

MEASUREMENTS. — Length 25.00 to 30.00 in.; spread 53.50 to 56.00; folded wing 15.00 to 17.17; tail 4.50 to 6.00; bill 1.80 to 2.43; tarsus 2.90 to 3.46. Weight of young 3 lbs. 8 oz. to 4 lbs. 4 oz.; in February 4 lbs. 8 oz.

Molts. — During the first winter the molt is nearly continuous; before juvenal plumage disappears white feathers appear in head and neck, and in spring greater part of head becomes white with more or less of a dark line on back of head and hind neck; tail is molted in spring, beginning sometimes late in February; probably there is a complete molt in summer, after which bird becomes practically indistinguishable from adult, but another year may be required to produce highest perfection of plumage with pure white head and upper neck; adult birds, with back, rump, upper tail-coverts and under surface of body all white, may be merely birds that have come to full maturity.

Field Marks. — *Adult:* Larger than Brant, smaller than Canada Goose; dark with white head and upper neck; sometimes white on lower surface of body. *Young:* Dark below with dark head and neck; hard to distinguish in field from young White-fronted Goose (which, however, has light yellowish feet and light bill); wings broader and more rounded than those of Canada Goose and wing-beat more rapid; flight more like that of Brant.

Voice. — Like that of Snow Goose; "a single high-pitched *quop.*"

Breeding. — Unknown. *Eggs:* Laid in captivity are pyriform; 3.10 by 2.05 in. — one specimen (R. M. Barnes).

Range. — West central North America to Atlantic coast. Breeding range unknown but probably includes Baffin Island and interior of northern Ungava (northern Quebec); winters mainly on or near coasts of Louisiana and Texas; recorded in winter from Nebraska, southern Illinois and Ohio; line of migration probably through Mississippi Valley; rare to casual in migration in California, from Ontario, Quebec and Maine to Florida, Cuba and Bahamas.

Distribution in New England. — A very rare straggler in migration. Records are: *Maine:* Lake Umbagog, October 2, 1896, young bird recorded by Brewster at "Lake Umbagog, Maine"[1] (but said by O. W. Knight to have been actually killed in New Hampshire); Little Spoon Island (near Isle au Haut), bird shot November 13, 1913;[2] Lubec, immature bird taken Sept. 27, 1924, by Charles Sheehan Jr. and in collection of Clarence H. Clark of Lubec.[3] *Massachusetts:* Gloucester (West Parish), young female taken October 20, 1876;[4] Plympton (Silver Lake), bird shot in late November, 1914;[5] South Hingham (Accord Pond), bird shot October 29, 1920;[5] Mashpee (Johns Pond), female taken October 30, 1920.[6] *Rhode Island:* Westerly, young male taken March 16, 1894;[7] Dyer's Island, adult female shot by Sinclair Tucker November 9, 1912.[8]

Haunts and Habits. Breeding of Blue Geese in great swamps in the interior of northern Ungava is reported by Indians, and Eskimos report these birds in southern Baffin Land, where Capt. Donald B. MacMillan says he found many of them in the breeding season. As great flocks go up and down the east side of Hudson Bay in migration and as very few are seen on the west side, both Eskimos and Indians may be right. Blue Geese migrate southward in October across the region of the Great Lakes and appear in great numbers on the Gulf coast in winter. In June they appear again on the east coast of Hudson Bay on the way to their unknown breeding-grounds. Comparatively few are taken during their migrations or in their winter haunts, as they are very shy and probably fly high. Little is known of their habits while in the far North where they feed largely on open tide flats. Probably they always will be stragglers here as New England does not lie in their regular line of migration. Their food consists largely of the roots and other parts of aquatic plants.

[1] Brewster, William: Auk, Vol. XIV, 1897, p. 207.
[2] Clarke, Chas. E.: Auk, Vol. XXXIII, 1916, p. 197.
[3] Clark, Clarence H.: *in litt.*
[4] Jeffries, William A.; Auk, Vol. VI, 1889, p. 68.
[5] Phillips, John C.: Auk, Vol. XXXVIII, 1921, p. 271.
[6] Lamb, Charles R.: Auk, Vol. XXXVIII, 1921, p. 109.
[7] Hathaway, H. S.: Notes on Rhode Island Ornithology, Vol. I, 1900, p. 19.
[8] Brooks, W. Sprague: Auk, Vol. XXXII, 1915, p. 226.

ECONOMIC STATUS. In their winter home in southern Louisiana the Blue Geese, on account of their great numbers, do much harm to pastures. In the Belle Isle region they frequent areas of marsh which have been burned over to bring in new green food for cattle. To get at the roots of the grass they dig holes which immediately fill with water; and after a continuance of this mode of feeding shallow ponds result. The numbers of these geese are so great that they cannot be driven away and as a result hundreds of acres of "pasture" land have been abandoned (McAtee in Auk, Vol. XXVII, 1910, pp. 337–338).

Ánser álbifrons gámbeli HARTLAUB. White-Fronted Goose.

Other names: SPECKLE-BELLY; GRAY BRANT; LAUGHING GOOSE; YELLOW-LEGGED GOOSE.

Plate 19.

NOTE. The subspecific name *gumbeli* is now given by some authors to a western race of the White-fronted Goose.

DESCRIPTION. — Nostrils in basal half of bill, their front ends reaching to its middle; tarsus shorter than middle toe and claw; tail-feathers normally 16. *Adults (sexes alike)*: Above and all of neck mainly grayish-brown, darkest on back, feather-edges (on back and wings) paler (ashy); forehead, fore face (narrowly around base of bill) and upper tail-coverts mainly white; white of fore face bordered behind by blackish; rump slaty-brown, tail the same or dusky, edged and tipped white; wings chiefly slate-gray above and below, greater coverts tipped white which forms a white wing-bar; primaries dark slate above; secondaries blackish above; quills of all flight-feathers mainly white; sides, and under surface of wing including axillars, glossy silvery slaty-gray; flanks colored like back but with white line along their upper edges; breast and belly brownish-gray or grayish-white with cross patches of very dark brown or blackish (very variable), sometimes in high plumage this area nearly all blackish; females average less of these markings than males; ventral region and under tail-coverts white; iris and naked edges of eye-lids sometimes gray or brownish-gray; bill varying from pale or whitish flesh-color to orange-yellow or orange, nail whitish; legs and feet orange-yellow or orange. *Young in juvenal and first winter plumage:* Similar, *but no white* on face (except sometimes on chin) which is all brown, sometimes darker about base of bill; no blackish patches on under plumage, but breast often mottled with small blackish spots; tail-feathers and wing-coverts rather narrower than in adult and head and neck darker grayish-brown; bill dull-yellowish or yellowish-gray or grayish-flesh color or "gray with lilac tinge," nail usually darker than in adult, becoming white toward spring; legs and feet dingy yellowish or orange-yellow; toward spring some white may appear in front face and some black feathers on breast; bill and feet brighten. *Downy young:* Variable; top of head, entire upper plumage of body, and thighs sooty olive-brown to "buffy olive"; faint dusky-olive stripe from bill through eye; nape and back of neck olive-yellow; below yellow, variable, growing lighter on abdomen; "bill brown with light colored nail" (A. C. Bent); some young are grayish-white below.

MEASUREMENTS. — Length 26.70 to 30.00 in.; spread 54.25 to 62.00; folded wing 14.20 to 17.50; tail 5.15 to 6.40; bill 1.60 to 2.35; tarsus 2.25 to 3.30. Weight of young in October 3 lbs. 10½ oz.; weight of adult 4 to 6 lbs. (Popham). Female averages slightly smaller than male.

MOLTS. — Juvenal plumage worn without much change during first winter and spring, but some white appears in frontal feathers of head and a few black spots in breast; tail is molted in spring and in summer a complete postnuptial molt produces practically adult plumage (A. C. Bent); probably another year is often required to bring adult plumage to highest perfection; adult has but one complete molt in summer and autumn, though some molting may occur in winter and spring (February and March) during which some feathers of head, neck and body are shed.

FIELD MARKS. — Smaller than Canada Goose; flies in similar formation, but no black on head or neck; at a distance looks gray; white front, light colored bill, legs and feet, and black marks on under plumage distinctive in adults but visible only at close range; distinguished from Canada Goose by light bill, legs and feet and absence of black head and neck; young resemble young of Blue Goose, but have lighter colored legs and feet.

VOICE. — "A loud *wah wah wah* somewhat like the laugh of a man" (Grinnell, Bryant and Storer); when rising harsh cackling tones, somewhat like a mingling of the notes of crows with those of a pair of Canada Geese (J. G. Peters, Jr.).

BREEDING. — Generally not far from coast, on flat or tundra; sometimes in woods; near fresh water. *Nest:* On ground, of grass and feathers lined with down. *Eggs:* 6 to 8; 3.41 by 2.33 to 2.93 by 1.99 in.; dull yellowish-white or greenish-yellow, usually with some discoloration. *Dates:* Latter half of June, Alaska.

RANGE. — Northern Hemisphere. Breeds on and near Arctic coast from northern Alaska east to northeastern Mackenzie, south to lower Yukon and on west coast of Greenland (said to have bred on Vancouver Island); breeds in Iceland, Lapland, Novaya Zemlya and Arctic Asian coasts and islands to Bering Strait; winters from southern British Columbia south to southern Lower California and Jalisco, and rarely from southern Illinois and southern Ohio south to northeastern Mexico, southern Texas, Louisiana and Cuba; rare on Atlantic coast; in the Old World south to the Mediterranean, Caspian and Black Seas, India and Burmah (rarely), Corea, China and Japan.

DISTRIBUTION IN NEW ENGLAND. — *Maine:* about November 10, 1922, a goose, evidently dazzled by the lights, flew against the front of a motor car at Augusta and was killed. This bird was dressed and eaten, but the description led me to believe that the bird was a White-fronted Goose (T. A. James); a wing of the bird confirmed this identification. *Massachusetts:* Quincy, male shot some time about 1848–50, presented to Boston Society of Natural History;[1] Salisbury, two killed on marshes October 5, 1888;[2] Plymouth, male shot "a few days before" November 26, 1897;[3] Ipswich, wounded adult, caught alive by A. B. Clark, August, 1907;[4] Nantucket, two birds shot November, 1909, one of which was given to the Boston Society of Natural History by the late Thomas Arnold of North Abington (recorded by S. Prescott Fay);[5] the other was mounted on a panel and is in possession of Mr. Arnold's family; Raynham, young bird, unsexed, shot November 16, 1920, by Leonard F. Hoxie and now in possession of W. S. Willson; North Truro, immature female shot November 1, 1923, by Joseph G. Peters, Jr., out of a flock of seven and given to Boston Society of Natural History; Duxbury, two birds taken in 1919 at the Brewer stand on Duxbury Bay.[6]

HAUNTS AND HABITS. The White-fronted Goose is a rare bird in New England as its migration routes lie mainly in the Mississippi Valley and farther west. Its habits and flight-formation seem to be similar to those of the Canada Goose. It flies very high in migration and in descending to the water is said to tumble and gyrate in the most erratic manner. With us it usually appears singly and in company with Canada Geese. Its young are unsuspicious when compared with the Canada Goose. It is very largely a vegetarian. Young herbage and grass make up a large part of its food and in the west it does some damage in the grain fields.

ECONOMIC STATUS. This goose has considerable value as food; as a table bird it ranks high among the geese, but it is so rare in the east as to be of no economic importance here.

[1] Cabot, Samuel: Proceedings Boston Society of Natural History, Vol. III, 1848–51, p. 136.
[2] Allen, Glover M.: Auk, Vol. XXX, 1913, p. 22.
[3] Brewster, William: Auk, Vol. XVIII, 1901, p. 135.
[4] Townsend, C. W.: Auk, Vol. XXV, 1908, p. 80.
[5] Auk, Vol. XXVIII, 1911, p. 120.
[6] Freeman, A. J.: *in litt.*

NOTE. As this goes to press Mr. B. P. P. Moseley sends to the office a goose killed by him Sept. 25, 1924, at Parker River, Ipswich. The goose came in to decoys, flying very high and apparently wild; it circled about and finally came to the decoys and was shot. It appears to be a juvenile Pink-footed Goose (*Anser brachyrhynchus*) going into first winter plumage. This is the first record of this species on the continent of North America, although it is recorded from Greenland. The only doubt about this record is that the feet of the bird were slightly calloused, which may have been an indication that the bird had sometime recently escaped from captivity. The wings, however, were perfect. The bird somewhat resembles the young of the White-fronted Goose, but has a pink band entirely around the bill extending from the nail toward the nostril, and pink feet; also both base and tip of tail are white.

Bránta canadénsis canadensis (LINNÆUS). Canada Goose.

Other names: WILD GOOSE; HONKER; LONG-NECKED GOOSE.

Plate 20 and Fig. 24.

DESCRIPTION. — Tail-feathers normally 18, sometimes 20; long swan-like neck. *Adults (sexes alike):* Head and neck mainly black, a white patch extending across throat, sometimes including chin, and up across both cheeks to a point near nape, sometimes separated into two cheek patches by black stripe along throat; rarely, white feathers appear elsewhere on head; upper surface of body and wings mainly brown or brownish-gray, feathers edged and tipped gray or whitish, darker or blackish on rump; primaries and secondaries blackish; wing-linings and axillars light grayish-brown; upper tail-coverts white; tail black; under surface of body mainly pale ashy-gray with ashy feather-tips; sides and flanks usually darker; upper breast usually lighter often nearly white but sometimes brownish; lower belly and under tail-coverts white; iris dark hazel; bill, legs and feet black. *Young in juvenal plumage:* Similar to adult but smaller, feathers softer; colors rather duller; white on cheeks not so pure, sometimes speckled black, and black about the white not so clearly defined; iris brown; bill, legs and feet black. *Downy young:* Top of head and upper back olive or "yellowish olive"; patch of yellow behind each wing; forehead, sides of head, neck all round, variable light yellow; wings and tail light brownish-olive; under surface of body yellowish or buffy, all varying with age; bill and feet black or blackish.

MEASUREMENTS. — Very variable; length about 34.00 to 43.00 in.; spread 59.00 to 65.50; folded wing 15.60 to 21.00; tail 5.20 to 7.00; bill 1.55 to 2.80; tarsus 2.40 to 4.10. Weight 8 to 14 lbs.; young often weigh less than 8 lbs.; some very large northwestern birds reported as weighing up to 18 lbs. Female smaller than male.

MOLTS. — During fall and winter by molt or wear young become practically indistinguishable from adults, but adults in captivity do not breed until three or four years old, and probably being long-lived this goose does not reach full maturity until the third or fourth year. Adults have one complete molt in late summer and autumn when the flight feathers are shed.

FIELD MARKS. — Largest of our geese, known by abruptly black head and neck, white cheek patches, black bill and feet. In flight at a distance a flock of cormorants might be mistaken for Canada Geese; if geese usually they may be *heard;* cormorant flocks are commonly silent.

VOICE. — Said to be a *honk* but I never have been able to hear the *h* or the *k;* very variable in pitch; sometimes low and hoarse and again very high.

BREEDING. — Anywhere in extreme northern United States and in Canada to tree limit and even on tundra near fresh water. *Nest:* Usually on dry ground; sometimes on a beaver house or large rock if in wet or swampy place; rarely and locally in old nests of herons, etc., in trees; built of twigs, weeds, grasses, reeds, etc., lined with down. *Eggs:* 5 to 9; 3.71 by 2.47 to 3.06 by 2.10 in.; "ovate to elongate ovate"; pale, dull greenish, yellowish or buffy-white. *Dates:* Late April to July 19 in United States. *Incubation:* Period 28 to 30 days (Burns); by female. One brood yearly.

PLATE 20

PLATE 20

WHISTLING SWAN
Page 302

Adult

BLACK BRANT
Page 300

Adult

BRANT
Page 296

Adult

All one-eighth natural size.

CANADA GOOSE
Page 292

Adult

RANGE. — North America. Breeds in valley of Lower and Upper Yukon north to limit of trees and to borders of Barren Grounds in northwestern Mackenzie, and northern Manitoba, northern Ontario, northern Quebec, Labrador and Newfoundland and south to northeastern California, northern Nevada, northern Utah, northern Colorado, South Dakota, Nebraska, Indiana and Gulf of St. Lawrence; formerly also and perhaps now occasionally to New Mexico, northern Kansas, northwestern Arkansas, western Tennessee and Massachusetts; winters from southern British Columbia, northwestern Wyoming, South Dakota, southern Wisconsin, southern Illinois, Ohio, southern Ontario, Maine and Nova Scotia south to southern California, Mexico, Gulf coast of United States and Florida; accidental in Bermuda and Jamaica.

DISTRIBUTION IN NEW ENGLAND. — Common to abundant migrant in all the states; much less common winter resident coastwise in southeastern Massachusetts and Connecticut waters; occasionally winter visitant coastwise in Maine; also in Lake Champlain, Vermont, in mild winters when the ice breaks; casual in summer in Massachusetts, breeding formerly, but no recent records.

SEASON IN MASSACHUSETTS. — Seen every month in the year; individuals resident rarely throughout the year and nests of wild birds occasionally reported in southeastern Massachusetts — probably those of escaped birds or escapes mated with wild birds; * dates north of Cape Cod, March 8 to May 4 (summer); September 21 to January 3.

HAUNTS AND HABITS. Wild geese are the forerunners of winter and the harbingers of spring. While ice still covers our lakes, before even the wood frogs begin to croak, when the spring floods first begin to break up the frozen rivers, the geese are on their way; and when that "flying wedge" sweeps fast across the sky, it brings to all who see or hear the promise of another spring. The farmer stops his team to gaze; the blacksmith leaves his forge to listen as that far-carrying clamor falls upon the ear; children leave their play and eagerly point to the sky where the feathered denizens of the northern wilderness press steadily on toward the pole, babbling of the coming spring, carrying their message over mountain and plain to village, city and farm as far as open water can be found. Coming after the long, cold winter, not even the first call of the Bluebird so stirs the blood of the listener. Again in autumn when the last great flight passes southward, flock after flock winging steadily on, we know that frost has closed the northern waters and that winter is at hand.

The Canada Goose is a distinctly American bird. It is the most widely distributed and well-known water-fowl on this continent. It migrates over nearly all of it and formerly bred over half the United States. Its habits are so well known that no extended description of them is necessary. The goose is a model of domestic faithfulness. Ordinarily a pair is mated for life. The young birds usually mate and breed in the third year. While the female incubates, the male keeps guard over her, and he is so strong and fierce in her defense that he will drive a fox, deer or even an elk away from the nest. When the downy young are hatched he still guards his little family. In July while the adult birds are molting, they lose all the flight feathers of their wings and for a time are unable to fly. At such times they skulk amid water plants or readily dive to escape observation or the attacks of eagles. If surprised on land, they lie flat on the

* "A set of two eggs of the Canada Goose was taken the last of April [1888] at Lexington." (Ornithologist & Oölogist, Vol. XIV, 1889, p. 14.)

ground with outstretched neck, and if the surroundings lend themselves to the deception the back of the prone bird may be mistaken for a rock. Wounded geese often lie flat along the surface of the water with outstretched neck and so swim away. If waves are running high, they are then difficult to see at a distance. If closely pursued, they can dive and sometimes escape. Their flight is deceptive. The wing-beats are rather slow, but the great birds pass with such speed that the novice firing at the leader of a small flock is likely, if he scores at all, to hit one of the last birds in the flock. The goose breeds freely in captivity.

When the geese have a good breeding season in the north, flocks begin to appear in Massachusetts in September and all through October flock after flock passes southward, usually increasing in frequency toward the last of the month. All through November the flight continues but usually is at its height during the last ten days. If November is mild, however, this flight may continue into December and small flocks sometimes pass as late as the first week in January. A large part of the fall flight comes down the coast from the Gulf of St. Lawrence. Others coming south from the interior join it, turning southwest when they reach the coast. When strong westerly winds blow, the flight may be drifted out over the sea and so many pass over Cape Cod; strong easterly winds on the contrary may send them inland. Usually many pass over the lakes of Plymouth County, and yearly large numbers are killed there. Many geese remain about the ponds of Marthas Vineyard, on the coast of Connecticut and sometimes about Muskeget all winter, except in very severe seasons. Sometimes during a January thaw some of these geese will make excursions into the interior, and then we hear of geese flying north; but there is rarely any real northward movement inland until late February or early March when geese begin to move eastward along the coast and if the weather is mild, penetrate into the interior. They have been known to reach Prince Edward Island by March 9, but this is a very early date. In the interior they must wait until the ice breaks up and probably they cannot reach their most northern breeding-grounds until well into the month of May.*

In spring and summer the Canada Goose feeds largely on insects, grasshoppers being a favorite food; and doubtless along the sea-coast in migration they get a few small clams and other shell-fish. Earthworms are not disdained but the principal food seems to be vegetal in great variety. The roots of rushes and other parts of water-plants, tender grasses and shoots of grain, many seeds and grains including wild rice, berries, eel-grass and algæ, all are taken.

ECONOMIC STATUS. The only harm done to Massachusetts agriculture by these birds seems to be damage to certain fields of winter rye near some of their favorite lakes, but in the West they are said to injure grain by pulling up young sprouts in the spring and by eating the seed in autumn. The Canada Goose is very important economically. It supplied much toothsome food to the early settlers and still supplies a large quantity of such food annually. Its feathers and down were formerly in great demand for feather-

---

* For geese frozen to ice around water holes see Oölogist, Vol. I, 1884, p. 130.

beds and pillows, and vast quantities have been used for this purpose in the United States. Considerable money is now expended by men of means in the maintenance of shooting stands, and in the care of live decoys used largely for the purpose of shooting Canada Geese and Black Ducks. I have described this method of stand shooting.[1] Messrs. E. A. Samuels [2] and A. C. Bent [3] have described it also.

Branta canadensis hútchinsi (RICHARDSON). Hutchins's Goose.

Other names: SHORT-NECKED GOOSE; LITTLE GOOSE; MUD GOOSE.

DESCRIPTION. — Sexes alike; almost exactly similar in all plumages to Canada Goose, but tail normally of 16 feathers (sometimes 14 to 18) instead of 18 or 20; typical examples are said to have bill and neck relatively shorter.

MEASUREMENTS. — Length about 25.00 to 34.00 in.; spread 45.00 to 54.50; folded wing 14.75 to 17.93; tail 4.75 to 6.00; bill 1.20 to 1.50; tarsus 2.25 to 3.20. Weight 3 lbs. to 4 lbs. 8 oz., rarely perhaps 5 lbs. to 6 lbs.

MOLTS. — Probably same as in Canada Goose.

VOICE. — Like that of Canada Goose but less "deep and sonorous" (Grinnell, Bryant and Storer).

BREEDING. — Similar to that of Canada Goose but nests more on Barren Grounds and open tundra near Arctic Ocean. *Nest:* Like that of Canada Goose. *Eggs:* Like those of Canada Goose but smaller, averaging about 3.08 by 2.12 in. *Dates:* May 17 to July 14 (A. C. Bent). *Incubation:* By female. One brood yearly.

RANGE. — Chiefly western North America. Breeds from Kowak Valley and Point Barrow, Alaska, east in Barren Grounds and along Arctic coasts and islands from about latitude 70° south to Melville Peninsula, Southampton Island, Hudson Bay and southern Baffin Island, also on Commander and Kurile Islands; winters from southern British Columbia, Nevada, Colorado, Nebraska, southern Wisconsin (rarely) and southern Illinois south to San Rafael, Lower California, Texas and Louisiana, and on Asiatic coast south to Japan; rare in migration east of Mississippi Valley, but recorded on Atlantic coast from Maine to Virginia; has been taken in Pribilof Islands; accidental at Vera Cruz, Mexico, and Greenland.

DISTRIBUTION IN NEW ENGLAND. — Apparently not very rare in 19th century; now a rare or accidental migrant. The records are: *Maine:* Knight gives records of five birds, one taken at Cape Elizabeth, November 13, 1894, three taken near Portland in 1899 and another said to have been shot in the Rangeley region.[4] Rich (1907) asserts that he had four "shortnecked geese this spring" of which one was doubtful and three "undoubtedly" of this subspecies.[5] *Massachusetts:* Abundant here in winter of 1836–37 and some seasons not uncommon near Boston (T. M. Brewer).[6] One shot at Bridgewater by Frank C. Drake and Irving A. Hall, recorded by Arthur C. Dyke.[7] Mr. F. H. Briggs informs me that in 1919 Waldo C. Turner shot seven birds at Oldham Pond, Pembroke, which he called Hutchins's Geese; the largest weighed only 6 lbs.* *Connecticut:* Sage, Bishop and Bliss give Linsley, George Bird Grinnell and E. H. Austin as authorities for the occurrence of Hutchins's Goose in Connecticut but the last record was "about 1900."[8]

---

[1] A History of the Game Birds, Wild Fowl and Shore Birds, 1912, pp. 536–539.
[2] Birds of New England, 1870, p. 490.
[3] Bulletin 126, Smithsonian Institution: United States National Museum, 1923, pp. 60–62.
[4] Knight, O. W.: Birds of Maine, 1908, p. 123.
[5] Rich, Walter H.: Feathered Game of the Northeast, 1907, p. 270.
[6] Baird, Brewer and Ridgway: Water Birds of North America, Vol. I, p. 466.
[7] Dyke, Arthur C.: Auk, Vol. XXIX, 1912, p. 536.
* Gunners occasionally report a flight of very small geese the size and weight of which fall within the limits of this subspecies, but such reports should be received with caution. I have measured but one bird taken in Massachusetts that in any measurements came within the limits of this race and this was plainly an intermediate.
[8] Birds of Connecticut, 1913, p. 41.

HAUNTS AND HABITS. Hutchins's Goose occurs in Massachusetts but how often can be determined only by careful measurements. If sportsmen securing very small geese would submit them to an ornithologist for measurement and comparison, more authentic records might result. The haunts and habits of this goose do not differ widely from those of the Canada Goose except that it is more northerly in its breeding range, breeds more in the open, north of the tree limit and feeds more on the tide-flats of the Arctic Ocean. Being much more western in its distribution than the Canada Goose it is considered rare in migration east of the Mississippi.

ECONOMIC STATUS. In the past it was even more abundant on the Pacific coast than the Canada Goose. It furnished the settlers, and later the markets, a bountiful food supply and it was very destructive to grain at times. It never has been important in the East.

Branta bérnicla glaucogástra (BREHM). Brant.

Other names: WHITE-BELLIED BRANT; SEA BRANT.

Plate 20 and Fig. 25.

DESCRIPTION. — *Adults (sexes alike)*: Head, neck and a little of fore part of body black; a small streaky patch of white on each side of upper neck and often small white touches on chin and eyelids; rarely head and neck entirely black; upper plumage chiefly brownish-gray or brown, many feathers having paler tips; middle rump darker; flight-feathers, primary coverts and tail blackish; sides of rump and upper tail-coverts white; breast, sides and flanks light ashy-gray or brownish-gray, feathers with white or whitish tips; under plumage fading gradually into white on belly; ventral region and lower tail-coverts white; iris brown; bill, legs and feet black. *Young in juvenal plumage*: Generally browner; wing-coverts with more prominent whitish edges and tips of secondaries white; black of head and neck less deep, rather brownish-dusky, and streaky white neck-patch, very faint or lacking; less contrast between breast and belly. *Downy young*: Top of head, middle of nape, whole upper body, and sides "pale mouse gray", with some "grayish-white" tips; chin, throat and rest of neck white; rest of under down "ashy white."

NOTE. There are two color phases of this bird. The above description applies to the common eastern American form with a white belly, commonly known as *Branta bernicla glaucogastra*, but now believed to be a color phase. Both white-bellied and gray-bellied birds breed together in Spitzbergen and Kolguev.

MEASUREMENTS. — Length 23.00 to 30.50 in.; spread 42.00 to 52.00; folded wing about 12.00 to 14.50; tail 3.75 to 4.60; bill 1.25 to 1.40; tarsus 2.20 to 2.40. Weight 3 to 4 lbs. Female smaller than male.

MOLTS. — In juvenal plumage, which resembles that of adult, young bird has no white on neck, but during winter "molting or wear of contour feathers especially about head and neck" produces an advance toward maturity; white patch appears on neck in January but wings remain as juvenal until summer; complete molt in summer, followed by plumage indistinguishable from that of adult (A. C. Bent); adult has complete molt in summer.

FIELD MARKS. — Smallest wild goose in New England; not much larger than Black Duck but neck longer; small size, *black head, neck and upper breast* and irregular flock formation in flight distinguish it from Canada Goose; Brant is also more extensively white above tail; rarely flies in V-formation; in adult, white patch on side of neck may be seen with a telescope.

VOICE. — A guttural *car-r-rup* or *r-r-r-ronk* (D. G. Elliot); *ruk-ruk* (Warren Hapgood).

Fig. 24. — Nest and Eggs of Canada Goose

From Bird-Lore, Courtesy of Dr. Frank M. Chapman and D. Appleton and Co.

Page 292

Fig. 25. — Nest and Eggs of Brant

Littleton Island, Smith Sound, 78° 21' North latitude

Page 297

Breeding. — On marshy ground; on coasts or sea-islands. *Nest:* A depression, lined largely with down. *Eggs:* 4 to 8; 2.65 to 2.87 by 1.75 to 1.95 in. (Coues); "elongate ovate"; white or whitish. *Dates:* June 14 to July 13, Greenland (A. C. Bent). *Incubation:* By female.

Range. — North of the Tropic of Cancer, in North America, Europe and western Asia. Breeds north of latitude 74° on Arctic islands west to about longitude 110°; from about 73° north latitude on both coasts of Greenland as far north as explorers have gone, and on Arctic islands north of Europe and western Asia, east to the Taimyr Peninsula; winters coastwise from Massachusetts to North Carolina and rarely Florida and in Europe south to the Mediterranean and northern Africa; in migration rare to casual west to Lakes Ontario, Erie and Michigan; reported by Coues on Missouri River; many doubtful (and some authentic) records in interior west to Colorado and south to Louisiana and Texas; rare to accidental in Manitoba, British Columbia, California, Labrador, Nova Scotia and West Indies.

Distribution in New England. — Common to abundant migrant locally on east coast; much less common in Rhode Island and Connecticut waters; rare migrant in Vermont; winters except in very severe seasons in variable numbers in waters about Nantucket, Marthas Vineyard and Cuttyhunk; also occasional in winter off shores of Rhode Island and Connecticut.

Season in Massachusetts. — (September 11, 18) October 12 to December 19; winters; March 9 to May 17.

Haunts and Habits. The Brant is among the wariest of New England wild-fowl. Formerly its great flocks were seen both fall and spring in every land-locked bay and harbor where eel-grass grew upon the tide-washed flats, but as settlement increased and civilization extended all along the coast the Brant, unprotected, constantly persecuted in migration and decreasing in numbers, withdrew, until at last it frequented only a few isolated points and islands such as Monomoy, Muskeget and the southeastern points of Long Island. Since spring shooting has been prohibited, it has begun to come back into such favorable waters as Waquoit Bay, from which long ago it was practically banished; but probably it will never return in its former numbers to Boston Harbor, where human activities constantly increase. There are many tales of its former abundance there, but the limits of space will allow but one.

Mr. Henry Fenno of Westborough tells me that his grandfather, Jesse Fenno, lived in Quincy and used to shoot on Half Moon Island in Quincy Bay, a part of Boston Harbor. There were large flats about the Island where Brants then fed in great flocks. Mr. Henry Fenno says that his grandmother told him that his grandfather paid for his farm with game brought down by his gun and that a large part of the money came from the sale of Brant feathers which the "nobility" then used for their feather beds. Brants and geese fairly swarmed in the bay in those days (about 1810). An old clock, formerly the property of the Fenno family and now owned by the Henry Faxon heirs, is ornamented with a picture representing Jesse Fenno bringing down thirteen Brants at one shot.

The habits of the Brant on our coast are well known. In ordinary flight over the water they fly low but when they go overland they fly high, out of gunshot range. In migration the flocks are more likely to form in wide ranks or curved lines with the birds flying side by side than they are to assume a V-shape or any other definite formation. Often the flocks are "bunchy." As they come on, the black heads and necks are conspicuous, and as they pass, the white hinder parts are prominent in contrast with the black fore parts. Wilson likens their notes at times when distant to the cry of a pack of hounds, but Audubon disagrees with this.   William Thompson says in support of Wilson's contention that when the birds are "swimming in order," their cries "are not sufficiently varied to be musical" but that when they are "veering about on wing, or swimming in different directions" the sound "strongly resembles what Wilson has compared it to," and he relates that once when his horse, "a hunter," heard the music of a flock of about 500, a sound like that of a "pack of hounds in full cry," he became very "impatient," restless and "spirited" as long as he was within hearing of the sound, as he would have been had it been produced by a genuine pack.   The Brant is an excellent swimmer, but seldom dives even when wounded and closely pursued, preferring usually to swim rapidly away with its head and neck stretched flat on the water, apparently in the hope of escaping observation.   On land it is very nimble and light of foot.   It runs at need almost with the agility of a sandpiper.   Brants eat much sand as an aid to digestion, and just before beginning a migratory journey they are said to fill up with "sand ballast."

The Brant breeds so far north that the ancients, having never known it to nest, believed that it was bred from barnacles or boring sea-worms that attack wood.   The route by which it comes down in autumn from its breeding-places in far polar regions has never been fully worked out.   It is known, however, that the birds that breed on the northwest coast of Greenland and those of the great lands lying to the westward of it begin to move southward late in August and early in September, as soon as the young are grown.   It is believed that in some seasons wintry storms destroy the young either when small or before they can fly, or else drive the parents southward before the young are able to go; and in this case the Brants make their long pilgrimage with very few young in their ranks.   They pass southward over desolate lands and freezing seas down the Boothia Peninsula and the west coast of Hudson Bay, into and down James Bay, and then turning to a point south of east they must cross the base of the Labrador Peninsula to the St. Lawrence River and the Gulf of St. Lawrence.   There are rivers and lakes in the Labrador wilderness where they can rest in safety if rest becomes imperative. Mr. R. D. Ware writes to me that they come from overland to the Bay of Chaleur in the Gulf of St. Lawrence and that the largest flights come on a northwest wind which is a fair wind from James Bay.   The birds which come across the Province of Quebec and cross the St. Lawrence River and the Gaspe Peninsula here save many miles over the route down the river; others apparently reach the Gulf farther east and go between Anticosti Island and the mainland; all turning south pass across Prince Edward Island and the neck of the Nova Scotia Peninsula and so on down to Cape Cod, Nantucket, Block Island and Long Island, while many pass on to Virginia and North Carolina.   The majority arrive in October and November in Massachusetts waters.   Considerable numbers now winter along the islands south of Cape Cod and on the coast of Long Island except when very severe winter weather, covering the flats with ice, drives them southward.

They begin to move north from the southern parts of their range in February, and in March their numbers considerably increase in their winter haunts in Massachusetts.

They continue to move northward past our coasts until well into May. In April large numbers have reached the Gulf of St. Lawrence by retracing the route followed in the fall, passing over Prince Edward Island. From June 10 to 15 large flocks leave the Island for their northward journey. Many flocks are said to turn up the St. Lawrence River in a general southwest direction, but apparently they all cross the base of the Labrador Peninsula somewhere and make for James Bay. Mr. Hoyes Lloyd informs me that he has information from Fort George on the east coast of James Bay that the Brants always go north in the spring along this coast, and as they are not seen at that season on the west coast of Hudson Bay, they probably follow up the east coast directly north and so on by the shores of Baffin Island to their final destination, which they first reach about mid-June. On the way many cross Baffin Bay to west Greenland, while others may go more directly north to Ellesmere Island where numbers breed. It is probable that, as in the case of the White-winged Scoter, another flight goes north by the inland route, from Long Island Sound by way of the Hudson Valley and Lake Ontario. Dr. Louis B. Bishop writes as follows:

"Professor A. E. Verrill informed me that on May 17, 1914, he saw, with Mr. G. E. Verrill, many flocks of Brant flying north up the Housatonic Valley near the mouth of the Housatonic River; that most were high in the air, but some almost within gunshot; also that he saw others flying northwest while at Outer Island, Stony Creek, about May 22."[1] Mr. Wendell P. Smith of Wells River, Vermont, tells me that he has heard flocks of Brants passing along the Connecticut Valley at that place at night.

Major Mark Robinson writes to me that flocks of Brant sometimes come into the lakes at Algonquin Park, which lies in the highlands well to the northward of Lake Ontario almost directly northwest from Long Island Sound. This may be near the route of the Brant from Long Island Sound to James Bay.

The principal food of the Brant in our waters is the common eel-grass (*Zostera marina*) of the tide flats. This they pull up when the water is low enough for them to reach (for they very seldom if ever dive for their food) and leave much of it floating on the water where they can feed on it again at high tide. Mr. William E. Smith informs me that Brants were feeding at one time in winter on frozen quahaugs (*Venus mercenaria*), and mussels also are taken, but this species is believed to take chiefly vegetal food. In its northern homes it eats a variety of mosses and lichens and the stalks and leaves of Arctic plants, and in captivity it readily and eagerly feeds on corn and other grains.

ECONOMIC STATUS. The Brant when in good condition and properly prepared is one of the most savory of all water-fowl. Its feathers and down make the finest filling for pillows and feather beds. It does not injure crops. Its pursuit requires special devices in the way of sunken boxes, floating "batteries" or sink boxes, and much money changes hands to enable the sportsman to procure this highly-valued bird. There are, however, but few places along the New England coast today where Brant shooting can be followed successfully. Monomoy and Muskeget are the two principal points, and even in those

[1] Auk, Vol. XXXVIII, 1921, p. 584.

places the activities of fishermen or scallopers are likely to disturb the birds, while in autumn and early winter, storms and ice may interfere with the sunken boxes. For these reasons comparatively few people now hunt the Brant in New England.

Branta nígricans (LAWRENCE). Black Brant.

Plate 20.

DESCRIPTION. — Similar to Brant but darker. *Adults (sexes alike):* Black of head and neck not ending abruptly on breast but extending in a wash over breast and much of belly; broad white collar on upper neck, broken by black of hind neck, but less streaked with black than in Brant; dark wings unmarked with white. *Young in juvenal plumage:* Similar to adult, but head, neck and breast sooty-black, fading slightly below; feathers of back edged whitish; wing-coverts, secondaries and tertials broadly edged white; belly and flanks sooty, unbarred; little if any white on neck. *Downy young:* Upper half of head sooty-brown; chin white; upper half of body largely hair-brown; flanks and chest fading below to light drab; throat and belly whitish.

MEASUREMENTS. — Practically same as Brant (see page 296).

MOLTS. — Similar to those of Brant; young birds begin early to molt parts of juvenal plumage; white collar often is conspicuous in autumn when birds are moving south.

FIELD MARKS. — Readily distinguished in flight from Brant by dark breast and lack of abrupt contrast between black neck and lower breast.

VOICE. — Low, guttural *gr-r-r-r* (E. W. Nelson); "a mellow *cronk, cronk, cronk*" (W. L. Dawson).

BREEDING. — Usually on the tundra. *Nest:* A deep bed of dark brownish-drab down. *Eggs:* Similar to those of Brant but variable in shade. *Dates:* June 8 to July 7, Arctic Canada (A. C. Bent). *Incubation:* By female. One brood yearly.

RANGE. — Western North America and northeastern Asia. Breeds on Arctic coasts and islands; from Alaska to about 100° West longitude (Banks Island, etc.), north to Melville Island and west on Siberian coast to Taimyr Peninsula and New Siberia Islands; winters on Pacific coast (mainly of United States) from British Columbia to Lower California, inland in Oregon and Nevada, and on Asiatic coast to northern China and Japan; in migration on Pribilof Island and inland to Utah; casual or accidental on Atlantic coast; recorded in Massachusetts, New York and New Jersey.

DISTRIBUTION IN NEW ENGLAND. — *Massachusetts:* Bird sent to C. I. Goodale of Boston, killed at or near Chatham in spring of 1883;[1] bird shot at Chatham April 15, 1902, recorded by S. Prescott Fay, now in the collection of W. A. Carey of Boston.[2]

HAUNTS AND HABITS. Though the Black Brant has been taken but twice in New England, there are three records for New York and two for New Jersey, and it is likely that a few Black Brant may occur unnoticed among the large flocks of the Brant that annually seek our shores. Black Brant and Brant are said to intergrade where their breeding ranges meet or overlap, and if they interbreed we must expect that an occasional Pacific bird will follow the Atlantic Brant in migration. Probably all the Brants intergrade and will be recognized eventually as races of one species. The haunts, habits and food of the American birds are very similar except that *nigricans* migrates normally to the Pacific coast and *glaucogastra* to the Atlantic.

ECONOMIC STATUS. See page 284.

---

[1] Cory, C. B.: Auk, Vol. I, 1884, p. 96. [2] Auk, Vol. XXVII, 1910, p. 336.

Branta leucópsis (BECHSTEIN). Barnacle Goose.

DESCRIPTION. — Tail usually of 16 feathers; female slightly duller in color than male. *Adults:* Front and sides of head, chin and throat cream white; broad dark stripe from base of bill to eye; rest of head and neck black, the black extending on upper back and fore breast; scapulars, wing-coverts and inner secondaries bluish-gray, feathers with subterminal black crescentic bands and tipped white, giving a barred effect; flight-feathers blackish, darkening toward ends, a trifle ashy on exposed surfaces; middle part of rump and tail black; upper and under tail-coverts, sides of rump, belly and lower breast light grayish or whitish, sides and flanks shaded gray; axillars and wing-linings "ashy-gray," latter partly tipped white; iris hazel; bill, legs and feet black. *Young:* Similar to adults but black areas browner, and white face speckled with black; general plumage washed reddish-brown, more or less marked, according to age.

HEAD OF BARNACLE GOOSE
About ½ natural size.

MEASUREMENTS. — Length 25.00 to 28.00 in.; spread 52.00 to 56.00; folded wing about 17.00; tail about 6.00; bill about 1.50; tarsus about 2.75; very variable. Weight 2 lbs. 8 oz. to 5 lbs. Female averages much smaller than male.

MOLTS. — Most juvenal body feathers are molted in autumn and winter, and after a complete post-nuptial molt in the succeeding autumn young birds apparently become as adult; adult molts completely (July to December) and may have a partial spring molt.

FIELD MARKS. — "Boldly contrasting black and white plumage"; white face and forehead with wide black line from bill to eye; top of head and entire neck black; black legs, feet and bill.

VOICE. — A cackling note (C. F. R. Jourdain).

BREEDING. — On rocky hillsides or cliffs, in rock caves or on a rocky pinnacle. *Nest:* Usually on a projecting rock; a mound lined with white or light grayish down. *Eggs:* 3 to 6; white. *Dates:* Month of June, Spitzbergen. *Incubation:* By female. One brood yearly.

RANGE. — Northern part of Eastern Hemisphere. Breeds in northeastern Greenland and Spitz-bergen and probably in Novaya Zemlya and other Arctic islands and in northern Siberia; winters in northwestern Europe south to Baltic and North seas and British Isles, occasionally to Switzerland and Austria, and rarely to Azores, Spain and Italy; in migration to Iceland and western Greenland; casual or accidental in Labrador, James Bay, Vermont, Massachusetts, Rhode Island, Long Island and North Carolina.

DISTRIBUTION IN NEW ENGLAND. — A mere straggler probably from Greenland. *Vermont:* Marsh-field, head and neck of a Barnacle Goose (all that was unplucked) was found by Outram Bangs "in the Boston market this winter [1877–78 Ed.] which was shot in Marshfield, Vt."[1] Mr. Bangs states that this bird was with a lot of geese which were said to have come from Marshfield. *Massachusetts:* North Eastham, adult killed November 1, 1885, and mounted by N. Vickary.[2] J. A. Farley, who with W. E. Freeman secured the specimen for the William Brewster collection, says that this bird, shot by Joseph Dill, was one of three or four "presumably of the same species." J. G. Peters, Jr., wrote me in September, 1920, that on the flats at Wellfleet he saw a bird that he was sure was a Barnacle Goose. The

---

[1] Brewer, T. M.: Proceedings of the Boston Society of Natural History, Vol. XIX, 1876–1878, p. 307; Howe, R. H., Jr.: Contributions to North American Ornithology, Vol. II, 1902, p. 10.

[2] Ornithologist and Oölogist, Vol. XI, 1886, p. 16, where the locality is incorrectly given as "North Chatham." This error was again made in the Birds of Massachusetts by Howe and Allen.

bird was not wild and might readily have been taken, but Mr. Peters did not have a gun.   The tameness of this bird may indicate that it had escaped from captivity.   *Rhode Island:* Block Island, Miss Elizabeth Dickens reports that just at sunset one Sunday night in October, 1909, one was shot by Mr. Lovell Dickens.   *Connecticut:* Linsley records this species as occurring at Stonington,[1] but as he gives no definite data this record must be disregarded.

HAUNTS AND HABITS.   The Barnacle Goose is a mere straggler on the coasts of New England, probably from the shores of Greenland.   Though it is found mainly on the coast, it is not so maritime as the Brant, but sometimes visits inland districts.

Along the coast it feeds on the mud flats when the tide is out and at high tide repairs to the grassy banks of lake or river to feed.

SUBFAMILY **CYGNINÆ**.   SWANS.

Number of species in North America 3; in Massachusetts 1.

Swans are of large size, with necks extremely long, of 22 to 24 vertebræ.   The legs are placed far back.   Bare skin extends from eye to bill.   The tail is short and the plumage usually white, though in one species black and in another a contrast of black and white. Swans, like geese, are widely distributed and their ranges in some cases extend into the Arctic regions.   There are about ten species.

ECONOMIC STATUS.   Swans are valuable as food, as game and as domesticated fowls; they also furnish the swansdown of commerce.   Their food is chiefly vegetal, though they are alleged to destroy small mollusks and the spawn of fish.

NOTE.   In the journal of the Maine Ornithological Society (Vol. VI, 1904, p. 1) the capture of a "Trumpeter Swan" was reported.   This bird which was shot September 10, 1903, at Poke-a-moonshine Lake, Washington County, Maine, was afterward identified as a specimen of the Whooper Swan *Cygnus cygnus* (Linnæus) of the Old World, and is recorded as such by Knight in his Birds of Maine, 1908, p. 124, and in the Auk, Vol. XXVII, 1910, p. 79.   This specimen is said to have passed into the possession of the late John Lewis Childs of Floral Park, Long Island, New York.   I have been unable to trace it and have not seen it.   The measurements seem unusual for a Whooper Swan and even if correctly identified, it may have escaped from captivity in this country.   The occurrence of the species here in a wild state may be doubted.

Cÿgnus columbiánus (ORD).   Whistling Swan.

Other names: WILD SWAN; AMERICAN WHISTLING SWAN.

Plate 20.

DESCRIPTION. — Bill as long as head; less lengthened and less expanded at end than in Trumpeter Swan; distance from front angle of eye to hind end of nostril more than thence to end of bill; usually a yellow spot on naked skin before eye near base of bill; tail-feathers normally 20.   *Adults (sexes alike):* Plumage white, tail yellowish; some have rusty wash, chiefly on head; iris brown; bill, legs and feet

---

[1] Linsley, James H.: A Catalogue of the Birds of Connecticut; The American Journal of Science and Arts, Vol. XLIV, 1843, p. 269.

black. *Juvenal plumage:* "Sooty-brownish" with leaden shade about top and sides of head; neck and throat all round light dull leaden-ashy; back, tertials and wing-coverts dull leaden-ashy with silvery-gray luster, especially on wings; rump ashy-white, this deepening to dull leaden-ashy on tail coverts and tail; flight-feathers white mottled with ash-gray, this mottling increasing on terminal third and decreasing to nearly white toward base; under surface white with gray wash; "bill purplish-flesh color," nail and border along gape black; iris hazel; legs and feet livid flesh color (E. W. Nelson); general color gray, sometimes nearly a lead color first year (D. G. Elliot). *Downy young:* Pure white; bill, legs and feet yellow (D. G. Elliot).

MEASUREMENTS. — Length about 48.00 to 55.00 in.; spread about 72.00 to 88.00; folded wing 20.35 to 23.00; tail 7.00 to 8.50; bill about 3.55 to 4.00; "from eye to tip of bill under 5"; rear of nostril to tip of bill 1.86 to 2.16; tarsus 3.80 to 4.54. Weight 12 to 20 lbs. Female slightly smaller than male.

MOLTS. — Apparently no great change takes place in plumage of young during first winter, but they gradually assume lighter plumage and during next summer have a complete molt when wing-quills are shed; the young, now about 15 months of age, become practically as white as adults; some may require another year; the swan, a long-lived bird, may not reach full maturity before its fourth or fifth year; Dr. Brewer says that the bill is black in the 3d year, and that until the bird is fully 5 years old an occasional feather is still gray.[1] Adults have a complete molt in summer.

HEAD OF WHISTLING SWAN, AND OUTLINES OF BILL AND FOREHEAD, SEEN FROM ABOVE

Compare with head and bill of Trumpeter Swan (page 305).

FIELD MARKS. — *Adults:* Large size, pure white color, V-shaped flight-formation, very high flight with comparatively little wing movement and *extremely long necks;* no other birds resemble swans in flight. *Young:* Gray or dirty white.

VOICE. — A high-pitched plaintive *oo oo* uttered in couplets, probably by leader of flock; a high "flageolet-like" note (D. G. Elliot); harsh and striking notes or "soft musical trumpetings"; soft laughter, suggested by the syllables *wou how ou* (A. C. Bent); sounds like a slow shake of two notes on a clarinet (E. S. Cameron).

BREEDING. — On marsh or tundra near water. *Nest:* A heap of rubbish, moss, etc., concealed by moss or tussocks of grass. *Eggs:* 2 to 7; "4.00 by¯2.25 to 4.50 by 2.50 inches" (Coues); dull white with more or less discoloration. *Dates:* May 29 to July 5, Arctic America (A. C. Bent). *Incubation:* Period "said to be from 35 to 40 days" (A. C. Bent); by female. One brood yearly.

RANGE. — North America. Breeds mainly north of Arctic Circle and from northern Alaska and St. Lawrence Island south to Alaska Peninsula, east to Baffin Island and from Arctic islands (about latitude 74°) south to Barren Grounds of northern Canada and islands in Hudson Bay; in migration west rarely to Bering Island; winters on Pacific coast from southern Alaska rarely south to southern California; in interior in large bodies of open water from Lake Erie and southern Illinois to coast of Louisiana and Texas; and on Atlantic coast from Delaware and Maryland to South Carolina; rarely north to Massachusetts and south to Florida; casual in New Mexico and Mexico; accidental in Scotland, and Bermuda and Commander Islands.

---

[1] Baird, S. F., Brewer, T. M., and Ridgway, R.: Water Birds of North America, Vol. I, 1884, p. 427.

DISTRIBUTION IN NEW ENGLAND. — Rare migrant in all New England states chiefly in autumn; formerly winter resident in Massachusetts.

SEASON IN MASSACHUSETTS. — October and November; winter; March.

HAUNTS AND HABITS. To an ornithologist there is no more thrilling sound than the high double or triple note of the leader of a flock of swans and no more thrilling sight than that of the flock far up in the azure heights, their long necks stretched toward the pole, their glistening white plumage catching the rosy rays of the rising sun as they sweep grandly onward in V-shaped flock formation toward their home in the Arctic wilds. In New England we rarely see or hear them now. Once they were abundant in migration along our coasts and many a lake, swamp or point of land received its name from them. Swan Lake, "Swanholt," Swan Neck, Swan Point, names not rare in New England, indicate the former presence of these noble birds. Now the few that pass over or through our territory fly so high that they rarely are noticed, or they keep well out on wide water during daylight. Rarely their call is heard as they pass in the night to or from their inland feeding grounds in the lakes or rivers. During the last five years I have attempted to collect sight records of the passage of these birds, but the task is complicated by the fact that there are at large a few park swans of the European Mute species which are seen frequently at various points. It is evident, however, that small numbers of Whistling Swans still migrate through New England quite regularly. I have heard them passing in the night. Small flocks were seen in 1921 in Duxbury Bay, and others (a few) in various years in Cape Cod, Marthas Vineyard, Nantucket and Plymouth County ponds, and at the mouth of the Connecticut River. As they are protected by law, it is difficult to get the facts when one is killed.

Swans feed mainly by floating upon shallow water, thrusting down their heads to the bottom and digging up roots or breaking off other parts of aquatic plants. They rarely dive for their food. They have been known to dive and swim under water, however, when wounded and pursued, when mating, or when in summer while molting and unable to fly they seek by diving to escape from eagles. Swans are powerful birds, extremely rapid swimmers and strong, swift fliers. They are so heavy that they must flap and paddle along the surface for some distance before they can clear the water, but when once in the air they probably can exceed the speed of any of our ducks or geese. In alighting they sail down to the water and glide along the surface like a boat, but hold the wings partly spread until their impetus is spent.

Their food consists of a great variety of vegetation, both aquatic and terrestrial, and various forms of animal life which they glean mainly from the bottom in shallow water.

ECONOMIC STATUS. See page 302.

Cygnus buccinátor RICHARDSON.   Trumpeter Swan.

DESCRIPTION. — Bill longer and relatively wider at tip than that of Whistling Swan, rather longer than head; frontal outline of forehead where it meets upper surface of upper mandible more acute than in Whistling Swan; tail normally of 24 feathers. *Adults (sexes alike):* General plumage white, sometimes with rusty wash on head, and more rarely on neck and under plumage; iris brown; bill, naked lores and feet entirely black. *Young:* Smaller than adults; plumage grayish-brown or brownish-gray, head and upper neck with more or less rusty brown; bill and feet not entirely black; in first winter "feet dull yellowish brown, tinged olive, webs blackish brown" (Audubon).

MEASUREMENTS. — Length 58.50 to 72.00 in.; spread 8 to nearly 10 feet; wing 21.00 to 27.75; tail 8.00 to 9.60; bill 4.11 to 5.00; nostril to tip of bill 2.00 to 2.70 (position of nostril very variable and *not always diagnostic*); tarsus 4.00 to 5.25. Weight 15 to 31 lbs.; said rarely to reach 35 or even 36 lbs.; very large one recorded at "38 lbs." (Audubon).

MOLTS. — Young swans apparently have partial molt succeeding juvenal plumage during or after first winter, and complete molt in succeeding autumn, after which or during the following season most of them probably assume white plumage of adults, though perhaps not fully mature and in some cases showing some grayish feathers; adults have complete post-nuptial molt beginning in late July or in August, when flight-feathers and tail are shed; probably the Trumpeter molts as do other swans.

FIELD MARKS. — Adult like Whistling Swan but much larger; probably indistinguishable from it in the field, except close at hand, when black unmarked bill can be plainly seen; lack of knob at base of upper mandible distinguishes Trumpeter from ordinary park swans (*Cygnus olor* Gmelin). *Young in spring:* Has the body grayish-brown or brownish-gray, while young of Whistling Swan has body dirty white.

HEAD OF TRUMPETER SWAN, AND OUTLINES OF BILL AND FOREHEAD, SEEN FROM ABOVE

Compare with head and bill of Whistling Swan (page 303).

VOICE. — The Kootenai Indian name for a swan, *Ko-hoh*, pronounced with a guttural intonation "is a very good reproduction of the notes of a Trumpeter Swan" (E. S. Cameron). Resonant trumpeting tones. Sonorous, resembling the notes of a "French horn" (Hearne).

BREEDING. — Usually on an island or near some large body of water. *Nest:* on a slight elevation, a large structure of sods, grass, rushes, etc., lined with down and some white feathers; muskrat or beaver houses often adapted, flattened and used as nests. *Eggs:* 2 to 8, elliptical or oval, rough-shelled, pale yellow or creamy white; 4.38 to 4.51 by 2.78 to 3.06 in. *Dates:* April 7, Alberta, June 17 to July 9, Arctic Canada (A. C. Bent). *Incubation:* Period unknown. Probably about 40 days; by both sexes.

RANGE. — North America, chiefly south of the Arctic coast, formerly ranging to the Atlantic and Pacific coasts; now confined to the interior; bred formerly from Rocky Mountain region east to west coast of Hudson Bay and from near Arctic coast south to Indiana, Missouri, Nebraska, Montana, Idaho, and casually west to Fort Yukon, Alaska, British Columbia and probably western Washington; wintered from southern Montana, southern Indiana, and southern Illinois, south to Louisiana and Texas, and from southern British Columbia to southern California; formerly accidental or occasional in migration on Atlantic coast from Maine to the Carolinas; now approaching extinction; breeding now very sparsely in western and northwestern Canada, and possibly in some wilder parts of Montana, present winter range not well known.

DISTRIBUTION IN NEW ENGLAND. — An accidental straggler. Belknap (1792), who rates the Trumpeter as a migrant in New Hampshire, says that "our swan" makes a sound "resembling that of a trumpet" and that it has been known to weigh 36 lbs. and to reach 6 ft. in length when stretched.[1] These are the dimensions of a large heavy Trumpeter. The Whistling Swan never attained such a size. Merriam reports the Trumpeter Swan as probably formerly occurring at East Windsor Hill, Connecticut, but no specimens were taken.[2] The only definite New England record substantiated by a specimen is the capture of a Trumpeter Swan which was found exhausted and taken alive Nov. 25, 1901, at Lewiston, Maine. This bird was sent to the New York Zoölogical park.[3]

HAUNTS AND HABITS. The Trumpeter Swan, a splendid white bird, the largest of all American wild-fowl, formerly nested on islands in many lakes or marshes in the latitude of New England and still farther south. It may have bred as far east as Ohio or western New York, but there are no definite records and so far as we know the bird always bred only in the western states and in Canada. Formerly it frequented ponds of no great size, as well as large lakes, but was mainly a fresh-water fowl, rarely seen off the coast. Its habits are similar to those of other swans. It seldom dives except to escape an enemy, but it can swim long distances under water. It gradually disappeared before settlement and the advance of civilization. Its eggs were taken and used as food. Its young were caught or shot for food before they were able to fly, and adult birds were killed at all seasons and at every opportunity. In Canada the same methods were used to bring about its extermination, and the trade in swans-down offered further incentive for the destruction of the species. Today there may be a few birds breeding in some of the wilder parts of Montana and Wyoming, otherwise they have retired to remote wildernesses in Canadian wilds seeking safe nesting places. In 1915 Mr. H. K. Coale could find but sixteen specimens with authentic data preserved in museums.[4]

The following paragraph is taken from my Game Birds, Wildfowl and Shore Birds.

"At the approach of the frost king the Trumpeter leaves its breeding-grounds in the northwest and moves southward in triangular flock formation. The flocks move on like those of the Canada Goose, led by some old male, who, when tired of breasting the full force of the air currents, calls for relief, and falls back into the ranks, giving way to another. In migration they fly at such immense heights that often the human eye fails to find them, but even then their resonant, discordant trumpetings can be plainly heard. When seen with a glass at that giddy height in the heavens, crossing the sky in their exalted and unswerving flight, sweeping along at a speed exceeding that of the fastest express train, traversing a continent on the wings of the wind, their long lines glistening like silver in the bright sunlight, they present the grandest and most impressive spectacle in bird life to be found on this continent. When at last they find their haven of rest they swing in wide majestic circuits, spying out their landfall, until, their spiral reconnaissance ended and their apprehensions quite allayed, they sink gently down to the grateful waters to rest, drink, bathe and feed at ease."

[1] Belknap, Jeremy: History of New Hampshire, 1792, p. 167.
[2] Merriam, C. Hart: Review of Birds of Connecticut, 1877, p. 120.
[3] Coale, Henry K.: Auk, Vol. XXXII, 1915, p. 87.

[4] Auk, Vol. XXXII, 1915, p. 90.

PLATE 21

PLATE 21

GLOSSY IBIS
Page 309

ADULT

GREEN HERON
Page 334

ADULT

CORY'S LEAST BITTERN
Page 323

ADULT MALE

LEAST BITTERN
Page 321

ADULT MALE

ADULT FEMALE

All one-fourth natural size.

BITTERN
Page 315

ADULT MALE IN BREEDING
PLUMAGE

The Trumpeter's food is largely vegetal, pondweeds and the roots, stalks, leaves and seeds of many water-plants are eaten. It is said also to take mollusks and crustaceans.

ECONOMIC STATUS. Young swans, properly cooked, were said to resemble roast goose, and even some of the old birds when hung long enough were palatable. The contents of swans' eggs were edible, and that of one egg would nearly fill an ordinary drinking cup. Swans-down was for many years a staple article of commerce. The Trumpeter is a valuable bird and apparently harmless, but doomed.

ORDER HERODIONES. HERONS, STORKS, IBISES, ETC.

Number of species in North America 20; in Massachusetts 11.

This Order includes long-legged, long-necked, long-billed, short-tailed waders that feed in shallow water along shore, on muddy flats or in marshes and swamps. The bill is long and straight or curved. The wings are long, broad and rounded. The toes are usually long, slender, never fully webbed. All members of the order can perch in trees. The food is principally aquatic or amphibious animal life and also terrestrial insects.

SUBORDER IBIDES. SPOONBILLS AND IBISES

Number of species in North America 5; in Massachusetts 1.

FAMILY THRESKIORNITHIDÆ. IBISES.

Number of species in North America 4; in Massachusetts 1.

Ibises have the bill very long, slender, cylindric and curved downward like that of a curlew; a deep groove extending down each side of one or both mandibles nearly to tip which is rather obtuse, broad and depressed; the size is rather large; the legs of medium length. There are about 32 species widely distributed.

ECONOMIC STATUS. Ibises are important as destroyers of locusts and other insect pests. In ancient Egypt the Ibis was considered a sacred bird, largely because of its value to the agriculturist. About 200,000 Ibises nesting in a large swamp in Australia were estimated to consume 25 tons of grasshoppers and other insects daily.[1]

Guára álba (LINNÆUS). White Ibis.

Other names: SPANISH CURLEW; WHITE CURLEW.

Fig. 27.

DESCRIPTION. — Upper mandible grooved from nostril to tip; most of face, forehead and chin bare; toes webbed basally. *Adults (sexes alike):* Plumage white except "deep glossy steel-blue" tips of several outer primaries (these appear black at a distance); most of bill bare; skin of face and of legs flesh color, orange or a shade of red or carmine, according to season; bill pale reddish, flesh color or

[1] LeSoeuf, W. H. D.: American Forestry, Vol. XXVI, 1920, p. 410.

orange toward base, tipped dusky (all bare parts said to be carmine at height of nuptial season); iris "pearly blue," "light blue" or straw, according to season. *Young in transition plumage:* Dull brown, with rump showing whitish feathers; tail gray; bill yellowish-orange; iris brown; legs bluish-gray. •*Juvenal plumage:* Dull brown, head and neck streaked with whitish; rump, upper tail-coverts, base of tail and all under plumage white; iris blue, brown or hazel; bare skin of head pink; legs "cream" or bluish-pink.

MEASUREMENTS. — Very variable; length 21.50 to 27.50 in.; spread 37.00 to 40.00; folded wing 10.30 to 12.50; tail 4.00 to 5.00; bill 4.15 to 7.00; tarsus 3.10 to 4.00. Weight 2 lbs. (Audubon). Female averages smaller than male.

MOLTS. — Young molt from juvenal plumage rather late (December or January); molt continues more or less through first winter and spring; white feathers appear gradually in the plumage; most young birds appear to become pure white and indistinguishable from adults the next summer, while a few are still brown and white in June and may require another year to assume white plumage; adults apparently molt both in autumn and in late winter and spring, but material examined is insufficient to determine this.

FIELD MARKS. — *Adult:* Might be mistaken for Wood Ibis (which is very much larger and has a much heavier bill); pure white plumage, black wing-tips, long, slender, curved bill and size (rather larger than Green Heron) render them otherwise unmistakable. *Young:* Appears much lighter than young of Glossy Ibis and dull brown, *not* dark, glossy-green.

VOICE. — A hoarse cackle (G. B. Grinnell); resembling the syllables *hunk, hunk, hunk* (Audubon).

BREEDING. — Usually in southern swamps or marshes. *Nest:* In bushes or trees, in reeds or tangles; built mainly of reed-stalks and weeds or sticks and twigs. *Eggs:* 3 to 5; 2.25 by 1.60 in.; dull white, spotted and blotched with "pale yellowish and dark reddish-brown," these spots usually most numerous at larger end. *Dates:* March 28 to May 1, Florida. *Incubation:* Period 20 to 23 days (Beebe); 21 days (Burns).

RANGE. — Subtropical North America to northern South America; from Lower California, Texas and South Carolina south to West Indies, northern Brazil and northern Peru; breeds from southern South Carolina, southern Mississippi, southern Louisiana, southern Texas and northern Mexico southward; casual to north central Utah, South Dakota, Illinois, eastern Pennsylvania, New Jersey, Long Island, Connecticut and Vermont; winters from Gulf coast and central Florida southward.

DISTRIBUTION IN NEW ENGLAND. — Accidental visitant. *Vermont:* South Woodstock, bird taken "some 6 or 7 years ago the past summer" [1877 or 1878 Ed.].[1] *Connecticut:* Milford, May 23, 1875, adult seen at close range by Dr. George Bird Grinnell.[2]

HAUNTS AND HABITS. The White Ibis has been reported in Massachusetts,[3] but there is no record substantiated by the specimen or attested by any competent ornithologist. Nevertheless, as the bird is recorded in Vermont and Connecticut, probably it has appeared here at some time. I have seen it only in southern Florida where, when wading across partially submerged prairies, I have known a gunshot to start up hundreds if not thousands of these white birds and cause them to perform their graceful evolutions as they drifted and turned upon the wind. There is a northward movement in spring when some individuals occasionally get beyond the normal range, and toward the close of summer young birds and a few of the adults wander northward, as do many herons. One or the other of these movements accounts for most of the occurrences of this species in the northern states.

---

[1] Tracy, C. O.: Ornithologist and Oölogist, Vol. X, 1885, p. 10.
[2] Grinnell, G. B.: American Naturalist, Vol. IX, 1875, p. 470.
[3] DeKay: Birds of New York, 1843, p. 230.

The food of the White Ibis, as reported by Mr. W. C. Henderson of the Bureau of Biological Survey, after examining nine stomachs, includes crayfish, fishes, various beetles, snails, water-bugs, dragonfly nymphs and frogs.[1] Audubon includes small crabs, slugs, snails, flying insects and crayfish in its dietary.

Economic Status.   See page 307.

Plégadis falcinéllus (Linnæus).   Glossy Ibis.

Other name: Black Curlew.

Plate 21.

Description. — Bill long, regularly down-curved and grooved on sides of both mandibles from base to tip; skin before eye and around it naked, slaty-blue or "greenish"; claws all long, inner edge of middle one enlarged and incised 3 or 4 times; tail of 12 feathers. *Adults in breeding plumage (sexes alike):* Top of head, cheeks and chin glossy greenish-black, with violet-purple reflections; hind head, neck, fore part of back and fore part of lesser wing-coverts region rich reddish-chestnut, darkest on back; under plumage (except under tail-coverts, axillars and wing-linings) uniform bright reddish-chestnut, lighter than neck; remaining upper plumage, as well as wing-linings, axillars, tail-coverts and tail, glossy, metallic, dark purple, green, and bronze; under surface of wings and tail burnished metallic green, bronze and purple, tint varying with light; bill dark grayish-brown or blackish; "in this fresh-killed specimen it is very nearly clay color, with a tinge of green" (F. C. Browne); iris brown or hazel; legs and feet brown, dark brownish-olive or blackish. *Adults in winter plumage:* Similar to breeding plumage but head and neck brownish-black streaked white; below mostly blackish usually with some reddish-chestnut. *Young in first winter plumage:* Similar to juvenal plumage, but more iridescent above and browner below becoming much like adult winter plumage but juvenal wing-coverts retained. *Young in juvenal plumage:* Head and neck grayish-brown, streaked white; rest of upper plumage iridescent glossy green with little purple; under plumage dark, sooty brownish-gray; bill greenish-gray (almost black); bare part of head dusky; iris, legs and feet dark; "feet blackish-brown" (Audubon). *Downy young:* Blackish, usually with white band or patch on top of head and some white on throat; "bill yellowish and black; feet yellowish."

Measurements. — Length 22.00 to 25.00 in.; spread about 36.00; folded wing 10.00 to 11.85; tail 4.00; bill 4.30 to 5.50; tarsus 2.90 to 4.30.

Molts. — Juvenal body plumage is molted in late summer and autumn; and after complete molt during next spring young apparently resembles adult; adult has a nearly complete or complete pre-nuptial molt (January to May) and complete postnuptial molt (June to November).

Field Marks. — Size a little larger than Green Heron, heavier and longer down-curved bill; cannot be mistaken for a heron in flight as its neck is not withdrawn but stretched out like that of a duck or curlew; at a distance resembles a large curlew but appears *black*.

Breeding. — In tropical swamps. *Nest:* Usually in reeds or bushes. *Eggs:* 1.90 to 2.10 by 1.30 to 1.48; dark greenish-blue, like those of herons but rougher. *Incubation:* Period 21 days (Burns). Probably one brood yearly.

Range. — Tropical and subtropical regions, mainly Eastern Hemisphere; from Spain, Hungary, Greece, Persia, Turkestan and southern China south to southern Africa, Borneo and Australia; rare and local in southeastern United States from Louisiana to Florida, and in West Indies; casual north to Colorado, Missouri, Nebraska, Iowa, Wisconsin, Michigan, Ontario, Quebec, Nova Scotia and Prince Edward Island; reported in Arizona and California. (Most far inland records are questionable and may prove to be those of the White-faced Glossy Ibis.)

---

[1] Pearson, T. G.: Bird-Lore, Vol. XXVII, 1925, p. 77.

DISTRIBUTION IN NEW ENGLAND. — Accidental visitor. Records: *New Hampshire:* Alton, adult, October, 1858, Palmer.[1] *Massachusetts:* Nantucket, September, 1869, Allen;[2] Cambridge, May 8 (*circ.*), 1850, 1 taken out of 3 seen, Concord, May, 1850, 1 taken, Middleboro, May 6 or 7, 1850, 2 taken out of 3 seen, Browne;[3] Orleans, adult, May 5, 1878, Brewer;[4] Eastham, May 4, 1878, Cory;[5] East Orleans, May 5, 1878, Allen.[6] *Connecticut:* Stratford, Linsley in his Catalogue of the Birds of Connecticut reports that he "obtained 5 individuals about six years since" [1837 Ed.];[7] Middletown, bird taken May 9, 1850.[8]

HAUNTS AND HABITS. This bird is a mere straggler here from the tropics. Its movements are graceful and rapid. It is usually seen in flocks which wheel and turn in graceful evolutions. Nuttall says that "a specimen has occasionally been exposed for sale in the market of Boston,"[9] and he is cited by Peabody.[10]

The fullest account of the Glossy Ibis in New England is in Stearns and Coues' New England Bird Life, part II, 1883, page 255. The details of the taking of the five Ibises in May, 1850, are given fully by Mr. F. C. Browne in the Auk, Vol. IV, 1887, page 97 and the Middletown, Conn., bird is reported additionally and as fully by Mr. J. H. Sage on page 253 of the same Auk.

It will be seen that there have been two known flights or special irruptions of the Glossy Ibis into southern New England — one in 1850 and the other in 1878. Both were in May. As the authors of New England Bird Life truly say: "Doubtless [there were] many more than we have heard of." They are speaking definitely of the 1850 flight, but the remark applies as well to the flight of 1878, and is specially reinforced by the statement of Mr. William Brewster that he saw on July 14, 1878, in Belmont, a flock of 20 birds in flight which he believed were Glossy Ibises.[11] Furthermore, Dr. T. M. Brewer notes that in the following August [of 1878] several birds called locally "black curlews" were seen on Prince Edward Island and "one of them was shot . . . but not preserved." He adds: "Although inconclusive this evidence seems to indicate the presence of this species in a locality north of the United States."[12]

Dr. Samuel Cabot in his article on the 1850 "flight" in Proceedings Boston Society Natural History, June 19, 1850 (Vol. III, p. 314), referring to Nuttall's statement that a specimen has been occasionally found in the Boston market, says that "probably at the time when he made this observation there had been a flight of them into this state, similar to what has occurred this year."

[1] Palmer, Charles: American Naturalist, Vol. V, 1871, p. 120.
[2] Allen, J. A.: American Naturalist, Vol. III, 1870, p. 637.
[3] Browne, F. C.: Auk, Vol. IV, 1887, p. 97.
[4] Brewer, Dr. T. M.: Bulletin Nuttall Ornithological Club, Vol. III, 1878, p. 151.
[5] Cory, C. B.: Bulletin Nuttall Ornithological Club, Vol. III, 1878, p. 152.
[6] Allen, J. A.: Bulletin Nuttall Ornithological Club, Vol. III, 1878, p. 152.
[7] Linsley, Rev. J. H.: American Journal Science and Arts, Vol. XLIV, 1843, p. 266.
[8] Middletown Sentinel and Witness, May 21, 1850; see also Sage, Bishop and Bliss, Birds of Connecticut, 1913, p. 43; Sage, Auk, Vol. IV, 1887, p. 253; Stearns and Coues, New England Bird Life, Pt. II, 1883, p. 254 *et seq.*
[9] Nuttall, Thomas: Manual of Ornithology, Vol. II, 1834, p. 89.
[10] Peabody, Wm. B. O.: Report on the Ornithology of Massachusetts, 1839, p. 365.
[11] Birds of the Cambridge Region of Massachusetts, 1906, p. 131.
[12] Proceedings Boston Society Natural History, Vol. XX, 1878–80, 1881, p. 272.

The Glossy Ibis flight of 1850 (and that of 1878) probably was due to storms from the tropics.

In many respects the month of April, 1850, was unusual. It was unusually cold, south as well as north, along the Atlantic seaboard ("the coldest April in 30 years"), and was preceded in the tropics by atmospheric convulsions such as a "terrific tornado" at Nassau and a hurricane at Mexico City. The newspapers of Boston and Baltimore contain many allusions to the raw, rough weather of April. On the 13th there was a storm from St. John to St. Louis. In Boston this was a violent easterly gale of wind, rain and hail, while on the 14th at St. Louis 8 inches of snow fell. This "very extensive" storm was called "a tornado" in Boston and "a hurricane" in Jersey City. Again, on the 27th–29th in southern New England there was a tremendous downpour, with "high wind-squalls from the south"; this storm also was widespread. In Carroll County, Maryland, it was pronounced "one of the most fearful ever known." The low barometer (29.37) on the 29th in Providence indicates the severity of the storm. It was very cold the last of April and the first week of May in Boston. On May 1st, at sunrise, the glass registered only 37½ degrees. A high southwest wind prevailed and wires were down. On the 2d there was a very destructive hailstorm in Maryland. The copious rains swelled the Hudson, Connecticut, Merrimack and other streams so that the resulting freshets "proved very destructive in all directions." On Sunday, May 5th (day and night), again there were heavy rains which caused more freshets. This "spell of weather" lasted from the afternoon of May 4 to May 6. "For the past 36 hours . . . rain has fallen copiously nearly all the time," says the Boston Transcript. The Baltimore Patriot also refers to this Sunday night "blow." The high waters were widespread, for there was "a great flood in the lower Mississippi Valley" and the river was "miles wide at Vicksburg." To continue the tale: "Rain has fallen steadily and in quantity from an early hour this morning and many of the streets are running brooks; wind is south southeast" (Boston newspaper of May 9). Under caption of "The Great Storm" the New Orleans Picayune of May 10 describes this hurricane of May 8 on the Gulf coast, while the Boston Morning Advertiser of May 20 says that "evidences of the severity of the storm were seen at many points along the coast. . . ."

In connection with the Glossy Ibis irruption of 1878 it is of interest that the local records of the U. S. Weather Bureau show that on May 5 there was a gale from the south and southwest, its highest velocity (forty miles) being at 2.40 P.M. This velocity on land means at least a fifty-mile velocity at sea.

ECONOMIC STATUS. See page 307.

Suborder CICONIÆ. Storks, etc.

Number of species in North America 2; in Massachusetts 1.

Storks inhabit chiefly temperate and warm temperate parts of the world; bill, stout, straight or curved up or down; plumage without powder-down tracts; upper mandible not grooved.

Family CICONIIDÆ. Storks and Wood Ibises.

Number of species in North America 2; in Massachusetts 1.

Subfamily MYCTERIINÆ. Wood Ibises.

This subfamily has the bill long, very stout and broad at base; much heavier than in the true ibises and down-curved toward tip.

Myctéria americána Linnæus. Wood Ibis.

Other names: GOURD-HEAD; GANNET.

Fig. 26.

DESCRIPTION. — Basal half of bill straight, terminal part curved downward; whole head and back part of neck bare, less so in female, mostly feathered in young; front toes webbed at base and bordered to claws with a narrow membrane. *Adults:* Entire plumage white, except flight-feathers, primary wing-coverts and alula which are "dark, glossy green and purple," appearing black; tail rich, dark purple with greenish reflections, also appearing black at a distance; in high plumage linings of wings pinkish; bare head livid "grayish-blue and yellowish," its sides "dark bluish purple" (Audubon); bill dull yellowish or brownish horn color, edges yellow, ridge dusky; legs blue or dusky-green, toes blackish or yellowish and black, webs with yellowish tinge; iris dark brown or dark red. *Young in juvenal plumage:* Head and neck downy but feathered (except region about bill in front of eyes and on top of head between eyes) grayish-brown, growing darker on back and sides of neck; general plumage dark gray; wings and tail dusky or blackish.

MEASUREMENTS. — Length 35.00 to 47.50 in.; spread 62.00 to 66.00; folded wing 17.60 to 19.50; tail 6.30 to 7.85; bill 6.10 to 9.30, depth at base 2.00; tarsus 7.00 to 8.50. Weight male 11 lbs. 12 oz.; female 9 lbs. 4 oz. (Audubon).

MOLTS. — Some time during first winter and spring young bird molts from its juvenal plumage gradually assuming white plumage; meanwhile head becomes bare; young bird appears to assume plumage similar to that of adult the second summer, but Audubon says that the bird becomes fully adult in its fourth year; adults seem to molt at various times in spring and fall; probably the autumnal molt is complete.

FIELD MARKS. — Size near that of Canada Goose; dark, naked head, long extended legs, white plumage, black flight-feathers and down-curved bill; young are gray or only partly white; in flight head is not drawn close to breast as in herons; its long legs and curved bill distinguish it at once from the similarly colored Gannet.

VOICE. — Usually silent; a rough, guttural, croaking note when frightened (T. M. Brewer).

BREEDING. — In colonies; in swampy regions. *Nest:* In trees, sometimes very high; a platform of sticks. *Eggs:* 2 to 3; 2.75 by 1.75 to 1.80 in.; elliptical; rough; chalky white, more or less stained. *Dates:* December 8, January 5, March 14, Florida.

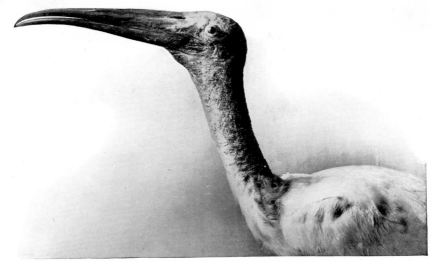

FIG. 26. — HEAD OF WOOD IBIS

From a specimen in Museum of Comparative Zoölogy

Photograph by Dr. Arthur A. Allen

FIG. 27. — WHITE IBIS

Page 307

RANGE. — Temperate and tropical America from central California, Arizona, Texas, Ohio Valley and South Carolina south to Argentina. Breeds over most of its range; casual north to Montana, Wisconsin, Michigan, Ontario, North Carolina, New York, New Jersey and New England.

DISTRIBUTION IN NEW ENGLAND. — Records: *Maine:* Berwick, bird shot July 16, 1896, and preserved in collection of Prof. J. Y. Stanton of Lewiston;[1] Harpswell, immature bird found dead August 10, 1922, at Mill Cove, Cundy's Harbor, and now in Lee Museum collection of Bowdoin College.[2] *New Hampshire:* Lancaster, adult taken in spring of 1922.[3] *Vermont:* Williston, bird taken "about 5 years ago" [1897 Ed.], and now in collection of the University of Vermont (one of two birds that remained for several weeks at a pond).[4] *Massachusetts:* Seekonk, young male taken July 17, 1896, and secured for the Brewster collection;[5] Chilmark, young bird taken November 26, 1918, by James A. Vincent and now in collection of Boston Society of Natural History.[6] (The Georgetown record, June 19, 1880, is doubtful.) *Rhode Island:* Barrington, young bird shot August 8, 1896.[7]

HAUNTS AND HABITS. The Wood Ibis is really a stork with a down-curved bill, and it is unfortunate that the name "Ibis" has become attached to it. It is a large, heavy, powerful bird, and in its full plumage is not likely to be mistaken for any other bird when seen close at hand. I have seen and taken it only in Florida, where it usually frequents swamps and marshes. It seems to be extremely gluttonous, but when well fed it often exercises its wonderful powers of flight by mounting to great heights and wheeling and sailing there somewhat after the manner of the White Pelican. Wood Ibises sometimes gather in enormous numbers in southern swamps. Dr. T. Gilbert Pearson says :

"Of all the various species of Storks known to inhabit the earth, only two are found in North America. One of these, the Jabiru (*Jabiru mycteria*) of tropical America, occasionally wanders north to Texas, but the other species, the Wood Ibis, is with us in goodly numbers. They breed in the southern United States, chiefly in Florida. They are gregarious at all times, although now and then small bands wander away from the main flock. I once saw at least five thousand of these birds in a drove, feeding on a grassy prairie in central Florida. When disturbed by the report of a gun they arose, a vast white and black mass, and the roar of their wings coming across the lake resembled nothing so much as the rumbling of distant thunder.

"They breed in colonies numbering hundreds or thousands of pairs, and they always select the tallest trees for nesting sites. For several years the Audubon Society has been guarding a colony in 'Big Cypress' swamp of south Florida. In the rookery nearly every tree has its nest and some of the cypresses with wide-spreading limbs hold six or eight of them. This colony occupies an area of from two hundred to five hundred yards wide and about five miles in length. Here, as in other rookeries, Fish Crows are a great

---

[1] Knight, Ora W.: Birds of Maine, 1908, p. 125.

[2] Gross, A. O.: Maine Naturalist, Vol. II, 1922, p. 59, and *in litt.*

[3] Howe, Miss Addie Inez: *in litt.*

[4] Perkins, Geo. H., and Howe, C. D.: A Preliminary List of the Birds found in Vermont, 1901, p. 12; and Howe, R. H., Jr.: Contributions to North American Ornithology, 1902, p. 11.

[5] Brewster, Wm.: Auk, Vol. XIII, 1896, p. 341.

[6] Brooks, W. Sprague: Auk, Vol. XXXVI, 1919, p. 565.

[7] Hathaway, H. S.: Osprey, Vol. I, 1897, p. 67.

scourge. All day a stream of Crows can be seen flying from the pine woods to the swamp, or returning with eggs stuck on the ends of their bills.

"I had the opportunity to witness the rather odd manner in which these birds sometimes get their prey. The water was low at this season and in the pine flats various ponds, which ordinarily cover many acres, were partially or entirely dried up. One of these, now reduced to a length of about one hundred feet and with a width perhaps half as great, contained many small fish crowded together. Thirty-seven Wood Ibises had taken possession of this pool and seemed to be scratching the bottom, evidently for the purpose of making the already thick water so muddy that the fish would be forced to the surface. The numerous downward strokes of the bare, bony heads fully demonstrated the effectiveness of their enterprise. 'Gourd Head,' 'Iron Head,' and 'Gannet' are the appellations given to these birds by many swamp-dwellers to whom the name Wood Ibis is unknown.

"After the breeding season these Storks wander north as far as Pennsylvania and Michigan. Often one may find them on the wide marshes, either salt or fresh water, standing perfectly still for an hour or more at a time, the long heavy bill pointed downward and resting on the skin of the thick, naked neck. On such occasions they seem to represent the personification of dejection." [1]

After the breeding season this stork straggles very rarely to New England.

The Wood Ibis' food is believed to be mainly fish, reptiles and other aquatic animals such as crayfish. Audubon says that it eats young rails.

ECONOMIC STATUS. The Wood Ibis is so rare as to be of no economic importance in the North.

SUBORDER HERODII. HERONS, EGRETS, BITTERNS, ETC.

Number of species in North America 13; in Massachusetts 9.

This order includes long-necked, narrow-bodied, long-legged wading birds with hind toe and its claw long, tarsi normally scaled and inner edge of middle claw pectinate. The bill is variable but usually narrow and wedge-shaped; the plumage with two to four powder-down tracts.

FAMILY ARDEIDÆ. HERONS, BITTERNS, ETC.

Number of species in North America 13; in Massachusetts 9.

In this family powder-down tracts (of oily specialized under down), reach high development (herons have two or three pairs, boat-bills, four); the feather tracts are narrow; the lower neck often bare behind, the feathers long and loose. Most species have crests and plumes, particularly during breeding season. The head, neck and body are narrow; lores naked; nostrils long, narrow; wings long, broad, ample; toes long, slender, outer usually connected to middle by small basal web; inner side of middle toenail with dis-

---

[1] Nature Lovers Library, Birds of America, Vol. I, 1917, p. 179.

tinct comb-like edge. All species are more or less maritime or aquatic; in flight the head is usually drawn in and the neck folded close to the breast.

ECONOMIC STATUS. Birds of this family feed largely on fish, frogs and other aquatic animals and to some extent on the enemies of fish. They eat some young birds but also kill enemies of birds, such as snakes, fish, mice, rats, etc. Many of them feed largely on destructive insects like locusts and cutworms. Their economic status is not well known, but doubtless they are indispensable aids in keeping true the balance of life.

SUBFAMILY **BOTAURINÆ**. BITTERNS.

Number of species in North America 2; in Massachusetts 2.

Bitterns are herons of rather inconspicuous colors; mostly without long crests or plumes in breeding season. The tail feathers usually are 10, broad and soft; the outer toe shorter than the inner; claws long, little, and curved. Bitterns do not commonly nest on trees in colonies but separately on or near the ground.

Botaúrus lentiginósus (MONTAGU). **Bittern.**

Other names: STAKE-DRIVER; INDIAN HEN; MEADOW HEN; BOG HEN; THUNDER-PUMP; PLUM PUDD'N; DUNK-A-DOO; MARSH HEN; BARREL-MAKER.

Plate 21.

DESCRIPTION. — Neck practically bare behind, its feathers and those of back of head long, loose; tail, 10 feathers, short, slightly rounded. *Adults (sexes alike):* General color light or tawny-brown; upper plumage rather inconspicuously marked and mottled with irregular spots, bars and freckles of various darker browns and buffy; chin and upper throat white or buffy-white with a median stripe of brown on throat; otherwise lighter below than above, the feathers with brown dark-edged stripes; top of head usually darker than general plumage, but sometimes rusty; a buffy stripe over eye; flight-feathers brownish-black (sometimes bluish), brown tipped; axillars finely barred and freckled with brown, wing-linings mainly buff, freckled brown; tail brown more or less mottled; center of belly and under tail-coverts pale buff with few if any brown freckles; narrow brown stripe on each side of white chin, widening into a long velvety-black patch on side of neck; bill mostly pale yellowish or yellowish-green, ridge blackish; dark brown stripe on bare yellow skin of lores (sometimes continued on feathers behind eye); iris yellow; legs and feet yellowish-green or greenish-yellow. *Young in first winter plumage:* Like adult. *Young in juvenal plumage:* Like adult but no black patch on side of neck, plumage softer and markings not so pronounced; lighter markings more buffy or paler.

MEASUREMENTS. — (Very variable); length 23.00 to 34.00 in.; spread 32.00 to 50.00; folded wing 9.50 to 13.50; tail 3.00 to 4.00; bill 2.50 to 3.50; tarsus 3.10 to 3.95. Weight 1 lb. 6 oz. to 2 lbs. Female smaller than male.

MOLTS. — Young bird molts juvenal body-feathers (August to November) but retains wings and tail, becoming otherwise practically indistinguishable from adults the first winter; adults have complete molt (July or August to November), and some specimens show indications of partial prenuptial molt (February to May).

FIELD MARKS. — Size of Night Heron; a large, brownish, slow-flying bird, with wide black streak on side of neck, broad, brown, black-tipped wings and long yellowish-green bill; flies like other herons with neck drawn in and legs extended behind; alights usually on ground, rather rarely on bushes or trees, unlike young Night Heron, which lights commonly on trees and is often mistaken for Bittern.

VOICE. — A harsh, hollow croak, sometimes rattling and prolonged; usually while flying a nasal *haink* and croaking *ok-ok-ok-ok* (Wm. Brewster); also "a mere quack" (O. A. Knight); peculiar love notes like the sound of a wooden pump; young, when small, a "fife-like peep," later a harsh rattle (C. C. Abbott).

BREEDING. — In swamps or marshes, commonly amid marsh vegetation. *Nest:* Rarely in bushes or trees, usually on ground or matted marsh vegetation, rarely in hayfield, sometimes partly in water; when over water reeds may be bent over into a platform as a support for the nest; flat, usually of grasses, reeds, etc. *Eggs:* 4 to 6, sometimes 7; 2.25 by 1.80 to 1.90 by 1.40 in.; elliptical; varying in color; "olive-brown," "brownish-drab" or "pale olive-buff." *Dates:* May 1 to June 13, New England. *Incubation:* Period at least 4 weeks (Verdi Burtch); probably by female. One brood yearly.

RANGE. — Most of North America and Middle America. Breeds from central British Columbia, central Mackenzie, northern Saskatchewan, northern Manitoba, southern Ungava (central Quebec), southern Labrador and Newfoundland south to southern California, Mexico, northern Arizona, southern Colorado, Kansas, Arkansas (probably), Missouri, Alabama (possibly), Louisiana (casually), Kentucky and South Carolina, but rare to casual in southern part of this range; winters from southwestern British Columbia (casually), California, Arizona, southern Texas, Louisiana, lower Ohio valley and Massachusetts (casually), south to Bahamas, Porto Rico, Cuba and Panama; casual in Bermuda, Jamaica, Porto Rico and Europe.

DISTRIBUTION IN NEW ENGLAND. — Rather uncommon migrant and uncommon local summer resident in Maine, New Hampshire and Vermont; common migrant and rather uncommon summer resident generally in Massachusetts, Rhode Island and Connecticut; common summer resident, locally however, in marshy regions of Massachusetts, particularly in river marshes; casual in winter in Massachusetts.

SEASON IN MASSACHUSETTS. — March 15 to November 28 (winter); winter records: Fall River, January 4, 1907, Owen Durfee; West Falmouth, December 24, 1918, Louise Handy; Sandwich, December 8, 1922, "one seen and reported for the past month" (John F. Carleton).

HAUNTS AND HABITS. The Bittern is a hermit, dwelling in swamp and fen. Like all hermits, he is a peculiar character, and as the unusual piques our curiosity and even, among the ignorant, excites suspicion and superstition, the Bittern has been thought to have a sinister influence. Linsley tells how a countryman, hearing one in the marsh, thought the Evil One was pursuing him and how at another time 100 men turned out and scoured the meadows at Stratford until they had killed a Bittern.

Dr. Coues, who designated the bird as a shady character, characterized him as follows: "He prefers solitude and leads the eccentric life of a recluse, forgetting the world and 'by the world forgot.' To see him at his ordinary occupation one might fancy him shouldering some heavy responsibility, oppressed with a secret, or laboring in the solution of a problem of vital consequence."

Thoreau regarded him as the "genius of the bog." The bird seems to delight in the impassable morass where the "floating island" tempts the unwary and where the first false step may plunge the incautious adventurer into foul and slimy depths. By preference our peculiar fowl seeks quaking margins of so-called bottomless ponds, cedar swamps, cat-tail beds, river marshes and meadows, the muddy "thatch"-bordered shores of tidal streams, where it follows the receding tide, or stagnant pools in the salt marsh and froggy sloughs. In such surroundings the Bittern's inconspicuous colors furnish sufficient concealment the moment it crouches low or retires among the reeds and even when wading in open water it has only to point its bill upward and draw the feathers close to its narrow body to be passed unnoticed, so close is its resemblance then to a dead limb, crooked stake or stump-root projecting from the water.   One day when riding with a jolly company I observed a Bittern in this rigid position standing at the margin of a little pool by the roadside.   Our vehicle passed within 20 feet of the bird, but, though I called it to the attention of the company, their untrained eyes could not find it, and we left it there apparently immovable.*   The Bittern has such confidence in its invisibility that it often loses its life by starting up only when in danger of being trodden upon by the hunter.   It flies so slowly and presents so broad and tempting a mark that many are shot and left where they fall.   Therefore the Bittern is now becoming rare in many places in New England where formerly it was common.   It is so inconspicuous and ordinarily keeps so much in hiding by day and its loud "love notes" so much resemble the rural sounds of pumping and stake-driving that it is rarely noticed except by people who are much afield in its haunts or by those who are looking especially for it.   Thoreau wrote : "The Bittern pumps in the fen."   What a story these few words tell.   Again he remarks that the bird's notes sound "as if he had taken the job of extending all the fences up the river to keep the cows from straying."

The Bittern's so-called song and the accompanying contortions, together make up one of the most remarkable performances indulged in by any New England bird.   We cannot determine whether the sounds produced are all vocal or partly instrumental, nor can we say by what principle of acoustics this production, which never varies very appreciably, appears to imitate at one time pumping and at another stake-driving.

Bradford Torrey, who in 1889 gave an excellent description of the Bittern's pumping performance,[1] described the behavior of two birds, one of which he said was a "pumper" and the other a "stake driver."   This, I fear, gives a false impression, as the same bird produces both sounds at the same time but usually only one or the other can be heard distinctly.   Apparently the character of the sound which reaches the ear depends on the direction of the listener from the bird and possibly also on the point of the compass toward which the bird faces.

In 1922 I noticed that at my cottage at Wareham which was east of a meadow we heard only stake-driving, but when I went to the marsh due south of the bird only pumping could be heard.   The bird was perfectly concealed in the tall grasses and reeds so that one could not see which way he faced, but I passed carefully around him time after time and always heard on one side stake-driving only and on the other only pumping. There was a point, however, midway between the two where both could be heard together. The same experience was repeated day after day.   When another observer accompanied me he could hear only the stake-driving from the east while I heard only the pumping from the south or west ; while a third observer properly placed could hear both at the

---

* The bird is said to imitate . . . by a gentle swaying motion the waving flags and grasses that surround him as they are stirred by an occasional zephyr, and thus blends for the time into invisibility.   (Barrows, W. B.: Auk, Vol. XXX, 1913, p. 189.)

[1] Auk, Vol. VI, 1889, pp. 1–7.

same time. Distance from the bird made little difference. The sound was the same and seemed nearly as loud at 300 yards as at 30. One could account for this only on the supposition that the bird during its performance always faced in the same direction, which actually was the case with a Bittern which I was able to see plainly in the Concord meadows. Mr. Torrey tells us that his bird moved about and changed his position "between the acts." Probably should the Bittern face in different directions while pumping the "tune" would seem to change, but we have no proof of this. Mr. William Brewster asserts that "all three syllables may be heard usually up to a distance of about 400 yards, beyond which the middle one is lost" and the remaining two sound like "plum pudd'n," while at distances of more than half a mile the terminal syllable alone can be heard, resembling then the sound produced by driving an axe on a wooden stake. I had always supposed distance to be essential to produce the stake-driving effect, but this was not the case at Wareham. At the moment of emitting his dolorous love-song the violent contortions of the Bittern simulate those of a nauseated person in the very act of retching; yet the bird is not regurgitating food but apparently inflating its gullet with air.

Mr. Arthur J. Parker who, standing at a second story window in his house, has many times watched the Bittern pumping, thus describes a performance during which he could hear both pumping and stake-driving:

"The preliminary motions were each time the same; a forward (horizontal) thrust of the head with opened beak whereby air was gulped — the bill being audibly snapped upon each 'mouthful.' This swallowing motion would be repeated perhaps five or six times, and during the operation a strange swelling and contortion of the neck could be plainly seen — it was as if the bird had swallowed a large frog. There was a downward movement of the enlarged part of the neck. Then at once followed the explosive eruption of air — the *boom* — closely followed by the second sound, a clear syllable *ka*, like the stroke of a mallet on a stake. This second syllable gave the impression of being *vocal*, but we had no proof of that.

"The following spring (1921) Bitterns were again very bold back of our house, and one evening at dusk I crept up within about 30 feet of a bird absorbed in his music. But he had had warning, from Red-winged Blackbirds, of my approach, and although he kept on, the second note had already been muffled or disguised ere I got anywhere near him. When quite close, the snapping of the bill after the gulping could be plainly heard, the *boom* was fairly sonorous and hollow, but the sound that ended the call was a double note, suggestive of the stake-driving note but as if it had been cut in two, and the halves proportionately diminished!"

The utterance of the three "pumping" notes occupies a little more than one second. At the second note the bird's head is thrown up quickly, with bill pointing skyward. There is a disagreement among observers regarding the so-called snapping sound of the bill. Several observers are convinced that the quick closing of the bill produces this sound. Especially is this true of those who have observed the bird at such a distance that the sound reaches them just as the bill closes. Those who have been very close to the bird during the performance agree that the sound is vocal. Mr. Verdi Burtch [1] who asserts that he was within 40 feet of this bird when he witnessed this opening and closing of the bill says that it was a vocal sound. Mr. Manly Hardy who, sitting in a canoe, was able to drift quietly so that the stem "was within a paddle's length" of the bird, states distinctly that "the bill was opened with every noise; but the sound, which resembled the retching of a seasick person came from within, not from snapping the bill." Also he asserts that "when this noise was made there was not much distention of the throat, but when the pumping sound began the gullet was greatly enlarged at each noise." [2] The late Otis Fuller, who had an excellent opportunity to watch the bird as long as he wished, was positive that the so-called snapping of the bill was a vocal sound produced with the mouth open.[3] Mr. Frederick Hermann, in Bird-Lore for November–December, 1924 (Vol. XXVI, p. 441), well describes the Bittern's performance: "After giving the three introductory *clicks*, during which his breast became greatly inflated, the bird jerked his head suddenly downward until he appeared to have no neck at all, and uttered the first syllable of the triplet. Then, throwing his head as suddenly upward again, the second note was produced, and followed immediately by the last as the head was darted frantically forward. The second syllable was a note or two higher than the others and strongly accented, and all of them were accompanied by a peculiar undertone like a choking person gasping for breath."

The sound produced ("the song"), which it is agreed resembles the loud sucking of an old wooden pump, has been variously imitated in print by many writers, and to show what part imagination plays in such renditions, a few are herewith presented, all of which are supposedly descriptive of the same sounds: *Punc-a-pog; ugh plum pud'n'; plum pud'n'; pump-er-lunk; glump-te-glough; gung-gī-um; dunk-a-doo; pump-ah-gah; ponk-a-gong; chunk-a-lunk; kunk a whulnk; pomp aŭ gōr; pump ăŭ gah; umph-ta-googh; plunk a lunk; slug-toot; pung-chuck; chunk-a-lunk-chunk; quank-chunk-a-lunk-chunk; kung-ka-unk; puck-la-grŏŏk; waller-ker-toot.* A slight discrepancy in the consonants is noticeable. I doubt if the bird uses any. During the height of the mating season the Bittern has his "spasms" often. In late April or early May he may emit his call from five to eleven times in succession, but in June and July the notes become much less frequent. While the booming of the Bittern is commonly a spring sound, it is sometimes heard in autumn. The bird is likely to be most noisy between twilight and midnight.

The "stake-driver" note has been rendered thus: *Whack-a-whack, whack-a-whack.* At a distance only the reiterated *whack* reaches the ear.

The word "booming" is misapplied to the notes of our Bittern, though it may be aptly used to describe those of the European species.

No one yet knows just how the Bittern's pumping is produced. Mr. James P. Chapin [4] has shown by dissecting a male Bittern in the breeding season that the gullet or esophagus is much thickened and presumably strengthened at this season. When in-

---

[1] Bird-Lore, Vol. XVII, 1915, pp. 104–108.   [2] Auk, Vol. VI, 1889, p. 188.
[3] C. J. Maynard's Records, Vol. VI, 1913, p. 45.   [4] Auk, Vol. XXXIX, 1922, p. 196.

flated with air it may act as a resonator to magnify the sounds.   Mr. Chapin's paper should be read by all who are interested in this subject.

Mr. C. J. Maynard in 1889 made an exhaustive study of this bird, based on the dissection of a Bittern, taken in the breeding season.[1]

Mr. Maynard believes as a result of this dissection that the inferior larynx is nearly functionless and produces only the harsh croak that the bird emits when disturbed; also that the pumping sound is produced by the expulsion of the air from the gullet.

There is a display of light colored or white feathers which sometimes accompanies the above performance, especially when two males meet in the breeding season.   This display apparently was first recorded by Miss Agnes M. Learned [2] and was first fully described by William Brewster.[3]   It consists of about nine or ten light-colored, fluffy feathers which appear on the male during the mating season.   They are attached near the point of the shoulder or about where the humerus or arm bone springs from the body, and ordinarily are concealed under the wing.   In display these seem to be usually erected and spread, one on each side of the back, like ruffs or "little wings" nearly meeting behind the neck.   Although usually more or less buffy or yellowish, they appear pure white in the sunlight.   Another form of display is noted by Mr. Burtch who in the paper hereinbefore cited says, "as if by magic two beautiful, fluffy plumes arose from their concealment in the feathers of each shoulder and spread, fan-shaped, down around the neck to the breast."

Miss J. O. Crowell who has watched the latter performance repeatedly, believes that it is quite different from the display shown on the back which she has observed also; but she notes that the bird exhibiting this display showed no plumes on the back.

There is much variation in the size and color of the plumes or ruffs.   Females ordinarily do not have them.   Males begin to exhibit them about May 1.   In some individuals they are quite small, in some very buffy, in others large and nearly white.   Probably they increase in size and lighten in color until the bird reaches full maturity.

Miss Elizabeth Hill has watched a Bittern which she believes to be the same individual come yearly to a meadow in Groton.   She is positive that his plumes have grown larger and whiter year by year.

While the Bittern as ordinarily observed is motionless or very deliberate in movement, it can move quickly at need, and the stroke by which its long neck darts out the ready beak after its prey is *flashlike*.   Miss Hill describes the feeding of a Bittern which she watched practically all one day: "His song is short and of poor quality.   He stalks through the water and when over his depth *swims*.   He draws in his neck very suddenly, when a crow or hawk flies over.   Crows evidently do not approve of him, cawing or screaming at him.   He jumps as if startled when a frog starts up in front of him, then recovers himself, strides after the frog with neck outstretched, darts his bill upon him,

---

[1] Contributions to Science, Vol. I, 1889, p. 59; see also, Maynard, C. J.: Birds of Eastern North America, 1889, pp. 160–167.

[2] Bird-Lore, Vol. X, 1908, p. 107.

[3] Auk, Vol. XXVIII, 1911, pp. 90–100.

then gobbles him down. Now he lies down in the grass, sunning himself like a hen. He is gazing into the brook, he plunges in his bill and pulls out a flopping fish. After gulping, swallowing, stretching his neck, the fish disappears. The Stake-Driver walks across and disappears in the bushes."

If an intruder in the reedy marsh stumbles suddenly upon a Bittern, the bird rises from the oozy margin with a startling croak and rush of wing and flaps loosely and slowly away as if all the time in the world were at its disposal. If shot down but not mortally wounded, it turns upon its pursuer, partly spreading its wings and ruffling up its plumage until it appears more than twice its normal size, ready to stab with its sharp beak the incautious hand or eye that approaches too near for safety.

While not usually disposed to gregariousness, traces of the habit occasionally are observed. Four sets of eggs have been found in the space of a few rods square.

The migrations of the Bittern are made mostly at night. The greater part of the spring migrants pass through New England during the latter half of April and in early May. In autumn most of them move southward before October ends. An occasional famished straggler has been seen or taken in December and January.

The food of the Bittern consists mainly of frogs, snakes, small fish, crayfish and other small water animals, mice, moles and shrews, especially field mice, and a variety of insects. It is fond of grasshoppers and locusts and frequently may be seen in meadows or pastures near its usual haunts hunting grasshoppers.

"I once had the pleasure of watching a Greater Bittern dissecting out the dangerous dorsal and pectoral fin spines from a good-sized bullhead, preparatory to making a meal of him. . . . The bird placed the captured fish on the marsh grass between its feet and with sharp stabs destroyed the attachments of the spines. The work took some time as the fins of the catfishes are strongly connected with the bony framework. The bird was flushed before completing its work and I viewed the result after the disappointed Stake-Driver had departed. Two of the spines were found almost wholly torn loose, and the other about in shape for the feast." [1]

ECONOMIC STATUS. The exact value of the Bittern in an agricultural country has not been determined, but the destruction of mice and harmful insects is a strong point in its favor.

Ixobrýchus exílis (GMELIN). Least Bittern.

Plate 21.

DESCRIPTION. — Head slightly crested; bill slender; otherwise like Bittern in form but very much smaller. *Adult male:* Top of head, upper surface of body, back and tail glossy greenish-black; outer edges of scapulars buffy or whitish, back of neck, most of larger wing-coverts and outer webs of inner secondaries chestnut; other wing-coverts brownish-yellow or buffy; outer primaries slaty; flight-feathers (all or most) tipped pale chestnut; throat buffy white; sides of head and neck, and under plumage brownish-yellow or buffy-yellow, with some white or whitish along throat line and front of neck; blackish-brown patch on each side of breast; wing linings and axillars brownish-yellow and buffy-whitish;

---

[1] Gibbs, Morris, M. D.: Oölogist, Vol. 18, pp. 103-104.

bill largely pale yellow, ridge blackish; bare skin about eyes, and lores light green; iris and toes yellow; legs mostly green or greenish-yellow turning to yellow behind. *Adult female:* Similar to male except black of back and most of that of crown is replaced by purplish chestnut, and edges of scapulars form two brownish-white or buffy stripes, one on each side of back; throat and fore neck darkly streaked or lined. *Young in juvenal plumage:* Similar to adult female but feathers of back and scapulars tipped buff.

MEASUREMENTS. — Length 11.00 to 14.25 in.; spread 16.75 to 18.00; folded wing 4.00 to 5.25; tail 1.60 to 2.10; bill 1.60 to 2.00; tarsus 1.50 to 1.90.

MOLTS. — Apparently there is a partial molt during first autumn, after which young become practically indistinguishable from adults. Adults molt completely beginning about midsummer.

FIELD MARKS. — A small secretive bittern hiding in reed beds, etc.; not very shy but difficult to flush in daylight; male looks black on top of head and back; buffy below; unlike any other New England bird.

VOICE. — A mellow cuckoo-like call, *coo coo coo* from the depths of the marsh (E. H. Eaton); commoner variations: *cŏo', hoo hoo hŏo'* or *coo-coo, coo-hoo hoo';* also *co-co-co-co; co-co-ho-ho* or *co-ho-ho* without special emphasis on any syllable; when startled a loud, cackling *ca-ca-ca-ca* (William Brewster); *coo coo, whoo whoo, cuk cuk cuk cuk* (C. W. Townsend); male, guttural dove-like notes *ŭh-ŭh-ŭh-oo-oo-oo-oo-oooah* similar to one call of Pied-billed Grebe; female, *ŭk-ŭk-ŭk* (A. A. Allen); when startled, a low cry like *qua;* ordinary cry a rough croak, a feeble imitation of note of Great Blue Heron (T. M. Brewer); mated pair, "a low chattering hum" (C. C. Abbott).

BREEDING. — In fresh-water swamps and marshes. *Nest:* In reeds, cattails or low water bushes, usually over water; very rarely in trees; a flat structure of reeds (when in reeds) or twigs; usually well concealed. *Eggs:* 3 to 6; about 1.32 by 1.00 to 1.20 by .90 in.; elliptical; "bluish-white" or greenish-white. *Dates:* April 18, Florida; May 29, Pennsylvania; June 1 to 29, Massachusetts. *Incubation:* Estimated period 17 days (W. H. Bergtold), probably less; 15 days (A. A. Allen); by both sexes. One brood yearly in New England; possibly double brooded in the south.

RANGE. — Temperate and tropical North and South America. Breeds from British Columbia, southern Saskatchewan (possibly southern Manitoba), northern Ontario, Quebec and New Brunswick south to West Indies and Brazil; in migration east to Nova Scotia (where it breeds) and north to Manitoba; winters south from Florida and Gulf of Mexico.

DISTRIBUTION IN NEW ENGLAND. — Rare summer resident. *Maine:* Rare summer resident in southern counties. *New Hampshire:* Probably breeds. *Vermont:* Rare; taken in fall of 1909 at a small pond near Lake Bomoseen, Castleton;[1] bird seen August 7, 1903, and another May 13, 1908, both at Bennington. *Massachusetts:* Uncommon or rare and local summer resident, mainly near coast or in river valleys. *Rhode Island:* Rather common local summer resident; casual in winter. *Connecticut:* Not very common local summer resident.

SEASON IN MASSACHUSETTS. — (March 4); April 15 to September 26; (October 12).

HAUNTS AND HABITS. The Least Bittern is a queer little bird. Its slim head, and neck, and narrow, deep body fit it for passing between close-growing stems of reeds, flags and other water-plants, and it seems to be specially trained in climbing. I have seen it only when, like a rail, it was flying low and rather slowly over the tops of the reeds or climbing among their stems. When wading among tall reeds, one may rarely start this bird. It flies briefly in a rather bewildered way and drops down into the reeds a little farther on. It seems to keep more or less above the surface of the water, climbing about or running along from stem to stem, clasping them with its long flexible toes. When closely approached it is likely to straighten up, facing toward the intruder, with bill point-

---

[1] Kirk, George L.: Bulletin No. VI, Vermont Bird Club, 1911, p. 15; and *in litt.*

ing skyward, and in this position among the shadows of stalks and blades it seems a part of its environment and is exceedingly difficult to distinguish. "The young in the nest will often rise and stand thus like four little grotesque statues until the observer has passed on." [1] To show how readily this bird can pass between the crowded stems of reeds and flags, Audubon made an experiment with an individual alive. This bird was able to contract its body so as to pass between two books set an inch apart without moving them. When the bird was dead its body measured 2¼ inches in diameter. Occasionally it may be seen low down on some small tree or it may alight on a haycock or a fence rail. I have never heard of a real colony of this species here, but sometimes a few pairs breed not far apart. Probably the Least Bittern is not so rare in the marshy regions of New England as the published lists would seem to indicate. The bird is perhaps even more secretive than the rails and is rarely seen except by those who spend much time in the marshes. I have heard its strange cooing notes in many places where I have never seen it. Probably we know very little about its real distribution in New England in the breeding season. Its ordinary flight at that time, which probably occurs chiefly at night, is so low that some individuals have been killed by striking wire fences.

It migrates silently also at night, often flying rather low, and thus, like the Woodcock, is sometimes killed or injured in migration by striking telegraph wires. Its principal spring migration through Massachusetts probably occurs during the latter half of May, though stragglers arrive much earlier. In late August and September its principal southward passage occurs here, though stragglers appear later, and Fleming gives a late Toronto record, November 28, 1894 (Cooke). The behavior of both sexes at the nest is well described by Dr. Arthur A. Allen in the November–December number of Bird-Lore, Vol. XVII, 1915.

ECONOMIC STATUS. As the food of the Least Bittern is somewhat similar to that of the Bittern except that it feeds more on marsh insects and less on those of the uplands, and as it seems to be comparatively rare, it probably is of little economic importance.

NOTE. Cory's Least Bittern (*Ixobrychus neoxenus*), Plate 21, which has been taken in Massachusetts, has the *sides of head and throat "rufous chestnut"* and under tail-coverts dull black. As its range, so far as known, seems to coincide with that of the Least Bittern, probably it is identical with that species. Its difference in color may be due to melanism but probably it is merely a case of dichromatism, Cory's bird being a dark phase of the Least Bittern. Mr. Outram Bangs expresses this view (Auk, Vol. XXXII, 1915, pp. 482–483). It is mentioned here because it appears in the A. O. U. check-list.

SUBFAMILY **ARDEINÆ**. HERONS AND EGRETS.

Number of species in North America 11; in Massachusetts 7.

True herons differ from bitterns in having three pairs of powder-down tracts instead of two, 12 stiff tail-feathers instead of 10 soft ones, and much of the tibia bare. They develop plumes in the breeding season and some have two color phases — dark and white. Egrets are merely herons which are usually white and produce elegant long, loose-webbed

---

[1] Pearson, T. G.: Bird-Lore, Vol. XXV, 1923, p. 357.

plumes in mating time. The colors of bill, lores and feet are exceedingly variable among herons, not only with age and season but with different individuals. Sometimes one leg of a heron may not exactly match the other in color or size; also, there is great individual variation in size and in measurements of the parts.

Árdea heródias heródias. Linnæus. Great Blue Heron.

Other names: CRANE; BLUE CRANE.

Plate 22.

DESCRIPTION. — Bill stout at base but tapering to long, sharp end; neck and legs very long, neck well feathered all round; in breeding season the crest has two long feathers and lanceolate back plumage becomes longer. *Adults in nuptial plumage (sexes alike):* Forehead and middle of crown white or whitish; sides of crown and hind head bluish-black and crested, two longest feathers often exceeding 8 inches; chin, cheeks, sides of head, and throat mainly white (often mixed with rusty), fore neck streaked with double row of black; most of neck brownish-ashy, but lower neck with many long, pointed plumes of pale ashy or whitish which cover upper breast; breast and belly mainly black, latter streaked down the middle with white; under tail-coverts white; feathers on front borders of wings white basally, tipped chestnut; feathers of legs chestnut; sides bluish-ashy; upper part of wings, body and tail light bluish-ashy with long, pointed, paler or whitish feathers falling from scapular region over wings, back and tail; flight-feathers shading down from bluish-ashy inner secondaries to bluish-slate outer primaries; under wing-coverts and axillars bluish-gray; bill yellow or yellowish, in some individuals blackish or dusky-greenish on ridge; bare space from around eye to nostril variable but usually light purplish-blue; iris straw or pale yellow; legs where bare brownish-yellow above the joint and brownish-black, olivaceous or blackish below it; soles of feet yellowish. *Young in first winter and next summer plumage:* Much like juvenal but more uniform bluish-gray above; similar to juvenal below. *Young in juvenal plumage:* Variable; whole upper head dusky or dark slate, with no long crest feathers; no long plumes on lower neck, back or scapulars; bluish-gray above, tinged rusty; some white feathers about bend of wing edged chestnut; feathers of neck and wing-coverts edged brown or reddish-brown; feathering of legs much lighter than in adults; black of under plumage replaced by ashy and whitish, more or less streaked darker; upper mandible blackish, lower yellow; iris yellow; legs pale brownish or yellowish above tarsal joint, below joint and feet "slaty" gray.

MEASUREMENTS. — Length 42.00 to 52.00 in.; spread 65.00 to 74.00; folded wing 17.90 to 20.00; tail 7.00 to 8.00; bill 4.25 to 6.50; bare tibia 3.00 to 4.00; tarsus 6.00 to 8.25. Weight 6 to 8 lbs.; young in autumn 3 lbs. 8 oz. to 5 lbs. Female averages smaller than male.

MOLTS. — A partial molt of juvenal body plumage occurs in autumn and winter, while wings and tail are retained; in summer and autumn of the next year young probably undergo a complete molt after which plumage more closely resembles that of adult; after next molt in succeeding summer young apparently become indistinguishable from winter adults and the next spring they appear in adult nuptial plumage; adults apparently have a partial molt in spring after which the nuptial plumes appear and a complete molt in summer and autumn.

FIELD MARKS. — Great size; very long neck and legs and general bluish-gray color; in flight carries head drawn back to shoulders, legs trailing behind and it beats large, dark, eagle-like wings slowly and seemingly laboriously.

VOICE. — In migration a hoarse *honk*, having some of the same quality as that of Canada Goose but longer, flatter and harsher; when startled, guttural, raucous, rattling croaks and squawks.

BREEDING. — Usually in colonies in wooded swamps. *Nest:* Sometimes in bushes or even on ground or on cliffs in West where trees are wanting; usually high in large tree; built of sticks. *Eggs:* 3 to 6,

PLATE 22

PLATE 22

GREAT BLUE HERON
Page 324

YOUNG IN JUVENAL
PLUMAGE

ADULT IN BREEDING
PLUMAGE

EGRET
Page 328

ADULT IN BREEDING
PLUMAGE

BLACK–CROWNED NIGHT HERON
Page 336

ADULT IN BREEDING
PLUMAGE

YOUNG IN JUVENAL
PLUMAGE

SNOWY EGRET
Page 330

ADULT IN BREEDING
PLUMAGE

LITTLE BLUE HERON
Page 332

WHITE PHASE, OR
IMMATURE

DARK PHASE, OR
ADULT

All one-eighth natural size.

is Agassiz Fuertes

usually 3 or 4; 2.37 to 2.79 by 1.50 to 1.85 in.; elliptical-ovate, pale greenish-blue. *Dates:* Late April to May 25, Maine. *Incubation:* Period about 28 days (E. S. Cameron); by both sexes. One brood yearly.

RANGE. — North America from near southern border of Hudsonian zone to northern South America. The eastern form (there are various western subspecies) breeds from southern Manitoba, northern Ontario, Anticosti and Prince Edward Island south to northern Mexico, Texas and Georgia; winters from Oregon, the Ohio Valley and Middle Atlantic States, Massachusetts (rarely) and Maine and Vermont (casually) south to West Indies, Panama and Venezuela.

DISTRIBUTION IN NEW ENGLAND. — *Maine:* Common migrant and local summer resident throughout most of the state from coastal islands to Aroostook County (one wintering record).* *New Hampshire:* Common migrant and local summer resident; casual in winter. *Vermont:* Common migrant and local summer resident in northern part; casual in winter. *Massachusetts, Rhode Island* and *Connecticut:* Common migrant; occasional in early summer; bred not many years ago in Massachusetts; winters occasionally in Massachusetts and Connecticut.

SEASON IN MASSACHUSETTS. — March 15 to June 4; July 14 to December 30; winters occasionally in Cape Cod region, southern Bristol County and on Marthas Vineyard.

HAUNTS AND HABITS. The Great Blue Heron is by far the largest common wading bird of New England. It is also one of the wariest. Its great height, telescopic sight and acute hearing give it an advantage over all other denizens of the marsh. It is quick to take the alarm and those that are shot are mainly inexperienced young of the year. In early spring after the ice has gone out of the rivers it may be seen wading in shallow waters, stepping slowly along, raising each foot high and slipping it noiselessly into the yielding element. While searching for its prey or standing motionless for many minutes at a time knee-deep in the flood, it patiently waits with indrawn neck until some luckless fish or frog has ventured near enough, when the sharp bill and long neck shoot forward and downward, the wiry body sways forward on the reed-like legs and the unfortunate prey, transfixed, or seized in the serrated beak, soon disappears down the capacious gullet. Then the statuesque pose is resumed and another period of waiting ensues. The Great Blue Heron flies heavily but with considerable speed and its powers of flight are great. Mr. A. C. Bagg tells me that he saw one soaring in circles at such an immense height that until he had looked it over with his binoculars he mistook it for a hawk. Audubon tells how this bird sometimes pursues the Osprey and forces it to drop its fish, which the militant Heron appropriates, but this must be unusual. The Heron is regarded as a solitary bird and is often seen alone. During the breeding season, however, it lives in communities, and in migration it not only flies occasionally in companies and sometimes in large flocks, but in the autumnal migration I have seen from 10 to 20 feeding not far apart about a salt pond or immersed to their bellies in a tidal river and scattered in a long line over the submerged flats. At such a time each bird holds its head high and remains quiescent or moves slowly forward until it sees its prey. They are not always happy or fortunate in their catch. Mr. George W. Morse of Tulsa, Oklahoma, writes that he saw a heron strike at a small fish between its own legs, thereby tripping itself, and so, being upset, was carried by the swift current down stream on its back with legs in the air. How-

---

* One passed the winter of 1922–23 on the Androscoggin River below Brunswick. J. W. Walsh *in litt.*

ever, it held on to the fish.[1]　A correspondent of Forest and Stream reports finding a Great Blue Heron apparently choked to death by a shad fully a foot in length that had become wedged in the bird's throat.　The fins had prevented the bird from disgorging the fish.[2]

The stroke of a Heron's bill is notoriously dangerous; wounded birds should be approached with care.　A case is cited in which an enraged bird struck a pine-wood oar with such force that its bill protruded through it for two inches.

Mr. J. B. Smith tells us that about mating time the herons form a circle and that each adult male in turn shows off his plumage within the circle, surrounded by an appreciative throng.[3]　I have not seen the mating of this species, but in the nesting season I have climbed several tall trees to investigate the contents of the nests of heron communities.　These nests are often used year after year and added to each season.　When the parent comes with food, the well-grown young rise in the nest and as the adult usually alights at some distance from the nest and walks down a branch toward them the young reach, scramble and climb toward the parent, each one eager to be first at the feast. The cackling of the young ones and the croaking of their parents make up a distracting combination of discordant sounds.　The young are fed by regurgitation and from a distance the operation looks a little like an attempt at wilful murder as the parent stabs downward at the throats of the appealing young.　As the wings of the young birds develop they strengthen them by climbing about among the branches, flapping their untried pinions to keep their balance and using wings, beak and claws to keep from falling, though not always with success.　Occasionally one falls to its death on the ground far below while the wings are still too weak to support its weight.　Heronries are not always located in situations convenient for feeding, and the birds have been known to make daily round trip journeys of scores of miles to procure food.　When the young are fully fledged, they soon learn to fish for themselves and in late July or August they begin to scatter over the country, visiting practically all the lakes and large streams in New England.

From August until mid-November the birds are passing on their southward migration.　The great November flight (which in New England occurs mainly along shore) takes with it about all the remaining herons except occasional stragglers, a few of which may remain through the winter, though some such are starved and frozen before spring.

Miss Elizabeth Dickens of Block Island was the first to report the great November flight.　This was in 1910.　She writes:

"I'll never forget that flight of herons in 1910.　In the early morning I was attempting to feed a flock of 75 turkeys, when they suddenly all became sky-gazers.　Of course I did likewise and beheld 12 Great Blues circling above the flock.　Round and round and round they flew until I was almost dizzy trying to follow their motion with my eyes. At last they seemed to have had enough of this and flew away to the southeast.　A little later another dozen came from the west and alighted in a row along the edge of the bluff.

---

[1] Oölogist, Vol. XXXVIII, 1921, p. 67.
[2] A. F. R.: Forest and Stream, Vol. XX, 1883, p. 364.　　　　　　　　[3] Nidiologist, Vol. II, 1894, p. 10.

'Twas interesting to note their different heights and sizes. Then there came groups of threes and fives and nines, and so it continued at intervals all day. In the afternoon came one great flock of just a hundred birds. As they reached the land a life-saving (?) crew fired into them and the flock became two bunches of 40 and 60 birds each. I don't know how many herons I saw that day, but there must have been several hundred. In 1911 the flight was similar, tho' not as many birds. The dates were Nov. 10, 1910, and Nov. 13, 1911.

"The regular annual flight of Great Blue Herons usually occurs here about the middle of November and usually in the night altho' I have twice seen it during the day. This year (1918) it came between 2 and 5.30 A.M. Nov. 21. At least I was awakened twice by the calls of a host of these birds between those hours. Sometimes they were so near it seemed they must come in at the open window. Daylight revealed a few stragglers left behind on various parts of the island. My last record is Dec. 2, a single bird."

This flight probably consists of some of the maritime herons that breed far north, possibly on Anticosti or in some region where their presence has not been discovered. They usually appear during a northeasterly storm or a drop in the thermometer and probably are driven from their northern haunts by inclement weather. A few stragglers from this flight reach Cape Cod and Nantucket. A similar flight has been reported at Algonquin Park in Ontario.

In migration Great Blue Herons usually fly high enough to clear all obstacles, but one was brought to me in December from near the top of Mt. Wachusett where evidently its wing had struck a hard, sharp-pointed dead branch of some tree. The tip of the branch had pierced the wing and remained embedded there. Apparently the bird, either in its struggles or by its momentum, had broken off the branch in its wing and, unable either to fly or to find its way to water, had died of starvation and cold, as it was much emaciated. There is one case on record where a heron of this species in Iowa struck one of the many wires that cross the country, wrapping its long neck about the wire and so hanging suspended until decomposition released the remains.[1]

The Heron can alight on the water, swim and easily rise again and occasionally does so. Mr. P. A. Taverner asserts (Canadian Field Naturalist, Vol. XXXVI, 1922, p. 59) that at Big Lake he saw several herons from a large heronry drop into the middle of the lake and rest on the surface, and that his mother and sister reported a similar habit at Crow Lake. Mr. L. A. Fuertes informs me that he has seen one alight in deep water far out in a lake and rise again. Dr. John B. May states that he saw one alight in deep water, apparently catch a fish and rise with it. Mr. D. A. Cohen, Alameda, California, reports (Nidiologist, Vol. I, 1894, p. 77) that he saw two resting comfortably on the bosom of a slough deep enough to float a schooner. Dr. T. G. Pearson says in Bird-Lore (Vol. XXV, 1923, p. 77) that he once saw these birds feeding in a most unusual way. They would spring off into the water of the Cape Fear River and as the current carried them down they would continually strike "with their bills as if in the midst of a school of small fish."

---

[1] Barker, H. H.: Oölogist, Vol. XXXVIII, 1921, p. 99.

In their offshore migrations some have been overtaken by strong adverse winds and blown far out to sea. Herons have been reported as boarding vessels hundreds of miles at sea. They may rest upon the waves.[1]

The Great Blue Heron is largely but by no means wholly a fish eater. Knight records as its prey frogs, eels, horn-pouts, pickerel, suckers, shiners, black bass, herrings, "water-puppies," salamanders and tadpoles. The size of the fish eaten at times is surprising. Black Bass weighing not less than one pound and a half each have been regurgitated by a young heron, and a piece of eel eleven inches long by another. This Heron rarely frequents trout streams except where they flow through wide meadows, but often takes trout from artificial ponds; but it also takes minnows, crayfish and various enemies of food fish. It eats many large insects and is fond of grasshoppers and locusts. Sometimes in remote fields or pastures near the sea fifteen or twenty of these birds may be seen catching grasshoppers. They are expert also in capturing field-mice, shrews and ground squirrels and they feed many harmful rodents to their young. Rarely they have been known to destroy ducklings and in one case a chicken.

Mrs. Elizabeth L. Burbank of Sandwich reports a flock of 50 teal pursued by a Great Blue Heron. "Whatever change they made in their course, he did the same, and was close upon them."

Economic Status. Whether the good that this bird does from the human standpoint overbalances the evil has never been determined. Until this has been done it should be given the benefit of the doubt as it is destructive to harmful rodents and insects, and most of the fish that it eats are of little commercial value. Also it feeds on some destructive enemies of fish including water snakes which are pernicious enemies of young trout.[2]

Casmeródius egrétta (Gmelin). Egret.

Other names: GREAT WHITE EGRET; WHITE HERON.

Plate 22.

Description. — No plume-like crest; in breeding season long, loose-webbed feathers descending from scapulars over and beyond wings and tail (the larger egret plumes of commerce); neck close-feathered to near base where lower plumage is elongated. *Adults (sexes alike):* Chiefly pure white; dorsal plumes often slightly tinged yellowish; bare skin of lores pale green turning to pale yellow before eye; iris pale yellow or straw, sometimes nearly white; bill orange or orange-yellow; extreme tip of bill, legs and feet black. *Young:* Nestling, juvenal and first winter plumages all white; in juvenal plumage feathers of crown and lower neck shorter than in adult; no plumes; bill of young more or less black.

Measurements. — Length (tip of bill to tip of tail *not* tip of plumes) 34.75 to 42.00 in.; spread 50.50 to 58.50; folded wing 13.00 to 17.00; tail 4.00 to 6.50; bill 3.15 to 5.00; bare tibia 3.50 to 4.00; tarsus 5.60 to 6.80. Female averages smaller than male.

Molts. — The body plumage of the juvenal bird is shed, beginning in August. After the complete postnuptial molt beginning the next August immature birds in the second winter become practically indistinguishable from adults in winter plumage, though their nuptial plumes may not be as fully devel-

---

[1] Forest and Stream, Vol. LXXV, 1910, p. 732.
[2] Pearson, T. Gilbert: Bulletin No. 5, National Association of Audubon Societies, 1924, p. 26.

oped in the succeeding spring as those of mature birds. Adults have a partial molt beginning in late winter or spring (after which nuptial plumes are produced) and a complete molt beginning in summer or early autumn.

FIELD MARKS. — Smaller than Great Blue Heron, but being white appears as large or larger unless both are seen close together. At a great distance (especially in flight) might be mistaken for Snowy Heron or white young of Little Blue Heron, but these are *much* smaller and have bills mainly black, while the bill of Egret is largely or mainly yellow.

VOICE. — A very harsh, rattling croak.

BREEDING. — Breeds in communities in marshes or wooded swamps. *Nest:* Of sticks; usually on a tall tree, sometimes on bush or other growth in marsh. *Eggs:* 3 to 5; 2.20 to 2.28 by 1.45 to 1.60 in.; "dull pale blue." *Dates:* January 20, Florida to May 4, Louisiana; May 15 to June 1, Virginia. *Incubation:* Period probably about 28 days. Probably but one brood yearly.

RANGE. — Temperate and tropical America (formerly from southern Canada to Patagonia). Breeds in Oregon and California and from North Carolina and possibly Virginia and Missouri (formerly New Jersey, New York, Illinois, and Wisconsin) south to Patagonia; now rare in greater part of United States; winters from Gulf coast southward; casual in Manitoba, southern Ontario, southern Quebec, New Brunswick and Nova Scotia.

DISTRIBUTION IN NEW ENGLAND. — A rare or occasional summer visitor in the three northern New England states (but Dr. Wm. P. Coues records as many as nine at once at Scarborough, Maine in July, 1921[1]); and a rare (but probably regular) summer visitor in the three southern New England states; seen chiefly along the sea-coast in southern New England but may appear anywhere about swamps or ponds of interior.

SEASON IN MASSACHUSETTS. — (April); July to October (November 22).

HAUNTS AND HABITS. When as a boy in the wilds of Florida I first saw Egrets I was amazed at their apparently large size and snowy whiteness. Their imposing figures stood out in the full sunlight in the chaste purity of their dazzling whiteness against the dark background formed by the shadows and black water of a deep cypress swamp. Their great flocks in those days were indeed a wonderful spectacle. Their large size and graceful plumes lend them a certain dignity that smaller herons do not possess. As they alighted on the ground the plumes springing from their backs seemed to float or rise in the air.

This great Egret, sometimes misnamed "White Crane," probably always has been a regular summer visitor to southern New England. Since I have been collecting migration records from hundreds of observers, it has been reported in greater or less numbers every year (for six years) from July to September. Some of the comparatively few Egrets left to us continue to come north in summer. An extreme hot wave in July usually sends some of them up through the Middle States and into New England; if not they come with the high temperatures of August. In 1921 I received over 100 reports of White Herons in New England. Probably many of these were mere duplications, as the Egrets moved from place to place and came under the eyes of different observers, while fully half of them evidently were Little Blue Herons in white plumage. This migration of herons and some other birds to the northward after the breeding season is a well-known occurrence, and probably when the first settlers came to America, Egrets which once

---

[1] Letter to F. A. Foster of Edgartown.

bred in millions in southern swamps extended their regular summer migration over practically the whole United States and into Canada; but since then, through man's greed and woman's vanity, the Egrets have been killed in the breeding season for their plumes and have been so nearly exterminated that they are now rarely seen in the North. When I visited Florida in the winter of 1876–77, thousands of Egrets were flocking in the Indian River region; ten years later they had become rare and hard to find. They have been saved from extinction chiefly through the efforts of the National Association of Audubon Societies which, under the leadership of William Dutcher and T. Gilbert Pearson, have stationed armed wardens in many heronries to protect the birds from the plume hunter.

These great White Egrets are conspicuous, and usually they seem to be aware of this and are very shy. In the land of their nativity they serve as sentinels to warn the wildfowl of danger. I remember once as a boy on Indian River creeping through the grass to get a shot at a flock of Pintails. Success seemed certain as I had advanced nearly within gunshot range when an old Egret that had been wading in the shallows stretched up his neck, saw something suspicious and rising on broad wings cried to heaven with rattling screams the news that the enemy was at hand. Those ducks immediately disappeared from that landscape. In habits the Egret much resembles the Great Blue Heron and haunts the same localities.

Mr. George Morse, formerly in charge of the zoölogical garden at Franklin Park, Boston, reported (1920) that an American Egret lost a leg from the bite of a snapping turtle July 30, on Cape Cod. The bird was later captured and sent to Franklin Park.

The food of Egrets is mainly, if not wholly, animal. They feed largely on fish, but in the South they destroy great numbers of so-called crawfish which are enemies of fish and destructive to dikes and levees; also frogs, lizards and many insects, including grasshoppers, locusts and crickets. Wilson says that they devour mice, moles and seeds of the "splatter dock."

ECONOMIC STATUS. In the South Egrets do their part in restraining the superabundance of aquatic animal life. In New England they are too rare to be of any consequence.

Egrétta candidíssima candidissima (GMELIN). Snowy Egret.

Other names: SNOWY HERON; LITTLE WHITE EGRET.

Plate 22.

DESCRIPTION. — Similar to Egret, but much smaller; form less elongated. *Adults in breeding plumage (sexes alike)*: Pure white with up-curved crest of loose-webbed feathers on back of head and stiff-shafted, up-curved, loose-webbed plumes forming a train over back and tail; plumes shed after breeding season; bill black, yellow at base; bare skin of lores, iris and toes yellow (lores rarely orange); legs and claws black. *Young:* White, or nearly so, at all ages but lacking plumes; legs and feet at first olive (Audubon); young in October have legs "yellowish-green marked black and toes greenish-yellow."

MEASUREMENTS. — Length 20.00 to 27.75 in.; spread 34.00 to 44.00; folded wing 8.20 to 11.00; tail 3.00 to 4.00; bill 2.00 to 3.80; bare tibia about 2.50; tarsus 3.15 to 4.50. Weight about 12 oz. Female averages smaller than male.

MOLTS. — Juvenal body plumage is molted in August, September and October, but not wings or tail; in first winter plumage crest begins to show and feathers of neck and upper breast begin to grow longer; in spring a prenuptial molt takes place, after which in most young birds plumes like those of adults appear; adults have complete or nearly complete molt beginning in January and another molt beginning about June when nuptial plumes are shed, to be renewed in succeeding spring.

FIELD MARKS. — Nearly size of Night Heron but slimmer; *pure white;* usually no plumes when in our climate; *legs and bill mainly black, toes yellow;* may be confused with white young of Little Blue Heron which, however, has touches of bluish on primaries, and greenish legs; much more active than Little Blue Heron and uses its feet more to rake the bottom and stir up food; much smaller than Great White Egret.

VOICE. — In my experience a silent bird; have seen no description of its utterances.

BREEDING. — Usually in low trees or bushes in a swamp. *Nest:* Of sticks and twigs. *Eggs:* 3 to 5; about 1.67 to 1.85 by 1.20 to 1.34 in.; varying from elliptical to oval; "light bluish-green"; hardly distinguishable from those of Little Blue or Louisiana Herons. *Dates:* March, Florida; May 5, South Carolina; June 1, North Carolina. *Incubation:* Period probably about 21 to 23 days; by both sexes. Probably but one brood yearly.

RANGE. — Temperate and tropical America. Formerly bred south from Oregon, Nebraska, Indiana and New Jersey; breeds south to Chile and Argentina but rare in Rocky Mountain region and on Pacific coast; now breeds only locally in United States (as in Utah), mainly near coast from Virginia (possibly) and North Carolina to Louisiana and Texas; casual north to British Columbia, Alberta, Great Lakes, southern Ontario, New Brunswick and Nova Scotia; also in Bermuda.

DISTRIBUTION IN NEW ENGLAND. — Accidental visitor in Vermont, Massachusetts, Rhode Island and Connecticut; now practically extirpated. Records: *Vermont:* St. Albans Bay, two taken in October, 1890.[1] *Massachusetts:* Boston, bird shot in 1862;[2] Nantucket, one taken at Hummock Pond, March, 1882, by a member of the crew of the Life Saving Station;[3] Northampton, one taken by E. O. Damon, before 1887;[4] *Rhode Island:* Newport, bird in full plumage and perfect condition with prominent and fully developed aigrette plumes, picked up dead April 2, 1924, during a heavy snow storm, at the home of Charles A. Hall and given by him to A. O'D. Taylor;[5] *Connecticut:* Stratford, listed by Linsley but not taken;[6] Hartford, one taken by Dr. D. Crary prior to 1877;[7] Groton, "C. L. R." reports having seen "in early October" 11 at Groton Long Point at once, 9 at another time and smaller groups in other seasons;[8] Lyme, J. C. Comstock records five seen July 28 and thirteen, August 16, 1853.[9]

The species has been reported several times in Massachusetts and once in Rhode Island since 1917, but it is now so exceedingly rare and so likely to be confused with the white young of the Little Blue Heron that sight records can be accepted no more.

HAUNTS AND HABITS.   The Snowy Egret is the loveliest of our herons.   Its plumage when fully developed is pure and spotless white without any of the yellowish tinge often seen on the plumes of the Egret.   Its recurved crest and train are the acme of elegance and purity.

1 Howe, R. H.: Review of Perkins' Birds of Vermont, Contributions to North American Ornithology, Vol. II, 1902, p. 11.
2 Allen, J. A.: Proceedings Essex Institute, Vol. IV, 1864–5, 1886, pp. XXVIII and 85, 86.
3 Purdie, H. A.: Bulletin Nuttall Ornithological Club, Vol. VII, 1882, p. 251.
4 Clark, H. L.: Birds of Amherst and Hampshire County, Massachusetts, 1887, p. 46.
5 Taylor, A. O'D.: Auk, Vol. XLI, 1924, p. 473.
6 Linsley, James H.: A Catalogue of the Birds of Connecticut, American Journal of Science and Arts, Vol. XLV, 1843, p. 265.
7 Merriam, C. Hart: Review of the Birds of Connecticut, 1877, p. 111.
8 Ornithologist and Oölogist, Vol. XVI, 1891, p. 59. [This record is credited to "C. L. R. of Norwich" on p. 46 of Sage, Bishop & Bliss, Birds of Connecticut. But "C. L. R." means Calvin L. Rawson, and the O. & O. note was signed by "J. M. W." (Jennie May Whipple), Norwich (not C. L. R.), a nom de plume used by Mr. Rawson. (See pp. 240 and 254, of Birds of Connecticut.) Ed.]
9 Sage, Bishop and Bliss: Birds of Connecticut, 1913, p. 46.

It was my good fortune in the spring of 1877 when concealed behind some mangroves in a Florida swamp to approach within about thirty feet of a dozen birds of this species while they were engaged in their courtship evolutions. They were standing on black mud from which the water had receded, and against this dark background and that of the mangrove roots their immaculate forms stood out in such bold relief that every detail of movement, shape and plumage was plainly visible. They strutted about, raised, spread and lowered their lace-like plumes, pursued one another back and forth, bowed and turned about, apparently bringing into action all their muscles and displaying all their airs and graces. It seemed impossible that with all this impulsive constant activity, with the birds apparently heedless of consequences, they should not besmear their plumage with mud to some extent at least, but marvelous to relate I could not detect a single spot upon their snowy forms. They did not feed, as it was playtime, and they were so engrossed in their antics that they never noticed me until one incautious movement on my part put them all to flight. Had I realized at the time that within ten years the species then so abundant in that region would be practically wiped out, doubtless I should have made full notes describing the occurrence.

The millinery business brought this bird even nearer extirpation in the United States than it did the Egret. A few colonies have been saved by the efforts of the National Association of Audubon Societies, and Mr. E. A. McIlhenney has established and protected a large community on his estate in Louisiana. This bird, like the Egret, is prone to wander north in summer, but its numbers in the United States are now so few that it can be regarded as a mere accidental straggler in New England. It is practically extirpated here where once it was not exceedingly rare. Reports of this species in this region should be received with caution as the Little Blue Heron is likely to be mistaken for it.

When here the Snowy Egret usually seeks the seacoast and the marshes along shore. Its food is similar to that of the Egret but it probably takes more insects. Unlike most other Herons, it rushes on its prey and turns and darts about in a very active manner. Mr. Oscar Baynard, who made a study of this species in Florida for the National Association of Audubon Societies, found that it destroyed many cutworms.

ECONOMIC STATUS. See page 315.

Flórida cærúlea (LINNÆUS). Little Blue Heron.

Other names: WHITE HERON; LITTLE WHITE HERON.

Plate 22.

DESCRIPTION. — *Adults (sexes alike)*: Head and neck usually purplish-red or maroon; a few slender, much elongated feathers on crested head and a tuft of lanceolate, long, close-webbed feathers on lower neck; body and wings nearly uniform dark slate-blue; said to be sometimes pied with white or practically all white, with tips of longer flight-feathers marked slate-blue; long, close-webbed, lanceolate feathers depending from scapular region cover lower back and rump extending beyond tail; tip of bill black; its base and the bare skin between it and eyes varying shades of blue; iris yellow or gray; legs and feet bluish-black. *Young in juvenal plumage:* White with more or less slate-blue markings, usually at or near end of longer flight-feathers, sometimes elsewhere; iris variable, changing with age, often yellow; legs, feet and bare lores, chiefly greenish-yellow, usually with some traces of bluish.

MEASUREMENTS. — Length 20.00 to 29.50 in.; spread 36.00 to 42.00; folded wing 9.00 to 11.50; tail 3.00 to 4.50; bill 2.70 to 4.00; tarsus 3.00 to 4.00.

MOLTS. — Juvenal plumage worn with little change during first winter. Molting begins in early spring and apparently continues through much of summer. The amount of slaty-blue in the white plumage gradually increases. In the ensuing winter and spring the white disappears entirely and the bird takes on a blue plumage with the long plumes of the adult. This plumage is worn through the second summer, most birds having a touch of maroon somewhere about the neck. In April of the fourth season, when about 3 years old, following the prenuptial molt the birds have maroon neck and become indistinguishable from adults. There may be a white phase of this species, as birds in white plumage have been known to breed. Adults have a partial prenuptial molt and a complete postnuptial molt.

FIELD MARKS. — Size of Night Heron but slimmer. Adults in blue plumage can be confounded with no bird except the smaller adult Green Heron with its chestnut neck which, seen at a distance through glasses, in some lights, may *appear* bluish above; but the Little Blue Heron is larger, slimmer, with legs and neck longer. The white young as seen in Massachusetts may be mistaken for the Snowy Egret in fall plumage except when the slaty-bluish spots on primaries or *greenish* legs can be made out. The Little Blue Heron is slow in movement as compared to the Snowy Egret.

VOICE. — "Peculiar squawks" and croaks.

BREEDING. — Usually in swamp. *Nest:* In bushes or trees, composed mainly of sticks. *Eggs:* 3 to 4; in size, shape and color like those of Snowy Egret. *Dates:* From April 1, Florida, to April 23, South Carolina, May 21, Virginia and June 18, North Carolina. *Incubation:* Period probably about 21 to 23 days. Probably one brood yearly.

RANGE. — North and South America, mainly in temperate and tropical regions. Bred formerly from Missouri, Indiana, Illinois and New Jersey to western Mexico and south to Peru and Argentina; now breeds locally in United States from North Carolina and possibly Virginia and Kentucky (rarely) to Florida, Alabama, Arkansas, central Texas and along Gulf coast; wanders north regularly as far as southern New England and occasionally or accidentally to Labrador, Nova Scotia, Quebec, Ontario, Michigan, Wisconsin, Iowa, Nebraska and Colorado; winters from North Carolina southward.*

DISTRIBUTION IN NEW ENGLAND. — Accidental visitor in northern New England. *Maine:* Scarborough, bird taken in September, 1881;[1] Popham, female taken May 19, 1901;[2] Vinal Haven, male taken April 1, 1902;[3] Whitneyville, bird taken August 16, 1906.[4] *New Hampshire:* Amherst, adult taken April 28, 1897.[5] *Vermont:* Newbury, bird seen August 16, 1912;[6] Wells River, bird seen June 5, 1919.[7] *Massachusetts:* Very rare spring visitor; rare but regular summer visitor. *Rhode Island:* Rare summer visitor. *Connecticut:* Very rare in spring; rare but probably regular summer visitor.

SEASON IN MASSACHUSETTS. — April 14 to September 27, not known to breed.

HAUNTS AND HABITS. The Little Blue Heron has always been considered a casual or accidental visitor in Massachusetts; but during the past six years (1917–1923) since I have been collecting migration data, I have been astonished each summer at the number of White Herons reported in Connecticut and Massachusetts, the greater part of which are "as small as the Night Heron or smaller." Some of these birds have been seen at

---

* The birds of the southern part of this range have been separated as subspecies (*cœrulescens*) including South American birds and some from Antilles and Central America. The dividing line between the two forms cannot be definitely given.

[1] Brown, N. C.: Bulletin Nuttall Ornithological Club, Vol. VII, 1882, p. 123.

[2] Journal Maine Ornithological Society, Vol. III, 1901, p. 29.

[3] Norton, Arthur H.: Auk, Vol. XIX, 1902, p. 285.

[4] Knight, O. W.: Birds of Maine, 1908, p. 133.

[6] Smith, W. P., *in litt.*

[5] Melzer, J. P.: Auk, Vol. XIV, 1897, p. 316.

[7] Cobb, Anna E.: Auk, Vol. XXX, 1913, p. 111.

close range and recognized as Little Blue Herons. Twice I have seen one at Wareham. Also, reports of small herons in the blue plumage have been received not only in summer but in spring. There have been some attempts to identify some of these birds as Snowy Egrets, but such records as a rule must be classed as doubtful. The majority of the reports of Little Blue Herons come from the coast or the Connecticut Valley, but they are scattered elsewhere. The bird is seen occasionally in small flocks of from 6 to 12, but many appear singly or in pairs. The greatest number seen in recent years came in 1921, when they were reported all along the coast from Long Island Sound to Maine. Like the Egret they usually appear in hot weather, either in July or August. They frequent the same localities as other herons, but are most commonly seen on salt marshes or about fresh-water pools near such marshes. They commonly alight in trees near water. Most of those seen here are nearly pure white young of the year with very little blue on the primaries, or adult birds in the blue plumage. No pied or patchy birds have been reported. Various authors state that this species feeds on fish, frogs, tadpoles, lizards, crabs, worms and insects, for which it hunts by pacing or wading about in a slow and stately manner.

ECONOMIC STATUS. See page 315.

Butorídes viréscens viréscens (LINNÆUS). Green Heron.

Other names: LITTLE GREEN HERON; GREEN BITTERN; POKE; FLY-UP-THE-CREEK.

Plate 21 and Fig. 28.

DESCRIPTION. — Head crested; back of neck bare like that of a Bittern, inclosed and covered by long feathers on sides of neck. Adults (sexes alike): Whole top of head and crest dark glossy green, growing blackish on forehead; back also dark green but covered by long, hoary gray scapulars and interscapulars with green gloss over all; wings and tail dusky glossy green, wing-coverts and other feathers narrowly tipped and bordered more or less with buff, yellowish-white or whitish; axillars and wing linings as primaries, but reddening toward fore edge of wing which is whitish; chin and narrow streak down throat white or yellowish-white, streaked brown; sides of head and neck "rich chestnut" to dark "vinaceous red" or maroon; lower surface of body "ashy-brown"; bill greenish-black above, lightening on under mandible, the basal part of which is yellow; iris orange or yellow; bare skin from bill to eye yellow or green and yellow; legs and feet yellow, more or less tinged greenish. Young in juvenal plumage: Somewhat like adult but much more spotted and streaked; head less crested; its top and crest greenish, its fore part usually streaked rusty; back without narrow, hoary, greenish plumes, but dark greenish; sides of head, neck and body rusty-brownish, streaked deep yellowish-buff; light borders of wing-coverts broader than in adult, some of them marked with wedge-shaped spots or streaks of buffy or whitish; tips of primaries (sometimes some secondaries) with whitish marks; under plumage white or whitish, streaked with light and dark brown; wing linings variegated; color of bill, iris, legs and feet resemble adult but somewhat duller or paler.

MEASUREMENTS. — Length 15.50 to 22.50 in.; spread 23.00 to 26.00; folded wing 6.30 to 8.00; tail about 2.50 to 2.70; bill 2.00 to 2.55; bare tibia .90 to 1.00; tarsus 1.75 to 2.15. Weight 6¼ to 7½ oz. (Audubon). Female smaller than male.

MOLTS. — The comparatively dull juvenal plumage of the young bird seems to change gradually by fall and spring molts, flight-feathers gradually losing white tips, until in second autumn it becomes as adult. Adults have partial prenuptial molt and complete postnuptial molt.

Photograph by Dr. Arthur A. Allen

FIG. 28. — GREEN HERON AND NEST

From Bird-Lore, courtesy of Dr. Frank M. Chapman

Photograph by Dr. Arthur A. Allen.

FIG. 29. — YELLOW-CROWNED NIGHT HERON AND NEST

VOICE. — A rattling *Oc-oc-oc-oc-oc;* a startling *scow* and a deep, hollow groan (William Brewster); in breeding season a surprising variety of "henlike cacklings, clucks and squawks"; a harsh *skeow;* an explosive *wowoogh* delivered in a stage whisper.

FIELD MARKS. — Size smaller than Bittern or Night Heron; longer than Crow because of length of neck but smaller and with less spread; always appears dark; back of adult looks bluish at a distance; flies, like other herons, with downward bend to wing-tips even more pronounced than that of Night Heron; alights commonly on trees, stumps and dead limbs and jets tail when alarmed, often raising crest; has been mistaken for larger and slimmer Little Blue Heron in adult plumage.

BREEDING. — Usually in woods near water. *Nest:* Usually in tree, generally from 5 to 25 feet up; more rarely, where trees are scarce, in bush in marsh, or on muskrat house; frailly built of sticks and twigs, often added to and made much more compact after eggs are laid. *Eggs:* 3 to 6; 1.56 by 1.20 to 1.38 by 1.12 in.; elliptical; pale greenish or greenish-blue. *Dates:* March 25 to June 1, Florida; April 30, Pennsylvania; May 5 to June 17, New England. *Incubation:* Period 17 days (Burns); by both male and female. Usually one brood yearly; second brood may be reared rarely, more commonly in south.

RANGE. — Mainly eastern North America from Canadian region southward. Breeds from southern South Dakota, northern Minnesota, central Michigan, northern Wisconsin, southern Ontario, southern Quebec, New Brunswick and Nova Scotia south to eastern and southern Mexico and Guatemala; winters in Mexico and southward to eastern Colombia, northern Venezuela and northern Brazil and rarely in South Carolina, Florida and southern Texas; casual in Oregon, Colorado, New Mexico, Texas and Nova Scotia.

DISTRIBUTION IN NEW ENGLAND. — Uncommon or rare and local summer resident in southern and southwestern counties of Maine; uncommon summer resident in southern half of New Hampshire and Vermont, and farther north in Connecticut Valley; common summer resident in Massachusetts, Rhode Island and Connecticut.

SEASON IN MASSACHUSETTS. — (March 21, April 6) April 20 to October 23; (December 3).

HAUNTS AND HABITS. Hardly a shallow pond or wide stream may be found in southern New England that is not visited either occasionally or frequently in spring and summer by one or more Little Green Herons. In the fall of 1922 a Green Heron remained for weeks at Boston Public Garden pond (W. Sprague Brooks, Auk, Vol. XL, 1923, p. 121). This, the smallest of our true herons, is commonly startled from its retreats by rowers, fishermen or idlers who frequent our lakes and waterways. Its usual manner of fishing is to steal carefully upon its prey with head drawn in and to strike like a flash when the proper moment arrives, but sometimes it varies this performance. Mr. Samuel H. Barker reports that in 1898 he saw one that had been standing on the edge of a plank projecting out of the water plunge in after a fish that had come to the surface three or four feet away. The bird missed the fish, turned about, rose readily from the water and flew to the plank. This perch, he says, "was surrounded on all sides by water ranging from three to six feet deep" (Bird-Lore, Vol. III, 1901, p. 141). Professor Lynds Jones tells of a Green Heron "stretched out flat on a slanting log at a point where it projected from the water." Beneath this log minnows found shelter. The bird rested motionless with its bill at the water's edge, when suddenly it darted its head under water and brought up a wriggling minnow in its bill and, having swallowed it, remained motionless and ready as before. The bird came daily to this feeding-station and sometimes had to wait 15 minutes before it could strike a fish. (Dawson and Jones, Birds of Ohio, Vol. II, 1903, p. 476.)

Where Green Herons are abundant they nest in small colonies. Colonies have been known to settle in apple orchards, but commonly in New England each pair nests by itself in some remote and quiet place near water. Mr. T. Gilbert Pearson records an unusual nesting site on a bush in a "sink-hole" or natural well at least 40 feet below the surface of the surrounding earth.[1]

Green herons usually nest from 15 to 20 feet from the ground in almost any dense tree. The white pine is a favorite. The stick nest is so frail that the eggs show through it, but after the young are hatched (or before) it is frequently built much larger and higher with grass and other warm material. In time the young learn to climb out of the nest.

Rarely we hear of a Green Heron found dead after some great storm in December or early March, but these are unaccountable accidents, as all members of the species should be in the far South during the winter months.

The food of this bird consists of small fish, frogs, leeches, snails and various other small aquatic animals, worms and many insects, including grasshoppers and locusts.

ECONOMIC STATUS. The Green Heron is said at times to destroy fingerling trout in artificial ponds. Against this habit may be set the destruction of crawfish and minnows and certain insect enemies of the fish that are taken in large numbers. Grasshoppers and locusts which it eats should be credited also. Apparently it normally does more good than harm, but its food habits have not been fully investigated.

Nycticorax nycticorax nævius (BODDAERT). Black-crowned Night Heron.

Other names: QUAWK; BUTTERMUNK; BITTRUN; BULL BITTRUN; "PLUNKET"; "WAGIN."

Plate 22.

DESCRIPTION. — Bill very stout for a heron and about as long as tarsus; no long plume-like feathers over breast or back; neck and legs rather stout for a heron. *Adults in nuptial plumage (sexes alike):* Forehead and line reaching from it more or less over eye, white; crown, back and scapulars very dark blackish with bluish or bottle-green gloss; 3 (sometimes only 2, rarely 4) long, narrow, white, tapering feathers (often appearing as one) depend from hindhead; rump and tail-coverts, wings and tail, pale bluish-gray, axillars and wing linings paler; under plumage white, tinged (except along throat) with cream and lilac or very pale bluish-gray; skin of naked lores green to "grayish-olive"; iris scarlet or blood red; bill black; legs and feet yellow. *Young in first nuptial plumage:* Similar to first winter but back practically unspotted; breast white with broad streaks of gray, belly also streaked. *Young in first winter plumage:* Same as juvenal but paler. *Young in juvenal plumage:* Very different from adult; variable; above grayish-brown (crown and back brown and dusky) with paler feather-edges, spotted and streaked whitish and rusty; *outer edge of primaries more or less tinged rusty* and small white or light spots on tips of flight-feathers; below mainly white or whitish, streaked grayish and brownish; sides of chin, head and neck streaked drab, sooty or brown and buffy; lower belly and region about vent unstreaked; bill variable in color; at 50 days of age upper mandible black, shading into ivory-yellow on sides, lower mandible horn color (A. O. Gross); bare skin of lores light green, shading to black at base of bill and to "dull green-yellow" about eyes; iris yellow.

MEASUREMENTS. — Length 23.00 to 28.00 in.; spread 43.00 to 48.00; folded wing 11.00 to 13.00; tail 4.20 to 5.00; bill 2.75 to 3.15; bare tibia about 1.00; tarsus 3.00 to 3.75. Weight 1 lb. 14 oz. (Audubon).

---

[1] Bird-Lore, Vol. XV, 1913, p. 198.

MOLTS. — Apparently there is little or no postjuvenal molt; juvenal plumage is retained through the first winter, paling somewhat by fading and wear; first nuptial plumage appears to be acquired by a partial molt (February to May) which does not include wings or tail; a postnuptial molt beginning in August or September is followed by second winter plumage in which bird becomes nearly white below, while crown and back show many blackish feathers; in winter and early spring a complete prenuptial molt apparently occurs after which, in May, immature bird resembles adult, but dark crown and back are duller with less green-black on crown and with markings (mostly feather-edgings) of brownish on dark upper plumage; head plumes present in this plumage but usually shorter than in adults; following the postnuptial molt bird assumes adult winter plumage when about 2½ years of age and in the following spring full adult nuptial plumage is assumed; adults have prenuptial molt in late winter and spring and postnuptial molt in late summer and autumn, preceding which long feathers of head are shed; these feathers are doubtless renewed in autumn as birds examined in October and February had them.

FIELD MARKS. — *Adult:* Size of Bittern; black bill, crown and back, light bluish-gray wings and tail and whitish under plumage are unmistakable; in flight, flaps rather slowly, at times sailing with wings slightly curved downward. *Young:* Often mistaken for Bittern but spotted with whitish, not so reddish-brown as Bittern, and without the long black splashes on sides of neck, which adult Bittern shows.

VOICE. — Ordinarily a hoarse, abrupt *quock;* when disturbed on breeding-grounds a variety of harsh squawks and croaks; a loud *wock-o-wock-wock*, etc.; also some clucking, cackling and henlike notes.

BREEDING. — Usually in wooded swamp or marsh but sometimes on a dry hillside. *Nest:* Commonly in trees, less often in bushes and sometimes on ground or reeds in marsh; built of sticks and twigs and sometimes when in marsh contains stalks of weeds, rushes, etc. *Eggs:* 1 to 6 (rarely 7 and 8); 2.23 by 1.50 to 2.00 by 1.40 in.; pale light bluish-green; "glaucous-green" (A. O. Gross). *Dates:* May 6 to June 20, New England. *Incubation:* Period 24 to 26 days (A. O. Gross); by both sexes. Usually one brood yearly in North; said to be double-brooded in south.

RANGE. — Most of North and South America. Breeds from southern Saskatchewan, northern Oregon, Nevada, Utah, southern Wyoming, Colorado, southern North Dakota, Manitoba, Minnesota, Wisconsin, southern Ontario, Quebec and New Brunswick south to Patagonia; winters from northern California, Virginia and Gulf States southward; casual in winter north to Massachusetts and northeastern Illinois; casual in summer north of breeding range to Alberta, northern Quebec, Prince Edward Island and Nova Scotia.

DISTRIBUTION IN NEW ENGLAND. — Common to abundant migrant and local summer resident in coastal regions from Hancock County, Maine, westward and southward; less common migrant and summer resident in interior; rare migrant in extreme northern and eastern sections, except about the larger bodies of water; winter resident locally and casually near coast in Massachusetts, Connecticut and rarely in Rhode Island; in eastern Massachusetts breeds now (or formerly did) at Newburyport (Plum Island), Rowley, Ipswich, Georgetown, North Beverly, Saugus, Dedham, Quincy, Braintree, Kingston, North Falmouth, Barnstable, Chatham, Wellfleet, Truro, Provincetown, Edgartown, Gay Head and No Man's Land, and in interior towns in Worcester, Hampden and other inland counties.

SEASON IN MASSACHUSETTS. — March 20 to November 1; a few winter or have wintered at Cambridge, Quincy, Duxbury (probably), Plymouth, on Cape Cod and Marthas Vineyard and (irregularly) in southern Bristol County.

HAUNTS AND HABITS. The Black-crowned Night Heron, as its name implies, is a night-bird. Its harsh cry is one of the well-known "voices of the night" that may be heard in the dusk of summer evenings almost anywhere along the Massachusetts coast. Its great red eyes seem to have some of the powers of night-sight that are bestowed upon the owl, as otherwise it could hardly see to fish at night. Nevertheless, it is not by any means altogether a night-bird as, like all coast fishermen, it regulates the time of its fishing in coastal waters more or less by the tides, and like the owls it is often quite active in cloudy weather during the day.

There is an ancient tale which has come down to us from the dim past to the effect that the Night Heron can throw out a light from its breast which shines on the water and attracts its finny prey, thereby enabling the canny bird to direct that swift stroke of its powerful beak by which it seizes the luckless creature. I have talked with two

NIGHT HERONS IN THE TREE-TOPS

reputable eye-witnesses of this alleged light. In one of these cases the bird was actually shot while the light was shining; also I have received letters from three others who claim to have seen such a light which they attributed to the Night Heron. As the story is told, the light shines from the fore part of the bird's body, and is as bright as the glow of a number of fireflies. Nevertheless, though I have kept the bird in confinement and watched it in the dark and have lain all night near a great heronry, I have never seen any indication of such a light, and so far as I know no ornithologist has ever seen it. Probably those who have reported the light saw something, but what they saw remains to be determined. Such a light has been attributed also to the Bittern and to other herons. The powder-down tracts on the breast are supposed to be its source. Other species, however, have powder-down tracts to which no light has been attributed. Ornithologists generally are very skeptical about the probability of any light emanating from the Night Heron. Dr. A. O. Gross may be considered an authority on this bird, as he has published a paper on the species which shows thorough and painstaking investigation and rises almost to the dignity of a monograph.[1] He says: "Thus far I have not substantiated the statements frequently made that these tracts are phosphorescent organs, nor have I been able to find any reliable observer who has seen light produced by these patches of downy feathers. Some of the fishermen along the Cape relate startling stories of how the Herons produce a luminous glow in order to attract fish and other prey at night, but after studying the birds confined in cages and others at their feeding grounds at night, I am inclined to believe that the phosphorescence is a product of the imagination."

His article was based largely on investigations made at the Sandy Neck heronry in Barnstable. For many years there have been at least two heronries there; and in the past 20 years I have visited the herons there in six different localities, as the birds move from time to time, either because of persecution by crows or by man or for the reason that in time the trees on the breeding-grounds die and afford no shelter. Following is a description, taken from my unpublished manuscript, of a heronry among the sand dunes of Sandy Neck, Barnstable, which I visited in July, 1908:

"As I neared the spot a few herons flapped stiffly away, with hoarse 'quoks.' Some

---

[1] Auk, Vol. XL, 1923, pp. 1–30 and 191–214.

croakings and many machine-like 'chippings' were heard; and when at last my load dropped from my weary shoulders in the welcome shade of an oak grove, the heronry was so near at hand that the audible cries of both young and old had increased to a steady chorus.

"Evidently some enemies of the birds had been before me, for they had left their signatures on the visitor's book — a stretch of sand along the edge of the marsh. Tracks of foxes, old and young, and those of cats, crows and skunks, led into a little hollow, where a mat of dry creek grass had been thrown by the highest tides; and here well-worn paths led direct to the heronry, showing where nocturnal marauders had passed in to feast on young birds, eggs, dead fish, squids or other food dropped by the birds. Deeply indented hoof-marks in the sand showed where a big buck had passed along the edge of the wood, browsing as he went. The heronry was in a hollow among wooded hills, where there had been a pool in the spring, which was now dried up. The borders of the place were hedged about with thorny smilax and poison ivy, but inside the heronry the ground was comparatively clear. Here, well up on the trees, the large straggling nests were placed, from three to six nests on each tree. Young herons are inured to hardships from

YOUNG BEGINNING
TO CLIMB

THE GOAL OF THE YOUNG
CLIMBERS IN THE TREE-TOPS

THE USE OF THE HEAD IN
CLIMBING UNDER DIFFI-
CULTIES

the first. Resting on the hard sticks which compose their crude unlined nests, exposed to every wind that blows over and through the ramshackle structure, they must become hardened or perish. The windless air was stagnant and fetid; swarms of stinging midges, deer-flies and mosquitoes attacked at will; and vicious wood-ticks, hanging from the vegetation, reached for me with their clinging claws, and crawled upon my limbs, seeking an opening to bury their heads in my flesh.

"Croaks and calls, flat cries and choking gasps filled the air, as the great flocks of the heronry took flight, flapping and wheeling overhead. Here was a beautiful and stirring sight! Hundreds of waving plumes, pale, delicately tinted breasts, great red eyes, and wide-spreading pinions sailing over me just above the trees. The young birds, homely, awkward, speckled things with staring yellow eyes were now out of the nests and had climbed to the tree tops high above that pestilential hole to a place where they could escape the mosquitoes, feel the breeze and get a breath of the free air of heaven. They become adepts at climbing even before they finally leave the nest.   On the approach of an intruder some will climb out and into the tree tops, to return again after the alarm has passed.   In climbing they use feet, wings and bill and even the head.   Rarely one will

hook its head into a crotch from which it is unable to withdraw.   I have seen them thus hanging dead.   If one misses its footing and falls to the ground, it may become the prey of fox, cat, snapping turtle or other lurking enemy.

"While still in the nest they will strike at an intruder, opening the mouth widely, and making as formidable an appearance as possible, at the same time uttering a loud '*kak*' and perhaps also discharging the contents of the gullet at the enemy.   Even now some of them, when approached, threw up gobs of half-digested fish that struck the ground with a thump.   It is only courteous to proffer a visitor a meal, but these birds actually rob themselves to present one with a meal that they have already eaten !

RESULT OF IN-EXPERIENCE IN CLIMBING

"The day had been murky, hot and still, with hardly a breath of wind. On the ground under these trees the odor of ancient fish and that of the ammoniacal fumes accompanying decay were so nauseating that, having taken a few hurried snap-shots, I was ready to seek the open air to alleviate certain disagreeable symptoms.   What a contrast in emerging from such a place to breathe the delicate fragrance of azaleas, and to hear mingled with the racket of the heronry the melodious voices of the Catbird and the Yellow-throat.

"I had intended, in my ignorance, to encamp for the night in that heronry ; but this was plainly out of the question, and I determined to lie just outside, and so get the full benefit of the night wind over the water.   So, at a bend in the shore line nearest the heronry, where the creek grass or thatch lay dry and deep, I shook down a bed, arranged my blankets and head net, and crept in to escape the flies, midges and mosquitoes that swarmed in one grand chorus as the light began to fail.   Thus protected, molested only by a few hungry wood-ticks which penetrated my defenses, I lay awake far into the night, listening to the sounds of heronry, marsh and shore.

"Slowly the dull murk cleared away, then the rosy light melted out of the western sky, and the stars came out, but they were soon obscured by dark, drifting clouds.   One star still burned clearly miles to the eastward, but that was the beacon of a lighthouse ; and another light was shining from some window across the bay, where someone kept a late vigil, or some poor mortal tossed on a bed of pain.   The sweet west wind blew in little gusts out of the dark silences over wide marshes and lapping waters.   Shapeless and indistinct, seen darkly through my cheesecloth netting, some creature, perhaps a fox, stole swiftly across the strip of white beach sand ; but, for the most part, all was still save in the heronry close by.   There pandemonium had broken loose — evidently the birds were making a night of it.   I had long wished to spend 24 hours at a night heronry, out of curiosity to know whether these birds really turn night into day, as their name implies.   My experience here inclines me to the belief that, if they sleep at all, they must slumber in relays or take cat naps.   In the twenty-four hours that I remained within hearing, there was not a minute when the sound of their voices was stilled, and there were always birds flying away to sea, shore or marsh, and others returning.   They were quietest just after noon, and noisiest about all night, I believe; for, though I slept a little, sound or continuous slumber was impossible.   I never before passed such a night except in some of the crowded swamps of Florida.   No moon was shining, but nevertheless the babel of sounds increased as the night grew darker, until a nervous person might have imagined that the souls of the condemned had been thrown into purgatory, and were bemoaning their fate.   One bird in particular in the edge of the wood near me set up a succession of most dismal groans, as if it were suffering slow torture.   It kept up the performance intermittently throughout the night.   The frog chorus of the young birds was varied.   It sounded in some cases more like a hen calling for her chicks; now and then heavier notes were heard, reminding me of an old rooster clucking to his harem; cat-calls, infant screams, shrieks, yells and croaks swelled the chorus, all intermingled with the beating of heavy wings and the harsh '*quoks*' of individual birds that swept low over my camping place.''

When the young birds are well able to fly, they scatter in all directions from their breeding-place in search of food.   Many of them go to the northward, sometimes hundreds of miles, others go west or south (see map, page xxiv).   In late September or October the adult birds gather in flocks and move southward.   They assemble toward night and move in the dusk of evening; some flocks assume a V formation; while at other times immense irregular flights gather and flap away into the night.

Night Herons feed mainly along the shores of tidal rivers and estuaries, about the shores of fresh-water rivers and lakes or in fresh or salt marshes.   Their food is taken either by silent watching or by walking or wading about and hunting over flats and marshes. At need some individuals do not hesitate to alight in deep water or to swim out into it.

Dr. L. C. Jones, of Falmouth, tells me that he saw a Night Heron wade into a small river and swim across it to some other herons on the farther shore.   Mr. C. W. Vibert, of South Windsor, Conn., wrote to me on August 8, 1920, that he had seen the Black-crowned Night Heron alight in the middle of the Connecticut River in deep water, and swim about like a Gull.   He stated that he saw this once in 1919, and in 1920 witnessed a similar occurrence, once one day and three times on another day.

The food of the Night Heron seems to be mainly animal in its nature — mice, a few young birds, especially young ducklings,* frogs, toads, tadpoles, lizards, fish, squids, crustaceans, such as crawfish and shrimps, and insects; so far as known the vegetal food is chiefly algæ.   I once came upon a group of young Night Herons at a heronry in Barnstable that were feeding on beach plums.   They had stripped the bushes of the fruit as high as they could reach.

---

* Several people have informed me that they have known Night Herons to take ducklings.   Mr. Lee Crandall of the New York Zoölogical Park tells me that individuals of a colony of Night Herons in the Park destroy many young ducks there.

ECONOMIC STATUS. The Black-crowned Night Heron is accused of being injurious to the fishery interests. Where trout are reared artificially in small ponds, individual birds doubtless commit some depredations, and probably they secure some fish that are taken in fish-traps and weirs, but ordinarily, so far as my observations go, they get comparatively few edible fish. There has been no thorough investigation of their food habits.

Nyctanássa violácea (LINNÆUS). Yellow-crowned Night Heron.

Fig. 29.

DESCRIPTION. — *Bill short and extremely stout* for a heron, much shorter than tarsus; eyes large. *Adults in breeding plumage* (*sexes alike*): Plumage generally light grayish-blue or bluish-gray; two long, narrow, white feathers 7 inches more or less in length hang from back of head, with others shorter, some white and some black; crested top of head and elongated patch on side of head from below eye to ear-region white, former (in some individuals both) sometimes rusty specked as if stained and (in life) tinted with primrose-yellow which is said to fade to white after breeding season; rest of head and nape black; rest of neck ashy; upper body feathers streaked broadly centrally with black and narrowly edged pale bluish-gray; scapulars extremely long, loose-webbed, tapering, extending beyond tail; wing-coverts very dark slate, edged pale gray; primaries bluish-gray; secondaries same, edged paler; under plumage plain, pale bluish-gray; bill black; iris reddish-orange; bare skin before eye green; legs and feet yellow. *Second summer plumage:* Similar to adult breeding plumage but general color of upper plumage darker, especially on back and scapulars. *Young in first summer plumage:* Similar to juvenal plumage but wanting the spots and showing indications of adult markings on head, with undeveloped long white plumes on back of head and some long feathers on back and scapulars. *Young in first winter plumage:* Similar to juvenal but back nearly or quite spotless. *Young in juvenal plumage:* Similar to that of juvenal Black-crowned Night Heron, but *darker brown,* more narrowly streaked and spotted whitish and rusty; flight-feathers slate, without a trace of reddish-brown; bill *shorter,* stouter.

MEASUREMENTS. — Length 22.00 to 28.00 in.; spread 34.00 to 44.00; folded wing 10.50 to 12.65; tail 4.00 to 5.00; bill 2.50 to 3.10, over .50 deep at base; bare tibia 2.00; tarsus 3.10 to 4.20. Weight 1 lb. 7 oz. (Audubon). Female slightly smaller than male.

MOLTS. — Similar to those of Black-crowned Night Heron (see page 337), but long white feathers on head begin to grow in first summer plumage; these head-plumes together with the long plumes of the back in adult are doubtless renewed in the fall.

FIELD MARKS. — Adult may be distinguished from Black-crowned Night Heron by darker plumage below, streaked back, black head with white stripe on cheek and yellowish or white crown; young of the two species are indistinguishable in field.

VOICE. — Similar to that of Black-crowned Night Heron; but "not so harsh and seldom given" (C. J. Maynard).

BREEDING. — Mostly in swamps. *Nest:* Placed variously from tops of tall trees down to low bushes; constructed of sticks. *Eggs:* 3 to 6, "2.00 by about 1.50 to 1.90 by 1.40" (C. J. Maynard); pale greenish-blue to yellowish-green. *Dates:* April 2 to 25, Florida; April 20, South Carolina. *Incubation:* Period probably about 24 days and by both sexes. Two broods yearly.

RANGE. — Warm temperate and tropical America mainly, ranging farther north in summer in eastern North America. Breeds from southern Lower California, Kansas, southern Illinois, southern Indiana and South Carolina south to Brazil and Peru; casual north to Colorado, Nebraska, Iowa, Minnesota, Ontario, Maine and Nova Scotia; winters from southern Lower California, southern Texas, southern Florida, Cuba and Bahamas southward; casual in Bermuda.

DISTRIBUTION IN NEW ENGLAND. — Accidental visitor. *Maine:* Portland (Deering), female taken April 13, 1901;[1] female taken April 11, 1906;[2] Monhegan Island, bird seen Aug. 13, 26 and 27, 1916.[3] *New Hampshire:* Portsmouth, adult seen July 8, 1920.[4] *Massachusetts:* Ashland, bird taken "about forty years ago" [1857 Ed.];[5] Lynn, bird taken in October, 1862;[6] Somerville, young bird taken July 30, 1878;[7] Provincetown, adult male taken April 8, 1891;[8] another adult seen later, and young female taken July 18, 1891;[9] Malden, bird (one of two) taken in summer, about 1893;[10] adult male taken April 20, 1897, skin by M. A. Frazar for Brewster collection, and now in Museum of Comparative Zoölogy collection; Gloucester, immature female taken Aug. 2, 1903, in collection of Hon. John E. Thayer; Falmouth, bird seen May 22, 1919, by Dr. L. C. Jones,[11] "undoubtedly *violacea*"; Sherborn, bird seen May 23, 1920, by John D. Houghton.[12] *Rhode Island:* Tiverton, male taken April 23, 1886;[13] Newport, young female taken August, 1892;[14] Block Island, male in fine plumage taken April 18, 1925.[15] *Connecticut:* South Norwalk, adult taken April 21, 1922 (bird found exhausted two days before and died two days later);[16] Hartford, bird seen Sept. 16, 1922;[17] Southport, bird seen Aug. 11 to Sept. 14, 1923;[18] Southport, bird seen Aug. 29 to Oct. 9, 1924 ("undoubtedly the same that I saw and reported last summer").[19]

SEASON IN MASSACHUSETTS. — April to October.

HAUNTS AND HABITS. The Yellow-crowned Night Heron in full breeding plumage is a striking and conspicuous bird. Though regarded as an accidental visitor in New England it probably occurs more often in summer than the records indicate. The tendency of young herons in America to migrate northward in summer is well known, and the young of this species so closely resemble those of the Black-crowned Night Heron that they may escape notice. The former resembles the latter in its habits, and haunts similar retreats. The yellow-crowned bird, although it migrates at night and moves about much on clear nights, is often abroad during the day. Audubon asserts that if when flying over a line of gunners this bird is shot at and missed, it will dive toward the ground and will continue to do this time after time whenever fired at. In this it differs from its black-crowned congener which under such circumstances usually stops for no dive but turns away from the gunner and devotes its best attention to getting out of gunshot range.

[1] Swain, J. Merton: Journal Maine Ornithological Society, Vol. III, 1901, p. 29. Brock, Henry H.: Auk, Vol. XIX, 1902, p. 285.

[2] Norton, Arthur H.: Auk, Vol. XXIII, 1906, p. 457.

[3] Munroe, E. A.: *in litt.* 1918.

[4] Coolidge, John T. Jr.: Bird-Lore, Vol. XXII, 1920, p. 285.

[5] Morse, A. P.: Birds of Wellesley, 1897, p. 15.

[6] Allen, J. A.: American Naturalist, Vol. III, 1870, p. 637.

[7] Brewster, Wm.: Bulletin Nuttall Ornithological Club, Vol. IV, 1879, pp. 124–125.

[8] Small, Frederic L.: Ornithologist and Oölogist, Vol. XVI, 1891, p. 64.

[9] Small, Frederic L.: *Ibid.,* p. 135.

[10] Forbush, E. H.: Auk, Vol. XI, 1894, p. 55.

[11] Jones, L. C.: *in litt.*

[12] Houghton, John D.: *in litt.*

[13] Howe, R. H. Jr., and Sturtevant, Edward: Birds of Rhode Island, 1899, p. 45, and Random Notes on Natural History, Vol. III, p. 49.

[14] Livermore, J.: Auk, Vol. XI, 1894, p. 177.

[15] Dickens, Miss Elizabeth: *in litt.*

[16] Smith, Wilbur F.: Bird-Lore, Vol. XXV, 1923, p. 393 and *in litt.*

[17] Vibert, C. W.: *in litt.*

[18] Lacey, Milton S.: Bird-Lore, Vol. XXV, 1923, p. 393 and *in litt.*

[19] Lacey, Milton S.: *in litt.*

The food of this heron is somewhat similar to that of the Black-crowned Night Heron, but it seems especially fond of crabs and crawfish. Audubon says that it eats small quadrupeds, young birds that have fallen from their nests, leeches and snails.

ECONOMIC STATUS. See page 315.

ORDER PALUDICOLÆ. CRANES, RAILS, ETC.

Number of species in North America 21; in Massachusetts 9.

This order contains all marsh birds of the type of cranes and rails as distinguished from herons on one side and shore birds on the other. The species of the various families within the order differ widely in size, form and general appearance, but they are practically all runners, although many of them have great powers of flight. The distinctions between this group and those arranged next to it are rather difficult to define but obvious on comparison. Although cranes and rails differ widely, there is a general similarity between them.

SUBORDER GRUES. CRANES, COURLANS, ETC.

Number of species in North America 4.

This group is represented in North America by Cranes and Courlans and in South America by the Agamis.

FAMILY GRUIDÆ. CRANES.

Number of species in North America 3.

Cranes have the bill deeply grooved laterally. They resemble rails more than herons in the shape of the bill (which is nearly straight, with a curved ridge) but average larger than herons and much heavier (wing over 16 inches, tarsus over 7); some are gigantic birds. The neck and legs are long and the plumage is compact in contrast to the loose plumage of herons. In place of the elongated scapular plumage of herons, cranes have the tertials lengthened and curved. There are no powder-down tracts. Cranes have the upper part of the head more or less bare, bristles on lores, no comb-like edge on inner side of middle toe nail, hind toe elevated. They may be distinguished from herons when in flight by the fully extended neck.

ECONOMIC STATUS. Cranes have considerable food value. Probably they are of some service in destroying pests, but they sometimes eat corn.

Grus americána (Linnæus).   **Whooping Crane.**

Whooping Crane
From a drawing by Annie Chase.

Description. — *Adults* (*sexes alike*) : Bill stout, tapering, straight or slightly curved.   Bare part of head extending from bill past eye to hind head and on either side to a point much below and behind eye, carmine sparsely sprinkled with black, hair-like feathers ; small, slaty-blackish patch on back of head and nape; plumage generally white; primaries, primary coverts (including shafts) and alula or bastard wing, slaty-black; bill "wax yellow," often tipped black or dusky-greenish; iris yellow; feet and legs black or bluish-black. *Young:* Head fully feathered; general plumage whitish, varied with rusty brown; rusty tips of feathers sometimes give general plumage a rusty tint; feathers on parts of head which finally become bare darker than the rest; primaries and their coverts similar to those of adults.

MEASUREMENTS. — Length about 49.00 to 56.00 in.; spread about 76.00 to 92.00; folded wing 22.00 to 26.00; tail 7.00 to 9.50; bill 5.10 to 6.00; tarsus 11.00 to 12.00. Weight 8 lbs. 12 oz. to upward of 12 lbs.

MOLTS. — During first winter tips of feathers of upper plumage fade somewhat, and in late winter or spring there is partial molt; some immature birds may become as adults after complete molt during next autumn, when more than a year old, but probably in most cases some rusty-yellow tips of upper plumage persist longer; Audubon believed that cranes required four or five years to reach full maturity; authorities differ here; adults apparently have complete autumnal change and partial spring molt.

FIELD MARKS. — Largest of American wading birds. *Adult:* White with black wing-tips; at a long distance it might be mistaken for a Wood Ibis or a White Ibis, both of which show dark wing-tips; but at ordinary distances its great size is distinctive. *Young:* More or less rusty or brownish; flies with slow heavy flappings or sails high in circles with neck always fully extended and legs trailing horizontally behind.

VOICE. — Occasionally "a loud ringing resolute whoop" (J. W. Preston); in migration loud intermittent croakings like hounds on a cold scent (Goss); sound like *kewr, kewr, kewrook* (Audubon).

BREEDING. — On open marsh or prairie. *Nest:* a platform of flags, rushes and weeds, often in water and solidly built. *Eggs:* 2; 3.75 to 4.08 by 2.50 to 2.60 in.; elliptical-ovate or elongate-ovate; light brownish-drab to greenish-brown, spotted thickly with brown or chocolate and light reddish-brown or buff, with some obscure purplish markings; shells very rough, even "warty." *Dates:* May 2, Iowa. *Incubation:* Period not definitely known, but probably at least 33 days; probably by female. One brood yearly.

RANGE. — Most of North America. Bred formerly from northern Mackenzie and Hudson Bay to the north central United States and possibly east to Ohio or western New York, and in migration occurred on the Atlantic coast from New England southward; now probably restricted mainly to southern Mackenzie, and in migration to the Mississippi Valley region; winters south to Texas and central Mexico.

DISTRIBUTION IN NEW ENGLAND. — Believed to have been an occasional or casual migrant here during the early history of the colonies; the only definite and recent record is that of a specimen taken in 1908 in extreme southwestern Connecticut, now mounted in the collection of the Boston Society of Natural History (further data lacking); reports of the species in Maine, Vermont and Massachusetts during the last century are not substantiated by specimens.

HAUNTS AND HABITS. In size the great Whooping Crane stands alone, a relic of the past. It overtops all North American waders even the Flamingo, which though nearly as tall is less in bulk. A search through the writings of the early explorers and settlers on the Atlantic coast leads to the belief that this great bird was once a transient there, and was at least an occasional visitor to some New England states. Emmons in his list of Massachusetts birds (1833) rates the Whooping Crane as a rare but regular visitant, "breeding in this climate." Dr. Thompson in his Natural History of Vermont (1842) says that it is seen in the state only in migration. DeKay (1844) includes it in his list of the birds of New York. Being an edible fowl, however, and of great size, it gradually disappeared before the rifle of the hunter and the settler, and is now confined mainly to the interior of the continent, where it is nearing extinction.

In moving about on its feeding-grounds this species flies low and heavily, but in migration it rises to tremendous heights from which however its resonant cries may be clearly heard. Audubon asserts that he has heard its call at a distance of three miles. This bird like the Trumpeter Swan has a long convoluted windpipe which is sometimes nearly five feet in length and which is believed to add force and resonance to its voice. Nuttall in describing the flight of cranes up the Mississippi Valley in 1811 said that the bustle of the great migrations and the passage of the mighty armies filled the mind with wonder.

Its chief inland haunts are savannas, marshes, prairies and the low grassy shores of rivers, lakes and lagoons, while formerly on the Atlantic coast it frequented river valleys and the lowlands of the coastal plains. It is extremely wary, feeding usually in open regions where its great stature enables it to keep watch in all directions. Its food consists largely of vegetal matter — grain, seeds, roots, etc. — and it also takes a large quota of animal food, consisting of mice, moles, snakes, lizards, frogs, insects, worms and many small forms of aquatic animal life. Aughey lists the species as one of the enemies of the Rocky Mountain locust.

ECONOMIC STATUS. See page 344.

Grus canadénsis (LINNÆUS). Little Brown Crane.

HEAD OF LITTLE BROWN CRANE, SHOWING BARE FRONTAL SPACE

DESCRIPTION. — *Adults (sexes alike)*: Bare skin, extending from bill to top of head and down to level of lower edge of eye, granulated, red (sometimes mottled with yellowish), sparsely furnished with scattering hair-like black feathers; feathers of back of head extending forward in wedge-like form into bare space; plumage generally light ashy-gray, except bastard wing, primary coverts and primaries which are darker ashy-brown to brownish-black; primary shafts more or less white, or at least lighter than webs; cheeks and throat usually lighter, sometimes almost white; *much individual variation*; often a rusty-brownish wash on part of plumage, especially on feather-tips (but such birds probably immature); iris crimson, pale orange, or orange-yellow; bill blackish, often paler at tip; legs and feet black. *Young in juvenal plumage*: Similar to adult, but lighter and browner; head entirely covered with feathers; much rusty on back of head; more or less rusty-brown tips, conspicuous on back and wing coverts; bill flesh-colored at base, lighter at tip.

MEASUREMENTS. — Length 33.30 to 39.50 in.; spread 72.50 to 75.00; folded wing 17.20 to 20.20; tail 6.50 to 8.10; bill 2.90 to 4.40, depth at base .75 to .95; tarsus 6.58 to 8.50. Weight "on an average not more than 7 lbs." (Hearne).

MOLTS. — See "Molts" under Whooping Crane (page 346).

FIELD MARKS. — *Adult:* Size about that of Great Blue Heron but heavier; a gray bird that flies with neck stretched to full length and legs trailing straight out behind; bald red forehead may be seen under favorable conditions. *Young:* Similar, but much browner above; indistinguishable in the field from Sandhill Crane.

VOICE. — A loud, hard, rolling *kr-roo, k-r-r-r-r-oo, ku-kr-r-roo* (E. W. Nelson).

BREEDING. — On grassy flats or tundra. *Nest:* A mere hollow in ground, on knoll or high part of flat; usually lined with grasses and straws. *Eggs:* 2; 3.70 by 2.40 to 3.33 by 2.21 in.; similar to those of Whooping Crane; elongate-ovate; "pale greenish-clay" to "buffy brown" or warm brownish, irregularly marked with elongated spots and blotches of chocolate brown, "most numerous at the large end" (E. W. Nelson). *Dates:* Late May to June 20, Alaska. *Incubation:* Period about 30 to 33 days; by female. One brood yearly.

RANGE. — North America. Breeds from western and northern Alaska, Melville Island and Baffin Island south to central Alaska, southern Mackenzie and southern Keewatin; migrates down Pacific coast and through interior of Canada and United States, and winters from California and Texas to Jalisco, Mexico; casual or occasional in northeastern Siberia.

DISTRIBUTION IN NEW ENGLAND. — Cranes are now merely accidental in New England, and when reported (in flight) are seen at such a distance that the species cannot be identified; the only definite and authentic record of the capture of this species in New England is that of a specimen taken at Natick Hill, Rhode Island, Oct. 8 or 9, 1889, recorded by William Brewster.[1]

HAUNTS AND HABITS. Little is known of the habits of the Little Brown Crane except that in its northern home, as in the South, it associates with the Sandhill Crane and cannot readily be distinguished from that species in the field. It frequents the same localities and seems to have the same habits and food. Its method of courtship is much the same as that of the Sandhill Crane. Dr. Nelson says that in Alaska late in July and during August the cranes frequent the hillsides to feed upon berries growing there.

ECONOMIC STATUS. See page 344.

Grus mexicána (MÜLLER). Sandhill Crane.

DESCRIPTION. — Almost exactly like Little Brown Crane (*Grus canadensis*), with similar individual variations, molts and changes of plumage, but a larger bird; also in specimens examined by me the bill seems relatively a little more slender and the tarsus relatively longer.

MEASUREMENTS. — Length 40.00 to 48.00 in.; spread about 80.00; folded wing 21.00 to 22.50; tail 8.00 to 10.00; bill 5.00 to 6.00, depth at base .95 to 1.10; tarsus 9.20 to 10.65. Weight up to 12 lbs. 8 oz.

MOLTS. — Apparently like those of Whooping Crane and Little Brown Crane.

FIELD MARKS. — Like those of Little Brown Crane from which it cannot be told in the field.

VOICE. — Like that of Little Brown Crane, a loud whoop or croak repeated several times and carrying far.

BREEDING. — Usually in marshes, wet prairies or savannas. *Nest:* Of grasses, weeds, roots, mud, etc., sometimes bulky, often on a platform of dead vegetation in shallow water of marsh or small marshy

---

[1] *Auk*, Vol. VII, 1890, p. 89.

pond. *Eggs:* 2; 3.40 to 4.10 by 2.10 to 2.60 in.; indistinguishable in color from those of Whooping Crane (page 346) but a little smaller. *Dates:* March 2, Florida; April 14, Oregon; May 5, Indiana; May 30, Wisconsin; June 5, Colorado; June 9, North Dakota; latest June 30, Michigan. *Incubation:* Period not definitely known, probably about 30 to 33 days; apparently by female. One brood yearly.

Range. — North America south of the Hudsonian region. Breeds from southern British Columbia, southern Alberta and southern Saskatchewan (formerly Manitoba and western Ontario) south to Cali-

SANDHILL CRANE
From Game Birds, Wild-fowl and Shore Birds.

fornia, northern Arizona, Colorado, Nebraska, Iowa and northern Indiana (formerly Illinois and Ohio); breeding now largely local and restricted, particularly in United States; resident in Florida, Louisiana and Cuba; migrated formerly on Atlantic coast from New England southward as well as through Interior; now rare or casual east of the Mississippi except in Florida where decreasing; winters from California (casually Colorado) and Gulf States through Mexico to latitude of Yucatan.

Distribution in New England. — Apparently more or less common locally during settlement, now practically extirpated; the two definite records are those of a specimen recorded by William Brewster, taken in 1896 or 1897 at Lovell's Pond, Wakefield, New Hampshire, and preserved in Museum of

New Hampshire Agricultural College at Durham;[1] and another shot on Connecticut River at Lunenburg, Vermont, and preserved in the Vermont State Museum;[2] may appear again in New England as an accidental straggler.

HAUNTS AND HABITS. The great Sandhill Crane once roamed the Atlantic coast in migration, and probably was the only crane that was ever common in any part of New England. Like the wild turkey it disappeared with the coming of settlement and civilization and is no longer found on the Atlantic coast north of Georgia, except as an extremely rare straggler. Probably it never came to New England in very great numbers, as this is largely a hilly forested country, and cranes prefer more level and open lands. When here it doubtless frequented the coastal marshes and the more open river valleys. It is an extremely wary bird. It feeds usually in open meadows, marshes, savannas or prairies, taking its food mainly from the ground or near it and raising its head frequently to watch and listen for danger. It is very difficult to approach, within gunshot range, as it always shows great fear of mankind, but when wounded and brought to bay, it exhibits the utmost courage and fights desperately. Audubon tells of being driven into a river up to his neck in water to escape an enraged crane with a broken wing which waded into the water to its belly in pursuit. A wing-tipped crane is exceedingly agile and is capable of evading blows and darting its long bill through a man's eye to his brain. I can well believe Audubon's tale as I once had a fencing match with a winged bird which attacked me so savagely that I felt obliged to end the contest with a charge of shot. This species can defend itself successfully against any dog, and doubtless has few dangerous enemies besides man. Like the other cranes it has a so-called mating dance which I once observed. The birds usually assemble in some numbers on a knoll and dance about, skipping high in air and even flying up a little way from the ground occasionally, turning about, moving with high prancing steps and bowing repeatedly in all directions. Both males and females engage in the dance. At times a single pair may be seen so occupied and even a lone bird may take a few "dance steps" from time to time.

In Florida the Sandhill Crane is not confined to the prairies and savannas, but may be seen at times in the open piney woods, where its raucous resounding cries arouse the echoes. There I was able easily to find its nests by climbing tall trees which gave me an outlook over the saw-grass ponds.

This crane, like its relatives, takes much vegetal food. The roots of plants and tubers including potatoes and sweet potatoes, corn and other grains and seeds make up a part of its food. It destroys the eggs and probably the young of rails. On the other hand, it feeds on mice and insect pests. Aughey found it to be destructive to the Rocky Mountain locust and other insects. Mrs. L. H. Touissaint states that in one morning a pet bird of this species captured and consumed "148 grasshoppers, 2 moths, a roach, a lizard, 2 grubs and 11 spiders."[3]

---

[1] Brewster, Wm.: Auk, Vol. XVIII, 1901, p. 274.
[2] Perkins and Howe: A Preliminary List of the Birds found in Vermont, 1901, p. 13.
[3] Bird-Lore, Vol. XVI, 1914, p. 359.

ECONOMIC STATUS. The only appreciable harm done by this bird seems to be due to its fondness for corn and potatoes. It has considerable value as a game bird as, when young, it is thought to be a delicate dish for the table. Morton, who lived at Mount Wollaston near Boston, writes (1632) that the crane is "a goodly Bird in a dishe and no discommodity." [1] A bird weighing 8 to 12 lbs. might well take the place of the turkey on Thanksgiving or Christmas, and often did so. In the early settlement of California by the Americans, cranes were said to have commanded from sixteen to twenty dollars each, to be used in place of the Christmas turkey. [2]

NOTE. The Cuban variety of this Crane is now regarded as a subspecies by some ornithologists. It is probable also that the Little Brown Crane and the Sandhill Crane may be eventually rated as two races of one species.

SUBORDER RALLI. RAILS, GALLINULES, COOTS, ETC.

Number of species in North America 17; in Massachusetts 9.

FAMILY **RALLIDÆ**. RAILS, GALLINULES AND COOTS.

The suborder RALLI is represented in New England by the single family *Rallidæ*. The species are chiefly marsh birds of small to medium size with body compressed to enable them to pass between the stems of reeds, long, strong legs and thighs for running and climbing, comparatively weak, short wings and very short tail; head completely feathered.

SUBFAMILY **RALLINÆ**. RAILS.

Number of species in North America 13; in Massachusetts 9.

Wading birds, with body compressed in front and adapted to push through narrow places; tail very short, rounded, of 12 feathers; toes extremely long, not webbed or lobed, but usually a slight basal membrane between front toes for assistance in swimming; bill long or short; rails inhabit all temperate countries.

ECONOMIC STATUS. No exhaustive study of the food of New England rails has been made. They are known to feed largely on seeds of wild marsh vegetation and insects and are not known to consume any appreciable quantity of the products of man's industry. As game birds they are of considerable importance and immense numbers are killed annually for food. However, not many rails are killed in New England for either sport or food except along the meadows of the Connecticut River and in the marshes of southern Connecticut. The greatest numbers are taken in the Middle Atlantic States and along the coast of some southern Atlantic States, where rails are more numerous in migration than they are in New England.

---

[1] Morton, Thomas: New English Canaan. Publications of the Prince Society, 1883, p. 192.
[2] Report of the California Fish and Game Commission, 1896, p. 42.

Rállus élegans AUDUBON. King Rail.

Other names: MEADOW HEN; FRESH-WATER MARSH HEN; MUD HEN.

Plate 23.

DESCRIPTION. — Bill longer than head, down-curved and slender. Much individual variation in intensity of coloring and distinctness of markings: *Adults (sexes alike)*: Above rich, olive-brown, distinctly streaked with brownish-black (and in some cases, with olive-gray), with sometimes a tawny or yellow tinge, turning to chestnut on wing-coverts and dark brown on hind neck and top of head; "brownish-orange" or brownish-white line over eye, turning to brownish-gray behind it; rest of side of head dusky bluish-ash; chin and upper throat whitish; wings mostly brown of varying shades; sides of neck and entire chest mainly reddish-brown or cinnamon, darkest on breast, fading to whitish from belly to under tail-coverts; flanks and wing linings dark brown to blackish, barred white; bill (ridge and tip) "deep brown," with lower mandible and edges of upper orange-red or brownish-yellow, tinged olive; iris red; "iris light brown" (B. H. Warren); bill dark yellowish especially at base of lower mandible; legs and feet apparently variable, reddish-brown, "pale flesh-brown," or "slaty or grayish maroon" (Ludwig Kumlien) or "yellowish-brown with a grayish-orange tinge" (G. Trumbull). *Young in juvenal plumage:* Similar to adult but usually duller, darker above, paler below. *Downy young:* Glossy black or blackish.

MEASUREMENTS. — Length 17.00 to 19.00 in.; spread 21.25 to 25.00; folded wing 6.00 to 7.00; tail 2.50 to 3.50; bill 2.00 to 3.00; tarsus 2.10 to 2.75. Weight 10 to 18 oz. Female smaller than male.

MOLTS. — Apparently young birds become indistinguishable from adults after the first prenuptial molt; adults appear to have a partial prenuptial molt in late winter or spring and a complete postnuptial molt beginning in July.

FIELD MARKS. — Largest of New England rails; larger and brighter in color than Clapper Rail, breast cinnamon rather than buffy or grayish as in Clapper; and very much larger than Virginia Rail which otherwise it resembles.

VOICE. — Harsh, clattering, hen-like; apt to be confused with that of Clapper Rail, but rarely heard in salt marshes which Clapper inhabits; a loud *bŭp, bŭp, bŭp, bŭp, bŭp, bŭp*, increasing in rapidity to a roll and then ending in about 5 seconds, somewhat as it began (F. M. Chapman); a grunting *umph, umph, umph, umph*, all on same key and separated by rather wide intervals, deep and guttural, sometimes harsh and vibrant (Wm. Brewster). J. C. Peters saw one walking calmly about meanwhile uttering a "series of loud, abrupt squawks" (Bird-Lore, Vol. XIII, 1911, p. 251). Call note *creek, creek, creek;* flight note, *cark, cark, cark* (B. F. Goss); when caught, cries like a common fowl (Audubon).

BREEDING. — In fresh-water marshes. *Nest:* Of weeds, grasses, etc., usually on or near ground or just above surface of water, in long marsh-grass, reeds or low bush. *Eggs:* 6 to 16; 1.80 by 1.10 to 1.50 by 1.05 in.; buffy or creamy-white, blotched or speckled with reddish-brown and lilac. *Dates:* June 17 to June 25, Connecticut. One brood yearly.

RANGE. — Eastern North America. Breeds from Nebraska, southern Minnesota, Wisconsin, southern Michigan, southern Ontario, New York and Connecticut south to Texas and Florida; winters mainly in southern part of breeding range; casual north to North Dakota and southern Manitoba and occasional northeast to Maine.

DISTRIBUTION IN NEW ENGLAND. — *Maine:* Occasional fall visitor. Knight gives records of 8 Maine birds[1] (three of which may have been Clapper Rails), all of them previously published in The Auk or the Bulletin of the Nuttall Ornithological Club. A late date for *Maine* is Nov. 22, 1909, when a fine male King Rail was taken at Bucksport by A. G. Dorr.[2] *New Hampshire:* Hampton, female taken Dec. 7, 1924 by Peter B. Olney.[3] *Vermont:* Bennington, a King Rail heard and seen in May, 1910.[4]

[1] Knight, O. W.: Birds of Maine, 1908, p. 138.
[2] Phillips, C. L.: Auk, Vol. XXXVI, 1919, p. 277.
[3] Smith, J. D.: *in litt.*
[4] Ross, Lucretius H.: Auk, Vol. XXX, 1913, p. 436 and Vermont Bird Club Bulletin No. VI, 1911, p. 21.

PLATE 23

PLATE 23

KING RAIL
Page 352
ADULT IN BREEDING PLUMAGE

CLAPPER RAIL
Page 354

ADULT IN BREEDING
PLUMAGE

VIRGINIA RAIL
Page 355
YOUNG IN JUVENAL
PLUMAGE

ADULT IN BREEDING PLUMAGE

SORA
Page 357

YOUNG IN AUTUMN

ADULT IN BREEDING
PLUMAGE

YELLOW RAIL
Page 360

BLACK RAIL
Page 361

All one-third natural size.

Massachusetts: Rare summer resident and occasional at all seasons. In Game Birds, Wild-Fowl and Shore Birds, Massachusetts Board of Agriculture, 2d Edition (1916), p. 203, I gave many records, most of which had been recorded elsewhere. Mr. S. Prescott Fay gives records in Auk, Vol. XXVII, 1910, p. 220, and Vol. XXVIII, 1911, p. 121; and Dr. C. W. Townsend gives two more records in his Supplement to the Birds of Essex County, 1920, p. 71. The following winter record is unrecorded (doubtless there are others): Sandwich, Feb. 14, 1919, bird caught in trap, A. W. Higgins. *Rhode Island:* Rare visitor and may breed. Three records are given by Howe and Sturtevant,[1] and others by Harry S. Hathaway.[2] *Connecticut:* Rare summer resident and occasional visitor. Sage, Bishop and Bliss give many records in the Birds of Connecticut.

HAUNTS AND HABITS. This great rail is the largest and handsomest representative of the family in New England. Tall grasses, reeds, sedges, arums and cat-tail flags commonly screen it from human eyes, except on those rare occasions when startled by a sudden intrusion it rises and flaps or flutters slowly along for a short distance above the tops of the marsh vegetation. It is more partial to uplands than most of our rails and sometimes wanders into grass or grain fields. It frequents fresh-water marshes, though often found near the sea-coast or even occasionally within the confines of salt marshes. When not in fear of molestation it sometimes leaves its cover and comes out on mud flats or into stubble fields. In seasons of high spring floods it has been known to retreat from its flooded marshes and nest in fields and on hillsides. It seems to be an erratic wandering bird. Mr. G. A. Abbott reports that during balmy nights of May and June it was not an uncommon occurrence near his home to hear one of these birds about the dooryard at least a mile from its actual abode. He asserts that frequently one will stand under an electric light and give vent to its clucking notes and says that he knows of one instance wherein one of these rails wandered into the parlor of a residence in the early morning in house-cleaning time when the doors were ajar. (Oölogist, Vol. XXV, 1908, p. 133.)

Nevertheless, the bird is more often heard than seen. It is considered as merely an occasional visitor in Massachusetts, but as large rails are reported on Cape Cod in summer with young, this species must breed occasionally in that region. The only positive breeding record reported is that of Dr. L. C. Jones, who tells me that somewhere about 1880 he found a pair of adults with a brood of young in Sandwich, several of which he caught in his hands. The adults were so fearless that they came within a few feet of his position and he had an excellent opportunity to identify them.

Some King Rails seem to remain in the North or to wander northward in autumn or winter. There are winter records in Wisconsin, Michigan, Ontario, New York, Connecticut, Rhode Island, Massachusetts, New Hampshire and Maine. Mr. J. A. Farley secured a specimen in Cambridge, Mass., Dec. 30, 1896, which was recorded in The Auk (1905, p. 409).

ECONOMIC STATUS. This rail destroys many grasshoppers and locusts as it feeds about the edges of uplands. Oats are the only product of man's industry that it is known to eat. It is so rare in New England that it is of no economic consequence.

---

[1] Birds of Rhode Island, 1899, p. 45.   [2] Hathaway, Harry S.: Auk, Vol. XXX, 1913, pp. 549–550.

Rallus crépitans crepitans GMELIN.   Clapper Rail.

Other names: MUD-HEN; SALT-MARSH HEN.

Plate 23.

DESCRIPTION. — Similar to King Rail in form but somewhat smaller, colors paler or grayer, more suffused, and markings less conspicuous. *Adults (sexes alike)*: Above ashy olive-gray, streaked inconspicuously with olive-brown; crown and nape brown or dusky; eyelids and line from bill over eye brownish-white or whitish; wings and tail brown; wing-coverts dull olive, tinged gray; wing-linings dark brown barred whitish; sides of head, neck and body ashy olive-gray, turning whitish on upper throat and chin, and pale brownish-yellow or buffy on lower fore neck and breast; flanks somewhat darker, barred whitish; abdomen and under tail-coverts whitish barred brownish-gray (middle abdomen usually not barred); bill yellow, dusky on ridge and tip; iris reddish-brown to pale yellow; legs and feet "gray with yellow or orange tinge at tibio-tarsal joint." *Young in juvenal plumage:* Similar to adult but darker above and soiled white below. *Downy young:* Chiefly black with some whitish below.

MEASUREMENTS. — Length 13.50 to 16.00 in.; spread 19.00 to 21.00; folded wing 5.00 to 6.30; tail 2.00 to 2.50; bill 2.00 to 2.50; tarsus 1.67 to 2.27. Weight 8 to 14 oz. Female smaller than male.

MOLTS. — Similar to those of King Rail (page 352).

FIELD MARKS. — Size near that of King Rail but smaller; gray and buffy rather than brown and ruddy; much less distinctly marked; rarely seen away from coastal region.

VOICE. — A harsh, clattering cackle; *cac, cac, cac, cac, ca, caha, caha* (Audubon); begins extremely loud and fast, ends lower and slower; where numbers cry together there is some resemblance to the cries of the Guinea Hen; "a rail-like crake, a harsh scream when annoyed" (C. J. Maynard).

BREEDING. — In salt marsh or on coastal islands, rarely in upland fields. *Nest:* On ground under lodged drift trash or in tussocks concealed by a canopy of grass. *Eggs:* 8 to 13; 1.72 by 1.20 to 1.63 by 1.13 in.; glossy buff or clay color, speckled and blotched with different shades of reddish-brown and fainter markings of lavender and gray; similar to those of King Rail but averaging smaller. *Dates:* April 27 to June 1 and July 1 to 20, Virginia; May 24, Long Island. *Incubation:* Period 14 days (Audubon). Usually one brood yearly; possibly double-brooded in southern states.

RANGE. — Salt marshes of Atlantic coast of North America. Breeds from Connecticut to Virginia; winters mainly south of New Jersey; casual in Maine.

DISTRIBUTION IN NEW ENGLAND. — Accidental visitor on southwest coast of Maine and in New Hampshire (Portsmouth)[1] and Vermont (Burlington);[2] occasional visitor in Massachusetts and may breed in southeastern coastal region. Howe and Allen give various records,[3] and there are others in the second (1916) edition of my Game Birds, Wild-Fowl and Shore Birds, Massachusetts State Board of Agriculture. A. C. Bent tells me that he picked up a dead Clapper Rail which had struck the telephone wires at West Harwich, Sept. 4, 1923. Mrs. George E. Burbank of Sandwich states that a Clapper Rail was caught in a trap Nov. 2, 1923, in Sandwich, was banded and released; one week later it was caught again and again released; finally in January, 1924, the bird was found dead. Rare visitor and summer resident in Connecticut. Sage, Bishop and Bliss give various records, four of them breeding records.[4]

HAUNTS AND HABITS. The Clapper Rail is so rarely seen or taken in the greater part of New England that it might be regarded as accidental were it not for its habit of skulking in the marsh and not showing itself in daylight unless forced to do so. It is a rather common breeder on the south shore of the east end of Long Island. Probably it breeds on Cape Cod. Miss J. Olivia Crowell of Dennis writes me that she saw a Clapper

---

[1] Dearborn, Ned: Birds of Durham and Vicinity, 1903, p. 29.

[2] Perkins, Geo. H., and Howe, C. D.: Birds of Vermont, 1901, p. 13.

[3] Birds of Massachusetts, 1901, p. 17.

[4] Birds of Connecticut, 1913, pp. 48–49.

Rail walking there by the river in May, 1918, and that she has seen this species year after year in that region. Doubtless most of the so-called Clapper Rails recorded from the interior are really King Rails. The Clapper Rail resembles the latter in habits, but unlike it is rarely found far away from coastal islands or salt marshes. Like all the rails it migrates chiefly at night, flying low.

The Clapper Rail feeds on fish-fry, crustaceans, snails, insects, and other small forms of animal life found in the marshes, and on the seeds and other parts of water plants.

ECONOMIC STATUS. This bird is of no economic importance in New England, but in the southern states was formerly so abundant that its eggs were gathered in large numbers for food. According to Prof. W. W. Cooke, about 10,000 Clapper Rails were killed in two days in 1896 near Atlantic City, New Jersey. (U. S. Department of Agriculture, Bull. 128.) In the Game Survey of Virginia for the hunting season of 1922–23 it is estimated that 25,000, valued at $7,500, were killed that year in that state.[1]

Rallus virginiánus LINNÆUS. Virginia Rail.

Other names: SMALL MUD-HEN; LONG-BILLED RAIL.

Plate 23.

DESCRIPTION. — A miniature of King Rail; colors distributed in a similar manner but usually a little darker and sides of head grayer, flanks usually darker; chin and throat often darker but variable; "bill vermilion, culmen and tip dusky, feet dull red, iris bright red" (Allan Brooks); bill, legs and feet usually as in King Rail; ventral region and under tail-coverts almost invariably marked chestnut; female has dark upper tints lighter than male and under plumage less bright. *Young in first winter plumage:* Similar to adult but somewhat duller. *Young in juvenal plumage:* Mainly dull black, but wings and tail (and sometimes head in transition) much as in adult; chin and throat white; some white elsewhere on lower surface of body; under tail-coverts marked cinnamon. *Downy young:* Glossy greenish-black, with bill scarlet or orange red, black at base and crossed by black band; bill "pinkish-white" (Oölogist, Vol. XIX, 1902, p. 52); outer digit of wing has a tiny claw.

MEASUREMENTS. — Length 8.50 to 10.50 in.; spread about 13.00 to 14.50; folded wing 3.45 to 4.40; tail 1.50 to 2.00; bill 1.25 to 1.65; tarsus 1.25 to 1.50. Weight about 3 to 4 oz. Female smaller than male.

MOLTS. — A postjuvenal molt (July to October) is succeeded by first winter plumage (one specimen retained juvenal plumage until April) which apparently is as adult; adults have a partial prenuptial molt (March) including body-feathers and some wing-coverts and a complete postnuptial (beginning late July).

FIELD MARKS. — Smaller than Bob-white; not half size of King Rail; near that of Sora, but distinguished by long bill, slightly downcurved, red eye and reddish breast.

VOICE. — When undisturbed a sharp squeak; when much annoyed a low chuckle (C. J. Maynard); call, *kep kik* or *kip;* also a *grunting* sound; a *wak-wak-wak;* and cut, *cutta-cutta-cutta;* anxious female, *ki ki ki* or *kiu,* like a Flicker (William Brewster); an ear-piercing *spee* or *see;* a loud and disdainful *eh, eh;* song, *ki d-ick ki d-ick ki d-ick* "delivered with great vigor and rapidly repeated" (C. W. Townsend); also "a series of notes" alternating by a rising and falling inflection of the voice (G. A. Abbott); call of female to young a soft *ka ka ka ka ka,* song of male *kid kid ic kid ic kid ic kid ic* (Verdi Burtch); "on a still day the metallic *keks* may be heard a long way" (J. A. Farley).

---

[1] Commonwealth of Virginia. Department of Inland Fisheries and Game. Game Survey, season ending Feb. 1, 1923, p. 6.

BREEDING. — In fresh-water marshes or along bushy banks of small marshy streams. *Nest:* Of weeds, grasses, dead stalks, etc., in tussock or on pile of broken-down reeds or driftwood; often well concealed. *Eggs:* 5 to 12; 1.30 by .96 to 1.23 by .90 in.; oval to ovate; colored like those of King Rail but much smaller, very variable, sometimes almost white, spots of varying shades of brown, purple, etc., and rather sparse. *Dates:* May 12 to July 18, New England. *Incubation:* By female. Probably but one brood yearly.

RANGE. — North America from near southern limit of Hudsonian Zone to Tropical Zone. Breeds from British Columbia, southern Saskatchewan, Manitoba, Ontario, southern Quebec, New Brunswick and Nova Scotia south to southern California, Utah, Colorado, Nebraska, Missouri, southern Illinois, Kentucky, southern Ohio, New Jersey and (casually) North Carolina and in Toluca Valley, Mexico; winters from southern British Columbia, Utah and Colorado to Lower California and Guatemala, also in lower Mississippi Valley and Gulf states and from North Carolina (casually Massachusetts) to Florida; casual north to Alberta, Hudson Bay, northern Quebec and Newfoundland, also in Bermuda and Cuba.

DISTRIBUTION IN NEW ENGLAND. — Rare local summer resident in Maine, New Hampshire and Vermont; local summer resident in Massachusetts, more common near coast; common local summer resident and common migrant in Rhode Island and Connecticut; casual in winter in southern New England. Albert Landon reported a Virginia Rail Dec. 24, 1921, at New Britain, Connecticut; E. W. Schmidt reported one Jan. 1, 1922, at the same place; and one was seen Dec. 14, 15, and 19, 1922, by S. G. Emilio at Danvers, Massachusetts.

SEASON IN MASSACHUSETTS. — April 3 to November 30; (winter).

HAUNTS AND HABITS. The Virginia Rail frequents such localities as those inhabited by the King Rail and has similar habits. Like the latter, it is, for the most part, a bird of fresh-water marshes, rarely breeding in salt marsh. In autumn it sometimes may be found in grain fields or stubble fields. It seems more secretive than the King Rail. Although secretive like all rails, it is not usually so shy as the Sora and, while keeping more or less hidden, will often come near an observer or permit a close approach. It is fond of marshy, oozy pools where button bushes grow, of jungles of cattails and of river meadows flanked by wild roses. Among reeds, bushes, briars, rushes, grasses and wild rice it follows the numerous hidden passages, which cross and recross one another, in which, unseen, it can race rapidly from place to place at the least alarm. It runs at great speed and passes readily between stems set so close that passage seems impossible. Its flight is feeble and it rarely flies where it can escape under cover. If forced to the brink of a swampy pond and in immediate danger of discovery, it may plunge in and swim away under water by using its partly spread wings, and may hide beneath some stump or bank or conceal itself among the water-plants with only the bill above water. If there is but a small ditch or slough to cross, it may run lightly over the surface on lily pads or other floating vegetation or, if the water is clear, it may swim quickly across, its head bobbing forward with each foot stroke, until it disappears on the farther side in the moving greenery of marsh vegetation. This bird is much more common in its favorite retreats than our infrequent views of it would indicate. Like all rails it is active in the twilight, and its common notes may be heard sometimes intermittently for hours along our river marshes. During the breeding season its rarer grunting notes also are uttered.

The Virginia Rail is often brave to foolhardiness at its nest. Mr. J. A. Farley says: "I have had a female Virginia, whose nest with 10 eggs was much exposed, being in a small (and the only) tussock in an open space, with bare mud flats surrounding, coolly walk around and around me within a yard or so. Such pluck deserved its own reward and I left the brave bird and her eggs unharmed.

"A more interesting case was that of another Virginia Rail which absolutely refused to leave her eggs as she sat on them in her cosy nest in a tussock of a grassy meadow and which, just like a bantam hen, picked my fingers when they came too near her as she nobly refused to leave even for one second her treasures. Her bravery too had its own reward."

This bird is a rapid and excellent climber, scaling at times rushes, shrubs, vines and even small vine-embowered trees in its search for seeds and berries or in pursuit of insects, of which it destroys quantities. It seems to be especially eager in quest of locusts, grasshoppers and beetles. It is fond of wild rice, wild oats and the seeds of grasses and reeds. It takes small crustaceans and even small snakes and fishes and also feeds on earthworms, snails and other of the smaller aquatic animals of the marsh.

ECONOMIC STATUS. No exhaustive study of the food of this bird has been made but so far as is now known it is harmless and beneficial. As an object of sport it ranks below the Sora Rail which apparently is more numerous and generally more accessible to the sportsman.

Porzána carolína (LINNÆUS). Sora.

Other names: SORA RAIL; CAROLINA RAIL; RAIL-BIRD; CHICKEN-BILL: MEADOW-CHICKEN; CRAKE.

Plate 23.

DESCRIPTION. — Bill short and stout. *Adults (sexes similar):* Top of head and back of neck deep olive-brown; a blackish stripe through center of crown; upper surface of body, wings and tail olive-brown, streaked black, with some white or whitish feather-edges; bend of wing and first primary edged white; fore part of head black, the black extending back to inclose eye and well down the center of throat and fore neck; small whitish spot behind eye; line from forehead over eye, sides of head, neck and breast slaty or lead color; flanks brown and grayish barred white; axillars and wing-linings similarly barred; lower belly and under tail-coverts white or whitish; bill pale yellow, tip black or greenish; iris brown or carmine; legs and feet light yellowish-green. *Young in juvenal plumage:* Similar to adult but *no black on face or throat;* no slaty on breast; throat whitish and breast washed with light brown or cinnamon. *Downy young:* Black with a tuft of orange, bristle-like feathers on throat, "a gold-thread goatee"; bill yellow with a red protuberance at base; legs and feet as adult.

MEASUREMENTS. — Length 7.85 to 9.75 in.; spread 12.00 to 14.50; folded wing 3.90 to 4.50; tail 1.50 to 2.16; bill .67 to .90; tarsus 1.18 to 1.44. Weight about 3 to 4 oz. Female smaller than male.

MOLTS. — A partial juvenal body molt (July to winter) is succeeded by first winter plumage, and after spring molt the birds are practically as adult, but black on throat often not quite so extensive as in fully adult birds; adults have a partial prenuptial molt in winter and early spring and a complete molt usually beginning in July.

FIELD MARKS. — Not much smaller than Virginia Rail, but distinguished from it at once by short, yellowish bill and in adult by black fore face and throat; much larger than Yellow or Black Rails.

VOICE. — A clear whistled *ker-wee;* a high-pitched, rolling whinny, often repeated all over the marsh (F. M. Chapman); the whinny consists of 12 or 15 short whistles, clear as a silver bell, first 8 or 10 uttered very rapidly in descending scale, rest more deliberately in uniform key; bird sometimes utters a *cut-cut-cutta* less loud and vibrant than that of Virginia Rail; a sweet, plaintive *er-e* with rising inflection, suggesting a "scatter call" of Bob-white; when very near sounds like *kae*, is repeated many times in succession; heard at early morning, after sunset and through the night (Wm. Brewster); a subdued *ca-weep-eep, ca-weep-eep-eep-ip-ip ip*, like a flock of young chickens; also *crek, crek, crek* (P. L. Hatch); a variety of other short, sharp cries when startled; "notes not as rapid as with Virginia Rails; some short chuckles" (C. J. Maynard).

BREEDING. — Usually in fresh water marshes or meadows, in similar situations as Virginia Rail; but sometimes in grass fields or grain fields. *Nest:* Usually supported by stems of grass, raised above surface of water and concealed by grass tops; usually on hummock; rarely in a briar patch, sometimes set on ground; composed of grasses, weeds and last year's rush-stalks. *Eggs:* 4 to 17; 1.20 to 1.38 by .85 to .90 in.; ovate; deep cream, light brown, drab, "or a yellowish-drab with an olivaceous tint"; darker than those of Virginia Rail, with much larger scattered markings of reddish-brown and purplish-gray. *Dates:* May 15 to July 5; according to latitude or altitude; May 20 to June 11, Massachusetts. *Incubation:* Period probably about 14 days; by female. Probably a single brood yearly.

RANGE. — North America; north into Hudsonian zone and south to northern South America. Breeds from central British Columbia, southern Mackenzie, Saskatchewan, northern Manitoba, Gulf of St. Lawrence and New Brunswick south to southern California, Nevada, Utah, Colorado, Kansas, northern Missouri, (probably Tennessee and Arkansas), southern Illinois, southern Ohio, Pennsylvania and Maryland; winters from northern California, Illinois and South Carolina, in Bermuda and through West Indies and Central America to Venezuela and Peru; straggles in winter north to Minnesota and Massachusetts; casual or occasional in Greenland, Labrador and Newfoundland; accidental in England.

DISTRIBUTION IN NEW ENGLAND. — Rather an uncommon and local summer resident in Maine, New Hampshire and Vermont, becoming rarer and more local in Vermont; common local summer resident and an abundant migrant in river meadows in Massachusetts, Rhode Island and Connecticut. There is a winter record for Rhode Island — Feb. 23, 1924, at Block Island. (Miss Elizabeth Dickens: *in litt.*)

SEASON IN MASSACHUSETTS. — March 20 to December 20. (East Sandwich, Feb. 12, 1919, one tracked in snow and found near a spring by Harry Torrey.)

HAUNTS AND HABITS. The Sora is the Rail-bird of New England. It is a more abundant migrant in our meadows and marshes than any other rail and probably outnumbers them all. Its favorite breeding-haunts are river meadows, cattail swamps and fresh-water marshes in general, together with brackish marshes near the sea; in migration it frequents also salt marshes and tidal streams. Lowlands along slow flowing rivers such as the Concord, the Ipswich and the lower reaches of the Connecticut are favorite spots for migrating Soras. The term "thin as a rail" applies to this as well as to all rails. Any rail can compress its narrow body at will. At the least alarm the Sora slips easily and rapidly away amid the grass stems, or if pressed too hard by a fast dog, it rises above the grass tops, flutters away weakly like a wounded bird, with legs dangling loosely, and drops to earth again almost at once as if unable to fly far. But the short-winged fluttering Sora has landed on vessels hundreds of miles at sea. Numbers fly to Bermuda, about 600 miles from the Continent. The bird goes north to Greenland and is supposed even to cross the Gulf of Mexico. Probably favoring winds assist it in its long migratory night flights.

Like all rails it takes readily to water, swimming on the surface, diving at need and using its wings for propulsion under water. Mr. C. J. Maynard asserts that he once saw one run nimbly along the bottom of a brook in water about one foot deep. It was able to do this, he says, by clinging to aquatic plants, and it went about 15 feet while thus submerged.[1]

When closely pursued, this rail hides readily beneath the surface by clinging to grass or reeds with its feet and breathing through its upthrust bill, or sometimes it crosses narrow waters by fluttering and splashing along the surface like a Coot. While naturally secretive, it is also curious, and I have seen it come out from its hiding places to survey a slowly drifting canoe or a gunner hiding in the marsh. In September a loud shout, a gunshot or a paddle struck upon the water will sometimes start the Soras to cackling and their *cuck cuck* may be heard all over a marsh where not one of the birds is visible. If one wishes to see them, he must sit down quietly in some open spot and wait. If his patience is greater than that of the birds, they may appear. Occasionally a dog may force one to fly and even overtake and catch it in the air, so low and slow is its flight. Where unmolested it becomes quite tame, and it is said that on the western prairies it formerly came about the farm-houses and fed with the chickens.

This rail has a wonderful variety of notes which it gives forth at night as well as by day, and it is sometimes unusually vocal on moon-lit nights. Apparently individuals have some ability as imitators. On three different occasions I have heard a very remarkable avian monologue, interspersed with apparent imitations of Whip-poor-will, Flicker, Screech Owl and Bob-white which I could only attribute to the Sora, and during which several common notes of the Sora were given frequently. Once I had a very brief glimpse of the performer as it plunged into the water, but can only say positively that it was a rail of some kind.

This species is most abundant in Massachusetts in its migrations in September and early October. Severe frosts send it south, but in mild seasons numbers sometimes stay with us until November. Its food resembles that of other small rails. It feeds on small mollusks and crustaceans, grasshoppers and other insects, worms, and on the seeds of wild rice, wild oats and many reeds, grasses and some small grains.

ECONOMIC STATUS. Doubtless this bird is of some service as a destroyer of insect pests. As an object of sport it is prominent. Its flesh is said to be delicious and is much superior to that of the Clapper Rail. In the fall, when fattened on wild rice, hundreds of thousands of this species have been killed along the tidal estuaries and marshes of the Atlantic coast where the rising tide makes it possible to pursue them in boats. One man poles the skiff while another shoots the birds that are driven to fly from the marsh-grass by the close approach of the flat-bottomed craft. Under the circumstances the slow flying birds offer about as difficult shooting as would a tin can floating down a rapid current or a toy balloon drifting with the wind. Some birds, however, turn and swing about the boat making the shooting more difficult for the shooter and dangerous for the boatman. Formerly when the bags were unlimited, in the days of muzzle-loading guns, an expert could kill 100 birds or more on a single tide. Even as late as 1880 Morris

---

[1] Maynard, C. J.: Birds of Eastern North America, 1896, p. 131.

Ketchum killed on the Housatonic River in Connecticut 181 birds in one day and 145 on another, according to records of the shooting kept by Charles T. Johnson; [1] and even now, though rails have decreased and hunters increased, this bird is an important object of the chase.

Cotúrnicops noveboracénsis (Gmelin). Yellow Rail.

Other names: LITTLE YELLOW RAIL; YELLOW-BREASTED RAIL.

Plate 23.

DESCRIPTION. — Bill short and rather stout. *Adults (sexes alike)*: Above streaked yellowish-brown and blackish, narrowly barred and mottled white; dusky from bill to below eye; line over eye, sides of head and neck, and under plumage yellowish-brown or brownish-yellow, paling to whitish on belly and nearing white on chin; breast feathers more or less tipped dark brown; flanks blackish, barred white; upper wing-coverts varying from brownish to blackish, margined rusty and spotted white; flight-feathers grayish, some finely and sparsely spotted white; much white toward ends of secondaries, center edge of wing tinged white; axillars and wing-linings mainly white; tail, concealed by coverts, short, blackish; under tail-coverts reddish-brown; bill greenish-dusky at base, rest orange-yellow; iris hazel or drab to brownish-yellow; legs and feet greenish to pale brownish-yellow or flesh color. *Young in first winter plumage:* Lighter and more yellowish with fewer dark markings both above and below; no white barring on head and neck; markings more suffused than in adult; this plumage (or one like it) apparently is retained throughout the first winter and first summer. Second winter takes on more white barring and head is darker on top with some white spots.

MEASUREMENTS. — Length 6.00 to 7.75 in.; spread 10.00 to 13.00; folded wing 3.00 to 3.80; tail 1.00 to 1.75; bill .50 to .64; tarsus .75 to 1.02. Weight 2 to 2¾ oz. (Audubon). Female smaller than male.

MOLTS. — There is a partial autumnal molt of young, after which (August to October) not much change in appearance results until postnuptial molt in second autumn, when immature birds in their second winter plumage apparently become as adult; adult molts not examined.

FIELD MARKS. — Very small size; general yellowish coloring, darker above; in flight, wings show conspicuous white patch.

VOICE. — *Kik-kik-kik-queah;* more rarely *kik-kik-kik-kik-kik-kik-kik-kik-ki-queah* and a *chip* exactly like that of the Indigo Bunting (J. H. Ames); at morning and evening a note resembling flint striking steel; at other times a shrieking noise (Hutchins).

BREEDING. — Near marshes. *Nest:* On ground. *Eggs:* 4 to 15, usually 8 to 15; 1.15 by .85 to 1.05 by .80 in.; warm deep buff or pinkish-buff, marked chiefly about the larger end with small dots of "orange cinnamon" or "reddish chocolate", "mikado brown and vinaceous drab."

RANGE. — Chiefly eastern North America, but not well known. Breeds from southern Mackenzie, probably Saskatchewan, northern Manitoba and southern Ungava (northern Quebec) south to North Dakota, Minnesota, Illinois, Ohio and Maine and possibly farther south; winters in the Gulf States and north to South Carolina (casually to Rhode Island); also rarely in California, Illinois and North Carolina; casual in Oregon, Nevada, Colorado, Arizona, Utah and Bermuda.

DISTRIBUTION IN NEW ENGLAND. — Rare local migrant generally, though not uncommon in the southern Connecticut Valley and locally along the Massachusetts coast in autumn; said to have bred in Maine near Calais and in Connecticut at Middletown; may have bred in all the New England states, but records are lacking; one found dead about Feb. 20, 1922, on shore of Warren River in Barrington, Rhode Island. *

SEASON IN MASSACHUSETTS. — April to May 26; September 2 to October 22 (Nov. 25).

---

[1] The Sportsman's News of Connecticut, Vol. I, 1923, p. 1.

* "From all appearances the bird had recently died, was not injured in any way, and it is a mystery how such a bird, so sensitive to cold, could have lived during that severe winter, when everything was deeply buried under snow and ice." Harry S. Hathaway *in litt.*

HAUNTS AND HABITS. The Yellow Rail is not uncommon locally at times in New England. It is so secretive that it might even be abundant at times and no one be aware of it except an occasional marsh-haunting gunner. I have talked with intelligent hunters who claim to have killed two or three a year in certain years in Massachusetts. It is difficult to flush one without a swift dog and even then the dog is quite as likely to catch the bird alive as to start it from the grass. When once in the air it flutters along a few yards and drops into the grass. It may even breed here unseen. In 1889 a bird which it was thought might be a Black Rail was often heard in Cambridge and was believed to have bred there; but its notes, as described by William Brewster [1] (and other ornithologists who heard them both there and in several other towns at dates between 1899 and 1901) were like those of a Yellow Rail which was kept alive by Mr. J. H. Ames (Auk, Vol. XIX, 1902, p. 94). Mr. Arthur T. Wayne, who spent about 5 hours in collecting a pair of Black Rails and their nest and eggs and who both saw and heard them, did not hear at any time the note of the supposed Black Rail as recorded by Mr. Brewster.

The Yellow Rail seems to prefer the higher margins of marshes, grass-meadows and savannas. It is sometimes found in grain fields and among garden crops. It frequents wet meadows and the higher parts of salt marshes.

ECONOMIC STATUS. See page 351.

Creciscus jamaicénsis (GMELIN). Black Rail.

Other name: LITTLE BLACK RAIL.

Plate 23.

DESCRIPTION. — Smallest of North American rails. *Adults (sexes similar)*: Head, neck and under plumage dark lead or slate, darkest (often nearly black) on top of head and turning brownish-black on abdomen and under tail-coverts, both of which, with flanks, barred white; nape and back dark chestnut or reddish sooty-brown; rest of upper plumage brownish-black, with narrow irregular bars and small dots of white; flight-feathers and tail dusky, with white spots; female duller than male and slightly lighter below; bill black; iris red; "feet bright yellowish-green" (Audubon). *Young in juvenal plumage:* Similar to adult but under plumage "dull ashy"; throat whitish and crown tinged reddish-brown. *Downy young:* Bluish-black.

MEASUREMENTS. — Length 5.00 to 6.00 in.; spread 10.50 to 11.50; folded wing 2.50 to 3.25; tail about 1.30 to 1.35; bill .50 to .60; tarsus .85 to .90. Female smaller than male.

MOLTS. — Not sufficient material examined to determine molts of immature bird; apparently it becomes as adult in second winter after the first postnuptial molt; before this there seems to be little change. Adult has a complete molt in autumn beginning in late July or August and probably a partial body molt in spring.

FIELD MARKS. — Size of sparrow; appears like a little black chicken; black with black bill but at very close range white cross-bars on upper plumage may be seen; *black downy young of other rails frequently mistaken for this species.*

VOICE. — A cry of more than three syllables like *chi-chi-croo-croo-croo*, repeated several times, sharp, high-toned notes (W. T. March); female, *croo-croo-croo-o*, "and then again"; almost exactly like commencement of song of Yellow-billed Cuckoo; male, *kik, kik, kik* or *kuk, kuk, kuk, kuk* (Arthur T. Wayne).

[1] Auk, Vol. XVIII, 1901, pp. 321–328.

BREEDING. — In marshes, grass meadows or grain fields. *Nest:* On ground, in a depression composed of grasses like a Meadowlark's. *Eggs:* 6 to 9 or more; about 1.00 to 1.03 by .75 to .79 in.; "creamy white" or "light buffy white, profusely speckled with reddish-brown and lilac." *Dates:* May 7, Michigan; May 27, southern Minnesota; June 6 to July 10, Connecticut; May 26 and June 10, South Carolina.

RANGE. — Chiefly eastern North America. Breeds from Kansas, Iowa, Illinois, southern Ontario, Connecticut and Massachusetts south to Florida; winters probably mainly south of United States to Jamaica and Guatemala; reported from southeastern Oregon and Colorado; casual in Bermuda. (The Black Rail of the Pacific coast is now regarded as a subspecies.)

DISTRIBUTION IN NEW ENGLAND. — Probably erroneously recorded from Maine (Scarborough, Oct. 4, 1881); rare summer resident in Connecticut and southeastern Massachusetts, which state probably is near the northern limit of its range. Records: *Massachusetts:* Plymouth (Clarks Island), bird found dead August, 1869;[1] Boston, bird caught in street, Sept. 20 (*circ.*) 1873 or 1874;[2] Chatham, pair with young, July, 1884, and nest with four eggs, May, 1885;[3] Milton, bird caught May 16, 1904;[4] Chathamport, one seen Sept. 9, 1918;[5] West Tisbury, one killed by mowing machine Aug. 26, 1920, and wing sent to me by Mrs. Johnson Whiting for identification; Yarmouthport, one seen Nov. 9, 1923.[6] *Connecticut:* Saybrook, nest with 10 eggs, July 10, 1876;[7] Saybrook, nest with 9 eggs, June 13, 1884;[8] North Haven (Quinnipiac Marshes), bird flushed July 11, 1893 and Aug. 12, 1904; Essex, young bird taken Sept. 14, 1904;[9] Hazardville (Enfield), found breeding "a number of years ago" by J. H. Batty.[10] [Given as "Hazenville" by Dr. T. M. Brewer in Proceedings Boston Society Natural History, Vol. XVII, 1874–5, p. 447.]

SEASON IN MASSACHUSETTS. — May 16 to September 20 (November 9).

HAUNTS AND HABITS. The Little Black Rail is not so rare within its range as it is supposed to be, but probably the region about Boston is near the northern limit of its normal distribution on the Atlantic coast. Cape Cod seems to be well within its range, and the bird doubtless is not very rare in certain suitable localities from the Cape southward. It should be looked for in the marshes and damp meadows of Cape Cod, Marthas Vineyard and Nantucket, where undoubtedly it breeds, and in Rhode Island and Connecticut as well. It is not particularly shy but is very secretive and keeps well under cover, running with head low and neck extended so that it might readily be mistaken for a field mouse. Sometimes when frightened it squats close to the ground and hides, pushing its head under cover. In this position it is occasionally caught by man, dog or cat. It rarely flies until almost trodden upon. Its small size and skulking habits serve as its best protection and as it frequents marshes overgrown with rank vegetation and nests there or in fields of rank grass and grain, it seldom emerges from cover and is an extremely difficult bird to find or observe. Like all rails, it is more or less nocturnal, flies and migrates chiefly at night, and is heard far more than seen. Its characteristic

---

[1] Purdie, H. A.: Bulletin Nuttall Ornithological Club, Vol. II, 1877, p. 22.
[2] Curtis, D. T.: Forest and Stream, Vol. VIII, 1877, p. 129.
[3] Allen, J. A.: Revised List Birds of Massachusetts, 1886, p. 236.
[4] Cobb, Stanley: Bird-Lore, Vol. VIII, 1906, p. 136.
[5] Bassett, Bartlett: *in litt.*
[6] Abbott, Henry W.: *in litt.*
[7] Purdie, H. A.: Bulletin, Nuttall Ornithological Club, Vol. II, 1877, p. 22.
[8] Clark, John N.: Auk, Vol. I, 1884, pp. 393–4.
[9] Sage, Bishop and Bliss: Birds of Connecticut, 1913, p. 51.
[10] Morris, R. O.: Birds of Springfield, 1901, p. 13.

notes when heard will identify it, but a sagacious bird dog is usually required to take it or at least to assist in its capture.

ECONOMIC STATUS.   See page 351.

Crex crex (LINNÆUS).   Corn Crake.

Other names: CREAK; EUROPEAN LAND RAIL.

DESCRIPTION. — Bill short like that of Black Rail.   *Adult:* Above, grayish-brown or light drab, conspicuously striped black; wings reddish or chestnut with indistinct white cross-spots on larger coverts; linings of wings and axillars soft cinnamon, former edged white; head ashy-gray with indistinct stripe of grayish-blue running from near bill above and behind eye; top of head like back; throat, belly and region about vent white; fore neck and breast pale drab, tinged gray; sides and under tail-coverts cross-barred buffy-brown and white; bill dusky or pale brownish; iris brown; legs and feet bluish flesh color.   *Young:* Similar, but no gray on head.   *Downy young:* Dark sooty-brown; head blackish; bill dusky.

MEASUREMENTS. — Length about 10.00 to 10.50 in.; spread 17.00 to 18.00; folded wing 5.50 to 6.00; tail about 2.00; bill .80 to 1.00; tarsus 1.50 to 1.60.

MOLTS. — Apparently there is a partial molt of juvenal feathers beginning in September after which young bird becomes as adult; adult has partial postnuptial molt (December to March) and complete molt in August and September.

FIELD MARKS. — Size larger than Sora.   When in its grassy coverts difficult to distinguish, but if forced to fly its yellowish or buffy body plumage and chestnut wings are unmistakable.

VOICE. — A *creak;* a "low guttural sound" when disturbed; call of the male a "loud rasping dissyllabic and long maintained *aerp-aerp,* uttered in spring and early summer by day and night; other notes growling and grunting cries" (Witherby's Handbook of British Birds).

BREEDING. — In grass, grain or clover.   *Nest:* On ground.   *Eggs:* 5 to 8; 1.44 to 1.48 by 1.00 to 1.05 in.; light, reddish-buff spotted reddish-brown.   *Incubation:* "by female; period 17 days (in confinement) probably single-brooded" (Handbook of British Birds).

RANGE. — Europe and northern Asia; south in winter to Africa, Arabia and northern India; casual in Greenland, Madeira, Newfoundland, Bermuda and eastern North America, from Nova Scotia to New Jersey.

DISTRIBUTION IN NEW ENGLAND. — Accidental visitor from Europe. *Maine:* Falmouth, bird taken Oct. 14, 1889, by John Whitney.[1] *Rhode Island:* Cranston, one taken about 1857, Newton Dexter.[2] *Connecticut:* Saybrook, adult male taken October 20, 1887.[3]

HAUNTS AND HABITS. The Corn Crake is believed to be a straggler from Europe. But how can a bird with such short wings and so apparently weak in flight reach the United States from Europe; and why is it that, if a mere straggler from abroad, a bird so secretive as this rail has been taken and *recorded* by naturalists at least 14 times on this side of the Atlantic, to say nothing of Greenland records? Considering the habits of the bird hundreds may have occurred in this country where not more than a dozen birds are thus recorded. Probably if this rail comes to us from Europe, it journeys here by the way of Greenland. Its haunts and habits are much like those of American rails except that it frequents higher grassy lands and cultivated fields as well as meadows. As it has been taken in Maine, Rhode Island and Connecticut, probably it has occurred in Massachusetts, where it should be confidently looked for.

SUBFAMILY **GALLINULINÆ**. GALLINULES.

Number of species in North America 2; in Massachusetts 2.

Gallinules are rail-like birds but unlike rails have an extension and expansion of the ridge of the bill forming a horny plate on the forehead. The bill is somewhat like that of the short-billed rails, but in most cases stouter; the body is not so narrow and compressed as in rails but is narrower than in coots; the toes are long and rail-like and neither webbed nor lobed, but sometimes slightly margined. Gallinules inhabit borders of reed-margined streams or ponds and marshes. Like some of the rails they often build sham nests; and sometimes rail's eggs are found in Gallinule's nests.

Ionórnis martínicus (LINNÆUS). **Purple Gallinule.**

Plate 24.

DESCRIPTION. — *Adults (sexes alike):* Head, neck and under plumage purplish-blue, deepening about face and blackening on abdomen; upper surface of body bright olive-green, tinted bluish on back of lower neck and wing-coverts; flight-feathers and tail dusky-brown but glossed greenish on outer webs; sides and wing-linings bluish-green; under tail-coverts white; frontal shield dull blue or bluish-white; bill carmine or vermilion, tipped greenish-yellow or yellowish-white; legs and feet greenish-yellow. Little seasonal difference in plumage, but out of breeding season legs are duller, also bill, a duskier color replacing more or less of its red, while plate is darker than in full breeding plumage. *Young in juvenal plumage:* Unlike adult; no blue or purple. Head, neck and upper plumage more or less brownish; wings greenish or olivaceous; under plumage lighter, buffy, more or less whitish on throat and abdomen; frontal shield small; bill without red; size same as young Florida Gallinule, but *nostrils oval;* middle toe shorter than tarsus, and inner hind surface of tarsus *scaled. Downy young:* Glossy black; many white, hair-like feathers on head and throat; bill yellowish at base, black at tip.

---

[1] Brock, Henry H.: Auk, Vol. XIII, 1896, p. 173.
[2] Random Notes on Natural History, Vol. I, No. 6, 1884, p. 3.
[3] Clark, J. N.: Ornithologist and Oölogist, Vol. XIII, 1888, p. 45.

PLATE 24

PLATE 24

COOT
Page 369
ADULT IN BREEDING
PLUMAGE

NORTHERN PHALAROPE
Page 375
ADULT FEMALE IN BREEDING
PLUMAGE

ADULT MALE IN BREEDING
PLUMAGE

WINTER PLUMAGE

FLORIDA GALLINULE
Page 366
ADULT IN BREEDING
PLUMAGE

PURPLE GALLINULE
Page 364
ADULT IN BREEDING
PLUMAGE

All one-fourth natural size.

RED PHALAROPE
Page 372
WINTER PLUMAGE
ADULT FEMALE IN BREEDING
PLUMAGE

ADULT MALE IN BREEDING
PLUMAGE

WILSON'S PHALAROPE
Page 377
ADULT FEMALE IN BREEDING
PLUMAGE

MEASUREMENTS. — Length 12.00 to 14.00 in.; spread about 22.00; folded wing 6.50 to 7.50; tail 2.50 to 3.00; bill from gape to end about 1.25, including frontal shield 1.85 to 1.95; tarsus 2.25 to 2.50.

MOLTS. — Not enough molting material examined to determine all molts exactly. Apparently there is a nearly complete molt (January–April), including wings, after which young birds assume a plumage similar to that of adult, but not quite so brilliant. After a postnuptial molt young birds probably assume adult plumage. Adults apparently have a complete molt in autumn, and one specimen showed evidence of slight molt on the head and neck in April.

FIELD MARKS. — Size near that of Coot but slimmer; deep purplish-blue head and neck (appearing black at a distance) and bright, glossy green upper plumage distinguish the bird.

VOICE. — Loud and hen-like.

BREEDING. — In swamps and marshes. *Nest:* A platform of rushes etc., like a shallow basket suspended among and woven into marsh vegetation. *Eggs:* 6 to 10; 1.63 by 1.16 to 1.54 by 1.13 in.; soiled white, creamy or pale buff, sparsely spotted chiefly about larger end with brown, umber and neutral tints. *Incubation:* Period 23 to 25 days (Whitaker).

RANGE. — Tropical, subtropical and temperate America. Breeds from Texas, Louisiana, Tennessee and South Carolina south through Mexico and West Indies to Ecuador, Paraguay and Argentina; winters from Texas, Louisiana and Florida southward; irregularly north in summer to Arizona, Colorado, Nebraska, Wisconsin, Illinois, Ontario, Quebec, Nova Scotia and New Brunswick; accidental in Bermuda.

DISTRIBUTION IN NEW ENGLAND. — *Maine:* Accidental; Boothbay, one taken alive in the latter part of September, 1877; [1] South Lewiston, one taken by John Turner April 11, 1897; [2] Eastport, male taken April 2, 1898, and now in the mounted collection of Hon. John E. Thayer; Winter Harbor, one taken Nov. 7, 1899.[3] *New Hampshire:* Accidental; Dover, Rye;[4] Plainfield (Meriden), one taken alive about May 1, 1925, and given by Mrs. Elsie E. Wheeler to the Franklin Park Aviary, Boston.[5] *Massachusetts:* Occasional, for in the Game Birds, Wild-Fowl and Shore Birds of Massachusetts, 1916, Massachusetts State Board of Agriculture, I gave eleven records, eight of which are given by Howe and Allen in their "Birds of Massachusetts" 1901, p. 19, and three by Dr. C. W. Townsend in his "Birds of Essex County," 1905, p. 161. One published record is that of a pair in June.[6]

There is another (unpublished) June record of a pair seen at Lake Quinsigamond, Worcester, one of which (the male) was shot May 30, 1888, and is preserved in the mounted collection of Hon. J. E. Thayer at South Lancaster. Col. Thayer furnishes the following hitherto unpublished record: Brant Rock, male taken Oct. 15, 1898; specimen preserved in his mounted collection. There is also in the Thayer collection a skin of a male of this species which was caught in Randolph, May 24, 1904, and kept alive for several days.[7] Still another unpublished record is that of the bird caught alive on the morning of April 2, 1924, near Everett Square, Everett. Mr. Fred Cross caught the bird during a snowfall which was the end of the snow storm of April 1–2, one of the great gales of the season. This southern stranger was a beautiful bird and was kept alive for many months in good health and spirits in the Franklin Park Aviary, Boston.

This bird is also a rare visitor in Rhode Island and Connecticut, there being eight published records for the former state, two of these being of summer birds;* and four records in the "Birds of Connecti-

---

[1] Purdie, H. A.: Bulletin, Nuttall Ornithological Club, Vol. V, 1880, p. 242.

[2] Knight, Ora W.: Birds of Maine, 1908, p. 144.

[3] Swain, J. M.: Journal Maine Ornithological Society, Vol. II, 1900, p. 34.

[4] Dearborn, Ned: Birds of Durham and Vicinity, 1903, p. 30.

[5] Day, Chester S: *in litt.*

[6] Farley, J. A.: Auk, Vol. XVIII, 1901, p. 190.

[7] Howe, Reginald Heber, Jr.: Auk, Vol. XXII, 1905, p. 319.

* A mid-winter record is that of the adult found dead Jan. 13, 1889, at Warren Point, Little Compton. Mr. Newton Dexter, who recorded this bird in Forest and Stream, Vol. XXXIII, 1890, p. 364, inquired: "How could this semi-tropical bird have reached this bleak coast and in the bitter freezing weather?"

cut," 1913 (p. 51), by Sage, Bishop and Bliss.   One of these latter was of a female taken June 26, 1903, at Bridgeport.   An early record for Connecticut is that of the bird seen at Stratford, April 16, 1920, by Dr. Charles W. Packard.[1]

SEASON IN MASSACHUSETTS. — April to June; October.

HAUNTS AND HABITS.   The elegant and tropically-colored Purple Gallinule is second in grace and beauty among the water-birds only to the male Wood Duck.   It seems to be a great wanderer and its wanderings occasionally bring it to New England.   Its long-toed yellow feet enable it to run rapidly over lily pads and other water vegetation, but unless frightened or pursuing elusive prey it is rather deliberate in its movements.   It is a great runner, however, and an active climber and does not hesitate to climb into shrubs, vines and trees where it often perches.   It swims well but usually keeps more to cover than to open water.   It feeds on insects, worms, small snails and other small aquatic animals and wild fruit seeds and other parts of plants.

ECONOMIC STATUS.   In the West Indies this bird is sought for the table; here it is so rare as to be of no economic consequence.

Gallínula chlóropus cachínnans BANGS.   Florida Gallinule.

Other names: GRAY POND-HEN; MEADOW-HEN; KING RAIL; RED-BILLED MUD-HEN.

Plate 24.

DESCRIPTION. — *Adults (sexes alike)* : Head and upper neck blackish-slate, turning to bluish-slaty-gray on lower neck and body; brownish-olive on back, scapulars and wing-coverts; under surface of body more or less whitish; flight-feathers blackish; feathers of flanks streaked broadly white; axillars and wing-linings ashy-brown, latter more or less edged and tipped white; tail black, central under tail-coverts black, outer white; outer edge of wing and half of outer web of first primary white; bill, tipped greenish-yellow, rest and large frontal plate sealing-wax red; iris deep red or brown; ring around upper leg next to feathers red; leg below this and foot greenish-yellow; joints tinged bluish; leg greenish-black (Stanley C. Arthur); olive-green (Cory); pea-pod green (Trumbull); in high plumaged birds in spring outside of tarsus also becomes bright scarlet in an elongate patch, not present at other times (Fuertes).   *Young in first summer plumage:* Similar to adult, but lacking bright tints of bill and legs; bill and forehead brownish; more or less white below; similar to young Purple Gallinule but nostril linear, tarsus *reticulate not scaled on its inner front edge*, otherwise scaled, and middle toe longer than tarsus.   *Young in first winter plumage:* Similar to adult but much more whitish on under plumage and some whitish about sides of head and throat.   *Young in juvenal plumage:* Top and sides of head sooty black, paler on sides where also sparingly flecked with white; chin and throat white, flecked with slate-gray; whole neck dull black; rest of upper surface brown, red-toned on back, more blackish from rump backward; breast and sides of body pale slate-gray, many of the feathers extensively tipped white; middle of belly white; flanks and rest of under surface pale brown; feet proportionately large, as in adults (but red color of bill seen in downy young and adults is wanting in the juvenal).   *Downy young:* Greenish-black above, sooty below, with bristly silvery beard; bill red.

MEASUREMENTS. — Length 12.00 to 14.75 in.; spread 20.00 to 23.00; folded wing 6.50 to 7.50; tail 2.75 to 3.00; tarsus 2.10 to 2.30; bill to end of frontal shield 1.32 to 1.85, to gape about 1.25 to 1.50.   Weight 14 oz. (Trumbull).   Female smaller than male.

MOLTS. — Juvenal plumage apparently is molted (August to November).   No molting young examined.   Adults have a complete molt annually in late summer and autumn.

---

[1] *Bird-Lore*, Vol. XXII, 1920, p. 160.

Field Marks. — Resembles the next species but adult distinguished at once by *broad red* frontal plate and red bill; Coot's bill is staring white.

Voice. — "A succession of hen-like *cucks*, given rather slowly," frequently ending *kee'-ar-r, kree'-ar-r*; clucks and loud screams like a squawking hen, occasionally *kr-r-r-r, kruc-kruc, krar-r*; *kh-kh-kh-kh-kea-kea*, delivered rapidly and falling toward the end; a low *klŏc-klŏc* or *klŏc-klŏc-klŏc*; an explosive, frog-like *kup* (Wm. Brewster); a harsh rail-like *kea* repeated several times; a metallic *chuck* if annoyed (C. J. Maynard); many other calls and cries, most of them loud and hen-like, given in the breeding season.

Breeding. — In *fresh*-water marshes or near water. *Nest:* Rather like that of grebe; a hollowed heap of reeds, grass or flags among clumps of tall water-plants, on platform of broken down flags, sometimes half afloat, sometimes on ground near water; rarely in thorny vines two or three feet above water (Arthur T. Wayne). *Eggs:* 8 to 14; 1.95 by 1.30 to 1.54 by 1.15 in.; varying shades of brown or buff, spotted dark brown or pale reddish and lavender; darker than those of Purple Gallinule and spots longer and bolder than on either those or the Coot's. *Dates:* May 21, South Carolina; May 22 to July 17, New England. *Incubation:* Period unknown, probably variable and about 22 to 25 days.

Range. — Tropical and temperate America. Breeds from central California, Arizona, Nebraska, Minnesota, Ontario, New York and Vermont south to Argentina; rarely recorded outside breeding range, but regarded as casual in South Dakota, Colorado, Quebec, Nova Scotia and Maine; winters from southern California, Arizona, Texas and Georgia south to Argentina.

Distribution in New England. — *Maine:* Rare migrant and probable summer resident. *New Hampshire:* Very rare migrant and probable summer resident. Rollinsford, immature bird taken.[1] *Vermont:* Local summer resident at Lake Bomoseen and in tributaries of Lake Champlain; St. Albans; rare migrant. *Massachusetts:* Rare local summer resident, chiefly near coast, and rare migrant. *Rhode Island* and *Connecticut:* Uncommon local summer resident.

Season in Massachusetts. — April 29 to October 25 (November 9); (December 30).

Haunts and Habits. The Florida Gallinule is the water-hen of America. Its generic name (*Gallinula*) means "little hen," and it walks, talks and squawks like a veritable "biddy" of the barn-yard. It behaves, however, like a connecting link between the hens and the ducks, as it swims and dives like a duck. It prefers to keep under cover, but when forced into open water it often dives to escape observation, and when pursued can conceal itself under water as readily as on land. In habits it resembles the other gallinules and even the Coot, except that it is less inclined to swimming and more to wading than is the latter. While the Coot keeps much in open water, the Gallinule keeps more under cover. Like the Purple Gallinule, its large, long-toed feet serve like snowshoes to support it as it walks or runs over the surface of the water from one lily pad to another or over the tangled leaves and stems of other floating water-plants. Though not usually very shy it is secretive like the rails and by keeping under cover eludes observation. Thus where uncommon, as in New England, it might escape notice were it not for its loud calls in the breeding season which are so much like the common clucks and cackles of the barn-yard that when coming from the henless watery waste of the marshlands they attract the attention of the ornithologist. When the bird is discovered it is usually walking about with quick upward jerks of the tail, the white of the under tail-coverts flashing as the tail is alternately raised and lowered. If swimming, the bird rests lightly on the water like a duck, its head moving forward and backward

[1] Dearborn, Ned: Birds of Durham and Vicinity, 1903, p. 30,

with every stroke, like that of a Coot. When feeding in shallow water it sometimes "tips up" in the manner of surface feeding ducks. Although it prefers the cover of the marsh rather than the open water, it is unlike the rails in that it is rather more readily flushed. In the breeding season the bright scarlet of the bill and frontal plate is conspicuous.

Brewster described the wooing of the bird as follows:

"Late one afternoon we suddenly heard a great outcry, and soon our pair of Gallinules appeared; the female, who was much the plainer-colored in every respect, swimming swiftly, her tail lowered and about in line with the back; the male flapping his wings on the water in his eagerness to overtake her. This he soon succeeded in doing, but just as he clutched at her with open bill, evidently with amorous designs, she eluded him by a sudden clever turn. He then swam around her in a narrow circle, carrying his tail widespread and erect, his neck arched, his scarlet front fairly blazing and apparently much enlarged and inflated. Seeing that she would not permit his approaches, he soon gave over the pursuit and returned to his favorite raft, while the female swam into the bushes. During the chase one of the birds, presumably the male, uttered repeatedly the following cry: *ticket — ticket — ticket — ticket* (six to eight repetitions each time). This was doubtless a wooing note, for we heard it on no other occasion." [1]

The eggs of this and the preceding species are found in different stages of incubation and some of the young hatch much earlier than others. The nestlings resemble little black chickens, and like the young of rails they run about soon after they are hatched.

It is a well-known fact that the Florida Gallinule builds several nests other than the one in which the female deposits her eggs. According to Mr. Norman McClintock and the Warden employed by the National Association of Audubon Societies, at Orange Lake, Florida, this species utilizes its nests in the following manner: At this place the extra nests, which are built by the male, are placed on a floating growth of water-plants. The female at twilight, or just after sundown, conducts or calls the young to one of these nests, where she broods them during the night. If she is disturbed at this nest, she occupies another on the succeeding night. Mr. McClintock actually secured motion pictures of the young birds going to the nest at the call of the mother.

The Florida Gallinule usually arrives in Massachusetts from the south in May and disappears in October. Its notes usually may be heard in the latter half of May, at early morning or at night in its breeding-places.

Its food is both vegetal and animal; grass-seed and small grains (in the south particularly rice) are eaten, but it also destroys many aquatic insects, grasshoppers and locusts.

ECONOMIC STATUS. The Florida Gallinule is not common enough in New England to be of much economic importance. As it destroys nothing of consequence to man (the grain that it eats being mostly waste), it probably is beneficial as an insect destroyer. Many are shot by gunners, but the bird should be preserved for its grace and beauty alone.

[1] Auk, Vol. VIII, 1891, p. 4.

Subfamily **FULICINÆ**. Coots.

Number of species in North America 2; in Massachusetts 1.

Bill and frontal plate somewhat as in gallinules; form stouter; body depressed, wider than in rails and gallinules, and covered with dense down to resist water, as in ducks; feet lobed for swimming somewhat as in grebes and phalaropes.

Fúlica americána GMELIN. Coot.

Other names: BLUE PETER; BLUE MARSH-HEN; CROW DUCK; CROW-BILL; PELICK; PULDOO; SEA-CROW; POND-HEN; POND-CROW; MEADOW-HEN; WATER-HEN.

Plate 24.

DESCRIPTION. — Bill short, pointed; forehead with more or less of a shield; feet with large lobes. *Adults (sexes alike):* Head and neck blackish, sometimes small whitish spot below eye; general plumage bluish-slaty, lighter below; back and scapulars tinged olive; flight-feathers slate; wing edged narrowly white and secondaries tipped same, forming white bar which hardly shows on closed wing; primaries growing blackish at tips; region of vent black, which color extends in form of wedge over central under tail-coverts; outer under tail-coverts white, forming a V; bill whitish, tip horn color, banded near tip of upper mandible with chestnut, spot of same below it on lower mandible, edged below with yellow; shield on forehead "dark chestnut brown"; iris red; legs and feet yellowish-green; lobes light leaden-gray. *Young in juvenal plumage:* Similar to adult but generally more olive and lighter above and more whitish below and bill even whiter, lacking spots; iris brown. *Downy young:* Blackish, with elongated, crinkled, bristly, orange feather-tips on throat, cheeks, neck, wings and back; some hoary tips on under surface of body; bill orange-red, tipped black.

FOOT OF COOT

MEASUREMENTS. — Length 13.00 to 16.00 in.; spread 23.00 to 28.00; folded wing 6.70 to 8.00; tail 2.00 to 2.75; bill, tip to gape 1.25 to 1.50; tarsus 1.86 to 2.36. Weight 1 lb. to 22 oz.

Molts. — Young bird appears to undergo a postjuvenal molt in late summer and autumn in which the body-feathers are shed, after which it becomes as adult but retains juvenal wings and tail; adults apparently have one complete molt in late summer and autumn; there seems to be little if any molt in spring.

FIELD MARKS. — Size of a small duck, but small head and short *white* bill distinguish it from all ducks, grebes and gallinules; a slaty bird with black head and neck; in full flight white on ends of secondaries is conspicuous, neck is stretched out, bill pointed a little downward, legs extended backward and a little upward, and large, clumsy feet protrude beyond tail.

VOICE. — Explosive, cackling; usual call note *pulque, pulque, pulque* (Grinnell, Bryant and Storer); a noisy bird; its *coo-coo-coo-coo* heard day and night; also it has a *squack* similar to quack of a duck (Ralph Hoffmann); half melancholy whistles followed by a guttural chuckle (C. J. Maynard).

BREEDING. — Often in colonies, about reedy sloughs, pools and sluggish streams. *Nest:* Like that of gallinules, a heap of reeds or flags, etc.; sometimes half afloat, sometimes on ground near water. *Eggs:* 6 to 15; 1.76 to 2.05 by 1.20 to 1.45; pointed ovate, like hens' eggs; clay color to creamy white, rather uniformly dotted with small spots of dark brown or blackish, usually pin-head size, sometimes larger. *Dates:* May 11 to 27, northern United States. *Incubation:* Period said to be about 27 days, but probably individual eggs hatch in less time, as some are deposited and incubated before others.

RANGE. — Chiefly temperate and subtropical North and Middle America, but extending into Canadian region. Breeds from central British Columbia, northern Mackenzie, central Saskatchewan, Manitoba, Ontario, Quebec and New Brunswick south to northern Lower California, northern Mexico, Texas, Arkansas, Tennessee, Pennsylvania, New Jersey and probably in Florida; also in southern Mexico, Yucatan, Guatemala and West Indies; not recorded as breeding in central Mexico; winters from British Columbia, Colorado (casually), Illinois, Indiana, Virginia and Massachusetts (casually) south to Colombia; casual in Alaska, Greenland, Labrador, Newfoundland, Nova Scotia and Bermuda.

DISTRIBUTION IN NEW ENGLAND. — *Maine:* Migrant, mainly in fall. *New Hampshire:* Uncommon migrant, chiefly in fall and in southern part. *Vermont:* Uncommon migrant and rare local summer resident (at Lake Bomoseen). *Massachusetts:* Rare spring and rather uncommon fall migrant; formerly bred (Nuttall) and may still breed rarely; pair at Cheshire Reservoir, June 21, 1892; rare to casual winter resident near coast. *Rhode Island* and *Connecticut:* Common fall migrant, less common in spring; winters casually in Connecticut and may breed.

SEASON IN MASSACHUSETTS. — March 26 to June 3 (June 21); (August 16); September 1 to November 22; (winter).

HAUNTS AND HABITS. The Coot is a rather clumsy, simple bird with a gawky, silly expression of countenance, whence perhaps its name and the expression "a silly coot," as applied to human beings. It is chiefly a fresh-water bird, though sometimes seen in salt marshes or on the surface of bays or estuaries of the sea. It should not be confused with the scoters commonly called coots alongshore, for these are actually ducks, not coots, and in New England are chiefly seen on salt water.

Formerly the Coot was much more abundant through most of its range than it is today. It is so unsuspicious that it is easily taken. Millions doubtless are killed annually by sportsmen, boys, settlers, farmers, and by all kinds of novices in the use of a gun. Probably for this reason Coots, being prolific breeders, go south in the fall in numbers much greater than those that return in spring.

In California, according to Grinnell, Bryant and Storer, Coots are so numerous still that they are a nuisance on the preserves of the gun clubs, eating the food provided by the clubs for the ducks, and getting in the way of the shooters. Hundreds, if not thousands, have been killed there merely to get them out of the way.[1] In some localities gun clubs hold what they call a "Mud-hen shoot" on the first day of the open season and "as many as 5,000 Coots have been killed in a day on one preserve in Merced County."[2]

Their only safety lies in betaking themselves to wide waters or to ponds and sloughs surrounded by impenetrable morasses. These are the situations they love, and in the South in winter they gather in such waters until their dark masses cover practically the entire surface. At a sudden alarm there arises an uproar of wings and splattering feet, for the Coot must run splashing and fluttering along the surface when it starts to fly. Almost immediately the pond is cleared, but the Coots, instead of departing for parts unknown at the first alarm, like a wild duck, have only retreated into the cover of the surrounding morass and soon appear again along the margin, spreading gradually over the water until the pool is again covered with their gabbling hundreds. While wading in such morasses in water and mud waist or armpit deep for want of a better method, I

[1] Game Birds of California, 1918, p. 319.
[2] Tyler, J. G.: Some Birds of the Fresno District, California; Cooper Ornithological Club, Pacific Coast Avifauna, No. 9, 1913, p. 23.

have observed their antics and studied their simple habits. Some authorities assert that Coots do not dive for their food, while others aver that they are excellent divers. Both are wrong in part and in part right. Some individual birds will go down and bring up food in water 20 feet or more in depth, while others seem to find it almost impossible to get under the surface. Coots seem to dive more quickly and directly downward than ducks. Mr. Walter H. Rich avers that they use both feet and wings together beneath the surface,[1] while Mr. C. J. Maynard says that they do not use the wings under water.[2] Whether individuals thus use the wings or not probably depends upon circumstances.

In rising from the water Coots flutter and flap along, splashing and paddling with both wings and feet until, clear of the water, they flutter feebly into the air with legs and feet hanging, but when well under way they make fairly good headway, with feet trailing behind. In habits they resemble both gallinules and ducks. They search for food by both wading and swimming as well as by "tipping up" and diving. When in cover they are prone to hide like rails and are not so easily flushed as are the gallinules.

The little, black, downy young tumble out of the nest into the water soon after they are hatched, but often when these first reach the water there are others still unhatched and the eggs must be cared for. So the mother remains on the nest and continues incubating, while doubtless the father cares for the earliest chicks. For many nights the mother calls them all back to the nest where she broods them through the hours of darkness.

Coots feed very largely on vegetable matter. They eat tender grass in the manner of domestic fowls and are fond of various pondweeds (*Potomagetons*), but they do not disdain their share of animal life, particularly in the breeding season when insects and snails form a good part of their fare. Roots, bulbs, buds, blossoms and seeds of various tender water-plants are eaten.

ECONOMIC STATUS. Although the Coot is not considered a table bird by sportsmen, it has formed a staple dish among settlers and farmers in many states. As the bird was formerly very abundant, it was not difficult for most "blunderers with a gun" to shoot into its dense masses and secure a dozen or twenty birds at a shot. When feeding on wild celery its flesh becomes almost the equal of that of the best ducks. Its eggs also have been used in great numbers for human food, but their flavor does not equal that of the "fruit of the hen."

ORDER LIMICOLÆ. SHORE BIRDS.

Number of species in North America 69; in Massachusetts 42.

Shore birds are snipe-like or plover-like waders which differ from herons or marsh birds in having the body rounded or slightly depressed rather than narrow and compressed. They average rather small in size. The bill is usually slim and straight or slightly curved. The head in most cases is fully feathered. There are 10 well-developed

---

[1] Feathered Game of the Northeast, 1907, p. 247.   [2] Field Ornithology, 1916, p. 223.

primaries and a rudimentary 11th; the wings are long; the tail is short. The legs are commonly lengthened and the toes slim and unwebbed or only partially webbed, and relatively shorter than those of herons and rails. The hind toe when present is short and elevated. Unlike the herons most of the species build no real nest and the young are not helpless but run about and secure their own food from the day they are hatched.

Economic Status. Shore birds undoubtedly are of some service to mankind, by reason of the injurious insects that they consume. Many species destroy the larvæ of mosquitoes, and mosquitoes carry from man to man the germs of such serious and often fatal diseases as malaria and yellow fever. Many shore birds destroy such pests as grasshoppers, cabbage worms, army worms, cutworms, cotton worms, boll weevils, rice weevils, Texas fever ticks and horse flies. Shore birds have been hunted from time immemorial. They are highly appreciated by the epicure and as objects of sport they take a high rank. They bring sportsmen customers to seaside hotels, bring business to boatmen and guides, and in the past have proved very profitable to market hunters and marketmen. This source of revenue is now cut off in this country by excessive destruction of these birds for market which has resulted in prohibition of their sale.

Family **PHALAROPODIDÆ**. Phalaropes.

Number of species in North America 3; in Massachusetts 3.

Phalaropes are "swimming sandpipers" with tarsi excessively compressed and *front toes lobed, hind toe elevated.* Their under plumage is thick and gull-like with heavy under down like that of ducks. These characters enable them to swim with ease and they are at home on the ocean. After the breeding season they go to sea. The females are larger and handsomer than the males. They take the lead in courtship while the male assumes the usual office of the female, preparing the nest, incubating the eggs and caring for the young. The family contains but three species — one peculiar to America.

Phaláropus fulicárius (Linnæus). **Red Phalarope.**

Other names: Gray Phalarope; Gray Bank-Bird (applied to all phalaropes collectively); Herring-Bird; Whale-Bird; Jersey-Goose; Mackerel-Goose; Sea-Goose.

Plate 24.

Description. — Nostrils well in advance of head feathers; bill rather short, broad and flattened; tail much rounded, under tail-coverts very long, sometimes projecting beyond tail; front toes generously lobed and basal half webbed; tarsus not longer than middle toe with claw. *Adult female in breeding plumage:* Chin, fore part of head about base of bill, top of head and back of neck (narrowly) blackish-slate or very dark gray, sides of head around eye white, graying before eye and behind ear where a gray streak runs down to center of nape; *rest of neck and all under plumage deep vinaceous chestnut-brown or* "*purplish cinnamon,*" some of which mixes with slate gray of hind neck; back and scapulars "cinnamon buff and pinkish buff" (fading to "light buff" as season advances) and striped black; central feathers of rump and upper tail-coverts ashy-gray deepening to dark mouse-gray on tail; sides of rump white; outer upper tail-coverts orange-cinnamon; "wing-coverts slate or deep slate gray," greater coverts broadly tipped white, flight-feathers dusky slate; "bill waxy yellow in spring with jet black tip; feet and tarsus dull yellowish" (E. W. Nelson); iris very dark brown. *Adult male in breeding plumage:* Similar to female but smaller and duller; white area of side of head smaller, top of head and back of neck streaked black and cinnamon; colors about base of bill lighter, less pure, often intermixed; under-plumage and side of neck lighter, and duller, often intermixed white; central tail-feathers dark, outer ones pale sepia; bill, iris, legs and feet like those of female but duller; "legs and feet horn colored, webs yellow" (Practical Handbook of British Birds). *Adults in winter plumage (sexes alike):* Head, neck and under plumage mainly white with imperfectly concealed dark bases to feathers of crown, a dusky patch on hind head, another in front of and below eye extending back over ear-region but leaving most of eyelids white; dusky tint continues down back of neck; sides of lower back, rump and outer upper tail-coverts white; rest of upper plumage mainly ashy-gray darkening to "deep mouse gray" on wings and tail; scapulars and tertials bordered white; some primary, middle and greater coverts tipped white, latter broadly; feathers on sides of breast ashy-gray, tipped white; wing-linings and axillars mainly white, mottled along edge of wing; bill, legs and feet dark horn color. *Young in first winter plumage:* Like adult winter; distinguished by juvenal tail and wing coverts. *Young in juvenal plumage:* Resembles adult male in breeding plumage above but forehead light buffy or white; feathers of upper back and scapulars, wing coverts, tertials, back, rump and upper tail-coverts edged but not tipped cinnamon-buff; fore neck, sides of breast, sides and flanks reddish-buff, other under plumage mainly white. *Downy young:* Head buffy, deepening to cinnamon-buff on forehead and crown; broad stripe on each side of crown and narrow stripe from bill to eye black, center of crown mixed black and cinnamon-buff, sides of nape latter color; blackish patch on ear-coverts; middle of nape black; back a mixed pattern of black, cinnamon-buff and buffy-white; rump with a median stripe of black bordered on each side by a stripe of buffy-whitish; cheeks, chin, throat, sides of neck and breast light buffy; rest of under plumage grayish-white.

FOOT OF RED PHALAROPE

MEASUREMENTS. — Length 7.50 to 9.00 in.; spread 14.00 to 16.00; folded wing 5.00 to 5.50; tail 2.00 to 2.80; bill .75 to .96; tarsus .75 to .90. Weight 1¾ oz. (C. L. Bonaparte). Female larger than male.

MOLTS. — Following natal down juvenal plumage is assumed in summer; in autumn apparently most body-feathers are molted but wing and tail retained; in spring a prenuptial molt of body-feathers and tail occurs, including some smaller wing-feathers; after this molt, except for partial juvenal appearance of wings, bird becomes as adult; adults have complete molt (July to December) and another (March to May) in which body-feathers and tail are molted but not wings, except perhaps some coverts and tertials; some specimens have winter plumage nearly perfect in August, while others have not finished molting in October.

FIELD MARKS. — Size of Sanderling, very unsuspicious, admits close observation; in winter plumage in which chiefly seen at sea, from late July onward, is very white on head, neck and below, with black patches on crown and side head; bill rather short, stout and deep at base; compared with bills of other phalaropes, more like that of Knot or Sanderling; swims buoyantly like a gull and looks larger, stockier and rather grayer above than Northern Phalarope; unmistakable in breeding plumage, with its reddish neck and breast, black crown, white sides of head and yellow, black-tipped bill; a broad white wing-bar in all plumages; uncommon inland on lakes and rivers.

VOICE. — "A low, musical *clink clink*" (E. W. Nelson); a clear whistle, sometimes a *creak* (C. W. Townsend).

BREEDING. — On low, moist flats, islands and broken ground near swampy pools. *Nest:* A mere depression in ground, moss or gravel, sometimes slightly lined with leaves, sometimes built of grass, in tussock. *Eggs:* 3 to 6; 1.15 to 1.30 by .85 to .89 in.; pear-shaped or ovate; "stone color" to "olive," blotched and spotted blackish-brown to umber-brown and pale chocolate with a few ashy spots; markings much darker and larger than those of Northern Phalarope, often many large confluent spots at large end, almost hiding ground-color. *Dates:* June 1 to July 10, Alaska; late June and early July, Spitzbergen. *Incubation:* Period 14 to 16 days (Hantzsch); by male. One brood yearly.

RANGE. — Cosmopolitan; Arctic to south temperate regions. Breeds in North America from northern Alaska, Melville Island, northern Ellesmere Island and northwestern Greenland south to mouth of Kuskokwim River, northern Mackenzie, northern Manitoba, Hudson Strait and southern Greenland; in Eurasia on most Arctic coasts and islands, Iceland, Spitzbergen and Novaya Zemlya and Siberian coasts; winters probably on oceans; recorded in winter south to Patagonia; in Mediterranean, Azores, Africa, southern India and China and casual in Kauai and New Zealand (one record each); migrates mainly off shores of continents, often far at sea; in North America rare migrant (so far as known) in Great Lakes region and casual in southern California, Colorado, Kansas, Alabama, New York, Pennsylvania and Maryland. Spitzbergen birds have been described as a separate race.

DISTRIBUTION IN NEW ENGLAND. — Usually rare on coast except when driven in by storms, when it sometimes enters estuaries and rivers; not rare at times in autumn in some of interior waters of northern New England; said to have bred near Calais, Maine; offshore migrant, sometimes common.

SEASON IN MASSACHUSETTS. — May 1 to 26; (June) July 11 to November 24.

HAUNTS AND HABITS. Phalaropes are shore birds on their breeding grounds but sea-birds on the New England coast. In the waning of the summer, far off shore from Cape Ann, Cape Cod or No Man's Land, we may see here and there in the distance on the smooth, glassy surface of the ever restless sea swell a little white speck like a dash of foam — the white breast of the Red Phalarope already taking on its winter plumage. The bird is so tame and gentle that it will hardly get out of the way of our boat until we are nearly upon it, when it flutters away for a few rods and again comes to rest upon the sea, attracted perhaps by some floating food. It rises easily from the water, flies in the manner of a Sanderling, which it somewhat resembles, swims fast and floats as lightly as an autumn leaf.

The idea of "women's rights" may well have originated with the phalaropes, for among these birds the female, being the larger and handsomer, does practically all the courting, while the male prepares the nest. After she has laid the eggs, her meek and gentle consort incubates them until the young are hatched and then takes upon himself the principal care of the little family while his "strong minded" spouse enjoys herself after her own fashion. This species is the most maritime of the phalaropes and breeds near the shores of the sea which it seeks continually. Phalaropes are believed to pass the winter at sea, and it seems remarkable that these delicate creatures should be able to withstand the storms of wide oceans, but after they pass our shores on their southward journey they disappear into the ocean wastes and are rarely seen again by human eyes until they return in spring over the same seas. In its summer home the Red Phalarope feeds largely on insects, but crustaceans, mollusks and jelly-fish are eaten, also sandworms, leeches and small fish. Phalaropes are believed to eat a small quantity of vegetal matter, including some weeds. Far at sea they seek floating masses of sea-weed about which they seem to find quantities of food and they follow right whales or bowhead whales which feed on small sea animals. The habit has given phalaropes the name Whale-birds or Bowhead-birds. Not infrequently their keen eyes discover a whale before the whalemen see it, and as these little birds hasten toward the gigantic animal they give notice to the lookout at the mast head that his prey is in sight. The rising and spouting of whales assure the birds that food in plenty may be found.

Economic Status. See page 372.

Lóbipes lobátus (Linnæus). Northern Phalarope.

Other names: Red-necked Phalarope; White Bank-bird. (See under Red Phalarope, page 372.)

Plate 24.

Description. — Bill slender, pointed, a little longer than tarsus, which is as long as middle toe without claw or slightly longer; outer toe longer than in Red Phalarope and not so fully lobed. *Adult female in nuptial plumage:* Above, including wings and tail, dull, dark "slate gray" or brownish-slate (a bluish suffusion on upper back) extending down on sides of breast and there mixing with white ground color; upper back and scapulars with two buffy or yellow-brown stripes forming a "V" on back; sides of lower back and rump largely white; outer upper tail-coverts white streaked or shaded gray; larger middle wing-coverts narrowly tipped white, greater wing-coverts broadly so tipped; sides of neck and fore neck "rich rust red"; chin, throat, small spot over eye, and under plumage white including axillars and most of wing-linings; sides and flanks white with dusky shaft-streaks; bill black; iris dark brown; legs and feet bluish-gray, to greenish-gray, lead color or dusky, webs lighter.

Foot of Northern Phalarope

Adult male in nuptial plumage: Similar to female but much duller in color; gray upper plumage duller, less uniform; fore face, including forehead, chin and throat, largely white; rusty red of neck much duller and largely confined to its sides; some reddish on back and scapulars; sides of breast mixed white and dark grayish, more or less tinged rusty red; iris brown; bill black; legs and feet dusky. *Adults in winter plumage (sexes alike):* Above chiefly gray; forehead, stripe over eye, sides of head and neck, and under plumage white; sides of upper breast washed, mottled or clouded pale gray, top of head grayish, feathers with dusky shaft-streaks and whitish edges; blackish spot before eye, dusky and grayish-white patch from below and behind eye to ear region; nape, back of neck and upper plumage generally ashy-grayish with white feather edgings which arrange themselves in stripes on scapulars and interscapulars; buffy or yellowish-brown "V" seen on back in breeding plumage now replaced by white; wings and tail much as in summer but more white on scapulars and tertials; eyes and bill much as in summer; legs and feet duller or livid. *Young in juvenal plumage:* Top of head dusky, feathers faintly margined or not with buffy; center of nape sooty-brown; forehead and face whitish or buffy, except dark patch from about eye to ear as winter adult; back, scapulars and tertials blackish, *feather margins warm buff* or "bright rusty-brown"; middle of back and rump sooty-brown; middle upper tail-coverts blackish-brown, mottled and tipped buff, outer ones white, brown-streaked; sides and flanks white with more or less buffy wash and central dark streaks; a dark or brownish suffusion across fore neck and upper breast, rest of under plumage white; tail-feathers narrower and more pointed than in adult; wing similar to adult but innermost secondaries and coverts with buffy edgings; lower middle wing-coverts widely edged white or buff; bill blackish; iris brownish-black; legs and feet bluish-flesh color. *Downy young:* Colored much as downy Red Phalarope but yellow of upper plumage brighter; no dark line at base of bill.

Measurements. — Length 6.40 to 8.00 in.; spread 13.00 to 14.50; folded wing 4.00 to 4.60; tail 2.00 to 2.50; bill .79 to 1.10; tarsus .75 to .88. Female larger than male.

Molts. — Young birds become nearly indistinguishable from adults by a postjuvenal molt in first autumn. They probably become absolutely indistinguishable from adults when, after the first post-nuptial molt, they assume second winter plumage. Adults have a partial molt of body-feathers, scapulars and some wing-coverts (February to June) and from July to January a complete molt.

FIELD MARKS. — Smaller than Spotted Sandpiper; smallest of phalaropes; distinguished from sandpipers by longer neck and more slender bill; distinguished in breeding plumage by rusty red on sides of neck sharply defined against white throat; in winter plumage (as usually seen in United States) back not pearly-gray as in Red Phalarope but dark gray marked white; compared with Red Phalarope it has an extremely slender head and neck; *a white wing-bar in all plumages.*

VOICE. — Call, a soft *pleep, pleep,* alarm note, "*prip, prip*" (C. L. Bonaparte) or "*chis-ick*" (Gladstone); other notes described as "a short *quit,*" a rapid "*ket-ket ket-ket,*" "*pe-et pe-et,*" "*wit, wit*" and "*chirra-chirra-chirra*"; "at times twitters like a Barn Swallow; at times emits a single harsh note like that of Eave Swallow" (C. W. Townsend); "on taking wing, this species utters a chipping note suggesting somewhat that of the Sanderling, either monosyllabic, 'tchip' or 'tchep,' or in two or more syllables" (J. T. Nichols).

BREEDING. — About the banks of ponds, sloughs or streams, often near sea, but fresh water apparently preferred. *Nest:* A depression in ground or moss, sometimes slightly lined with broken-down grass. *Eggs:* 3 or 4; 1.30 by .75 to 1.10 by .82 in. (Coues); pear-shaped; greenish or brownish-olive to drab, stone color or varying shades of buff, spotted boldly and splashed with blackish or dark chocolate and lighter shades of brown. *Dates:* Late May to early July according to latitude. *Incubation:* Period about 14 days (Hantzsch); about 18 days (Gladstone); by male. Probably but one brood yearly.

RANGE. — Both hemispheres, from Arctic coasts and islands to southern oceans. Breeds in North America from Pribilof Islands, northern Alaska, Melville Island and central Greenland south to Aleutian and Near Islands, upper Yukon, northern Mackenzie, northern Manitoba, southern James Bay and northern Ungava (northern Quebec) and in northern Europe and Asia, east to Commander Islands; winter range not well known, but migrates south on oceans and through interior Canada and United States and Eurasia, also off their coasts, and to Hawaiian Islands, Central and South America to Patagonia, Bermuda, Galapagos Islands, northern Africa, southern Asia, Malayan and Moluccan Islands, Aru Islands and Japan; supposed to winter mainly on oceans.

DISTRIBUTION IN NEW ENGLAND. — Common to abundant migrant off shore; not recorded from Vermont and accidental in Connecticut; irregular and uncommon in interior of other states and on our coast except when driven there by easterly storms; most common at outlying points like Cape Ann, Cape Cod, Nantucket and No Man's Land.

SEASON IN MASSACHUSETTS. — May 1 to 30; July 31 to October 13; (December 16; February 11).

HAUNTS AND HABITS. This gentle, active, graceful little bird is by no means rare at times in autumn on some of the inland waters of northern New England, and rarely considerable numbers are driven into estuaries by severe storms at sea. Brewster records a large number in the Charles River between Boston and Cambridge on May 20, 1894.[1] Sometimes they gather in considerable flocks off outlying points of the coast, and these flocks remain for days at a time only a mile or two off shore. Large numbers have been killed at times by flying against outlying lighthouses, but the species is usually uncommon or rare on the salt marshes, beaches and flats of Massachusetts. Sometimes on sunny days a few individuals alight in shallow fresh-water ponds where they spin or circle round and round on the water dabbing their bills into it very rapidly, apparently stirring up the mud or water and catching some minute forms of aquatic life. They pass our shores in greatest numbers about the middle of May, and during August and early September. Anyone cruising off shore at these seasons is likely to see them in numbers from one mile to 100 miles from land. They flock sometimes with Red Phalaropes, but

---

[1] Brewster, William: Birds of the Cambridge Region, 1906, p. 154.

more often by themselves, and they rest usually on the sea, often fluttering lightly from place to place.

Their food consists largely of small aquatic animals, including mollusks and crustaceans; when ashore they consume many insects including numbers of mosquito larvæ.

ECONOMIC STATUS. The Northern Phalarope is of no known economic importance while in New England waters.

Steganopus tricolor VIEILLOT. Wilson's Phalarope.

Plate 24.

DESCRIPTION. — Bill long, slender, about as long as tarsus; toes margined, rather than lobed, and very slightly webbed at base; tarsus decidedly longer than middle toe with claw; tail doubly emarginate. *Adult female in breeding plumage:* Forehead and crown pale blue-gray, with blackish border along each side; gray of crown fades into white or whitish on nape, continues down back of neck and again passes into blue-gray or slate-gray on back and scapulars and into dull brown on lower back and rump; dark stripe from bill to and below (or through) eye, becomes broader and blacker behind eye, and continues on side of lower neck, where it broadens and changes to chestnut, and passes backward, narrowing and often more or less broken on interscapulars; scapulars have similar chestnut striping; short stripe above eye (between the gray and black) not extending to bill, lower eyelid, lower face, chin and upper throat white; wings brownish-gray (shaft of 1st primary white); primaries and their coverts darkest, other coverts and tertials mar-gined paler; upper tail-coverts white, longer ones irregularly marked dusky; tail mouse-gray or "light drab," outer feathers barred or mottled with white on inner webs

FOOT OF WILSON'S PHALAROPE

and narrowly tipped white; fore neck and breast soft buffy-cinnamon, deeper on sides of neck and breast and fading gradually into white of rest of under plumage and into buffy suffusion on sides; wing-linings and axillars white (except some dusky mottling near outer edge of wing); bill blackish; iris dark brown; feet and legs blackish. *Adult male in breeding plumage:* Much duller in color than female, her beautiful color pattern similarly but faintly indicated on head and neck, but without chestnut in streaks on scapulars or interscapulars, and top of head mainly dull brown, becoming blackish-brown toward back and whitish on nape; back of neck reddish-brown; back and wings dull, dark brown, with lighter feather-edges (some marked rusty) giving a streaked appearance; rump drab, with white tips; feathers of upper tail-coverts centrally streaked light drab, margined white; under plumage similar to that of female but duller; wing-linings and axillars, bill, iris, legs and feet much as in female. *Adults in winter plumage (sexes alike):* Above plain light gray (occasional dark feathers sometimes present indicate imperfect plumage), feathers narrowly tipped whitish; upper tail-coverts, wide stripe over eye, sides of both rump and back and all under plumage mainly white; breast faintly tinged (mostly on sides) pale gray; flight-feathers darker than other upper plumage; tail much as in breeding plumage; bill black; eyes dark; legs and feet yellowish. *Young in first winter plumage:* Closely resemble winter adults; distinguished by retained juvenal wing-coverts. *Young in juvenal plumage:* Crown, back and scapulars dusky with buff or light rusty feather-margins, giving a streaked and mottled effect; wing-coverts and tertials similar, margined pale buff, rusty or whitish; lower throat and sides of neck washed buffy, sides also buffy, streaked dusky; otherwise as winter adults; "bill black, yellowish at base of upper mandible; legs flesh color, feet yellow" (Grinnell, Bryant and Storer); legs and feet dull greenish yellow (Ludwig Kumlien). *Downy young:* "Bright cinnamon-buff or tawny-buff," paler below; abdomen almost white; a central streak of black on nape branching on back of head into two narrow irregular lines; three broad stripes on lower back and rump, spot on each flank and bar crossing hinder part of body, black.

MEASUREMENTS. — Length 8.25 to 10.00 in.; spread 14.50 to 16.00; folded wing 4.60 to 5.50; tail 1.89 to 2.30; bill 1.08 to 1.50; tarsus 1.14 to 1.35. Female larger than male.

MOLTS. — Juvenal upper plumage (but not wings or tail) is molted (July to winter) and first winter plumage is assumed; spring molt of head, neck and body-feathers and wing-coverts is followed by a plumage which seems practically as adult and young bird becomes indistinguishable from adult after postnuptial molt of following fall; adults have an incomplete molt in spring and a complete postnuptial molt.

FIELD MARKS. — Largest of phalaropes; fully as large as Pectoral Sandpiper, but head, neck and bill slimmer than in Red Phalarope; bill longer, needle like; adults in full plumage unmistakable; in winter plumage or in partial winter plumage in which likely to be seen in New England they are pale birds, resembling winter Sanderlings, but with longer, slimmer bills; usually seen swimming rather than wading; very young birds are darker, resembling Pectoral Sandpiper but with slimmer, longer bill; unstreaked breast and white rump; *lacks in all plumages broad white wing-bar seen in other phalaropes.*

VOICE. — Female, a peculiar harsh note on arrival in spring (E. W. Nelson); both sexes, a weak nasal quack repeated six or seven times in succession (A. L. Kumlien); a nasal *oit, oit, oit* (W. P. Taylor); a soft trumpeting *yna, yna;* a soft *qua;* or *quok* (F. M. Chapman); when flushed, they utter a "peculiar grunting noise" (John F. Ferry); usually a rather silent bird in migration.

BREEDING. — In grass land or marsh land at varying distances from water. *Nest:* Collection of grasses or sedges, etc., with slight depression in center or a mere hollow in ground, lined with a little grass, usually concealed by overhanging grass or other vegetation (which may be drawn together by bird). *Eggs:* 3 or 4; 1.20 to 1.35 by .90 to .94; elongated pear-shaped; light buff to clay color or very light drab, marked with large splashes and spots and many specks and scratches of dark chocolate-brown or brownish-black and spots of pale olive or light brown, larger markings usually grouped about large end, smaller ones abundantly distributed over surface. *Dates:* Late May to end of June in northern states. *Incubation:* By male. Probably but one brood yearly.

RANGE. — Most of North America and South America. Breeds from southern British Columbia (probably), central Washington, central Alberta, central Saskatchewan, southern Manitoba and casually southern Ontario (one record), south to northeastern California, Nevada, Utah, Colorado, Nebraska, (formerly southern Kansas), central Iowa, northern Illinois and northwestern Indiana; winters from central Chile and central Argentina south to Falkland Islands; migrates largely in interior; occasional in migration from southern British Columbia to Lower California and casual from Ontario, Quebec and Nova Scotia to North Carolina and Gulf coast.

DISTRIBUTION IN NEW ENGLAND. — Very rare or accidental visitor chiefly in autumn. Records: *Maine:* Scarborough, 3 seen and 1 taken June 9, 1881;[1] Lewiston (Sabattus Pond), young bird shot in September or October, 1906.[2] *New Hampshire:* Rye Beach, bird taken August 15, 1872, by William Brewster.[3] *Massachusetts:* Boston, bird given to Audubon in winter of 1824 by John Bethune;[4] Nahant, female taken May 20, 1874, by George O. Welch, (recorded wrongly as male) and now in collection of Boston Society of Natural History;[5] Ipswich (probably), adult taken [about 1883 Ed.] and now in collection of Boston Society of Natural History (received from William Everett);[6] Nantucket, bird taken August 31, 1889, by George H. Mackay;[7] Marshfield, bird taken August 24, 1893, by Foster H. Brackett "in a heavy southeaster at the mouth of South River";[8] Salisbury, female obtained by John H. Hardy, August 18, 1907, and now in collection of Dr. C. W. Townsend.[9] *Rhode Island:* Newport,

---

[1] Smith, Everett; Forest and Stream, Vol. XX, 1883, p. 124.

[2] Knight, O. W.: Birds of Maine, 1908, p. 150.

[3] Baird, Brewer and Ridgway: Water Birds, Vol. I, 1884, p. 339, and Allen, G. M.: Birds of New Hampshire, 1903, p. 85.

[4] Audubon, John J.: Birds of America, Vol. V, 1842, p. 300.

[5] Baird, Brewer and Ridgway: Water Birds, Vol. I, 1884, p. 338, and Townsend, C. W.: Birds of Essex County (Mass.), 1905, p. 165.

[6] Allen, G. M.: Auk, Vol. XXV, 1908, p. 234.

[7] Auk, Vol. VIII, 1891, p. 120.

[8] Hagar, Joseph A.: *in litt.*

[9] Auk, Vol. XXV, 1908, p. 80.

male taken August 2, 1880, by F. T. Jencks;[1] female taken August 20, 1883, and now in collection of Boston Society of Natural History;[2] immature bird taken about September 13, 1886, and secured by J. Glynn, Jr.;[3] Little Compton (Sakonnet), bird taken August 24, 1899, and now in collection of Dr. G. T. Gardiner;[4] Quonochontaug, male taken August 28, 1909;[5] *Connecticut:* Bridgeport, female recorded by Linsley,[6] and now in collection of the Bridgeport Scientific Society.

Haunts and Habits. Wilson's Phalarope, one of the most elegant and beautiful of North American shore birds, is a mere straggler in New England. Its principal home is in the northern Mississippi Valley and contiguous parts of Canada, and New England is far from its regular route to South America as it migrates south mainly through the interior of the United States and along both coasts of Mexico and Central America. Its habits are similar to those of other phalaropes, but it is not so much of a swimmer and diver and seems to prefer land and fresh water to the sea. It feeds in shallow water, spins and bobs like other phalaropes and apparently rarely dives. In New England it has appeared chiefly along the coast and usually in autumn. Mr. E. W. Nelson has given an excellent account of its breeding habits.[7]

The females do most of the wooing. A single male is sometimes chased about by two or more ardent females, but when the nuptials are concluded and the honeymoon is over the henpecked father is said to assume most of the family cares. The young leave the nest soon after they emerge from the egg. The females are very active and vivacious in the breeding season when it is said a single female often has two mates and two separate families, each presided over by its faithful father.

Wilson's Phalarope feeds more on terrestrial forms of life than do the other phalaropes and destroys many insects. According to McAtee, it takes mosquitoes, crane-fly larvæ, leaf beetles and bill bugs.[8] It also destroys brine shrimps and alkali flies.

Economic Status. Doubtless this species is useful as an insect destroyer, but is so rare in New England as to be of little economic importance here.

Family **RECURVIROSTRIDÆ**. Avocets and Stilts.

Number of species in North America 2; in Massachusetts 2.

This small family is so named because of the peculiar, long, very slender, slightly upcurved bill, which, however, in some stilts is nearly straight. The legs are long and slender, particularly in stilts and the front toes are more or less webbed. Avocets, like phalaropes, have the body somewhat flattened and under plumage thick and duck-like. They usually wade but are expert swimmers.

[1] Bulletin, Nuttall Ornithological Club, Vol. V, 1880, p. 237.

[2] Rives, Wm. C.: The Birds of Newport, Proceedings Newport Natural History Society, 1883–4, p. 39, and in Newport Daily News, March 11, 1884.

[3] Rives, Wm. C. Jr., M.D.: Auk, Vol. IV, 1887, p. 73. See also page given in footnote 4 below.

[4] Howe and Sturtevant: Birds of Rhode Island, 1899, p. 48.

[5] Hathaway, Harry S.: Auk, Vol. XXX, 1913, p. 551.

[6] Linsley, J. H.: "A Catalogue of the Birds of Connecticut," American Journal Science and Arts, Vol. XLIV, 1843, p. 268. Bulletin, Nuttall Ornithological Club, Vol. II, pp. 338–365.

[7] A Contribution to the Biography of Wilson's Phalarope, Bulletin, Nuttall Ornithological Club.

[8] McAtee, W. L.: Our Vanishing Shorebirds; United States Department of Agriculture, Bureau Biological Survey, Circular No. 79, pp. 2 to 8.

Recurviróstra americána Gmelin. Avocet.

Other name: AMERICAN AVOCET.

AVOCET

DESCRIPTION. — Bill excessively slender, flattened on top, sometimes nearly straight, often much upcurved (sometimes downcurved toward tip, where upper mandible is slightly hooked), much longer than head, nearly as long as tarsus; front toes full webbed, hind toe elevated, very small. *Adults in breeding plumage (sexes alike)*: Variable; general color white, changing to light cinnamon-brown or rusty-brown on head, neck and breast; a whitish space around eye and another about base of bill; inner scapulars brownish-black; rump grayish; wings mainly black or blackish; tips of secondaries and terminal halves of greater coverts broadly white, latter forming white bar across wing; tertials pale drab; edges of wing, wing linings and axillars largely white; bill mostly black, often flesh-colored at lower base; iris brown, red or carmine; legs and feet mostly pale blue, webs more or less flesh color. *Adult and immature in winter plumage:* Similar, but rusty of head, neck and breast replaced above by pale gray, below by white.   *Young in juvenal plumage:* Similar to adult in winter but duller, primaries slightly tipped white; back feathers tipped and mottled more or less buffy and whitish; tinge of light reddish on nape; crown dull grayish.   *Downy young:* Top and sides of head mottled and mixed black, white and rusty-brown; hind neck and upper back similar, but more rusty; rest of upper plumage blackish with some rusty intermixed, becoming grayish on lower back and wings; a white spot on forehead and another in middle of chin; under plumage dull whitish.

MEASUREMENTS. — Very variable; length 15.50 to 20.00 in.; spread 27.00 to 38.00; folded wing 7.00 to 9.50; tail 3.00 to 4.48; bill 3.22 to 4.00; bare tibia 2.25 to 2.50; tarsus 3.27 to 4.00. Female smaller than male.

MOLTS. — Most juvenal body-feathers, apparently some wing-coverts and perhaps a few tail-feathers are molted beginning in midsummer and continuing more or less during autumn and early winter; from late February through spring prenuptial molt occurs, but immature bird now resembles first winter plumage and does not assume adult breeding plumage until another winter has passed; in following

May or June plumage seems to become as in adult; adults apparently have a complete postnuptial molt and a partial prenuptial molt (January to June).

FIELD MARKS. — Size of Green Heron; distinguished from all other shore birds by black and white plumage, brown head and neck, light blue legs and feet and upturned bill; it lacks solid black upper plumage of Stilt and has no black along back of neck.

VOICE. — A loud, sharp *plee-eek*, *plee-eek* (F. M. Chapman); *click-click-click* (Wilson).

BREEDING. — In colonies or small companies on islands, in shallow ponds or on grassy land near water. *Nest:* Sometimes on bare ground, more often among grasses; sometimes a mere ring of woven grass around eggs which rest on bare ground; again, a lining of grass, etc., in a hollow and sometimes a more pretentious nest. *Eggs:* Usually 3 to 4, but 5 to 8 have been known; very variable in shape and markings; 1.80 to 2.10 by 1.25 to 1.45; varying from dark olive or brownish-drab to light brown or even buff with profuse small spots of various shades of deep brown and markings of lavender or gray. *Dates:* May 3 to July 6, California; June 29, Colorado; June 2 to July 5, upper Mississippi Valley; *Incubation:* Period probably about 24 to 25 days. Probably but one brood yearly.

RANGE. — North America chiefly west of Great Lakes. Breeds from eastern Oregon, central Alberta, Saskatchewan (apparently no farther north), and southern Manitoba south to southern California, southern New Mexico, southern Texas, Kansas, northern Iowa, eastern Wisconsin (1870) and formerly Illinois and New Jersey; winters from southern California and southern Texas to southern Guatemala; casual in British Columbia and from Ontario and New Brunswick to Florida and West Indies; rare east of Mississippi.

DISTRIBUTION IN NEW ENGLAND. — Accidental visitor. Records: *Maine:* Cape Elizabeth, bird taken November 5, 1878.[1] *Vermont:* St. Albans, 1875 (fall) and 1890, bird taken by G. E. Edson. (The authority for these occurrences is George Edward Edson who is said by R. H. Howe, Jr. in his "Review" of Perkins' "Birds of Vermont" to have taken one at St. Albans. No date is given in the systematic list, but under "errata" the additional information is given that Mr. Edson writes that "a pair of young Avocets came to St. Albans . . . in the autumn of 1875" and "he also mentions the species as occurring in 1890"). *Massachusetts:*[*] Lynn, two birds reported taken many years ago on the marshes;[2] Natick, bird taken October 19, 1880, at Lake Cochituate;[3] Salisbury (probably), adult female taken May 23, 1887, by Benjamin F. Damsell and now in collection of Boston Society of Natural History;[4] Ipswich Neck (near Eagle Hill), three birds taken by A. B. Clark, September 13, 1896.[5] *Connecticut:* Between Saybrook and East Lyme, bird caught alive in 1871 in an old seine spread out on the beach to dry (J. G. Ely).[6]

HAUNTS AND HABITS. The Avocet, one of the largest and perhaps the most showy of all American shore birds, has been practically extirpated from the Atlantic coast, and if it is ever seen in New England again it will be as a mere accidental straggler from the West. In the early years of the nineteenth century Wilson reported that he found it breeding in the salt marshes of New Jersey; and Turnbull says that George Ord told him that during his [Ord's] excursions to the coast with Wilson, both the Avocet and Stilt were "quite plentiful." It is improbable, however, that the Avocet was ever common in New England, and the last record of the species in this territory was in 1896. Its

[1] Brown, N. C.: Bulletin Nuttall Ornithological Club, Vol. IV, 1879, p. 108.
[*] A. C. Bagg informs me that a mounted specimen now in the Public Library at Northampton was taken many years ago by E. O. Damon at Ipswich.
[2] Osgood, Fletcher: Shooting and Fishing, Vol. IX, 1890, p. 11.
[3] Purdie, Henry A.: Bulletin, Nuttall Ornithological Club, Vol. VI, 1881, p. 123.
[4] Allen, Glover M.: Auk, Vol. XXX, 1913, p. 23.
[5] Kennard, F. H.: Auk, Vol. XIV, 1897, p. 212.
[6] Merriam, C. Hart: Birds of Connecticut, 1877, p. 103.

habits and haunts have been described by Audubon, Wilson and Drs. Elliott Coues, Frank M. Chapman and T. Gilbert Pearson.

The following habit recorded in 1914 by Mr. Charles E. H. Aiken seems not to have been reported elsewhere:

"Aiken witnessed a curious performance of Avocets in Utah. In September, 1893, he visited the mouth of Bear River where hundreds of acres of mud flats and shallow water offer an attractive resort for various water-fowl. In a submerged grove where patches of mud appeared above the water hundreds of Avocets were congregated. One little mud island that differed from others in that it was quite round seemed to have a fascination for the birds, and they were packed together upon it in a mass which covered the island to the water's edge. As the island was about 12 feet in circumference the number of birds probably approximated 150. This mass of birds continued to revolve about from left to right, and being so crowded the movement was rather slow and their steps short and measured, so that the impression was that they were all marking time in the marching. Birds on the rim of the circle avoided walking off in the water and crowded inward against the mass. Every moment or two birds would leave the milling body and fly to a neighboring mud island, and as many from near by would fly to take their places and join the dance. Aiken advanced quietly to within 20 yards and viewed them for half an hour, but they continued undisturbed by his presence and he left them so. It appeared to be a diversion of the birds." [1]

It is not unlikely that the Avocet may be taken here again in years to come, if it can be protected on its western breeding-grounds.

ECONOMIC STATUS. The Avocet is a useful bird, as it is destructive to locusts and other injurious insects of grass lands. It is not highly valued for the table, as it is said to have a fishy flavor when on the sea-coast, caused perhaps by feeding to some extent on small fishes and crustaceans.

Himántopus mexicánus (MÜLLER). Black-necked Stilt.

DESCRIPTION. — Bill about twice as long as head, extremely slender, nearly straight, slightly up-curved, not flattened nor hooked at tip as in Avocet but needle-pointed; wings very long, tail short; legs very long and slim, feet small, hind toe wanting, front toes partly or slightly webbed. *Adult male:* Above, including eye, back part of head, back of neck, scapulars, upper back, and wings (both above and below) black, with some greenish reflections; forehead, most of eyelids, space above eye extending behind it, front face and lower face, sides of neck, lower back, rump, upper tail-coverts and under plu-mage generally white, with a pale pink tinge on white of fore neck and breast in breeding season; in some individuals white of breast continues around back of neck; tail drab in center, a little darker toward tip, outer feathers lighter or dingy whitish, shafts white; bill black; iris carmine, crimson or scarlet; legs and feet carmine, lake red or rose pink. *Adult female:* Similar but duller; upper back, scapulars and tertials brownish; pink on lower neck usually wanting. *Young in juvenal plumage:* Similar to female, but duller; feathers of dark upper plumage edged buffy or whitish; many flight-feathers nar-rowly tipped whitish. *Downy young:* Above, tawny and blackish finely mottled and mixed; long spot

---

[1] Aiken, Charles E. H., and Warren, Edward R.: The Birds of El Paso County, Colorado, Part I, 1914, p. 485.

on middle back and stripe on each side of back black; below "pale tawny" fading to whitish on belly; bill dark "mouse gray"; legs and feet grayish-blue.

MEASUREMENTS. — Length 13.12 to 15.50 in.; spread 26.00 to 30.00; folded wing 8.30 to 9.50; tail 2.75 to 3.25; bill 2.00 to 2.75; bare tibia 3.00 to 3.50; tarsus 3.81 to 4.83. Female averages longer than male but with slightly shorter legs.

MOLTS. — A part of the juvenal plumage (largely body-feathers) is molted in autumn and during late winter and spring there is apparently a molt of body-feathers, some tail-feathers and some wing-coverts, but juvenal wings are mainly retained; during postnuptial molt in next autumn quills of wings

BLACK-NECKED STILT

are shed and in second winter plumage young closely resembles winter adult; probably most individuals become about as adult in second summer when fully two years old; adults have partial molt in late winter and spring and complete molt in autumn.

FIELD MARKS. — About the size of Greater Yellow-legs, but taller and slimmer *with much longer wings and very long red or pink legs;* black or blackish above; white below; in flight body looks white, wings black.

VOICE. — A sharp, rapid *ip-ip-ip* when flying; a hoarse *k-r-r-r-r*-ing note when on ground (F. M. Chapman); in mating season, a "nasal *quănk*" (Grinnell, Bryant and Storer).

BREEDING. — In small colonies; on dry ground near water, on small island or even in shallow water among grasses, reeds or rushes, etc. *Nest:* Composed of grasses or other water-plants; sometimes a mere hollow in ground lined with grasses, etc., but when in water built up from 4 to 7 inches. *Eggs:* 3 or 4, rarely more; 1.60 to 1.88 by 1.10 to 1.25 in.; pear-shaped; from dark yellowish clay color to "greenish drab," "pale brownish olive" or buff marked with dark brown or blackish and gray or lavender; slightly glossy; usually smaller and somewhat darker than those of Avocet. *Dates:* Early April to early August, California. *Incubation:* Period probably a little less than 21 days; by both sexes; no accurate observations.

RANGE. — Temperate North America and northern South America. Breeds from central Oregon, northern Utah, southern Colorado south to southern California, southern New Mexico, Mexico, southern Texas and coastal region of Louisiana, and from central Florida (formerly New Jersey) and Bahamas through West Indies to northern Brazil and Peru; winters from southern Lower California, southern Texas, southern Louisiana and Florida through West Indies and Central America to northern Brazil, central Peru and Galapagos Islands; casual in migration north to North Dakota, Nebraska, Iowa, Wisconsin, Michigan, Illinois and New Brunswick, and in Bermuda.

DISTRIBUTION IN NEW ENGLAND. — An accidental visitor, formerly less rare in southern New England. Records: *Maine:* Rockland, bird taken early in May, 1889, and sent to Charles K. Reed of Worcester.[1] *New Hampshire:* Rye Beach: "Some years ago a summer visitor at Rye Beach brought a Black-necked Stilt to Mr. Shaw at Hampton to be mounted." [2] *Massachusetts:* Dr. J. A. Allen records two birds, noted by George A. Boardman in the Boston market and taken in Massachusetts; [3] there is a specimen in the Museum of Comparative Zoölogy at Cambridge labeled "Lynn." [4]

HAUNTS AND HABITS. The Black-necked Stilt is known in parts of its range as the "Lawyer" because of its vociferousness and is also called "Long-shanks," "Long-legs" and "Daddy-long-legs" in some localities. Despite its apparently unnecessarily long legs, it is a graceful and handsome bird. There is little to say of its habits in New England as it is a mere straggler here, but there is reason to believe that in the early part of the nineteenth century when it bred commonly as far north as New Jersey, it was less rare in southern New England than it is today. Dr. Brewer (1884) reported that several individuals had been taken at Grand Manan, New Brunswick, and that occasional instances of its capture near Boston were known.[5]

C. J. Maynard (1870) stated on the authority of gunners that it was seen occasionally along Massachusetts beaches.[6] Many years ago I heard similar reports but such evidence is too indefinite to be of much value. This bird, probably once common in suitable localities from the Atlantic to the Pacific, seems to be generally rare to accidental now east of the Mississippi Valley. I saw it in great abundance at Lake Harney, Florida, in March, 1878, where probably it is no longer common. It frequents the margins of grassy ponds, sluggish streams and marshes, both fresh and brackish, and feeds mainly by wading. It can swim and dive at need, but is not so expert a swimmer as the Avocet. In walking, it is a "high stepper" and when standing the legs are not spread but held parallel. It flies well with neck somewhat drawn in and long legs trailing behind. Often upon alighting it raises the wings straight up over the back, and in moving about on foot it frequently tosses up the head. It seems to be very suspicious and quite noisy when alarmed by the approach of a human intruder, and is likely to communicate the alarm to other wild denizens of the marsh or shore.

ECONOMIC STATUS. The Stilt feeds to some extent on grasshoppers, weevils and other destructive insects, and where it frequents agricultural lands it may be of some service to the farmer. It does no harm and should be perpetually protected by law as an unique example of specialized bird life.

---

[1] Ornithologist and Oölogist, Vol. XIV, 1889, p. 78.
[2] Dearborn, Ned: Birds of Durham and Vicinity, 1903, p. 31.
[3] American Naturalist, Vol. III, 1870, p. 638.
[4] Howe, R. H., Jr., and Allen, G. M.: Birds of Massachusetts, 1901, p. 34.
[5] Baird, Brewer and Ridgway: Water Birds, Vol. I, 1884, p. 346.
[6] Naturalist's Guide, 1870, p. 143.

PLATE 25

PLATE 25

WOODCOCK
Page 385

ADULT

WILSON'S SNIPE
Page 391

ADULT

DOWITCHER
Page 396

ADULT IN WINTER
PLUMAGE (AUTUMN)

ADULT IN BREEDING
PLUMAGE (SPRING)

All one-half natural size.

FAMILY **SCOLOPACIDÆ**. SNIPES, SANDPIPERS, ETC.

Number of species in North America 43; in Massachusetts 28.

This great family includes woodcocks, snipes, sandpipers, tatlers, ruffs, godwits and curlews, all closely related wading birds. They exhibit great differences in size and color, but are all of small or medium size, never reaching the average size of herons. The bill is usually long, rather straight, roundish and slim, but sometimes is curved up or down and in one genus is spoon-shaped. It is covered with a rather soft integument and in some cases the tip is very sensitive and is provided with muscles by which the upper mandible may be bent upward, thus opening the tip of the bill to seize food when the bill is thrust deep in soft mud. A long narrow nasal groove runs down each side of the upper mandible. The head is entirely feathered. The legs are long or of medium length but never very short. The toes may be either three or four, and in some cases they are webbed basally. The wings are long and pointed; the tail short. The family is represented in every habitable country on the globe, but its members breed mainly in northern regions. Many birds of this family make very extended migrations. In the autumn flights toward the south the young birds commonly precede the adults.

SUBFAMILY **SCOLOPACINÆ**. WOODCOCKS AND SNIPES.

Number of species in North America 5; in Massachusetts 2.

Birds of this subfamily are noted for a very long, rather slender, pliable bill, sensitive and somewhat expanded toward the tip. The gape is very restricted. The eyes are large and placed far back above the ears. The wings are long and pointed or rounded; the tail is short and variegated; the legs are rather short. The species are more or less nocturnal.

NOTE. The European Woodcock (*Scólopax rusticola*) has been taken casually along the Atlantic coast from Newfoundland to Virginia. It is about one-third larger than the American species, weighing 12 to 15 ounces, is more grayish below and the under plumage is distinctly barred. The first three primaries are not narrow and scythe-shaped as in our bird. *The 1st and 2d primaries are longest, 3d a little shorter, 4th much shorter; outer web of 1st whitish and barred.* Exceedingly large woodcocks have been reported in New England, some of which are believed to have been European, but there is no New England record substantiated by a specimen. The bird may be confidently looked for to occur here.

Rubícola mínor (GMELIN). **Woodcock.**

Other names: LITTLE WHISTLER; WHISTLER; BOGSUCKER; TIMBER DOODLE.

Plate 25 and Figs. 30 and 31.

DESCRIPTION. — Bill very long, straight and tapering in lateral profile; head large; neck rather short and thick; eye very large, far back and high in head; ear under eye; wing rounded; 1st primary shortest, 4th longest, three first narrow, scythe-shaped; tail rounded, of 14 feathers; legs rather short, tibia feathered. *Adults (sexes alike)*: Head, neck and under plumage pale cinnamon or dull cinnamon-buff suffused with grayish above and becoming brighter on sides and under wing-coverts; under tail-coverts with dusky shaft streaks; top of head black, crossed by 3 or 4 narrow bars of pale cinnamon;

a dusky streak from bill to eye, an oblique streak of same across cheek; above, general color cinnamon, mottled, and more or less intermixed with grayish, back and scapulars with rather large irregular black spots; outer webs of outer row of scapulars and interscapulars light gray forming 4 broad gray stripes; primaries brownish-gray; tail brownish-black above, broadly tipped light gray above and silvery-white below; bill dull grayish flesh color, dusky toward end; legs and feet same; iris dark brown. *Young in juvenal plumage:* Similar to adult but feathers softer and looser in structure; bill shorter. *Downy young:* Above "brownish-white" or pale "ochraceous buff"; a long patch on forehead and crown, a line from bill through eye to hind head, an oblique line beneath ear and several irregular stripes on upper body deep brown; below, deeper and more rufous, becoming pinkish-cinnamon in some cases.

MEASUREMENTS. — Length 10.00 to 12.00 in.; spread 16.00 to 19.55; folded wing 4.50 to 5.75; tail 2.20 to 2.60; bill 2.45 to 3.00; tarsus 1.20 to 1.40. Weight, male 5 to 6 oz., female 6 to 8, occasionally 9 oz.

MOLTS. — Juvenal body-feathers and some wing-coverts apparently are molted (July to October) and winter plumage then assumed is like adult; probably, however, at least another year is required by young to reach full maturity; adults have partial prenuptial molt in late winter and early spring and complete postnuptial molt during late summer and fall, beginning in July.

FIELD MARKS. — The Woodcock is more or less nocturnal and hides and sleeps by day; is seldom seen unless flushed; when rising, its stocky form, broad, fluttering wings, long bill and whistling sound identify it; Wilson's Snipe might be mistaken for it but has long, pointed wings and is slimmer in build, darker above and does not whistle.

VOICE. — A nasal *"peent"* something like common note of Nighthawk; somewhat resembling *kwank* (Audubon); a series of rather hard *paiks* (R. I. Brasher); while moving about in underbrush at evening *chip-per chip-per chip* or *bleat* or *bleat ta bleät ta* (E. A. Samuels); also many twittering, liquid and whistling sounds, but how many of these are attributable to the wings no one has been able to determine.

BREEDING. — In low, damp, bosky places, bushy meadows, brakes or damp woodlands, but sometimes far up in the hills on dry ground, even in an open pasture. *Nest:* Usually on dry ground surrounded by moist or wet land, near foot of tussock, bush or tree; occasionally on decaying log or stump; a mere hollow lined with a sprinkling of dead leaves and sometimes a little dried grass. *Eggs:* 3 or 4; 1.40 to 1.70 by 1.10 to 1.20 in.; *not pear-shaped* like those of most shore birds but *ovate*, varying much in shape and color; "creamy buff," "dark or light clay color," "ashy gray" or "buffy brown," beautifully spotted and mottled with various shades of brown and gray. *Dates:* February 15, South Carolina; February 25, Maryland; March 14, New Jersey; April 11 to May 6, Massachusetts; April 26 to May 19, Maine. *Incubation:* Period 20 to 21 days (Burns); by both sexes. One brood yearly.

RANGE. — Eastern North America. Breeds from northeastern North Dakota, southern Manitoba, northeastern Minnesota, northern Michigan, southern Ontario, southern Quebec, New Brunswick, Prince Edward Island and Nova Scotia south to eastern Colorado, Texas, southern Kansas (formerly), southern Louisiana and northern Florida; winters from southern Missouri, northern Indiana and New Jersey (rarely Long Island and Massachusetts) south to Texas and southern Florida; casual in Saskatchewan, northern Manitoba, Montana, Newfoundland and Bermuda; doubtfully reported from Labrador; possibly accidental in Jamaica; doubtfully recorded from Oregon.

DISTRIBUTION IN NEW ENGLAND. — *Maine:* Common but rather local summer resident except in York County where rare; common migrant; casual in winter. *New Hampshire and Vermont:* Rather uncommon migrant and local summer resident. *Massachusetts:* Common to abundant migrant and common to rare local summer resident except in Barnstable, Dukes and Nantucket counties where rare summer resident; winters casually. *Rhode Island:* Common to abundant migrant and rare local summer resident. *Connecticut:* Common to abundant migrant; rather common local summer resident and rare winter resident.

SEASON IN MASSACHUSETTS. — March 1 to December 11; (winter).

HAUNTS AND HABITS. According to the accepted definition of a game bird our Woodcock is supreme. It lies close, rises to a convenient height, offers a quick shot on the wing and when brought to the table is a most luscious and delectable morsel for the epicure. Properly prepared for the table it is said to be superior to the European Woodcock. As an example of how close the bird lies, let me relate that one day in August, while walking along a path near the Concord River with Mr. William Brewster, who was slightly in the lead, a Woodcock rose between us. One of the wings hit my companion's right ear and the bird passed close to my face.

Besides being a game bird of high excellence, the Woodcock is a most interesting bird. It has been studied by ornithologists for more than a century and still its periodical mysterious appearances and disappearances and its lines of migration are not fully understood. We know that the Woodcock is an early bird. Occasional individuals appear in February in Massachusetts. These may have wintered here or in Connecticut, but the main flight usually appears in March and the first part of April. We know that some of the early birds reach Nova Scotia and some of the later ones may go on even to Newfoundland; but we know little regarding the extent of their flight to the northeast. Even in the light of the twentieth century there is a dispute about just what part of the sounds that emanate from the bird in flight are emitted from its vocal organs and what are produced by its wings. Mr. Brewster assured us years ago that the Woodcock's whistle is caused by the wings, saying that he never heard a whistle from one that lacked the three peculiar outer primaries or from one not having them fully developed. He believed, however, that the "twitter" was vocal.[1] Mr. W. H. Harris asserts that he held a Woodcock by the bill which whistled three times with a rotary motion of body and wings.[2] Mr. J. M. Dinsmore held a Woodcock by the body and wings to prevent movement of these parts, and he says that this bird whistled through its mouth and throat.[3] Mr. H. Austin avers that he flushed a Woodcock that did not whistle, marked the bird and put him up again when he whistled,[4] which indicates that the bird may have made the sound with its vocal equipment.

Some of the Woodcock's common habits are well known and have been described often. We have read that its young are rather weak and dependent and, unlike the young of the Ruffed Grouse, easily taken; that they quickly learn to fly but in the meantime are frequently carried from place to place by the mother who clasps them between her thighs, or between her legs and her body, or with her feet. It is said that rarely she carries them on her back; that in the mating season the male, seeking the female at evening, bows and calls repeatedly and often rises high in air, with erratic flight and a variety of peculiar notes; that on returning to the ground he struts about with lowered wings and spread tail like a turkey-cock, and while strutting thus with his upraised tail almost touching the back of his retracted head, he is sometimes so absorbed that he actually trips over twigs or sticks in his path; that he bows, *peents* and sometimes raises his bill

---

[1] Forest and Stream, Vol. XXXV, 1890, p. 453.
[3] *Ibid.*, Vol. LXXXIX, 1919, p. 31.
[2] *Ibid.*, Vol. XLVII, 1896, p. 303.
[4] *Ibid.*, Vol. XXXVI, 1891, p. 3.

vertically as high as possible, stretching the neck to the utmost, and then pulls down his head until his eyes appear to lie on his shoulders.

To those who have not witnessed the song-flight of this bird, the following graphic description sent to me by Mr. Harry Higbee will be interesting:

"As the bird mounted into the air, it did so each time on a long plane, — exactly as an airship rises, — and the rapid wing-strokes and vibrant whistling notes given at the same time served to heighten the effect of this similarity.   When well into the air the bird turned and mounted higher and higher; still continuing its rapid whistling notes as it rose in diminishing circles.   When at the apex of this flight, — seemingly two hundred feet or more overhead, — these whistling notes were changed to louder and more distinct call notes, which were followed by the outburst of melody given in a descending scale, similar to the 'flight song' of the Ovenbird.   This song was given while the bird circled overhead, gradually descending on fluttering wings, and finishing with rapid downward sweeps and long 'volplanes' toward the earth, when it dropped suddenly down within a few yards of the place from which it had arisen.   The entire performance in the air seemed to occupy about five minutes and as soon as the bird alighted again in the grass it began the peculiar calls with which it had started.   These calls seemed to be given at intervals of about five seconds, and in some instances at least the bird moved about before it again arose.   Sometimes a low gurgling note, seeming to be given with a sudden expulsion of air, could be heard between these calls.   Once or twice an answering call was heard from the long grass near by, and just before dark another Woodcock, — presumably the female which had been the object of these outbursts, — flew up from the ground nearby and disappeared over the treetops, seeming to settle down again not far away.   This bird, which arose while the other one was in the air, made no distinguishable whistling sound as did its mate when rising."

Mr. H. W. Copeland says of this bird: "I have referred to several books, and while I notice that the various authors mention the three different notes, I do not see anywhere mention made of the fact that each note is uttered by the bird only in a certain part of the manœuver, *i.e.*, while the bird was on the ground the only note he uttered was a nasal '*peent*,' then as he rose in flight came the whistling sound which the bird kept making while he continued to mount in air.   As he descended, however, the whistling note changed to a *chipper-chipper-chip-chip* and he was on the ground again with his '*peent*.'"

Mr. James MacKaye, who noted this performance in May, 1924, in Shirley, reports that the average of ten flights by two different birds was only 1 minute 15 seconds from the "taking off" to the first "*peent*" after the return to earth.

We know that the Woodcock probes the soil with its long bill in search of earthworms and grubs, but beyond this we know little of its habits, for the bird is active during the twilight and in the night, and in daylight it may be as sleepy and stupid as an owl. Wherefore it lies to a dog until forced to rise, and then flutters up and over the tops of small trees or undergrowth, to drop again almost immediately into another hiding place.

The Woodcock, however, is not always asleep or inert in the daytime. Miss Bertha L. Brown of Bangor, Maine, wrote on March 12, 1920, that a Woodcock stayed all day about the home of one of her friends and from about 2 to 5 P.M. fed on the lawn directly in front of the sun-parlor windows where four people watched the bird boring and catching earthworms. Possibly it was unable to get food at night so early in the season owing to the freezing of the ground at night which, being later thawed by the noon sun, gave it the needed opportunity to feed.

But what can one say that is new about the Woodcock?

The function of the long, grooved, sensitive bill is understood to be that of feeling its way to grubs and worms buried in soft earth or mud, and then opening at the flexible tip to seize and draw them out. Wherever it feeds, its "borings" are found where its bill has probed deeply, and its "chalkings" (white excrement) also indicate its presence, for the Woodcock is a mighty eater and blessed with enormous digestive powers. Herbert K. Job informed me that a Woodcock that he kept for a time ate in 24 hours twice its own weight in earthworms. The Woodcock appears to work in different ways when hunting earthworms. These worms become active after sunset and by stirring or probing the earth they are brought to the surface. Mr. E. L. Ewbank asserts that a ramrod thrust into the ground will cause them to come out, and he assumes that they thus try to escape from any near-by disturbance of the earth such as is caused by moles which pursue them beneath its surface.[1] Mr. T. C. Homiller writes that he saw a Woodcock thrust its bill into the earth time after time, but that it did not pull out a worm, but waited for it to come out of the hole that had been made.[2] My old friend, the late Charles Hallock, writing editorially in Forest and Stream, relates that a Woodcock pecked away at the ground like a woodpecker, digging deeper and deeper, and having finished one hole, made another, and so on; then lay down "on his stomach" and beat the earth with his wings. As the worms or other insects come to the surface, he says, they are straightway caught by the Woodcock.[3] The earth vibrations or the sounds caused by the beating of wings on the ground may have simulated the beating of raindrops which so frequently bring worms to the surface.

Mr. C. J. Maynard, who kept a Woodcock confined, said that the bird walked "slowly and deliberately, pausing every instant or two as if listening intently"; then, giving several sharp, quick blows on the ground with one foot, it bowed its head close to the ground and listened again. Then turning suddenly right or left or moving a little forward it plunged its bill into the earth and drew out a worm, repeating this performance until it had eaten all that had buried themselves within the enclosure.[4]

Mr. Isador S. Trostler says that Woodcocks "often play in a very droll manner, running round and round each other in a small circle" with wings lifted and bills pointed nearly to the zenith. He gives an instance where, when frequently disturbed, the bird

---

[1] Forest and Stream, Vol. LXXXVIII, 1918, p. 604.
[2] *Ibid.*, Vol. LXXXVIII, 1918, p. 487.
[3] *Ibid.*, Vol. I, 1873, p. 251.
[4] Birds of Eastern North America, 1889, pp. 190, 191.

removed its eggs to another very crude nest, a mere hollow in mossy ground. He also asserts that in cold or wet weather both parents, facing in opposite directions, sit upon the nest.[1]

The primitive ground-nest of the Woodcock with its spotted gray or buffy eggs, which sometimes is buried by a late snowstorm; the close sitting of the parent bird which sometimes may be touched with the hand or even lifted from the nest (it is said that a dog cannot by scent find a female on her nest); * the stratagems by which the mother strives to entice the intruder away from her young; the bold front she sometimes assumes in the attempt to drive the enemy away — all these are but parts of an oft-told tale. The little chicks with their comparatively short bills and striped downy bodies are exceedingly interesting, readily tamed and might be artificially reared. If the breeding season be not too dry, young Woodcocks apparently prosper, but in a very dry season they seem to disappear, and then the fall flights are disappointing. The late spring, summer and autumn of 1923 were exceedingly dry in New England and in the Maritime Provinces except possibly in parts of eastern Quebec, Labrador and Nova Scotia. The birds largely disappeared that summer from their usual haunts in New England, and the autumn flight was exceedingly light until very late in the season. Then after rains during early November a great flight appeared near the end of Cape Cod. This flight may have come over the sea from Nova Scotia. Later, about December 10, a very considerable flight landed in central Massachusetts and remained a few days.

In July and August when molting, Woodcocks retire to briery thickets, and then and in September they are often found in the most unlikely places, such as pastures and fields of corn, strawberries, potatoes or asparagus. The movements of the birds in August cannot be fully accounted for. In southern New England some short migrating flights may begin before the month ends. During the September moon, however, many birds bred in the hill country move south or into the valleys, but the moonlight nights of October usually see the main flight. A very few Woodcocks winter irregularly in southern New England.

The numbers of the Woodcock are greatly reduced when, as sometimes happens in spring, they reach the North in March only to be overtaken by severe cold or overwhelmed by a blizzard. In the South they are sometimes driven by storms and cold from their wooded fastnesses in the hills and swamps to the coastal regions, where the starving birds die or are slaughtered. Sometimes also, in winter, high water in the swamps sends them out to meet death at the hands of the pot-hunter, but their greatest danger, the country over, lies in the multiplication of gunners. An expert shot with a good Woodcock dog can kill most of the birds his dog puts up. In the upper Mississippi Valley region the Woodcock is now practically a bird of the past. Its greatest refuge and breeding-ground at present is the Atlantic coast territory, particularly New

---

[1] Oölogist, Vol. X, 1893, pp. 278, 279.

* This is true of other birds besides the Woodcock; provided that the bird *does not move*, the dog fails to find her. I once killed a Woodcock stone dead in mid-air which the well-trained pointer could not find. Having seen the bird fall, I went to the spot and found it lying in a deep cow track.

Photograph by Daniel McDavid

FIG. 30. — YOUNG WOODCOCK IN NATAL SWAMP

Photograph by Daniel McDavid

FIG. 31. — NEST OF WOODCOCK

England and the southern part of the Maritime Provinces. If we do not adequately protect it here, its extirpation is only a question of time.

Sometimes, while wintering in the South, Woodcocks are driven out of the swamps by floods and appear in great numbers on the uplands. Again, during very dry seasons they swarm sometimes in such wet places as they can find. The following story comes from Mr. E. O. Damon and is taken from a letter written by him to Mr. A. C. Bagg. It relates to an experience in Peedee Swamp in South Carolina. Mr. Damon writes that he was in the swamp early one winter morning hunting turkeys and, coming out before light, he heard a confused noise, a sort of buzzing sound somewhat like that produced by great numbers of insects. As he and his companion came nearer the source of the sound it became so loud that he asked the cause of it. The man laughed and said it was "Woodcock." Mr. Damon asked where the birds were and his companion said that they were in what was called Indigo Field, some 200 rods away. As they approached the field the sound became louder and louder. It was indescribable — somewhat like the noise made by a huge cloud of buzzing flies. Just as light began to come in the east, the noise stopped and the birds began to fly; inside of half a minute they had disappeared from the field. This field was about 25 rods wide and "they went out of it," says Mr. Damon, "by thousands." The winter had been very dry, and they came into that field to feed because of its dampness.

The food of the Woodcock consists largely of earthworms. When the summer and autumn are unduly dry and worms go down into the subsoil, the birds lose weight rapidly, but they eat many beetles, grubs and other insects which they search for among the fallen leaves or dig from the ground.

ECONOMIC STATUS. In New England, most of the northern part of which is too cold for Bob-white, the Woodcock as an upland game bird is second in importance only to the Ruffed Grouse; and therein lies its chief economic value.

Gallinágo delicáta (ORD). Wilson's Snipe.

Other names: SNIPE; ENGLISH SNIPE; JACK SNIPE; ALEWIFE-BIRD.

Plate 25.

DESCRIPTION. — Bill usually as long as tarsus and middle toe or longer; wing ample as in Wood-cock but proportionally longer, less rounded, and *1st primary longest*, 2d often scarcely shorter; tail rounded, normally of 16 feathers, the 2 outer abruptly shorter and very narrow; lower part of tibia bare. *Adults in breeding plumage (sexes alike)*: Much individual variation; top of head black with a pale buffy-brown or whitish middle stripe and more or less streaked or flecked with pale buffy-brown; sides of head (and throat) pale buffy-brown or buffy-whitish becoming deeper or richer toward back of head and neck and crossed by a dark stripe of varying width from bill through eye, narrowing behind eye; another shorter stripe below ear; sides of head more or less spotted toward back of head and upper neck with dusky-brown; upper plumage generally variegated, dark dusky-brown or blackish and reddish-brown, tan or buff, striped light buffy or whitish; lower rump and upper tail-coverts light brownish-buffy, narrowly and irregularly barred dusky, bars darkest on lateral coverts, longest coverts tipped whitish; tail black with broad subterminal bar of bright reddish-brown or tawny, crossed near tip with blackish and tipped buffy and whitish, outermost tail-feathers pale buff or whitish, barred black; outer surface of closed wing mainly dusky-brown with buffy markings and buffy and whitish feather margins or tips; tertials brownish-black, narrowly margined whitish and narrowly barred buffy; secondaries dark brownish-gray, their terminal margins broadly white; primaries still darker, they and their coverts sometimes tipped whitish and outer primary margined whitish; neck, all around, pale brownish-buffy, darkly streaked and mottled dusky gray-brown, streaks darkest on hind neck; breast pale brownish-buffy or pale buffy-brown, spotted or clouded light gray-brown; under tail-coverts buff, with irregular V-marks of blackish; rest of under plumage white, wing-linings and axillars barred blackish, sides and flanks barred grayish-brown; bill blackish toward tip, greenish-gray elsewhere; iris dark brown; legs and feet pale greenish-gray or grayish-green. *Young in first winter plumage:* Like adult. *Young in juvenal plumage:* Similar to adult but stripe on middle of crown pinkish-white, cheeks and chin mixed white, black and tawny or cinnamon; outer surface of closed wing showing broad feather-margins of pinkish-buff; throat and breast pinkish-cinnamon, streaked dusky. *Downy young:* Bright brown, darkest on upper surface and marked there irregularly black and white; a whitish bar across forehead and another across crown; blackish line from bill to eye, another below it converging on it at base of bill; forehead white at base of bill, a white connecting line from bill to eye, spot below gape black, chin buffy.

MEASUREMENTS. — Length 10.25 to 11.75 in.; spread 16.25 to 20.00; folded wing 4.95 to 6.50; tail 2.00 to 2.50; bill 2.40 to 2.76; tarsus 1.15 to 1.50. Weight 3 to 5 oz. Female larger than male.

MOLTS. — Beginning in August, juvenal plumage is molted, and probably all young birds have assumed first winter plumage by end of autumn. In this plumage they are apparently as adult but may require another year to reach full maturity; adults have a partial prenuptial molt (February to May) including body-feathers and some wing- and tail-feathers, and a complete postnuptial molt from July or August to September or October.

FIELD MARKS. — Larger than Spotted Sandpiper; recognized by extremely long bill, dark striped plumage, white belly and its rather weak, harsh cry as it rises from the grass and goes off in zigzag or "crazy" flight; usually seen in low meadows or marshy land.

VOICE. — When startled and rising, a harsh, rasping *scaipe, scaipe,* not loud; otherwise given a "hoarse *cr-r-r-ack cr-r-r-ack* or *craik craik,* a distressed sound" (Thoreau); on ground *kuk-kuk-kuk* (O. W. Knight); in breeding season *yak-yak-yak-yak* or *ka-ka-ka-ka-ka* of far-reaching quality (Grinnell, Bryant and Storer); *kak-kak-kak,* a little like style of Virginia Rail but slower and on higher key (Kennicott).

BREEDING. — Mainly on meadows, open marshes or bogs and on floating islands in marshy ponds. *Nest:* On or near ground; sometimes in a tussock surrounded by water; a mere depression in grass or moss, lined perhaps with a little grass; sometimes more of a nest and raised slightly above the surrounding surface. *Eggs:* 3 to 4; 1.50 to 1.60 by 1.09 to 1.18 in.; pear-shaped; variable, "grayisholive" or "grayish-drab" to "greenish-brown" or "yellowish-ash," spotted and blotched sepia, grayishbrown, umber or chocolate and sometimes lines of black; markings numerous and bold, clustering toward large end. *Dates:* April 29 to May 26, northern states; May 28 and early June northern Canada and Alaska. *Incubation:* Period probably about 20 days, like that of European Snipe. Probably but one brood yearly.

RANGE. — North America and northern South America. Breeds from northwestern Alaska, northern Yukon, northern Mackenzie, northern Manitoba, northern Ungava (northern Quebec), northern New Brunswick, Magdalen Islands and Newfoundland south to northern California, northern Nevada, southern Colorado, eastern South Dakota, northern Iowa, northern Illinois, northern Indiana, Pennsylvania and New Jersey (rarely); winters from southern British Columbia, southern Montana, New Mexico, central Colorado, Arkansas and North Carolina (casually and locally north to Washington, Oregon, Nebraska, Minnesota, Illinois and Nova Scotia) south through Central America and West Indies to Colombia and southern Brazil; accidental in Greenland, Bermuda and Hawaii.

Distribution in New England. — *Maine:* Common migrant and uncommon and local to rare summer resident. *New Hampshire:* Common migrant near coast; less common in interior; probably rare local summer resident; very rare winter resident. *Vermont:* Uncommon migrant; rare winter resident; probably rare local summer resident. *Massachusetts:* Common to abundant migrant; rare, irregular summer resident; rare local winter resident. *Rhode Island:* Common migrant; rare local winter resident. *Connecticut:* Common migrant; rare local summer resident; rare winter resident.

Season in Massachusetts. — (March 2) March 20 to May 18; (summer) August 1 to November 30; (winter).

Haunts and Habits. When the spring rains and mounting sun begin to tint the meadow grass, when the alewives run up the streams, when the blackbirds and the spring frogs sing their full chorus, then the Snipe arrives at night on the south wind. Whoso wades in the marsh at this season will see the startled Snipe spring from the grass, rising up five or six feet perhaps against the wind, and with a harsh cry, *"escape escape,"* proceed to do so in the most erratic, crazy fashion.

Next to the Woodcock, Wilson's Snipe is the most important game bird among American *Limicolæ*. It breeds and feeds mainly in fresh meadows or marshes and in brackish marshes. It is very erratic and sometimes very wild but often lies well to a dog and furnishes good sport in the open. When flushed it veers and twists for the first 20 yards or so as if bent upon dodging a charge of shot. A wag remarked that when the Snipe got away in its burst of zigzag flight he was sure to miss it, for when he shot "zig" the snipe always went "zag." Some gunners wait until the birds have done twisting and then kill them at long range, and one that I know is so expert that he shoots them as they reach the highest point of their first rise. Sometimes in dull or rainy weather the first bird started or the first shot fired will flush every bird in a meadow, and they will go high into the air and after performing a few erratic aërial evolutions depart for parts unknown. Again, the meadow may contain hundreds of birds in the evening and not one the next morning.

The most remarkable performance of this bird is its song flight. Thoreau says of it: "Perhaps no one dreamed of a Snipe an hour ago, the air seemed empty of such as they; but as soon as the dusk begins, so that a bird's flight is concealed, you hear this peculiar spirit-suggesting sound, now heard through and above the evening din of the village." Again he says: "Persons walking up and down our village street on still evenings hear this *winnowing* sound in the sky over the meadows and know not what it is." Thoreau hears his first Snipe of the season "A-lulling the watery meadows, fanning the air like a spirit over some far meadow's bay." How few people seem to hear or recognize this remarkable sound! Sometimes on cloudy days (rarely in fair weather) this performance may be seen in full daylight in Massachusetts. It is called the booming, drumming or bleating of the Snipe, but these words entirely fail either to indicate or to describe the sound. In Massachusetts we may hear it more or less during the month of April about river meadows or isolated bogs. This flight is described as follows in one of my field notebooks:

"On April 30, 1911, a dark day with lowering clouds, I was standing near a bog in Westborough listening to a Brown Thrasher's rollicking song when I heard an intermittent *who-who who-who who-who who-who who-who* — a sound somewhat like the strong wing-beats of some powerful water-fowl in flight as its passing wings are heard in the dusk of the coming night. This occurred at intervals of a few seconds and shifted rapidly about in the sky. I looked in vain for the source of the sound, and as I moved on to the northward, it faded in the distance. Returning half an hour later I heard the winnowing sound again, and finally with my glass made out the bird against the sky. He was circling high — so high that when he passed over me I could barely see his long bill with the aid of my glasses! Each of his circuits must have covered a mile in its circumference and each encircled the Bittern's Bog, where possibly the female of his choice lay hidden. There was a strong breeze from the southwest. The Snipe seemed to rise diagonally through the air, with rapid wing-beats, and then to glide off sidewise and downward in a curious, wavering, sidelong manner, his wings apparently beating as before, but his body seeming to wobble a little, and his wings to pursue an erratic course. During the diagonal downward plunge the sound was produced, after which the bird continued on in its great circle, soon making another sidewise plunge from another point of the circumference of its line of flight. After I first saw the bird the performance lasted nearly half an hour. At times the bird was perhaps three hundred yards from the earth; at other times much lower, but always beyond gunshot. Finally at about 5.30 he circled directly over the bog, and with set wings pitched almost straight down into the grass."

The sounds produced in this flight are supposed to be made by the outer quills of the wings or tail. European ornithologists believe that the common snipe of Europe produces its so-called "bleating" by means of the two outer tail-feathers which stand out clearly from the others during the downward plunge.

The song flight apparently is a part of the mating display of this bird, but in courtship the male struts about the female in the manner of the turkey-cock with wide-spread erected tail, proudly carried head and drooping wings, sometimes ascending spirally into the air high above her, and uttering his love notes as he comes down. When the Snipe is on the ground, its striped plumage resembles so closely its environment that it has only to stand still or crouch in the open meadow to be perfectly concealed.

The Snipe can swim and dive and uses both wings and feet under water in its efforts to escape. Mr. Will C. Parsons writes that he shot one that fell into a little clear streamlet where later he found it dead, under water, grasping a rootlet in its bill. Later, on the Scioto River, as he relates, he shot another which fell into the river, and, turning, swam back toward the shore. On seeing him approach it dived, and he saw it grasp a weed with its bill. Wading in he secured the bird "stone dead."[1]

Snipes on the average are far more abundant in spring than in fall in New England. Considering the large number killed on the southward migration, the numbers should

---

[1] Forest and Stream, Vol. LXXXI, 1913, p. 103.

be less in spring. This anomaly must be accounted for by the fact that the greater part of the birds go south by sea in the fall and come north by land in the spring. Sea-going Snipes have reached Bermuda and many winter in the West Indies and eastern South America. Sometimes they are driven back by storms on Cape Cod, Nantucket, Marthas Vineyard or Block Island and some of them have been known to pass the winter in such localities. Locally a few winter on the mainland, near flowing springs or in springy swamps. While the Snipe is a ground dweller, it sometimes alights on trees and fences in the nesting season, and Mr. W. W. Castle, writing in 1869, asserted that multitudes crossing Lake Superior in spring alighted in the trees on the northern shore to rest.[1]

Wilson's Snipe walks usually with bill directed a little downward, and in feeding plunges it vertically down into the soft earth or mud. Sometimes it pulls out earthworms and at other times secures large numbers of crane-fly larvæ. Where it feeds, its borings are less prominent than those of the Woodcock on its chosen feeding grounds. It eats cutworms, grasshoppers, mosquitoes, wireworms, click-beetles, water-beetles, seeds of smartweed and other plants, and more or less other vegetal matter has been found in snipes' stomachs.

ECONOMIC STATUS. This Snipe is harmless and beneficial as it destroys injurious insects. As a game bird it takes high rank. When fat and feeding in fresh meadows it has not the sedgy taste so noticeable in birds that feed on the salt marsh, and it is superior even to the Woodcock. Perhaps there is in the world no more excellent small bird for gastronomic purposes. Market hunting, spring shooting and over-shooting generally have tremendously reduced its numbers. It can be saved and increased by preserving marshlands in which it feeds and breeds and by enforcing adequate protective laws.

SUBFAMILY CANUTINÆ. SANDPIPERS AND GODWITS.

Number of species in North America 22; in Massachusetts 17.

This is an extensive group showing many variable minor details of form and coloration. The bill in most species is more or less pliable and sensitive as in snipes; the gape is similarly restricted, but in sandpipers the bill is shorter than in snipes and either straight or slightly curved downward in most species. Birds composing this subfamily are mostly small or medium-sized as compared with the larger members of the *Limicolæ;* toes are four, except in one genus, and legs usually of medium length. In some members of this group the toes are cleft to the base and in others partly webbed.

The godwits, which are now included in this subfamily, are quite different superficially from the smaller members of the group. They are comparatively large (approaching the larger Curlews in size), with long legs and long bills, the latter slightly upturned and much less sensitive than in some other members of the subfamily. In size and shape they approach more closely to the Tatlers and Willets than to the generality of the species in this subfamily.

---

[1] American Naturalist, Vol. II, Feb., 1869, p. 663.

Limnódromus gríseus griseus (GMELIN). Dowitcher.

Other names: RED-BREASTED SNIPE; BROWN-BACK; RED-BREAST; ROBIN SNIPE; DRIVER; KELP PLOVER; DEUTSCHER; FOOL PLOVER; GERMAN SNIPE.

Plate 25.

DESCRIPTION. — Bill more than twice as long as head, tumid and wrinkled at base, much higher than wide, widened toward end; wing moderate, pointed, outermost primary longest; tail of 12 feathers; partial web between outer and middle toes. *Adults in breeding plumage (sexes alike)* : Above variegated with black and lighter colors, feathers edged and marked light pinkish-cinnamon or vinaceous-buff, sometimes edged whitish; top of head, hind neck and upper back thus streaked light and black, the black streaks very broad on back; scapulars irregularly spotted black or margined black at ends and barred with lighter ground color; anterior lesser wing-coverts "dusky grayish-brown," with narrow pale edges, middle coverts centrally blackish, edged pale "pinkish cinnamon" or "vinaceous buff," greater coverts dark grayish-brown, edges and tips white; secondaries similar but with much more white; tertials blackish, barred and edged cinnamon, primaries and their coverts dusky, quill of 1st primary very white; some inner primaries light brownish-gray, bordered by a dusky line and edged white; lower back, rump, upper tail-coverts and tail white, rump and uppermost tail-coverts spotted (some barred) and tail barred blackish; middle tail-feathers in some individuals tinged cinnamon; sides of head and neck, and under plumage light pinkish-cinnamon with a yellowish cast, often intermixed with some white below, more or less spotted dusky, particularly on breast, sometimes well down on abdomen; sides and flanks barred or spotted same; a broad line of fine spots from bill to and below eye, and dusky streaks in ear-region; axillars and wing-linings white, former with V-shaped bars or with inverted U- or V-shaped dusky marks; latter with similar U- or V-shaped marks; bill blackish or dark grayish, becoming greenish or olivaceous toward base; iris dark brown; legs and feet light yellowish or greenish-olive. *Adults in winter plumage:* Top of head, neck, upper back, scapulars and wing-coverts gray, more or less indistinctly streaked and otherwise marked darker or dusky; sides of head and eyelids white or whitish, a dark streak through eye, and cheeks streaked gray; fore neck, breast and sides of body more or less gray; hinder plumage and tail much as in summer, but with little or no tinge of cinnamon; rest of under plumage white; wing linings and axillars as in breeding plumage; bill, legs and feet as in summer (Turnbull). *Young in first winter plumage:* Similar to adult; feathers of upper plumage more or less edged whitish. *Young in juvenal plumage:* Top of head, upper back, scapulars and tertials largely black, many feather margins of clay color; under plumage dull whitish, more or less tinged buffy or clay color especially on upper breast which, with sides, is more or less speckled dusky; rest of plumage similar to winter adult.

MEASUREMENTS. — Length 10.00 to 12.50 in.; spread 17.50 to 20.00; folded wing 5.25 to 5.90; tail 2.13 to 2.60; *bill 2.01 to 2.56;* tarsus 1.20 to 1.55. Weight 3⅓ to 5 oz. Female larger than male.

MOLTS. — First winter plumage is acquired apparently by a partial postjuvenal molt of body plumage and some lesser wing-feathers (August to November); partial prenuptial molt (January to April or May) is followed by nuptial plumage, similar to adults, but often somewhat paler and retaining some feathers of winter plumage; in some individuals this molt apparently is omitted and these birds retain first winter plumage through spring and early summer; second or adult winter plumage is acquired by postnuptial molt beginning in late July or August after which bird becomes indistinguishable from adult; adults have partial prenuptial molt in late winter and early spring and complete postnuptial molt in fall.

FIELD MARKS. — *Long bill;* size close to Wilson's Snipe; rump and tail appear silvery gray at a distance; bird looks very dark at a distance, and so resembles Wilson's Snipe, but the Snipe does not habitually haunt sand bars, beaches and mud flats, as does the Dowitcher; in spring and summer reddish breast and long bill distinguish adult Dowitcher; in flight a narrow white patch shows on back, not so white as that of the Yellow-legs.

VOICE. — A shrill, quivering whistle (Wilson) flight-note suggests the bird's name *dowitch* or *dowitcher*; a soft rather abrupt whistle; *wheu-whup* or *whew-whup-whup*, subject to further variation (J. T. Nichols): "now and then a rapid series of rolling guttural notes"; a sharp *pip peep* or *pup*.

BREEDING. — Nest and eggs unknown, probably identical with those of Long-billed Dowitcher, but smaller.

RANGE. — Eastern North America (west in Canada to Alberta and probably to Pacific), West Indies and northern South America. Breeding range unknown; probably breeds in the same region as the Long-billed Dowitcher which seems to be identical with it except in size; winters from Florida and West Indies south to northern Brazil and Ecuador; migrates regularly on Atlantic coast and apparently also in the interior and on Pacific coast; non-breeding birds summer south to Florida; occasional in Great Britain; accidental in Prince Edward Island, Nova Scotia, Northern Idaho, Greenland, Bermuda and France.

DISTRIBUTION IN NEW ENGLAND. — Rather uncommon to abundant migrant coastwise, chiefly in fall; rare in interior; less common coastwise in southern New England; not recorded from Vermont but probably occurs there.

SEASON IN MASSACHUSETTS. — (March 8) May 1 to June 1 (June 18) July 4 to September 30 (October 23).

HAUNTS AND HABITS. Along the low sandy shores of the outer arm of Cape Cod the Dowitcher stops to rest and feed on its way to its northern home. It is a bird of inner beaches and still waters. It prefers inner beaches in sandy harbors near where the sea continually moans on outlying bars. Wide sand flats along the inner shores of Cape Cod Bay or small shallow ponds just inside the outer beaches are favorite resorts. At low tide it often feeds on sand or mud flats or along the estuaries in the salt marsh. In New England it is very rarely seen in fresh marshes where Wilson's Snipe sometimes abounds. In the spring migration it usually remains with us in small numbers during a brief period in the latter part of May or until early June, but in autumn its numbers are larger and, though usually not very common in its accustomed haunts, in some seasons a large flight of young birds passes south along our coast during the latter part of August. The species was once abundant on the New England coast. It became rare during the latter part of the nineteenth century and now is increasing again, owing to wise laws prohibiting shooting and sale. Early in July a few Dowitchers appear all along the Atlantic coast from Massachusetts to North Carolina. They seem to come overland from Ungava. Apparently the Dowitcher habitually migrates down the Atlantic coast. A part of the flight seems to leave the Carolinas in autumn and go by sea to the Antilles. In returning the majority of the birds appear to leave the coast of the Carolinas and migrate north through the interior. Dowitchers may be seen here in spring plumage in May and again in July, but most of the birds of the fall migration are in adult winter, first winter or changing plumage.

This species often feeds by thrusting its bill deep into mud and water, securing marine worms and other small animals buried there. If feeding on soft mud it seems to rest its weight partly on its bent tarsi, but on sand it runs about like any sandpiper. Often it wades in water up to its belly, probing the bottom. It swims readily, nodding its head and jerking its tail with each stroke. It does not habitually follow the receding waves but feeds in sheltered places. When resting on the beach at high tide Dowitchers often squat behind tufts of grass which they seek as a protection from the wind. Mr. Charles Whittle informs me that they often sleep standing with the long bill tucked under a wing and pointed straight back. The Dowitcher is normally a very unsuspicious bird. Dr. Winsor M. Tyler says that at Hampton, N. H., he approached so near one that he could hear a little click when foot and beak met as the bird used one foot to wipe a bit of sea-weed from its bill. This bird often may be found in the company of the smaller sand-pipers and also with the Yellow-legs, from which it may be readily distinguished by its long bill and shorter legs. In flight it is usually seen in small parties which move in concert, performing aërial evolutions, all moving together as one bird.

Among the food materials of the Dowitcher horse-flies, maggots, grasshoppers, leeches, worms, water-bugs, water-beetles, small mollusks and oyster worms have been reported.

ECONOMIC STATUS. See page 372.

Limnodromus griseus scolopáceus (SAY). Long-billed Dowitcher.

Other names: WHITE-TAILED DOWITCHER AND OTHERS APPLIED TO DOWITCHER.

DESCRIPTION. — This alleged geographic race has been accepted by the Committee on Nomencla-ture of the American Ornithologists' Union and I have followed them as in duty bound, but, in my opin-ion, individual variation alone will account for most of the supposed racial characters, and so far as these are concerned the two races are practically one and the same. It must be admitted, however, that most western birds examined by me are larger than eastern specimens. *Adults in breeding plumage:* Similar to Dowitcher but averaging larger; bill, tarsi and toes averaging longer; upper plumage generally darker; color of under plumage deeper (salmon), and extending over abdomen, which lacks white feathers; fewer dark spots and markings on under plumage; uppermost tail-coverts white, generally barred black; outer tail-feathers white, barred black, middle ones barred black and rufous; "iris dark brown; bill dull, yellowish, olivaceous, greenish at base; feet greenish" (F. Sumichrast). *Adults in winter plumage:* Similar to Dowitcher. *Young:* Like young of Dowitcher, but light border and marks of upper plumage deeper in color; bill, legs and feet blackish-green (Elliot); tips of middle tail-feathers barred black and reddish-brown; throat whitish, faintly marked; breast light salmon lightly marked with arrow-head spots of dusky; abdomen pale salmon (R. H. Howe, Jr.). *Downy young:* Top of head dark "burnt umber" brown, a stripe of dull buffy over eye, a blackish-brown streak from bill to eye and a wider dark brown stripe behind eye; ear-region pale buffy with narrow dark streaks across its center; upper plumage "dark burnt umber," intermixed with a little lighter shade of same and dotted grayish-white, this color forming two stripes lengthwise on back; chin and throat pale brownish-buff or buffy, whitish; rest of under plumage "pale brownish-buffy" becoming cinna-mon on breast.

MEASUREMENTS. — Length 10.81 to 12.50 in.; spread 18.00 to 20.50; folded wing 5.40 to 6.50; tail 2.20 to 2.70; bill 2.10 to 3.25; tarsus 1.36 to 1.75. Weight 4 to 5½ oz. Female larger than male.

MOLTS. — Same as Dowitcher. See page 396.

FIELD MARKS. — Same as Dowitcher from which it is indistinguishable in field.

VOICE. — In fall, a deep guttural chirp; a whistled note "much louder and clearer than that of Dowitcher" (N. T. Lawrence); also a "song" on its breeding-ground.

BREEDING. — In northern marshes on marshy or bare ground. *Nest:* In moss or grass or a slight depression in ground, often unlined. *Eggs:* Usually 4; 1.69 to 1.87 by 1.20 to 1.25 in.; pear-shaped; ground color, clay or grayish, sometimes with greenish cast, with large well defined dark umber brown spots, sparsely scattered except at larger end where crowded (Grinnell, Bryant and Storer). *Dates:* May 23, Mackenzie, to June 28, Point Barrow, Alaska.

RANGE. — Western North America. Breeds from Point Barrow to mouth of Yukon, east to northwestern Mackenzie (and probably much farther east) south to British Columbia; winters from Louisiana, Florida, Cuba, Jamaica and Mexico south to Panama and probably to northern South America; in migration most abundant in western Mississippi valley, but common on Pacific coast; rare on Atlantic coast from Sable Island southward and on northern coast of eastern Siberia; accidental in Japan.

DISTRIBUTION IN NEW ENGLAND. — Casual fall migrant in Maine; rare fall migrant in Massachusetts, Rhode Island and Connecticut. The records substantiated by specimens taken and carefully identified are few. *Maine:* Scarborough, one taken by John Petersen in first part of October, 1912, deposited in Museum of Portland Society of Natural History, recorded by Arthur H. Norton.[1] *New Hampshire:* Hampton, male taken by W. Olney, Sept. 15, 1918.[2] *Massachusetts:* Ipswich, specimen in Peabody Museum at Salem taken in 1871 by E. A. Smith; Salem, another in same collection taken October 14, 1876; Newburyport, young male taken September 20, 1904, now in collection of Dr. C. W. Townsend, all recorded by Dr. Townsend;[3] Cape Poge, male, August 16, 1904, in collection of Hon. John E. Thayer. *Rhode Island:* Middletown, female taken October 8, 1890;[4] Point Judith, female taken September 25, 1908, by Mr. C. B. Clark and recorded by Harry Hathaway. Mr. Clark asserted that he shot 11 of the same birds "12 or 14" years earlier;[5] *Connecticut:* North Haven, adult taken on Quinnipiac Marshes August 5, 1886, by Dr. E. L. Munson;[6] young male taken August 15, 1894, by Harry T. Flint at Grove Beach; North Haven, young female taken September 25, 1913, on Quinnipiac Marshes by Alanson Ganung; both the above recorded by Dr. L. B. Bishop.[7]

SEASON IN MASSACHUSETTS. — August 29 to November 3 (Howe and Allen).

HAUNTS AND HABITS. The haunts and habits of the Long-billed Dowitcher are the same as those of the Dowitcher when on our coast. The former is supposed to be much more western in distribution, but in the fall migration many wander eastward to the Atlantic coast. Probably this alleged race is not so rare here as the records would indicate as it is impossible to distinguish the two forms in the field and an expert can tell them apart only with difficulty even when in the hand. The measurements of bills of the two forms often overlap in length so that the length of the bill cannot be relied upon as a field mark. Dr. H. C. Oberholser informs me that he considers this a valid race of *griseus* and that if a sufficiently large number of specimens can be laid out side by side and properly graded the individuals of the two forms can be picked out. This kind of expert work, however, is of no service to the observer in the field and any attempt to separate these forms in the field would be merely guesswork. In the migration southeastward the Long-bill is said to reach Florida in larger numbers than does the other race, the majority of which are supposed to put out to sea before they reach the land of flowers.

The Long-bill feeds on the same food as the Dowitcher.

ECONOMIC STATUS. See page 372.

---

[1] Auk, Vol. XXX, 1913, p. 576.
[2] Smith, J. D.: *in litt.*
[3] Birds of Essex County, Massachusetts, 1905, p. 168.
[4] Howe and Sturtevant: Birds of Rhode Island, 1899, p. 49.
[5] Auk, Vol. XXX, 1913, p. 551.
[6] Sage, Bishop and Bliss: Birds of Connecticut, 1913, p. 55.
[7] Auk, Vol. XXXVIII, 1921, p. 585.

Micropálama himántopus (BONAPARTE). Stilt Sandpiper.

Other names: BASTARD YELLOW-LEGS; STILTED SANDPIPER; MONGREL; FROST SNIPE.

Plate 26.

DESCRIPTION. — Bill slender, straight or *very slightly* curved downward toward tip, expanded and flattened near tip, but slightly tapering in lateral profile; legs very long, slender; front toes basally webbed; tail-feathers 12. *Adults in breeding plumage (sexes alike):* Top of head and extreme hind neck streaked dusky and grayish-white, darkest on crown where dusky predominates; above varied with black, pale gray and light buff, black prevailing on back, scapulars and tertials, feather-edges buffy and pale gray; outer surface of closed wing (except primaries) mainly gray; wing-coverts deep brownish-gray, margined with pale gray; secondaries slightly darker, narrowly edged and tipped white; primaries and their coverts still darker; rump brownish-gray with paler feather margins; upper tail-coverts white, spotted or barred and streaked dusky; tail lighter brownish-gray than back; inner webs of all but two middle feathers more or less white, irregularly marked brownish-gray; sides of head, neck and under plumage generally varying from pale brownish to white; head, neck and under tail-coverts spotted or streaked dark brown or dusky, and other under plumage barred same; axillars and under wing-coverts white, sparsely marked grayish; broad streak over eye, chin and upper throat lighter than rest of head; broad stripe from before eye, passing under it, widening over ear-region (in some individuals also a streak bordering dark crown) light rust red; bill black and greenish on much of basal half; iris brown; legs and feet dull yellowish-green to yellowish-olive or olive-yellowish. *Adults in winter plumage:* Upper plumage mostly brownish-gray with narrow, light feather-edges; upper tail-coverts, tail and wings much as in summer plumage, but wings somewhat darker; sides of head, neck and under plumage mainly white, with little or no continuous barring on under surface of body; sides of head, sides and front of neck and upper breast, sides, flanks and under tail-coverts more or less streaked grayish; dark streak through eye, but no rusty-red on head; bill and iris much as in breeding plumage; legs and feet dark greenish. *Young in first winter plumage:* Similar to winter adults; only to be distinguished by retained juvenal feathers; legs and feet greenish-yellow or yellowish-green. *Young in juvenal plumage:* Top of head streaked dusky, and grayish; hind neck gray; back and scapulars blackish or dusky, feathers margined buffy or whitish; feather-edges on middle of back tinged rusty; wing coverts bordered pale buff or whitish; upper tail-coverts white, little marked; below dirty white, breast and sides tinged buff; neck, sides and flanks faintly and indistinctly streaked and spotted grayish.

MEASUREMENTS. — Length 7.50 to 9.25 in.; spread 15.50 to 17.00; folded wing 4.75 to 5.50; tail 1.90 to 2.35; bill 1.03 to 1.75; bare tibia 1.00 to 1.25; tarsus 1.50 to 1.75. Weight 2 to 2¾ oz. Female larger than male.

MOLTS. — Postjuvenal molt of young begins very early, but as some birds may arrive in New England in late July or in August, they may appear in juvenal plumage; during August and September first winter plumage is usually assumed, by a partial molt involving body feathers and some of wing-feathers and coverts; apparently there is a partial or possibly a complete molt (March to May) after which first nuptial plumage appears; second winter plumage is acquired by complete postnuptial molt (August, September) when bird becomes as adult; adults molt twice a year, partially in spring and completely in fall, autumnal molt is often later than in young birds and some adults may be seen here in July or August in worn summer or changing plumage.

FIELD MARKS. — A small bird, but its long legs and bill make it appear as large as a Dowitcher; in fall plumage it resembles young Yellow-legs, but its body is smaller and its legs are *greenish* and not bright yellow; the tail and tail-coverts show whitish in flight, but it lacks the long gray rump and the white on the back shown in flight by the Dowitcher; in spring it may be recognized by its dark back, barred under plumage and long, *greenish*-yellow legs; among small sandpipers it is readily recognized, as its long legs raise its body above the others.

PLATE 26

All one-half natural size.

Louis Agassiz Fuertes.

VOICE. — When disturbed, a sharp *tweet tweet*, resembling notes of Solitary Sandpiper (Audubon); a double or triple whistle (C. W. Townsend). Flight note "very like the single 'whew' of the Lesser Yellow-legs" (J. T. Nichols).

BREEDING. — On Arctic coast or about shores of Arctic lakes. *Nest:* On ground; a mere depression, lined with a little grass. *Eggs:* 3 or 4; 1.50 by 1.10 to 1.22 by .84; more or less pear-shaped; clay color to light grayish-drab, greenish-drab or grayish-white, with markings of chestnut-brown, umber, chocolate-brown or bistre and purplish-gray, heaviest and most massed about larger end. *Dates:* June 23 to 27, Mackenzie.

RANGE. — North and South America (except west of Rocky Mountains). Breeds near coast of Mackenzie, and probably in northern Manitoba; winters mainly in South America south to Uruguay, Argentina and Chile; occasionally in southern Texas and Mexico; migrates through western Mississippi Valley, West Indies and Central America and along Atlantic coast; practically unknown on Pacific coast; casual in British Columbia, Montana, Wyoming, Colorado, Alabama, Newfoundland and Bermuda.

DISTRIBUTION IN NEW ENGLAND. — *Maine and New Hampshire:* Rather rare fall migrant coastwise. *Massachusetts:* Uncommon to rare and irregular fall migrant coastwise. *Rhode Island:* Uncommon spring and not uncommon fall migrant. *Connecticut:* Rare migrant coastwise.

SEASON IN MASSACHUSETTS. — July 5 to September 29 (October 17).

HAUNTS AND HABITS. The Stilt Sandpiper is an unusual bird that seems nowhere to be very common now, although there is evidence in the western Mississippi valley as well as in New England that it was once common to abundant at times in migration. In spring it is a mere straggler in New England, as it passes north, mainly west of the Mississippi, arriving in Saskatchewan and Mackenzie soon after the middle of May. Little is known about its breeding range or breeding habits. As soon as the breeding season is over a part of the birds move south-eastward from Mackenzie or Keewatin toward the Atlantic coast. Some, going overland, apparently cross Ontario to New England, and either follow the coast line down or put out to sea on the way to South America. They are usually most common here during the month of August, though a few arrive in July. There was a large flight of this species here and on Long Island about August 12, 1912. This bird, like other sandpipers, when flying in flocks, wheels and turns, showing first the upper and then the under side. It is usually seen here singly or in very small numbers, sometimes with the Yellow-legs, along beaches, in salt marshes or on the flats where it wades deeply and plunges its bill (sometimes partly opened) into the mud.

It is said to feed occasionally like the Avocet or the Roseate Spoonbill by wading and swinging its partly opened bill through the water from side to side somewhat as a mower swings his scythe. In muddy pools it sometimes plunges its head beneath the surface in securing food from the bottom. Probably its food while here does not differ much from that of other sandpipers. Audubon found in the stomachs of some Stilt Sandpipers worms, small mollusks and vegetal matter.

ECONOMIC STATUS. See page 372.

Cálidris canútus (Linnæus). Knot.

Other names: RED-BREASTED SANDPIPER; GRAY-BACK; SILVER-BACK; ROSY PLOVER; ROBIN SNIPE; BLUE PLOVER; BUFF-BREAST; GRAY RED-BREASTED PLOVER; WAHQUOIT; WHITING.

Plate 26.

DESCRIPTION. — Form robust; bill straight, a little longer than head; tail nearly even; legs short; tarsus shorter than bill; toes with wide lateral margins practically cleft to base (with a very small basal web). *Adult male in breeding plumage:* Above mainly light gray, variegated with blackish and pinkish-cinnamon; top of head, hind neck and line through eye streaked pale gray and olive-blackish; rest of side of head, forehead, chin and throat light cinnamon-brown, with some whitish feather-tips; rump, pale gray, this passing into white on upper tail-coverts, both marked with bars and crescentic margins of dusky and sometimes with buffy or pinkish-cinnamon; tail pale brownish-gray, feathers narrowly margined white (sometimes marked dusky); folded wing chiefly light gray with darker feather centers and lighter (sometimes whitish) feather-edges and tips; some tertials darker and other flight-feathers dark brownish-gray with white shafts; below "pinkish cinnamon," except sides, flanks, lower abdomen and under tail-coverts, which are more or less white; sides mixed with cinnamon and marked dusky; flanks marked like sides; under tail-coverts with some small dusky markings; bill greenish-black; iris brown; feet dark greenish to "greenish-black" (Coues); bill (of one specimen taken August 27, 1924), a very dark olive-green, bordering on black; legs a medium olive-green (J. A. Hagar). *Adult female in breeding plumage:* Similar to adult male; not so bright above, with less pinkish-cinnamon; usually paler below and more often marked on sides with white and dusky; female, with a red breast, taken July 26, 1924, by J. D. Smith, had black iris, dusky-black bill, brownish-olive legs; both sexes very variable and often considerably unlike in markings. *Adult in winter plumage (sexes alike):* Above light brownish-gray, feathers with indistinct shaft streaks; rump, tail and flight-feathers about as in breeding plumage; cinnamon or reddish-brown of head, neck and under plumage replaced by white; eyes and bill much as in breeding plumage; legs and feet lighter; "iris darker; bill greenish black; feet yellowish green" (Audubon). *Young in first winter plumage:* Similar to juvenal plumage but white of under plumage usually tinged dull buffy, especially on breast. "Eye darker, bill and feet duller than in winter adults" (Audubon). *Young in juvenal plumage:* Head and neck whitish but streaked all round with blackish and drab; chin and stripe over eye whitish, nearly unmarked; elsewhere above grayish-brown with dusky shaft-streaks, narrow brownish-black feather margins, and whitish edges; flight-feathers and tail-feathers, rump and tail-coverts much as breeding adults; breast and sides whitish with narrow shaft streaks and other markings of brown; rest of under plumage white; bill greenish-black; legs and feet lighter than in summer adults, legs and feet "yellowish-green" (J. A. Hagar). *Downy young:* "Forehead warm buff, with a central black line; over the eye a double black line; crown, from center backwards, black slightly varied with rufous and dotted with buff; nape creamy buff, slightly varied with blackish; upper parts . . . black, slightly varied with reddish brown, and profusely dotted with creamy white; underparts very slightly washed with warm buff" (Dresser).

MEASUREMENTS. — Length 10.00 to 11.00 in.; spread 20.00 to 21.00; folded wing 6.00 to 6.75; tail 2.31 to 2.80; bill 1.25 to 1.50; tarsus 1.00 to 1.40. Weight 4 to 6½ oz. Sexes near same size; female usually larger than male.

MOLTS. — Juvenal plumage, which quickly follows natal down, is partially molted during fall; a prenuptial molt follows in late winter and early spring and a postnuptial molt, which is complete, precedes adult winter plumage; adults have a partial prenuptial molt, including feathers of head and under plumage and a complete postnuptial molt in fall; some individuals retain winter plumage through May and some are still in breeding dress in August.

FIELD MARKS. — Large and stout compared with small sandpipers; larger than Ruddy Turnstone; rounded chunky form; short legs; colored a little like Dowitcher, but short bill and gray back distinguish it; light rump not conspicuous in flight, as in Dowitcher or Yellow-legs and only a faint white line shows in wing; in breeding plumage, reddish breast distinguishes it from all but Dowitcher and Red Phalarope; young birds are gray above and white below.

VOICE. — Rather silent; occasionally emits a clear, double whistle (C. W. Townsend); a soft *wah-quoit* and a little *honk* (Geo. H. Mackay); a soft *whit whit* (like a man whistling for a dog) (R. Hoffmann); flight note "a low-pitched whistle with a peculiar whiz or buzz in it", *tlu tlu* (J. T. Nichols).

BREEDING. — On rolling ground or high, stony table-lands near Arctic coast, often on tundra. *Nest:* A shallow depression lined with a little dried grass or a few lichens. *Eggs:* 3 or 4; 1.64 to 1.97 by 1.14 to 1.33 in.; slightly pear-shaped; pale greenish-gray or clay color, with spots varying from yellowish to blackish-brown and pale violet-gray, all most numerous about larger end (Grinnell, Bryant and Storer); description of 3 eggs in Hon. John E. Thayer's collection: "ground color a soiled yellowish or greenish-white; speckled all over (heaviest at great end where spots are larger and clustered together thickly) with dark chocolate; there are a few underlying spots of a paler color." *Dates:* Last half of June and early July, Greenland. *Incubation:* Chiefly by female. One brood yearly.

RANGE. — Northern and Southern Hemispheres.* Breeds from northwestern Greenland and northern Ellesmere Island south to Melville Peninsula and Iceland and on New Siberian Islands and Taimyr Peninsula, Siberia; common in August at St. Michaels, Alaska; winters south to southern Patagonia, and from Mediterranean to southern Africa, India, Australia and New Zealand; casual in winter on Atlantic coast of United States and over most of Eastern Hemisphere; rare in interior of North America west of the Great Lakes and uncommon on Pacific coast.

DISTRIBUTION IN NEW ENGLAND. — *Maine* and *New Hampshire:* Rather uncommon migrant coastwise. *Massachusetts:* Fairly common migrant coastwise; casual inland; rarely wintering on Nantucket and Cape Cod. *Rhode Island* and *Connecticut:* Uncommon migrant coastwise. Evidently increasing on New England coast.

SEASON IN MASSACHUSETTS. — May 11 to June 5 (June 19 and 25); July 11 to November 8, 15; (winter).

HAUNTS AND HABITS. In the days of our grandfathers the Gray-backs or Wahquoits, as they were called, swarmed along the coasts of Cape Cod by the thousand. Spring and autumn their hosts were marshalled on the flats of Barnstable, Yarmouth, Dennis, Chatham, Monomoy, Nauset, Wellfleet and Billingsgate, and around Tuckernuck and Muskeget Islands they collected in immense numbers and rose in "clouds" before the sportsman's gun. As the nineteenth century closed they were becoming rare all along the coast, but now under protective laws their numbers are beginning to increase. They appear in spring usually during the latter half of May (about the 20th) and feed in company with Turnstones or Black-breasted Plovers, sometimes with Red-backed Sandpipers and a few Sanderlings. They usually pass rapidly on to the North. While here they feed much on beaches and flats at low water, wading in shallow small pools or little streams, that flow over the flats to the sea, retiring to the high beach or the salt marsh to rest and feed at high tide. They leave New England about the first week in June and proceed to Arctic regions. There in the breeding season the male has a pleasing flight song. By mid-July the adults are seen on their return to New England, some still retaining much of the breeding plumage. They continue to pass all through August. The young come later than the adults and are usually here in greatest numbers in the

---

* Since the American form of the species has been separated from the Old World forms and the exact distribution of each is not fully determined, the range of the species as a whole is given.

latter part of August and the first part of September. The Atlantic coast seems to be their chief route of migration between their Arctic homes and South America, though some pass through the Mississippi valley and down through Mexico.

The food of the Knot seems to consist largely of small mollusks, crustaceans and other small forms of life found on the beaches, flats and marshes. Dr. C. W. Townsend found small periwinkles and small mussels in the stomachs of some Knots that he examined.[1] It destroys many insects and Mr. George H. Mackay in his excellent account of the habits of the species says that it eats cutworms.[2] In the North it takes some vegetal food.

ECONOMIC STATUS. The Knot is highly regarded as a game bird and was formerly sold in large numbers in the markets of the Atlantic coast. It is perhaps of some service as an insect-eater in the West where, during migration, it takes numbers of locusts and other insects.

Arquatélla marítima marítima (BRÜNNICH). Purple Sandpiper.

Other names: ROCK-BIRD; WINTER ROCK-BIRD; ROCKWEED BIRD; ROCK PLOVER; ROCK SNIPE; WINTER SNIPE; WINTER PEEP.

Plate 26.

DESCRIPTION. — Form very robust; bill nearly straight, terminal half very slightly downcurved, longer than tarsus; legs short, toes unwebbed; tail slightly graduated, 4 middle feathers longer than rest. *Adults in breeding plumage (sexes alike):* Above generally dark gray or dusky; crown blackish-brown, feathers streaked buffy or whitish, head elsewhere and neck narrowly and faintly streaked same, head darkening in front of and below eye; some individuals have a grayish-white stripe over eye narrowly streaked dusky; eyelids white; scapulars and feathers of upper back "sooty black or blackish-brown" faintly glossed bronze or "purplish bronze," spotted or indented pale buff along edges and narrowly edged whitish or gray terminally; rump, upper tail-coverts and middle tail-feathers sooty-black; rump feathers usually faintly margined grayish; outer tail-feathers light brownish-gray, shafts and often terminal margins white; outer surface of closed wing deep brownish-gray, growing dusky on primaries, lesser and middle wing-coverts margined terminally white, primary coverts, greater coverts and secondaries tipped white, thus forming 2 white bars on wing; 2d bar narrower and shorter than 1st; innermost secondaries mostly white; shafts of innermost and outermost primaries white; lower front face, chin and throat a mixture of whitish and dusky streaks; breast grayish-white, heavily spotted dusky; rest of under plumage white; sides and flanks streaked and spotted grayish; under tail-coverts narrowly streaked dusky; axillars and wing-linings white; under fore wing and outer edge spotted brownish-gray; bill yellow or orange on basal third becoming dark brown or dusky toward tip; iris dark brown; legs and feet light yellow or orange; legs and feet greenish-yellow in all stages (C. J. Maynard); bill dark brown paler at base, legs and feet dull yellow (D. G. Elliot). *Adults in winter plumage:* Above light mouse-gray or light purplish-gray, deepening on scapulars, lower back and wings and before and below eye to sooty-blackish; crown sooty-brown, nape dusky-brown, both with feather-edgings dark ash-gray; eyelids white; indistinct whitish spot before eye at edge of forehead; scapulars, interscapulars and tertials faintly glossed purplish or magenta-purple, feathers broadly margined gray or (sometimes) buffy; chin and upper throat whitish, latter broadly streaked pale gray; upper breast brownish-gray with white feather margins, breadth of these margins increasing until merged into white under plumage;

[1] Birds of Essex County, Massachusetts, 1905, p. 169.   [2] Auk, Vol. X, 1893, p. 27.

otherwise as in breeding plumage; legs and feet "light straw color" (C. W. Townsend). *Young in first winter plumage:* Resembles adult winter plumage but usually duller, without gloss (Coues) and *broad* white edges to many wing-coverts. *Young in juvenal plumage:* Similar to summer adult but nape and cheeks "uniform smoky plumbeous"; upper plumage generally broadly margined and tipped "light buff or reddish-yellow"; pale margins to wing-coverts broader and more or less buffy or ashy instead of white; under plumage everywhere mottled dusky, deepest on breast and lower throat. *Downy young:* Fore part of head brownish-buffy, with blackish-brown streak back through center of forehead to crown, another from bill to eye, and a shorter one from base of lower mandible; elsewhere above, including back of crown, hind head and ear-coverts, velvety black-brown except nape and back of neck which are grayish-buffy, more or less mottled dusky; back and rump dotted whitish; below dull buffy-white.

MEASUREMENTS. — Length 8.00 to 9.50 in.; spread 14.00 to 16.00; folded wing 4.75 to 5.50; tail 2.25 to 2.66; bill 1.00 to 1.45; tarsus .75 to 1.00. Weight 3¼ oz. (Audubon). Sexes about same size, bill of female averaging slightly longer than that of male.

MOLTS. — Apparently a partial molt in autumn (September to December) precedes first winter plumage, and young birds become as adults after a partial prenuptial molt during the next spring; adults have a partial prenuptial molt in spring including many body-feathers and some wing-feathers, and a complete postnuptial molt (August to November).

FIELD MARKS. — About size of Sanderling, but more robust; the only shore bird commonly seen in the New England winter; *dark color*, white belly, *short legs and squat rounded figure* are sure field marks; yellow or orange base of bill is noticeable at close range; in flight the white in the dark wing is conspicuous.

VOICE. — A loud, shrill whistle; "a rather squeaky chip" (C. W. Townsend).

BREEDING. — About shores of northern fresh-water lakes or near sea "on moss-grown shingle," on tundra and even on hilly land. *Nest:* On ground; a mere depression lined with a little grass or with dead leaves. *Eggs:* 3 or 4; 1.44 to 1.50 by 1.00 to 1.10 in.; usually pear-shaped; pale greenish-drab or clay color, tinged olive, with large, bold, brown markings, varying in shade, largest and most numerous near large end and with underlying gray or violet-gray markings. *Dates:* Latter half of May to mid-June according to latitude. *Incubation:* "Chiefly by male, but female takes some share; period not less than 20 days; single-brooded." (Practical Handbook of British Birds.)

RANGE. — Eastern and northeastern North America,* Europe and northwestern Asia. Breeds from Melville Island, Ellesmere Island and northern Greenland, south to Melville Peninsula, Cumberland Sound and southern Greenland, and west probably to Banks Island; also in Iceland, Faroe Islands, Norway, Spitzbergen, Franz Josef Land, Novaya Zemlya, northern Russia and northwestern Siberia; winters from southern Greenland and New Brunswick south to Long Island and in Old World south to British Islands, North and Baltic seas and occasionally to Mediterranean; casual in migration to Great Lakes, Georgia, Florida, the Azores and Bermuda.

DISTRIBUTION IN NEW ENGLAND. — *Maine:* Rather common local migrant and winter resident coastwise; two (or more) summer records. *New Hampshire:* Winter visitor coastwise. *Massachusetts:* Common migrant, and fall and winter visitor coastwise. *Rhode Island* and *Connecticut:* Winter visitor on rocky coasts and islands.

SEASON IN MASSACHUSETTS. — (July 30) September 6 to April 19 (May 30).

HAUNTS AND HABITS. The Purple Sandpiper winters farther north on the Atlantic coast than any other shore bird. Those that visit New England breed in Arctic regions and winter mainly on sea-washed rocks lying off shore. All along the "North Shore" of Massachusetts from the ledges off Nahant to the Salvages off Rockport the bird is a common winter visitor but is rather rarely seen on the mainland. On the "South Shore"

---

* Its place is taken on the Pacific coast of North America by two allied races.

off Cohasset and Scituate it finds ledges to its liking and on the shores of the southeastern countries it is sometimes seen on stony and rocky beaches.   Thus it lives by the wintry sea, seemingly revelling in the commotion of the waters, feeding at low tide among the rockweed and when overtaken by the oncoming surge merely running and fluttering up the rocks to safety.   At high water the flocks rest or play upon the rocks.   They sometimes swim short distances from rock to rock.   Egg Rock off Nahant is a favorite feeding ground and from this they occasionally visit the ledges lying off shore near the Lodge estate at Nahant.   They frequent the rocks off Marblehead, Beverly, Magnolia and Gloucester harbor.   Some are seen about the Elizabeth Islands, the south shore of Marthas Vineyard and the shore of Westport in Bristol County.   From the latter shore they fly back and forth from the Hen and Chickens Reef, off shore, to the rocky seaward end of Gooseberry Neck.   Those arriving in Massachusetts in September are early stragglers.   The main flocks come in November or December, and remain until March. After that small straggling flocks continue to pass north, sometimes until May.*   Late in May or early in June the flocks first appear on their northern breeding-grounds.

The food of this species gleaned from the sea-wrack consists largely of mollusks, of which small mussels and snails form a considerable part.   It also eats some barnacles and insect food about the rocks.

ECONOMIC STATUS.   This bird appears to have little economic importance.   It comes at such a season, haunts such inaccessible places and is of so fishy a flavor that few ever find their way to the table.

Pisóbia maculáta (VIEILLOT).   Pectoral Sandpiper.

Other names: GRASS-BIRD; JACKSNIPE; BROWN-BACK; BROWNIE; MARSH-PLOVER; DOWITCH; SQUAT SNIPE; SQUATTER; CREAKER PERT; CREAKER.

Plate 26.

DESCRIPTION. — Bill nearly straight, slightly downcurved toward tip, but little longer than head; wings long, 1st primary decidedly longer than others; tail of 12 feathers doubly emarginate, two middle tail-feathers somewhat pointed and projecting beyond others; feet not webbed. *Adults in breeding plumage (sexes alike)*: Top of head streaked brownish-black and light chestnut; a narrow white ring round eye; an ill-defined white stripe over eye, narrowly streaked dusky; brownish stripe from bill through and beneath eye; cheeks, neck all round and upper breast dull pale brownish, streaked dusky, both streaks and brownish tint ending abruptly at lower breast; upper body generally brownish-black, with feather-margins of "ashy brown" and cinnamon or rusty-red, dark centers never distinctly indented by lighter color of margins; wing-coverts generally grayish-brown, drab or dusky, with paler tips and margins; primaries and their coverts dark grayish-brown; shaft of outer quill white, those of others light brown, becoming paler toward tips; secondaries colored as primaries, but lighter at tips; sides of lower back, rump and outer upper tail-coverts white, latter irregularly marked brown; middle tail-feathers brownish-black, lightening on edges, rest of tail light grayish-brown or pale drab, feathers narrowly edged and tipped paler; chin, upper throat and under plumage generally white, chin and throat sometimes tinged slightly buffy; sides sparsely streaked; axillars and wing-linings white, linings spotted

* "A Purple Sandpiper on May 4 was, I think, my most surprising spring record."   E. P. Bicknell, Hewlett, Long Island, *in litt.*

grayish-brown near edge; bill dull greenish-yellow basally, greenish-black toward tip; iris brown, legs and feet dull greenish-yellow or yellowish-green. *Adults in winter plumage:* Similar to summer plumage but feather margins of back and scapulars lack pronounced rusty tinge of summer and dark markings less distinct. *Young in juvenal plumage:* Similar to adult breeding plumage but long scapulars and back-feathers widely margined light chestnut and white, and breast more strongly buffy, or yellowish; legs and feet lighter or more yellow than in adults. *Downy young:* Forehead and sides of head yellowish buff; black middle stripe from upper base of upper mandible to crown, one from bill to below eye, one from bill to eye and another from above eye to upper ear-region, black; crown mottled black and tawny and dotted with irregular creamy tufts; nape yellowish-buff; upper body like crown but mixed with yellowish-buff; fore neck like sides of head; remaining under plumage white.

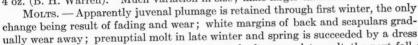
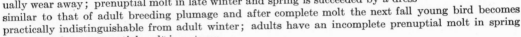

TAIL OF PECTORAL
SANDPIPER
(After Cory.)

MEASUREMENTS. — Length 8.00 to 9.62 in.; spread 15.00 to 18.00; folded wing 4.79 to 5.61; tail 2.12 to 2.67; bill 1.05 to 1.28; tarsus 1.00 to 1.21. Weight 2 to 4 oz. (B. H. Warren). Much variation in size; male larger than female.

MOLTS. — Apparently juvenal plumage is retained through first winter, the only change being result of fading and wear; white margins of back and scapulars gradually wear away; prenuptial molt in late winter and spring is succeeded by a dress similar to that of adult breeding plumage and after complete molt the next fall young bird becomes practically indistinguishable from adult winter; adults have an incomplete prenuptial molt in spring and a complete postnuptial molt in autumn.

FIELD MARKS. — Size of Sanderling or larger, smaller than Knot; stocky, short-necked, short-legged; legs yellowish or greenish; closely resembles Least Sandpiper in spring plumage but more than twice as large; has no white wing-bar, and white of lower breast and abdomen is more abruptly bounded by brownish or buffy, heavily-streaked, dark breast; streaks ending abruptly on fore border of white lower plumage; resembles Baird's Sandpiper, from which it may be told by its larger size, paler legs, longer and lighter colored bill, darker and more conspicuous breast-band; when on wing, the pale gray tail with dark middle feathers sometimes is noticeable; feeds chiefly on marshes and mud flats.

VOICE. — Notes have a reedy character. When startled and in flight, *kriek, kriek*, rather harsh; "two distinct notes, a short *kuk* or *chup* and a hoarse rolling whistle *k-r-r-r-u, k-r-r-r-u;* flight note *kerr*, confusable with *chrruk* of Semipalmated Sandpiper but heavier and huskier"; "short snappy chips" from the flock (J. T. Nichols).

BREEDING. — Largely on Arctic tundra. *Nest:* Usually on dry ground on banks of streams or pools; a depression in ground, grass-lined. *Eggs:* 3 or 4; 1.42 to 1.58 by 1.02 to 1.11 in.; pear-shaped, rather pointed; varying from pale greenish to pale brown, olive-brown or drab, spotted and blotched with umber and black and pale purplish-gray; markings thickest about larger end. *Dates:* Early June to July, Alaska.

RANGE. — North and South America. Breeds on or near Arctic coast from northern Alaska to mouth of Yukon and northeastern Mackenzie, east possibly to northern Ungava (northern Quebec), and in northeastern Siberia; winters in South America from Peru and Bolivia to northern Chile, Argentina and central Patagonia; rare in migration on Pacific coast south of Puget Sound except in Lower California; occurs in migration in Rocky Mountain region; common in fall migration in Mississippi Valley and on Atlantic seaboard; casual or occasional in Japan, Aleutian Islands, Greenland and England; accidental in Hawaii.

DISTRIBUTION IN NEW ENGLAND. — Rare spring and common fall migrant mainly coastwise; in Vermont uncommon fall migrant but not recorded in spring.

SEASON IN MASSACHUSETTS. — April 4 to May 28; (June 26) July 11 to October 30 (November 11).

HAUNTS AND HABITS. The Pectoral Sandpiper, known to many Massachusetts gunners as the Grass-bird, is well named, for it is mainly a bird of grassy lands. It prefers such environment and in its season may be found on the New England coast, chiefly in the upper parts of the salt marsh, where the "black grass" grows or even in fresh-water meadows or upland pastures. In the interior of the Continent it has been found in the mountains as high as 13,000 feet, but with us it prefers damp lowlands and sometimes may be found wading in mud holes in the marsh, running over mud flats or even occasionally following the retreating waves on the seashore. It usually comes in at night in small flocks, sometimes in considerable numbers or even great flights; in some seasons it is hardly seen at all. The flocks seem to prefer salt marshes, where the grass has been cut, and although they migrate in compact "bunches," when they alight they scatter about over the marsh to feed, singly or in pairs. When squatting or hiding in the short grass they seem to have confidence in their protective coloration and will often lie close, jumping suddenly and flying erratically away only when nearly stepped on by the gunner. In its Arctic home the male bird develops its gullet until when filled with air, it appears nearly as large as the bird's body. With the aid of this sac the bird in its nuptial flights produces a peculiar booming note. It also has a love-song which is described by Dr. E. W. Nelson.[1] The Pectoral Sandpiper arrives in New England in greatest numbers during the latter part of August or in September, though now and then a bird or two will appear as early as the last week of June. In May it is a rather rare migrant when on its way from South America to its home within the Arctic Circle.

Its food consists largely of insects. It takes grasshoppers, weevils, cutworms, beetles, wireworms, mosquitoes, horse flies, small snails, and small shell-fish, together with some vegetal matter.

ECONOMIC STATUS. Besides being beneficial in its insect diet, this Sandpiper when fat in autumn is considered one of the finest of table birds, and its value as a game bird is high, but like the rest of the smaller sandpipers it is now (1924) protected at all times by law.

Pisobia fuscicóllis (VIEILLOT). White-rumped Sandpiper.

Other names: BONAPARTE'S SANDPIPER; BULL-PEEP; WHITE-RUMPED PEEP; WHITE-TAILED STIB.

Plate 27.

DESCRIPTION. — Similar in form to Pectoral Sandpiper but rather more slim, and colored differently; 1st primary longest; bill relatively shorter, and a little stouter; toes long, slender, slightly margined. *Adults in breeding plumage (sexes alike)*: Narrow white ring round eye; head, neck and breast much as in Pectoral Sandpiper but sides of breast more distinctly spotted or streaked, and *color of breast fading gradually below;* feathers of top of head, back of neck, back and scapulars black centrally with margins of grayish-brown or brownish-gray, more or less tinged light rusty or cinnamon; light and dark colors on back arranged in stripes; rump dusky grayish-brown, feather-margins pale grayish-buffy; *upper tail-coverts white;* two long central coverts blackish-brown, edged or tipped grayish-white, outer ones each with a dusky mark on outer web; middle tail-feathers dusky, others grayish-brown, outer ones lightest, all narrowly edged paler and all except middle pair narrowly margined whitish around ends; wing-coverts

---

[1] Natural History Collections made in Alaska in 1877–81, 1886, p. 108.

PLATE 27

PLATE 27

RED-BACKED SANDPIPER

Page 416

Adult in Winter Plumage
(Autumn)

Adult in Breeding
Plumage (Spring)

WHITE-RUMPED SANDPIPER

Page 408

Adult in Breeding Plumage
(Spring)

Adult in Winter Plumage
(Autumn)

BAIRD'S SANDPIPER

Page 410

Adult in Breeding Plumage
(Spring)

All one-half natural size.

grayish-brown, darkest centrally, paling on margins, with indistinct dusky shaft-streaks, greater coverts narrowly tipped whitish; outer primaries and their coverts dusky; inner primaries and secondaries a little lighter, secondaries narrowly edged still paler and tipped whitish, tertials dusky grayish-brown, lightening toward edges; below, from breast to tail, mainly white; dark marks toward edge of wings; sides, wing linings and axillars white; sides and flanks streaked dusky; under tail-coverts very narrowly so streaked; bill black, sometimes lighter at base; iris very dark brown; legs and feet dusky-greenish or greenish-black. *Adults in winter plumage:* Wings, rump, upper tail-coverts and tail as in breeding plumage; rest of upper plumage brownish-gray or gray-brown, feathers with indistinct dusky streaks; line over eye whiter and line through eye darker than in breeding plumage; neck and breast gray or grayish-white, indistinctly marked dusky; eye, bill and feet, much as in breeding plumage. *Young in first winter plumage:* Similar to that of adult but some tawny edges to retained juvenal feathers of back and rump, and tawny or buff edges to wing-coverts. *Young in juvenal plumage:* Like adults in breeding plumage but less distinctly marked; crown streaked blackish-brown and tawny and nape "ashy brown" streaked darker; feathers of back and scapulars bordered rusty, many margined white around tips; tertials "blackish-brown, edged tawny"; middle and lesser coverts same, broadly edged white or light buff; some of innermost middle coverts edged tawny.

MEASUREMENTS. — Length 6.75 to 8.00 in.; spread 14.00 to 16.50; folded wing 4.35 to 5.12; tail 1.81 to 2.25; bill .85 to 1.00; tarsus .87 to 1.00. Sexes near same size; female often slightly larger than male.

MOLTS. — Juvenal body plumage undergoes a partial molt (September to January) which is followed by first winter plumage; a molt in late winter and spring produces a dress which in many or most cases probably is practically as adult; adults have a partial prenuptial molt in spring and a postnuptial molt of body-feathers beginning in August, but (in some cases at least) wing molt seems to be delayed until winter or even to March.

FIELD MARKS. — In breeding plumage resembles both Pectoral and Baird's Sandpipers (smaller than former, slightly larger than latter); distinguished from both in *flight* by white of its upper tail-coverts which extends *across* the rump; difficult to distinguish when on ground with wings covering white spot, but generally more black on back and scapulars than the other species, especially in midsummer; in winter plumage grayer than either; in transition plumage some black spots show in gray of upper plumage; larger than Semipalmated Sandpiper and in breeding dress breast is dark in front of wing where former is nearly white.

VOICE. — An exceedingly sharp, squeaky, mouse-like *jeet* uttered on the wing, unmistakable (J. T. Nichols); sharp piping *weet weet* (N. S. Goss); a high sparrow-like "*ssst*," in sharpness of pitch suggests song of Blackburnian Warbler (Winsor M. Tyler); "suggests at times call note of Pipit" (C. W. Townsend); "a low lisping sound," neither mellow nor whistling (T. M. Brewer); also a "cry loudly given and greatly prolonged, resembling the scream of a rapacious bird more than the whistle of a sandpiper" (C. J. Maynard).

BREEDING. — On Barren Grounds, shores of Arctic Ocean or banks of lakes and rivers. *Nest:* A depression in ground lined with a few dead leaves or a little grass. *Eggs:* 3 or 4, averaging 1.37 by .94 in.; pear-shaped; "olive-brown" or "light olive" spotted (finely as a rule) with chestnut-brown, "deep brown or black and dull purplish gray." *Dates:* Late June and first half of July.

RANGE. — North America mainly east of Rocky Mountains and South America mainly east of Andes. Breeds on or near Arctic coast from northwestern Mackenzie to Cumberland Sound, Baffin Island; occurs in summer west to Point Barrow and east to Greenland; migrates chiefly through Mississippi Valley; winters from Paraguay to southern Patagonia and Falkland Islands; casual in Bermuda, Azores, Franz Josef Land, Great Britain, West Indies and Central America.

DISTRIBUTION IN NEW ENGLAND. — Uncommon migrant, less common in spring than in fall; spring records very rare in Vermont and Rhode Island and Connecticut; more common coastwise than in interior but occasional there about shallow bodies of water in marshes or meadows.

SEASON IN MASSACHUSETTS. — (April 30) May 12 to June 5; July 10 to November 10.

HAUNTS AND HABITS. The White-rumped Sandpiper, or Bonaparte's Sandpiper, is not generally common on the northeastern Atlantic coast. Stragglers appear here from the north late in July but most of them come late in September or in early October. Again in May they return but usually in much smaller numbers. On the coast they come in small parties, by themselves, but often a single bird or a few are seen with Semi-palmated Sandpipers and "Ring-necks" on the beach. They are particularly fond of rocky beaches, where they run over the weed-covered rocks or wade up to their bellies in salt-water pools between tide marks. They frequent the borders of creeks and pools in the salt-marsh, and are seen also in springy places in the uplands. In the interior they may be found at times in meadows, sometimes in company with "Grass Birds" (Pectoral Sandpipers) or along the shores of shallow ponds or pools. In flight when seen from the rear their white upper tail-coverts are very conspicuous. In the late fall, as Eaton says, its habitat on the sandy shore, the plain gray of its winter plumage and the white of its rump suggest a diminutive Knot. It is usually rather unsuspicious, and allows a close approach wherever it has not been harassed by law-breaking gunners, but when molested soon becomes wild.

Mr. Samuel D. Robbins writes that on October 20, 1922, he saw a flock of White-rumped Sandpipers led by a lone Sanderling. When the Sanderling flew most of the Sandpipers flew with it or followed it.

This species remains in Argentina until late April and in Brazil until May. Most of the spring records in the United States are in May, and there are June and July dates in Ontario and Saskatchewan, respectively. In early July the southward movement begins and in early September the vanguard has reached Cape Horn, the southernmost part of the bird's range.[1] Thus this wonderful flight covers the entire length of both western continents.

The food of this species consists largely of small marine animals when on our coast, but in the interior it eats many insects, including grasshoppers and other pests of grass lands.

ECONOMIC STATUS. See page 372.

Pisobia baírdi (COUES). Baird's Sandpiper.

Other names: BULL-PEEP; GRASS-BIRD.

Plate 27.

DESCRIPTION. — Bill small, very slender, somewhat shorter than head, tip very slightly expanded, point extremely sharp; tail rather long, nearly even or slightly double-emarginate, two middle feathers rounded at tips and projecting but little beyond rest; upper tail-coverts extending to within half an inch of tail tip; toes unwebbed, cleft to base. *Adults in breeding plumage (sexes alike):* Above pale grayish-buff; top of head streaked sooty-black, hind neck more narrowly streaked same; interscapulars broadly black centrally, scapulars with large irregular black spots; wing-coverts light grayish-brown with narrow, indistinct dark shaft-streaks, and indistinctly margined paler; color darker and more uniform

---

[1] Cooke, W. W.: U. S. Department of Agriculture, Biological Survey, Bulletin No. 35, 1910, pp. 38, 39.

anteriorly; secondaries deeper grayish-brown, narrowly edged paler, which passes into white at tips; tertials deep grayish-brown (sometimes with more or less tawny tinge) passing gradually into white on edge of outer webs; primary coverts dusky, narrowly margined toward ends with whitish; primaries grayish-brown, narrowly edged paler or whitish; rump and upper tail-coverts mostly sooty-grayish-brown, indistinctly or narrowly edged pale brownish-buffy; outer tail-coverts whitish, each with a dusky V; two middle tail-feathers colored like middle upper tail-coverts but margined narrowly lighter; rest of tail-feathers paler (outer ones palest) grayish-brown, narrowly margined whitish; sides of head, sides of neck, fore neck and breast dull buffy or buffy-white narrowly streaked dusky, less streaked over eye; chin, throat and under plumage (breast to tail) white; axillars white and wing-linings mostly so; bill blackish, becoming lighter or brownish toward base; iris dark brown; legs and feet blackish or dark slate. *Adults in winter plumage:* Colors more blended and paler than in breeding plumage; above buffy-brownish, feathers with dusky centers and some shaft-streaks; below duller or more brownish-white, breast and sides of neck strongly tinged dull brownish-buffy, not so distinctly streaked; otherwise as in breeding plumage. *Young in first winter plumage:* Similar to adult winter plumage but distinguished by white or buffy-white edges to some retained juvenal wing-coverts (Practical Hand book of British Birds); white tips of juvenal back-feathers gradually wear off during winter. *Young in juvenal plumage:* Above and breast-band buffy, feathers of back, scapulars, wing-coverts and tertials

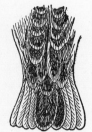

TAIL OF BAIRD'S SANDPIPER
(After Cory.)

darker centrally, margined at ends white or buffy-white, giving a scaled appearance; top of head streaked dusky; upper tail-coverts narrowly tipped buffy; otherwise similar to winter plumage, but breast more pinkish-buff than in adult and rather indistinctly streaked dusky; bill dusky, lighter at base; legs and feet "dark plumbeous." (Allan Brooks.) *Downy young:* Forehead whitish, with central black line running forward from crown not quite reaching base of bill; sides of head whitish with some tawny spots; short line extending back from bill to eye, and back coarsely mixed black and tawny with little tufts of whitish; below mainly white, chest shaded pale brownish-gray; ventral region and under tail-coverts similar in color to upper plumage.

MEASUREMENTS. — Length 7.00 to 7.60 in.; spread 15.00 to 16.50; folded wing 4.43 to 5.00; tail 1.90 to 2.25; bill .74 to 1.00; tarsus .86 to 1.00. Female slightly larger than male.

MOLTS. — Juvenal birds have partial molt in autumn, including most body-feathers, some wing-coverts and some inner flight-feathers but not all those of back, scapulars and wing-coverts; after prenuptial molt in spring young bird apparently becomes as adult; adults appear to have a prenuptial molt of body-feathers and sometimes wings in spring and a nearly complete postnuptial molt (August to late winter).

FIELD MARKS. Seen in New England chiefly in autumn. Most difficult of our sandpipers to identify in field; appears like a very large Least Sandpiper with breast tinted buffy; seen with Semi-palmated Sandpipers is a little larger, more buffy and breast darker; with Least Sandpipers, plainly larger; with White-rumps can be identified surely in flight by its dark rump; with Pectoral Sandpipers is smaller, not so brown, rather less distinctly streaked above and below and bill shorter and more slender; as this bird can be closely approached its short, straight, slender bill will help to distinguish it from larger shore birds; this readily separates it from Red-backed Sandpiper which has a longer, downcurved bill.

VOICE. — A rather shrill, trilling whistle like that of Semipalmated Sandpiper (C. W. Townsend); while feeding, a low, conversational twitter (Wm. Brewster).

BREEDING. — On higher, dry parts of Arctic tundra. *Nest:* A slight depression well hidden in grass and lined thinly with dead grasses or leaves. *Eggs:* Usually 4; 1.38 by 1.18 to .95 by .87 in.; pear-shaped; "clay colored," grayer or more buffy in different specimens, spotted with rich umber and chocolate-browns of various shades (Coues); markings usually fine and numerous, occasionally massed more and confluent at larger end. *Dates:* Mid-June to early July.

RANGE. — North and South America. Breeds along Arctic coast from Point Barrow to northern Keewatin and in northwestern Greenland; winters in Chile, Argentina and Patagonia; occurs regularly in migration from Rocky Mountains to Mississippi River, and in Central America and northern South America; irregularly in autumn on Pacific coast from Alaska to California, and on Atlantic coast from Nova Scotia to Virginia; practically unknown in southeastern United States and West Indies; occasional on Lake Erie; occasional or casual in Mexico, and Galapagos Islands; accidental in England, southwestern Africa and northeastern Siberia.

DISTRIBUTION IN NEW ENGLAND. — Rare fall migrant in all coastal states; not recorded from Vermont but probably occurs there.

SEASON IN MASSACHUSETTS. — July 27 to October 1 (Glover M. Allen) (Oct. 18).

HAUNTS AND HABITS. On the south shore of Marthas Vineyard where in West Tisbury and Chilmark shallow pools are formed from the overflow of ponds and marshes just inside the beach ridge — there Baird's Sandpiper loves to feed. In late August or early September when the grass has been cut, this bird comes in small parties of four to eight and hunts about the margins of partly dried out pools, threading its way among the stubble or poking about upon the bare mud. It is very intent on its own business, assumes a crouching attitude as if near-sighted, and works slowly along, weaving in and out among the Least or Semipalmated Sandpipers with which it associates. Under such circumstances it may be readily recognized, as it will allow a quiet observer to approach within 20 feet. Its larger size and generally buffy-brownish appearance distinguish it at once from its smaller and more agile companions. Probably in autumn it is less rare than it is rated on our coast, and a few may remain here later than the records show, as the bird is commonly confused with other small sandpipers. Occasionally it feeds on the beaches but seems rather to prefer inland ponds and even uplands. It is common in migration in the Rockies where it seeks grasshoppers and locusts on the high benches. It has been seen there near the summit of the highest mountains at an altitude of 14,000 feet and has been taken repeatedly in northern Chile at 10,000 to 12,000 feet. Therefore it is quite possible that this bird may occur anywhere in the interior of New England, as it often is found at considerable distances from water.

ECONOMIC STATUS. The food of Baird's Sandpiper in the interior consists largely of insects. According to McAtee it destroys mosquitoes, crane-fly larvæ, cutworms and clover-root curculios. It is a harmless, useful species and its protection at all times should be continued.

Pisobia minutilla (VIEILLOT). Least Sandpiper.

Other names: PEEP; MUD-PEEP.

Plate 28.

DESCRIPTION. — Bill slender, straight; *toes cleft to base;* smallest of our sandpipers; almost a miniature of Baird's Sandpiper. *Adults in breeding plumage (sexes alike)* : Darker and more richly colored above than Baird's Sandpiper and spots on upper breast rather more distinct; above generally with black or blackish feather centers, edged light gray or whitish and rusty; top of head light grayish-tawny or pale buffy, broadly streaked blackish; a broad light streak over eye, a dark one before and behind it, eyelids edged white; rusty or chestnut edges of scapulars usually scalloped into their black centers;

lower back, rump and middle upper tail-coverts blackish; outer upper tail-coverts white; flight-feathers blackish; secondaries and greater coverts tipped white; below white; lower neck and sides of breast washed ashy or brownish and streaked dusky; bill black; iris brown; legs and feet "greenish" to yellowish-green or greenish-yellow. *Adults and young in winter plumage:* Above deep brownish-gray or grayish-brown, feathers darker centrally; otherwise much as breeding plumage, but breast less distinctly spotted or streaked, distinguishable by lack of tawny and buffy markings. *Young in juvenal plumage:* Similar to adult breeding plumage but markings rather more blended and indistinct; feathers of upper plumage more or less margined and tipped white; wing-coverts margined pale tawny; breast-band indistinctly streaked. *Downy young:* Forehead and sides of head buffy-white; chin and throat pure white, a central stripe on forehead and one from bill to eye, black; top and back of head, other upper plumage and flanks mixed reddish-brown and black with feather-tips of buffy-white; below white, breast faintly tinted buffy.

MEASUREMENTS. — Length 5.00 to 6.76 in.; spread 11.00 to 12.17; folded wing 3.25 to 3.80; tail 1.50 to 2.00; bill .65 to .95; tarsus .68 to .80. Female larger than male.

MOLTS. — Part of juvenal plumage is molted in autumn — mostly body-feathers, and some wing-coverts and inner secondaries; there is a prenuptial molt in spring (March to June) after which most young become like summer adults; adults have a partial prenuptial molt (March to June) including body and tail-feathers and some wing-feathers, and a complete postnuptial molt during autumn.

FIELD MARKS. — Smallest of our sandpipers; sparrow size; known from Semipalmated Sandpiper by dusky-green, yellowish-green, "greenish yellow," lighter legs (never black or blackish like those of Semipalmated Sandpiper); neck and sides of breast usually more streaked in spring and darker in fall than those of latter; bill more slender. This point may be noted with a glass at close range.

VOICE. — A plaintive *pe-et pe-et* or *wheet;* faint *peeps* among members of flocks; in flight *wheet, wheet, wheet, whrr-terr-wheet* (Grinnell, Bryant and Storer); a simple trilling whistle (C. W. Townsend); flight note a grating *kreep,* the e e sound diagnostic (J. T. Nichols).

BREEDING. — About water on wet grassy ground; about small lakes, islets, etc.; sometimes on moist upland. *Nest:* A depression on ground or in moss on a rock, lined with a little grass and a few dead leaves. *Eggs:* 3 or 4; about 1.15 by .80; pear-shaped; light drab, pale brownish or grayish-buff, marked variably with rich browns or blackish and gray or ashy. *Dates:* June 13 to July 20, Labrador. *Incubation:* Largely by male. Probably but one brood yearly.

RANGE. — North and South America. Breeds from northwestern Alaska, northern Mackenzie near Arctic coast and on southern Arctic islands to Cumberland Island and south to southern Yukon, northern Manitoba, southern Ungava (central Quebec), Newfoundland, Magdalen Islands, Nova Scotia and Sable Island; winters from southern California, southern Arizona, Texas and North Carolina through West Indies and Central America to Brazil, Chile, Galapagos, Bermuda and central Patagonia; migrates throughout United States and west to northeastern Siberia and Commander Islands, north to latitude 69° West, Greenland, also to Bermuda; accidental in Europe.

DISTRIBUTION IN NEW ENGLAND. — Common to abundant migrant coastwise, less common in interior.

SEASON IN MASSACHUSETTS. — (April 18) May 5 to June 7; (summer); July 1 to September 21 (October 13).

HAUNTS AND HABITS. The Least Sandpiper or little Peep is naturally an exceedingly unsuspicious bird. If an observer remains motionless, the little things will sometimes come almost to his feet in their busy search for food. They run about the feet of much larger shore birds, and even associate with ducks feeding along shore. Apparently these larger birds seldom molest them. They are very gregarious, and frequent salt-marshes and mud flats on which they find their food, also inland meadows and the muddy margins of rivers and ponds, especially in August when the water is low.   They are not uncommon, however, on the sea beach, though not nearly so abundant there as are the slightly larger Semipalmated Sandpipers.   The male has a twittering, tremulo flight-song in the nuptial season, which may be heard occasionally over the marsh in late May or early June.   The habits of this species are well known, but anyone who has not observed them may easily do so, as they are always here during the month of May and during August and the first week of September.

In their migrations to South America they must fly long distances over the sea, as many arrive in the Bermudas during the autumnal migration.   These islands lie in a direct line and about halfway between Nova Scotia and the Lesser Antilles.

ECONOMIC STATUS.   As the food of the Least Sandpiper consists of insects and minute water animals and as they are known to destroy many grasshoppers and mosquitoes, they have a greater economic value as insect destroyers than as food and should be protected perpetually by law.

Pelídna alpína alpina (LINNÆUS).   Dunlin.

DESCRIPTION. — Bill rather long, longer than tarsus, tapering and slightly downcurved toward tip where somewhat expanded; tail slightly emarginate, two middle feathers pointed and extending beyond others; toes divided to their base.   *Adults in breeding plumage (sexes alike)* : Top of head streaked black or brownish-black and pinkish-cinnamon; nape and back of neck lighter or grayish, streaked dusky; upper plumage generally with black or brownish-black feather centers and broad cinnamon margins, broadest on scapulars, all giving a streaked appearance; rump grayish-brown, feathers with indistinct narrow, dusky centers and narrow indistinct ashy-brown end margins; central upper tail-coverts dark grayish-brown or dusky, sometimes irregularly marked cinnamon; sides of rump, and outer tail-coverts white; two middle tail-feathers dusky, edged paler, rest of tail pale brownish-gray, feathers narrowly edged white or whitish; wing-coverts brownish-gray, with dusky shaft streaks, narrowly margined grayish-white or buffy-white, greater coverts tipped white; primary coverts and flight-feathers dusky; some primaries edged white toward their bases, secondaries narrowly tipped white or margined white at tips; sides of head, chin, throat, fore neck and breast white or grayish-white, streaked or spotted dusky (except chin and upper throat), streaks becoming larger and more sharply defined on breast, where sometimes broken; abdomen more or less clouded blackish, which often forms a considerable area broken by some white feather tips; sides, flanks and under tail-coverts white, usually with a few conspicuous narrow blackish streaks; axillars and wing-linings mostly white; bill blackish; iris dark brown; legs and feet dark olivaceous.   *Adults in winter plumage:* Above mainly plain brownish-gray or "ash brown," sometimes with slightly paler feather tips on back; flight-feathers darker, some with white outer edges; a light stripe over eye, a broad, dark one through it; below white, neck and breast suffused with gray and (together with sides and flanks) sparsely spotted or streaked grayish and dusky; wings and tail as in breeding plumage.   *Young in first winter plumage:* Like adult winter, but some juvenal feathers retained on back, rump and wings.   *Young in juvenal plumage:* Similar to adult but feathers of upper plumage largely edged buffy; sides of head and neck light buff narrowly streaked dusky; lower throat and upper breast grayish, washed buffy and streaked dusky; flanks streaked and spotted dusky; belly more or less spotted and blotched dusky-brown.   *Downy young:* Upper plumage a mixture of black and rusty, interspersed with white tips; a short, very narrow black streak between bill and eye and a shorter one beneath it; sides of head and under plumage whitish.

MEASUREMENTS. — Length 7.50 to 8.00 in.; folded wing 4.30 to 4.75; bill 1.15 to 1.45; tarsus .85 to 1.00.

MOLTS. — A partial postjuvenal molt of body and wing-feathers (August to November) precedes first winter plumage; a partial prenuptial molt (March to June) is followed by first nuptial plumage, which closely resembles adults but retains some abraded juvenal wing-coverts; adults have incomplete molt (March to June) and complete postnuptial molt (July to November).

FIELD MARKS. — Cannot be distinguished from Red-backed Sandpiper except in hand. (See Field Marks under that species.)

BREEDING. — About moorlands and rough pastures. *Nest:* On ground; a cup of dried grass or leaves well hidden in a tussock. *Eggs:* 3 or 4, rarely 6, averaging close to those of Red-backed Sandpiper in size; pear-shaped; varying from pale bluish-green to yellowish; sometimes boldly blotched and spotted; sometimes finely speckled with chocolate-brown and with ashy-gray markings. *Dates:* Late May and June, British Isles. *Incubation:* Period 21 days (Evans), (hatching on 22d); by both sexes.

RANGE. — Eastern Hemisphere. Breeds in England, Scotland, the Faroes, Iceland, northern Russia and Siberia, apparently in Novaya Zemlya and on Spitzbergen and smaller islands of the Arctic coast; winters from Great Britain, Holland and Caspian Sea to northern Africa and Calcutta, India; accidental in North America.

DISTRIBUTION IN NEW ENGLAND. — Accidental visitor. Records. *Massachusetts:* Chatham, Mr. Charles J. Paine, Jr., reported a female taken August 11, 1900, by Mr. J. S. Cochrane, and deposited in the Brewster collection.[1]

HAUNTS AND HABITS. The Dunlin is a mere straggler here from the Old World. Apparently its haunts and habits are similar to those of the Red-backed Sandpiper.

In The Nation and The Athenæum of June 18, 1921, in "Birds in Marshland," Mr. H. J. Massingham writes charmingly of the Dunlin's evolutions in flight, as follows:

"April and September are the signal months for the great migratory flights of the dunlin, chestnut-backed, with a black patch on the lower breast in spring, and ash-gray and white when the nuptial dress is cast, the most commonly distributed of all the Limicolæ about our shores. The afternoon sun leans its rays into the repose of the marshes, when suddenly one of these tremendous floods of life surges over them, sweeping down in the distance like a cloud detached from the sky, an invasion of Valkyrie with all the wild discipline and exultation of speed and none of the menace or terror. The little birds approach over the water in a dense column of perfect order, in a humming volume of a sea-like monotone, accompanied by a soft purr from thousands of throats. Then, as though they swam into the spell of an influence breathed like a perfume from the brown flats beneath them, the determination of the course is stayed, and, swerving at right angles with a unanimous tilt of the body, flashing a single sheet of white from their breasts, they fall into a compact ballet of movement a few feet from the ground. Changing pattern, direction, color and formation with every turn, each individual yet keeps the same distance from his neighbor, the same momentum, and the same angle of the body, as though pulled hither and thither with lightning rapidity from the ends of an infinite number of invisible and equidistant threads, all radiating from a common point. Thus they cut one design after another out of the fabric of space — three thousand leaderless birds, executing intricate movements with the single cohesion of one body, supported upon one pair of wings, a thing more wonderful than a single thought issuing

---

[1] Howe and Allen: The Birds of Massachusetts, 1901, p. 41.

from the collaboration of a myriad brain-cells, since the myriad contained in one body have found subtle contact with those of thousands of other bodies as apart, and from that urge of harmonious energy blossoms one flower, dressed in thousands of petals, swaying to and fro in the varying breeze of its own delight and impulse. Thus the dunlin dance the air in chorus, until the marshland pulls them gently to its breast, and they sink into it, breaking up at once into a jargoning crowd of individuals, twinkling and dibbling helter-skelter over the saltings."

ECONOMIC STATUS. See page 372.

Pelidna alpina sakhalína (VIEILLOT). Red-backed Sandpiper.

Other names: AMERICAN DUNLIN; RED-BACK; LEAD-BACK; FALL SNIPE; BRANT-BIRD; CALIFORNIA PEEP; CROOKED-BILL; SIMPLETON; STIB; WINTER OX-EYE; LITTLE BLACK-BREAST; WINTER SNIPE.

Plate 27.

DESCRIPTION. — Similar to Dunlin (page 414) but with considerable individual variation at all seasons and averaging decidedly larger, with relatively slightly longer bill and legs, and in breeding season with upper plumage brighter, cinnamon markings brighter cinnamon, and black of under plumage richer, more extensive and contrasting more conspicuously with white or grayish-white of breast; bill and feet black; iris dark brown.

MEASUREMENTS. — Length 7.60 to 9.25 in.; spread 14.50 to 15.75; folded wing 4.31 to 5.00; tail 2.00 to 2.35; bill 1.38 to 1.73; tarsus .96 to 1.15. Weight about 1½ to 3 oz.; female larger than male.

MOLTS. — Similar to those of Dunlin (see page 415).

FIELD MARKS. — A little larger than Sanderling; size of Spotted Sandpiper but bill longer; unmistakable in spring plumage with red back, black belly and rather long, slightly curved bill; in autumn its dark plain brownish-gray or ashy-brown plumage and long bill, slightly curved downward toward tip, differentiate it from the light colored straight-billed Sanderlings with which it associates. It shows a grayish band across breast and in flight white lines in wings.

VOICE. — Call note, *che-ezp-ezp-ezp-ezp* run together in a rather rasping *cheep* hoarser than call of Least Sandpiper (Grinnell, Bryant and Storer); somewhat resembles word *purre*; recalls cry of Common Tern without its harshness; when disturbed, a short *kuk* (C. W. Townsend); flight song in breeding season, a musical trilling, like mellow tinkling of large water drops falling rapidly into a partly filled vessel (E. W. Nelson); flight note, "an emphatic near-whistled *chu* or *chru*" (J. T. Nichols).

BREEDING. — Near water on Arctic tundra or in Barren Grounds. *Nest:* Usually on dry knoll surrounded by wet land; a mere depression in ground, moss or grass, with little lining. *Eggs:* Usually 4; 1.36 to 1.60 by .93 to 1.10 in.; pear-shaped; buff of varying shades from grayish or olive to brownish, blotched, spotted and stained rich chestnut-brown of light shades, some pale gray marks; brown spots usually elongated and placed spirally about larger end. *Dates:* June 1 to July 3, Alaska. *Incubation:* By both sexes. Probably but one brood yearly.

RANGE. — North America and eastern Asia. Breeds on northern coast of Siberia west to mouth of Yenisei and from Point Barrow to mouth of Yukon, also in Boothia and Melville Peninsulas and in northern Quebec; may breed rarely between these two main breeding areas; winters on Pacific coast from southern British Columbia to southern Lower California, on Atlantic coast from New Jersey (rarely Massachusetts) south to southern Florida, Louisiana and southern Texas, and from China and Japan to Malay Archipelago; rare to common locally in migration in interior United States;[1] has been taken on Pribilof Islands; casual in Yukon, Arizona and Nicaragua (Cooke).

DISTRIBUTION IN NEW ENGLAND. — Rare spring and uncommon to common fall migrant, mainly coastwise, slowly becoming more common; not recorded from Vermont; rarer in spring to the north and

---

[1] Nice, Margaret M.: *in litt.*

east (along coast of Maine and New Hampshire) than to southward; sometimes rather common in spring in southeastern Massachusetts; very rare in interior.

SEASON IN MASSACHUSETTS. — (April 13) late April to May 31; (summer); September 1 to December 13; (December 31, January 2; winter). J. A. Farley reported the wintering of this sub-species in 1917 on Plymouth Beach — the first record of the wintering of this bird north of Cape Cod in Massachusetts.[1]

HAUNTS AND HABITS. When most of the smaller sandpipers have departed, when sharp frosts have closed the inland marshes and waters of the Arctic regions, when the honk of the wild goose is heard in the land, then in late September or October the Red-backed Sandpipers appear. In some seasons a considerable flight passes in November. A few of them reach New England early, in gay summer plumage but by the time the majority arrive they are mostly in modest gray winter dress, though some adults still retain some red feathers on their backs. They feed mainly on sand beaches and sand flats in company with Sanderlings or other lingering shore birds, but they appear often along the muddy margins of creeks in the salt-marsh. Usually they come in very small flocks or in companies of three or four. They are rather restless, run rapidly, and fre-quently fly from place to place. In spring their numbers are fewer, as they migrate northward largely through the interior and by way of the Great Lakes and Hudson Bay, but a few may be seen occasionally on wide sand flats in May in full spring plumage. Now and then a few are reported on our coast in June, July and August. The Red-backed Sandpiper flies in compact flocks, the members of which scatter over the flats to feed. On mud flats they move about rapidly, probing the mud with their bills, and sometimes even submerging the head in water in their eager search for food.

ECONOMIC STATUS. As the food of this species consists largely of crustaceans and insects and as, according to McAtee, it destroys oyster worms and water-beetles, it is not only harmless but possibly beneficial to the farming and shell-fish industries.

Erólia ferrugínea (BRÜNNICH). Curlew Sandpiper.

Fig. 32.

DESCRIPTION. — Bill much longer than head, slender, down-curved toward tip, *which is not ex-panded;* tail very short *and doubly emarginate;* legs rather long, slender, tarsus nearly as long as bill. *Adults in breeding plumage (sexes alike or similar):* Top of head and most of upper plumage brownish-black or greenish-black, feathers tipped and irregularly marked reddish-chestnut or "orange cinnamon"; rump brownish-gray, each feather margined much paler, with a dusky bar near end; upper tail-coverts white, broadly but sparsely barred dusky (in some reddish at ends); tail grayish-brown, two middle feathers darker, outer ones white-shafted, and margined white toward end; wing-coverts ashy-brown with dusky shaft-lines and lighter edgings, greater coverts tipped white; flight-feathers shading from grayish-brown on inner secondaries to dusky on primaries; shafts of primaries mostly white, inner primaries with outer edges white; head, except top, sides of neck, and under plumage reddish-chestnut or rusty, often with more or less white feather tips; under tail-coverts barred dusky, and somewhat indistinct dusky spots elsewhere below (some barred dusky on breast); axillars white and under

---

[1] Auk, Vol. XXXVII, 1920, p. 78.

wing-coverts mostly so; female sometimes somewhat duller above and paler below; bill olive-black, sometimes dusky at end, olivaceous (or dark olive-green) toward base; iris very dark brown or blackish; legs and feet "olivaceous," "greenish-gray" or "light green." *Adults in winter plumage:* Above mainly plain brownish-gray or grayish-brown, with dusky shaft streaks; white stripe over eye; under plumage white, chest indistinctly streaked grayish; otherwise as in breeding plumage with similar white upper tail-coverts. *Young in first winter plumage:* As adult winter, but middle and lesser wing-coverts edged buff. *Young in juvenal plumage:* Similar to first winter but back and scapulars dusky with dull buffy or yellowish feather-edgings and tips margined whitish; lesser and middle wing-coverts margined dull buff at tips; fore breast and sides of breast washed buffy, dusky shafts giving them a streaked appearance; middle tail-feathers with subterminal dusky border.

MEASUREMENTS. — Length about 7.00 to 9.00 in.; spread 14.50 to 16.00; folded wing 4.20 to 5.20; tail 2.05 to 2.50; bill 1.25 to 1.68; tarsus 1.00 to 1.50. Weight 1¾ to 2¼ oz. (Audubon).

MOLTS. — A partial molt of juvenal body feathers, scapulars and a few wing and tail feathers (September to December) is followed by first winter plumage; during second winter (if not before in some cases) young apparently become as adult; adults have partial prenuptial molt (February to July) and complete molt (July to winter).

FIELD MARKS. — Size of Red-backed Sandpiper but taller; in spring long, downcurved bill, long legs, slender form, upright carriage and rusty head, neck and under plumage distinguish it; in autumn ashy-brown or gray back, unusual bill and legs and white upper tail-coverts, shown in flight, mark the bird; bill slimmer than that of Red-backed Sandpiper; legs longer.

VOICE. — Alarm note, a shrill *wick-wick-wick* (Haviland); flocks in autumn, a low twitter (Coward).

BREEDING. — On Arctic coast or dry ridges in Arctic tundra. *Nest:* A hollow in moss. *Eggs:* 3 or 4; about 1.50 by 1.04 in.; pear-shaped; "greenish-gray, with rich, dark, red-brown blotches and purplish shell marks." *Dates:* Last week in June and first part of July, Northern Siberia. *Incubation:* By both sexes. One brood yearly.

RANGE. — Eastern Hemisphere; occasional in North and South America. Breeds in Arctic regions of Asia and in northern Greenland; winters in Africa (from Mediterranean to southern Africa), India, Malay Archipelago, Australia and New Zealand; in migration occurs from British Isles, Madeira, Canary and Andaman Islands to Madagascar, China and Philippines; recorded in Alaska, Ontario, Nova Scotia, New Brunswick, New England, New York and New Jersey; accidental in Grenada and other Lesser Antilles, Carriacou and Patagonia.

DISTRIBUTION IN NEW ENGLAND. — A casual visitor. Records: *Maine:* Scarborough, one killed September 15, 1881, at Pine Point, by Charles H. Chandler;[1] Oxford County (see Ridgway, Bulletin 50, U. S. National Museum, Pt. VIII, p. 251). *Massachusetts:* Has been recorded six times at least, as follows: Boston market, bird taken in autumn of 1865 on Cape Ann;[2] Nahant, specimen in the collection made by Baldwin Coolidge (now in possession of the city of Lawrence) taken about 1869;[3] Ipswich, female in collection of Peabody Academy at Salem, taken October 2, 1872, by R. L. Newcomb;[4] East Boston, bird taken in May, 1876;[5] another specimen in collection of John Fottler, Jr., taken on Cape Cod about May 10, 1878;[6] Chatham, male taken August 26, 1889, and came into the possession of Gordon Plummer.[7] *Rhode Island:* Doubtfully recorded. *Connecticut:* The two old State records are held to be not "absolutely trustworthy" by Sage, Bishop and Bliss in their "Birds of Connecticut," while Dr. Thompson's record was proven later to be that of the Stilt Sandpiper.

SEASON IN MASSACHUSETTS. — May; August to October.

---

[1] Purdie, Henry A.: Bulletin Nuttall Ornithological Club, Vol. VII, 1882, p. 124.
[2] Samuels, E. A.: Ornithology and Oölogy of New England, 1869, p. 444.
[3] Deane, Ruthven: Bulletin Nuttall Ornithological Club, Vol. IV, 1879, p. 124.
[4] Townsend, C. W.: Memoirs of the Nuttall Ornithological Club, No. 3, Birds of Essex County, 1905, p. 177.
[5] Brewster, William: Bulletin Nuttall Ornithological Club, Vol. I, 1876, pp. 51, 52.
[6] Deane, Ruthven: Bulletin Nuttall Ornithological Club, Vol. IV, 1879, p. 124.
[7] Ornithologist and Oölogist, Vol. XV, 1890, p. 110.

PLATE 28

PLATE 28

SANDERLING

Page 423

YOUNG IN JUVENAL PLUMAGE (AUTUMN)

ADULT IN BREEDING PLUMAGE (SPRING)

ADULT IN WINTER PLUMAGE
(AUTUMN)

SEMIPALMATED SANDPIPER

Page 419

YOUNG IN FIRST WINTER PLUMAGE
(AUTUMN)

ADULT IN BREEDING
PLUMAGE (SPRING)

LEAST SANDPIPER

Page 412

ADULT IN BREEDING
PLUMAGE (SPRING)

YOUNG IN FIRST WINTER
PLUMAGE (AUTUMN)

All one-half natural size.

HAUNTS AND HABITS. This straggler from the Old World may occur here more often than the records indicate. Apparently it has been taken and recorded at least twenty-five times on the Atlantic coast of the United States and no one knows how many captures have gone unrecorded. A late record is that of a bird in typical winter plumage taken by Mr. L. A. Fuertes, December 19, 1923, Fishers Island, New York.[1] When found it is likely to be with flocks of Red-backed Sandpipers and might readily pass unnoticed among them in autumn, when it resembles them closely. It frequents beaches, tide flats and estuaries and more rarely interior waters, and feeds on small crustaceans, worms and insects. As more specimens have been taken in Massachusetts than in any other state we may look for its occurrence here again.

ECONOMIC STATUS. See page 372.

Ereunétes pusíllus (LINNÆUS). Semipalmated Sandpiper.

Other names: PEEP ; SAND PEEP; BEACH PEEP; BUMBLE-BEE PEEP; HAWK'S EYE; OXEYE.

Plate 28.

DESCRIPTION. — Very small, *with distinct basal web between front toes;* bill rather short, as in Least Sandpiper, but not so slender; tail doubly emarginate. *Adults in breeding plumage (sexes alike):* Above light grayish-brown; sides of cap and some feathers of back and scapulars often but not always tinged pale buffy-cinnamon; top of head heavily streaked and back heavily spotted black; rump, middle upper tail-coverts and two middle tail-feathers dusky, feathers of rump narrowly margined brownish-gray; outer upper tail-coverts mostly white; all but middle tail-feathers brownish-gray, narrowly edged whitish at ends; wing-coverts mainly brownish-gray, darkest at shafts, narrowly edged paler or whitish around tips; greater coverts narrowly tipped white; primary coverts and flight-feathers dusky; outermost primary white-shafted, rest with partly white shafts; streaked white stripe over eye, dusky space before eye with streaks passing from its lower part over cheeks; ear-region also streaked grayish-brown; below white, breast slightly grayish and streaked or spotted sparingly dusky; bill blackish, slightly lighter at base; iris dark brown; legs and feet blackish. *Adults in winter plumage:* Brownish-gray or ashy above with dusky shaft streaks and feather centers; light line on wing formed by ends of greater coverts less conspicuous and not so white as in summer; below white, faintly streaked dusky on breast. *Young in first winter plumage:* Similar to adult in winter, with few indistinct breast markings. *Young in juvenal plumage:* Similar to adult breeding plumage but back and scapular-feathers margined white terminally, brown usually less rusty, and lower fore neck tinged pale grayish-buff; bill black; legs and feet "dark grayish-olive" (Allan Brooks). *Downy young:* Above pale tawny-brown laterally; centrally black with fine white tips over all; forehead dingy white, divided by a black streak up center; top of head light chestnut, marbled somewhat with black and white and mottled whitish at back, two dark lines before eye, the shorter running lower than eye; below whitish on abdomen and yellowish on fore neck.

FOOT OF SEMIPAL-MATED SANDPIPER

MEASUREMENTS. — Length 5.50 to 6.86 in.; spread 11.14 to 12.80; folded wing 3.25 to 4.00; tail 1.03 to 1.65; bill .50 to .90 (male .50 to .75, female .66 to .90); tarsus .60 to .98. Weight about 1 oz. Female larger than male.

MOLTS. — Much the same as those of Least Sandpiper (see page 413).

---

[1] Auk, Vol. XLI, 1924, p. 341.

FIELD MARKS. — A little larger than Least Sandpiper; similar but has a whiter, less streaked breast in fall and legs and feet very dark practically *black*, while those of Least Sandpiper are lighter and greenish, or greenish-yellow.

VOICE. — A quailing call like " '*to-weet, 'to-weet* "; a shrill, clattering whistle (T. Nuttall); a soft *peep peep* (O. W. Knight); a peeping chatter when in flocks; a rolling note, have sometimes described it as a whinney in syllables *eh eh eh* or *what-er, what-er* (C. W. Townsend); flight note *cher* or *che*, on being flushed *k-i-i-ip*. (J. T. Nichols).

BREEDING. — On Barren Grounds and Arctic coasts and islands. *Nest:* On ground; a hollow lined with a little grass. *Eggs:* 3 or 4; 1.15 to 1.25 by .80 to .90 in.; pear-shaped; color varies greatly; light grayish-buff or greenish-buff to greenish-drab, clay color or olive; finely speckled and dotted or coarsely blotched with dark brown, blackish-brown or reddish and lilac. *Dates:* June 12, Labrador; June 24, Ungava (northern Quebec); June 30, northern Mackenzie.

RANGE. — North and South America. Breeds from Arctic coast to Yukon mouth, east to northern Labrador and probably south to northern Saskatchewan; winters from Texas and South Carolina through West Indies and Central America (largely in eastern South America) to Patagonia; migrates mainly east of Rocky Mountains (but common in British Columbia), and along Atlantic coast, visiting Bahamas and Bermuda in autumn; casual in southern Alaska, Pribilof Islands and northeastern Siberia; accidental in Europe.

DISTRIBUTION IN NEW ENGLAND. — Common to abundant migrant mainly coastwise except in Vermont where rather uncommon migrant on larger lakes; rather less abundant in spring than in fall; a record date for Rhode Island is June 23, 1924, at Quonochontaug (H. S. Hathaway); non-breeding birds occur irregularly on coast in June.

SEASON IN MASSACHUSETTS. — (May 1) May 11 to June 22 (summer); July 3 to October 8 (November 11).

HAUNTS AND HABITS. The Semipalmated Sandpiper is the little Sand-peep of New England beaches. It runs along the beach, its little blackish legs twinkling over the wet sands, advancing and retreating with the wash of the surf, industriously gleaning its frugal fare from the "backwash" of that great fecund mother of abundant life, the sea. In August and September it appears in thousands on the sands from Ipswich to Monomoy. It is not confined to the sea beach, but occurs at low tide on wide sand flats and mud flats and in muddy creeks in the salt-marsh, all along our coast. Even in the interior in August when lakes, streams and ponds are low it may be found occasionally in small companies along sandy or muddy margins. Often it is abundant in May in southern New England, less so in Maine. Its habits are similar to those of the Least Sandpiper and the two species frequently associate on beach or flat, but the Semipalmated Sandpiper is more a sand bird than its smaller companion.

All the smaller sandpipers are now (1924) protected by law; nevertheless, complaints are heard often that many small sandpipers are crippled, being minus one leg, and the missing members are supposed to have been shot off by law-breaking gunners. Doubtless some have been thus crippled, but one observer counted 26 one-legged birds in one flock. The following extracts from my correspondence will explain what happens to most of the missing legs:

"I was watching a flock of Semipalmated Sandpipers feeding on the beach, dodging the incoming tide. Of the flock of twenty, about five occasionally detached themselves, drew up one leg into their plumage, and thrust their bills into the feathers of their backs, resting, I suppose. They were very tame and stood thus on one leg until I came within three feet of them. Then (and this is what struck me as peculiar) two or three of them started to patter along ahead of me as usual on two legs, but two or three others hopped along on one foot only, still keeping the second leg concealed, this even though I was walking right behind them. At first I thought one leg was shot off until I saw one bird after another repeat the act. They hopped along and fed, meantime, for a full ten feet before they called on the second leg for aid." (H. W. Copeland.)

"Together with Miss Viola Crittenden of Beverly, I found a flock of some dozen or fifteen Semipalmated Sandpipers above the tide line in some old seaweed that had been flung up on the beach.

" They and we were the only live things on the beach so we sat and watched them for more than half an hour. Each one in the small flock had but one leg. They all seemed rather stupid or under the weather, just standing in one place or at times hopping a bit and eating something found in the seaweed. We felt they had been left behind when the main flocks flew away because of their injuries and we were indignant over the brutes who had shot off their legs. Finally every last one of those little frauds put down a second perfectly good leg, ran off a short distance and then flew away." (Miss Caroline Hamilton.)

In northward migration the Semipalmated Sandpiper passes through New England rather rapidly, chiefly in the latter half of May, but on its return it lingers longer. As is the case with many shore birds the adults mostly come first, and the young ones begin to arrive usually after the middle of August.

Dr. C. W. Townsend well describes the habits of the species as follows:

"Semipalmated Sandpipers are fascinating birds to watch, whether on the wing, when the flocks twist and turn with military precision like one bird, alternately displaying their white breasts and gray backs, or whether busily engaged in feeding on the beach. At such times they occasionally find their small round mouth much out of proportion to the stretch of the end of the bill, and many shakings of the head are needed to get a large morsel past the sticking-point. I have seen one try several times to swallow a large beach flea, and then actually fly off with it in his bill. Their sleep in the daytime is taken at short snatches, standing or squatting for a few minutes at a time with bill concealed in the feathers of the back, not 'under the wing' as in poems. They also stand on one leg, even when both legs are intact, for cripples are common. They seem to yawn by stretching lazily one wing over a leg. They also spread both wings above the back as do many other shore birds, and they flirt their tail nervously from side to side, perhaps shaking the head at the same time. When gleaning food in the shallow water, they sometimes immerse their heads completely.

"Their call note is very much like that of the Least Sandpiper but is shriller and less musical. A harsh rasping note and a peeping note are sometimes heard. A low, rolling, gossipy note is often emitted when they approach other birds. This latter note is often imitated with success by gunners. In the spring, however, the bird is delightfully musical on occasions, and his flight song may be heard on the beach and among the bogs of the dunes. Rising on quivering wings to about thirty feet from the ground, the bird advances with rapid wing-beats, curving the pinions strongly downward, pouring forth a succession of musical notes, a continuous quavering trill, and ending with a few very sweet notes that recall those of a Goldfinch. He then descends to the ground, where one may be lucky enough, if near at hand, to hear a low musical *cluck* from the excited bird. This is, I suppose, the full love flight-song, and is not often heard in its entirety, but the first quavering trill is not uncommon, a single bird, or a member of a flock singing thus as he flies over. I have seen birds chasing one another on the beach with raised wings, emitting a few quavering notes, and have been reminded of a Long-billed Marsh Wren. I have also heard them emit at this time a sharp grasshopper-like sound." [1]

The Semipalmated Sandpiper feeds largely on small crustaceans and mollusks, but also destroys many insects, including mosquitoes, beetles, bugs, flies, grasshoppers and locusts and a few worms, with a very small quantity of vegetal matter, including a few seeds.

ECONOMIC STATUS. This bird is too small to be placed on the list of game birds. It is of some service in migration as an insect destroyer.

Ereunetes maúri CABANIS. Western Sandpiper.

Other names: WESTERN SEMIPALMATED SANDPIPER, AND OTHER NAMES APPLIED TO SEMIPALMATED SANDPIPER (page 419).

DESCRIPTION. — *Adults (sexes similar)*: Like Semipalmated Sandpiper but averaging a trifle larger with relatively longer bill (dimensions of bills of same sex in the two species rarely overlap), and with a tendency *in spring and summer* to brighter plumage above, a richer rusty or chestnut coloring on back and *heavier dark streaking on breast* sometimes taking the shape of arrow-heads which reach along sides and flanks; a more or less distinct stripe of rusty-cinnamon on each side of head and much of the same on crown. *Young in winter plumage:* Practically indistinguishable from that of Semipalmated Sandpiper. *Young in juvenal plumage:* much as in Semipalmated Sandpiper but with rusty-yellowish or cinnamon predominating on upper plumage; bill, feet and legs blackish.

MEASUREMENTS. — Length 5.78 to 7.00 in.; folded wing 3.52 to 3.90; tail 1.40 to 1.95; bill .83 to 1.25 (male .83 to .95, female .88 to 1.25); tarsus .82 to .98. Female larger than male.

MOLTS. — Similar to those of Least Sandpiper. (See page 413.)

FIELD MARKS. — Similar to those of Semipalmated Sandpiper (page 419); usually indistinguishable from that species in field in summer and autumn, the only seasons when seen in New England, but some adults in July or August may still retain some rich cinnamon on head; in spring, at *close range* with a good glass the rich, rusty cinnamon on sides and top of head and on back may be seen.

VOICE. — Similar to that of Least Sandpiper. Common call variable, *chee-up, cheep* or *cher-eep* (J. T. Nichols).

BREEDING. — Similar to that of Semipalmated Sandpiper.

RANGE. — North America and northern South America. Breeds on Alaskan coast, from Cape Prince of Wales to Yukon mouth; some individuals summer on Pacific coast from California northward; winters from North Carolina and from north central California to Venezuela and Peru; in migration

---

[1] Birds of Essex County, 1905, p. 178.

occurs largely west of Rocky Mountains but also in interior (not rarely on Great Lakes), and on Atlantic Coast north to New Hampshire, and in West Indies.

DISTRIBUTION IN NEW ENGLAND. — Uncommon or rare fall migrant mainly coastwise, except in Maine and Vermont, where it probably occurs; not recorded, however, from these states.

SEASON IN MASSACHUSETTS. — July 19 to September 20.

HAUNTS AND HABITS. In New England the Western Sandpiper is usually seen in company with the Semipalmated Sandpiper with which it visits the usual feeding-grounds and it seems to have precisely similar habits. It is a brighter colored bird in spring plumage but most of those seen in New England in autumn so closely resemble their eastern companions that it is impossible to separate them with certainty without careful comparison in hand. Therefore, it is quite probable that the western bird is much more common than the records would indicate.

The most remarkable feature in the life of this little bird is the long migrations that many of them are supposed to make from Bering Sea to the Atlantic coast and so on down to South America. Apparently numbers of them cross the Great Lakes and many reach the coast in New Jersey, New York and New England but more appear to go direct to the Carolinas, Georgia and Florida. In spring they return by a more western route as they do not appear in New England.

ECONOMIC STATUS. See page 372.

Crocethía álba. (PALLAS) Sanderling.

Other names: BEACH-BIRD; BULL PEEP; WHITEY; WHITING; SKINNER; STIB; WHITE SNIPE.

Plate 28.

DESCRIPTION. — Bill rather straight, stout and short, about as long as head or tarsus; tail short, doubly emarginate, central feathers projecting; toes (3) bordered with a very narrow membrane, hind toe wanting; (rarely a rudimentary hind toe). *Adults in breeding plumage (sexes similar)*: Top of head and hind neck pale rusty, mixed more or less with grayish-white and broadly streaked or spotted dusky or black; feathers of back and scapulars black centrally, widely margined rusty and grayish-white (toward summer rusty predominates); rump and shorter middle upper tail-coverts brownish-gray, each feather darker centrally, broadly margined pale gray and grayish-white (in some specimens indications of rusty on tail-coverts); longer middle upper tail-coverts and two central tail-feathers dusky, narrowly margined pale gray or grayish-white, rest of tail-feathers light grayish-brown, edged whitish, outer pair paler, with more white on outer web, shafts of all mainly white; wing-coverts dusky near bend; rest of lesser and middle coverts grayish-brown, paler along edges, often broadly tipped white or whitish; greater coverts brownish-gray, paler on edges, broadly tipped white, forming a white bar across wing; tertials brownish-gray narrowly margined white; basal half or more of secondaries white, becoming dusky toward tips; primary coverts and primaries dusky, some coverts broadly tipped white; dusky primaries, edged whitish at tips, shafts of all and basal half of inner ones white; sides of head and neck pale rusty with some white intermixed and slightly streaked and spotted dusky; side of neck and breast similar but spotted and barred dusky; rest of under plumage white, including axillars and wing linings except near outer border of wing where the usual dusky white edged feathers appear; iris dark brown; bill, legs and feet black. Female, grayer above and many areas usually paler, "sometimes legs and feet brownish" (Collector's Notes). *Adults in winter plumage:* Forehead white, elsewhere above pale gray or brownish-gray, with dusky or brownish shaft streaks and paler or whitish feather margins on back, scapulars, tertials and wing-coverts; a dusky area about bend of wing; sides of head and neck, and under plumage white; a slight, very indistinct, dusky line of specks through eye, and sparse, indistinct spotting and streaking on sides of head, neck and upper breast; otherwise about as in breeding plumage; eyes, bill and feet as in summer. *Young in first winter plumage:* Similar to adult winter but distinguished by some worn juvenal feathers retained (rump, scapulars and wing-coverts). *Young in juvenal plumage:* White forehead and line over eye sometimes washed buffy, streaks and tips dusky; top of head streaked blackish; upper surface of body variegated with pale grayish and blackish, with some whitish feather-tips; back and tertials largely blackish with feather-edgings pale grayish or whitish or even a suggestion of buffy; wing much as in adult but middle wing-coverts light sepia, shading to cream-yellow with a terminal dusky line, sometimes with a spot or bar of brownish-black near tips; lesser coverts brownish-black, some tipped cream; sides of head and neck white to cream, faintly streaked dusky; sides of breast creamy-yellow or buffy-white, feathers faintly tipped dusky; rest of under plumage white; eyes, bill and feet dark in all stages. *Downy young:* Forehead buff with central black line leading from middle base of upper mandible to top of head; nape buff; elsewhere above varied with light and deep buff and black, more or less spangled white; two black lines cross a buffy area from bill to eye, buff growing lighter on cheeks, chin and throat; white below.

MEASUREMENTS. — Length 7.00 to 8.75 in.; spread 14.00 to 16.25; folded wing 4.40 to 5.50; tail 1.85 to 2.25; bill .88 to 1.20; tarsus .80 to 1.10. Weight 2 to 3 oz. Female larger than male.

MOLTS. — Juvenal plumage largely shed by partial postjuvenal molt of body-feathers, tail-feathers, some scapulars and wing-coverts (September to December); then follows a partial prenuptial molt (March to May) which precedes first summer plumage, which is almost indistinguishable from adult breeding plumage; in following autumn a complete postnuptial molt is followed by adult winter plumage; adults have an incomplete prenuptial molt (March to May) and a complete postnuptial molt (July to winter).

FIELD MARKS. — Larger than Spotted Sandpiper; in flight shows a bold white bar along middle of wing in sharp contrast to blackish of flight-feathers; straight, short, black bill and black legs; in spring tawny or ruddy and black above and on *sides of neck and breast;* white below; in fall variable, spotted with black above or pale gray above, continuous *white below;* at this time whitest of shore birds.

VOICE. — "A not very loud *ket, ket, ket,* uttered singly or in a series and in a slightly complaining tone" (J. T. Nichols); a shrill but not unpleasant *wick* (H. E. Dresser); a short *chit,* a rasping note, a peeping note, or sometimes a sharp grasshopper-like sound; also a plaintive whistle like that of Semi-palmated Sandpiper.

BREEDING. — Not far from water; on Barren Grounds; sometimes on high ridges several hundred feet above sea or on bare raised islands of clay and stones in tundra. *Nest:* A hollow in ground, lined with dried grasses and leaves. *Eggs:* Usually 4; 1.30 to 1.50 by .95 to 1.03 in.; pear-shaped; pale olive-brown, spotted finely dark brown, markings often heavier at larger end. *Dates:* June 20 to July 15, northeast Greenland. *Incubation:* Period, 23 or 24 days (A. L. V. Manniche); by both sexes.

RANGE. — Nearly cosmopolitan. Breeds on Arctic coast and islands from Point Barrow, Alaska, to northern Greenland; also in Iceland, Spitzbergen and northern Siberia; winters from Washington, Texas, New Jersey (rarely Massachusetts) and Bermuda south to Patagonia; also from Mediterranean, Burmah and Japan to South Africa, Java, Ceylon, Borneo, the Philippines, Australia and various Pacific islands, including Hawaii.

DISTRIBUTION IN NEW ENGLAND. — *Maine:* Uncommon spring and common fall migrant coast-wise; casual in interior. *New Hampshire:* Uncommon spring and common fall migrant coastwise. *Vermont:* Rare migrant. *Massachusetts:* Common to abundant migrant, mainly coastwise; most numerous in fall; casual in June and July; winter resident south of Cape Cod and irregularly north to Plymouth County and north in December to Essex County. *Rhode Island:* Common migrant coastwise; casual inland; probably a rare winter resident. *Connecticut:* Not uncommon spring and fall migrant coastwise; casual in interior.

SEASON IN MASSACHUSETTS. — (April 7 and 26) May 11 to June 8 (summer); July 24 to November 25; (winter). J. A. Farley was first to report the wintering of the species north of Cape Cod in 1917 on Plymouth Beach.[1]

HAUNTS AND HABITS. Sanderlings follow the sea. They run over pale sand where storm-tossed breakers roar, for there in the wake of the storm they find their sustenance. The turmoil of the surf stirs up the sandy bottom and the rush of the waves throws many tiny waifs of sea life upon the shelving beach, where the backwash bears them again to the sea. Here, where breakers thunder down and flying spray obscures the scene, the little Sanderlings, ever on the alert, run nimbly into the returning flood to snatch up many a choice tidbit, and then trip lightly up the slope, ahead of the incoming wave. Sometimes they venture in too far, and must rise on fluttering wings to avoid the onset of the next surge. Real "children of the sand" they always may be found in their season along the open seacoast or on the shores of large bodies of fresh water, where the surf runs high. Elsewhere they are not so common, but they sometimes feed on wide sand flats at low water. When they are standing still or squatting on the sand their colors so blend with their environment that they become almost invisible; but when they rise and fly out low over the sea they become conspicuous against the dark water. They usually fly in small flocks along shore, close to the waves, barely rising above the curling tops of the surges, and sometimes disappearing in the hollows between them.

While passing through New England Sanderlings are changing plumage and may be seen in nearly all stages. Dr. C. W. Townsend thus describes some of the variations in plumage:

"In the spring migration, Sanderlings hurry through in the latter part of May. The plumage at this time is interesting, mainly because of the individual differences in time of molt. Thus on May 20, 1904, I saw two on the beach at Ipswich, both in light winter plumage. On May 27, out of a flock of thirty, eight had no rufous on the throat, two of these being in the snowy white winter plumage. Those with rufous on the throat had all degrees from a slight mottling to a general dark tinge. Unless the light is right, these rufous throats look black. On June 4, of two on the beach, one had a pure white throat, the other the rufous throat of the full nuptial plumage. Such differences as these at this late date suggest that some at least of the birds do not attain full nuptial plumage the first year. In the autumn migration the birds are moulting into winter plumage. Early arrivals in July are sometimes very ruddy on the back, throat, and breast and all stages up to the pure white throat may be found at the same time. There are great individual differences, and red throats may sometimes be found throughout August and even in September. Thus on August 4, 1904, all stages were to be found on Ipswich Beach. Of two specimens preserved, both males, one had a full ruddy throat, ruddy and dark back, and the primaries unworn. The other had only a few ruddy feathers in the throat,

---

[1] Auk, Vol. XXXVII, 1920, p. 78.

numerous scattering pearl gray feathers in the back, and the primaries much worn. Others had nearly perfect winter plumage, with pearl gray backs and white throats." [1] Such variations are likely to confuse the novice. Some early ornithologists mistakenly described individual Sanderlings in different plumages as distinct species.

Sanderlings with but one leg are frequently reported. The following from my correspondence is enlightening :

"Sanderlings often stand on one leg and hop on one. We saw a whole flock of one-legged Sanderlings one day last fall. Finally to our surprise the other leg of each bird appeared. I have often seen one Sanderling in a flock that I thought was one-legged, for it stood and hopped on that one leg so long I was convinced that it had but one. But since seeing that flock last fall I have begun to have my doubts about one-legged Sanderlings." (Miss J. Olivia Crowell.)

Where little waves break gently on the beach Sanderlings often hop nimbly into the water on one leg, hop out again, and continue to hop along the beach in search of food rather than dislodge that other leg from its warm covering of feathers.

Now and then, however, a shore bird loses a leg by some accident and, surviving, gets about very well on one leg.

In its migrations between northernmost Arctic lands and Patagonia the Sanderling passes through New England in greatest numbers during the latter half of May and in September. Its occurrence in Massachusetts in midsummer or midwinter is more or less irregular, but in ordinary winters it is not rare about Muskeget Island.

The food of the Sanderling on our coast consists largely of small mollusks, crustaceans, worms and beach insects. In the interior it feeds largely on insects and is said to eat the buds and seeds of Arctic plants, bits of moss and algæ. Dr. Townsend writes as follows of the feeding habits of this bird :

"On the hard wet sand of the beaches one may see in places the characteristic probings of the Sanderling without a trace of their foot marks, and these may be the cause of considerable mystery to the uninitiated. While the Semipalmated Sandpiper runs about with his head down dabbing irregularly here and there, the Sanderling vigorously probes the sand in a series of holes a quarter of an inch to an inch apart in straight or curving lines a foot to two feet long. Sometimes the probings are so near together that the line is almost a continuous one like the furrow of a miniature plough. The sand is thrown up in advance so that one can tell in which direction the bird is going. A close inspection of the probings often reveals their double character, showing that the bill was introduced partly open. The probings are for the minute sand-fleas and other crustaceans in the sand, their principal food. I have seen Sanderlings running about nimbly on the beach, catching the sand-fleas which were hopping on the surface. I have also seen them catching flies. I have the record of one I shot in 1884, whose stomach was stuffed with small specimens of the common mussel, *Mytilus edulis*." [2]

ECONOMIC STATUS. See page 372.

---

[1] Birds of Essex County, 1905, p. 180.   [2] Supplement to Birds of Essex County, 1920, p. 85.

PLATE 29

PLATE 29

LONG–BILLED CURLEW

Page 453

HUDSONIAN CURLEW

Page 455

ADULT

ADULT

ESKIMO CURLEW

Page 457

ADULT

HUDSONIAN GODWIT

Page 429

MARBLED GODWIT

Page 427

ADULT IN WINTER PLUMAGE
(AUTUMN)

ADULT

ADULT IN BREEDING PLUMAGE
(SPRING)

All one-fourth natural size.

Louis Agassiz Fuertes

Limósa fédoa (Linnæus). Marbled Godwit.

Other names: STRAIGHT-BILLED CURLEW; BRANT-BIRD; BADGER-BIRD; MARLIN; BROWN MARLIN; BIG MARLIN.

Plate 29.

DESCRIPTION. — Bill very long, longer than tarsus, slightly upcurved, feathers on side of lower mandible not extending far beyond those on upper; tail short and nearly even at end; legs rather long; toes short, stout, much flattened underneath, widely margined, outer and middle ones partly webbed, inner and middle with small basal web. *Adults in breeding plumage (sexes alike):* General ground color pale cinnamon, paling toward whitish on head; top of head thickly and broadly streaked dusky, narrow dusky streaks running from base of bill below eye to ear-coverts; back part of head, nape and entire neck all round streaked dusky-brownish; sooty-blackish predominates on upper back and scapulars, broken by broad bars and cross spots of ground color (pale cinnamon or vinaceous-buff); on lower back and rump each feather has a crescent-shaped spot of black near end; upper tail-coverts and tail barred dusky; lesser wing-coverts dusky grayish-brown, margined light cinnamon, rest of wing largely barred or marbled with ground color and darker or dusky; primary coverts and outer areas and tips of first four primaries *dark slate-brown or blackish;* other primaries mostly cinnamon; 1st primary with white shaft (the other shafts white only below); breast, sides, flanks and under tail-coverts narrowly and irregularly barred dusky; (in some individuals all under plumage including axillars and under wing-coverts, barred); axillars and under wing-coverts richer cinnamon than rest of under plumage, *axillars more or less barred with narrow zigzags of sooty-gray;* basal half of bill pale flesh color or reddish ("rose-pink" Nichols), growing blackish at tip; iris dark brown; legs and feet bluish-gray. *Adults in winter plumage:* Similar to breeding plumage but lacking barring on front of breast, sides and flanks; very indistinctly barred or not at all. *Young in juvenal plumage:* Similar to adult winter but cinnamon deeper; markings above, especially on head and neck, less sharply defined; below cinnamon, paling to buffy on throat, sparingly and faintly streaked dusky on lower neck and little if any barring on flanks. *Downy young:* Pinkish-buff, brightest on sides and neck; paler below, fading to near white on throat, chin and sides of head; back of head and neck, back, rump and wings blotched with seal-brown or clouded with hair-brown, becoming gradually buff on sides; a narrow stripe from bill to eye and dark brown central stripe running from base of bill over top of head.

MEASUREMENTS. — Length 16.00 to 20.50 in.; spread 30.00 to 40.00; folded wing 8.46 to 10.00; tail 3.00 to 4.00; bill 2.90 to 5.50; tarsus 2.50 to 3.07. Weight about 30 oz. (Wilson). Female decidedly larger than male.

MOLTS. — Not sufficient material examined to determine molts. Adults have a complete molt July to December; the change into nuptial plumage in spring is not great and is believed to be due to a shedding of tips and margins of body-feathers, taking place without molt; immature birds probably become as adults the second winter.

FIELD MARKS. — Great size (largest of our shore birds except Long-billed Curlew); light reddish color and long, straight or slightly upturned bill; *no white patch at base of tail,* as in Hudsonian Godwit.

VOICE. — *Ter whit ter whit* or *godwit godwit;* when disturbed sounds more like *kerweck kerwee-eck;* sometimes a long scream, *qu-a-ack* or *quoi-oick* or even *ker-kor-koit* (A. C. Bent); call of the flock *queep, queep, queep, queep, queep* (Florence M. Bailey).

BREEDING. — On dry prairie or in meadows or marshes, usually not far from water. *Nest:* In hollow, on ground, often formed by treading down grass. *Eggs:* 3 or 4; 2.14 to 2.37 by 1.50 to 1.61 in.; somewhat pear-shaped or elongate-ovate; varying tones of buff, with underlying spots of drab or lilac and superficial ones of deep brown or yellowish-brown. *Dates:* April 20, Iowa; May 16, South Dakota; May 20 to June 15, Saskatchewan. *Incubation:* Probably by both sexes. One brood yearly.

RANGE. — North America, Middle America and northern South America. Breeds from Saskatchewan valley (eastern Alberta and Saskatchewan), southern Manitoba and both coasts of James Bay south to southern North Dakota (formerly Utah, Nebraska, Iowa, Wisconsin and northern Ohio); winters from southern Lower California, Louisiana, Georgia and Florida to Ecuador and Peru (formerly Argentina); casual in California in December; occurs in migration on Pacific coast north to Vancouver Island and on Atlantic side (chiefly in autumn) to Maritime Provinces and southern Hudson Bay (formerly at least) and south to Lesser Antilles; casual in Alabama; accidental in Alaska and probably Bermuda.

DISTRIBUTION IN NEW ENGLAND. — Formerly an uncommon or rare migrant, mainly coastwise; now an accidental transient visitor. The records since 1900 are: *Maine:* Popham Beach, female taken September 13, 1900;[1] Scarborough, female shot August 16, 1904, by George H. Cushman, and preserved in the collection of Dr. H. H. Brock.[2] *New Hampshire:* Seabrook, bird taken August 17, 1912, near Massachusetts line. *Massachusetts:* Sandwich, male taken August 27, 1902 and mounted and preserved in the collection of Hon. John E. Thayer; Newburyport, bird taken September 5, 1904, by S. J. P. Eaton and preserved in the collection of Dr. C. W. Townsend;[3] Eastham, bird taken August 10, 1912, by Augustus Hemenway and given to William Brewster;[4] Essex, female taken August 31, 1921.[5] Newbury, male taken August 27, 1924, at Parker River by Dr. Thos. C. Barbour; another bird of same species seen by Dr. Herbert Maynard but did not come within gunshot.[6] *Rhode Island:* Little Compton, bird taken August 29, 1900, at Sakonnet by Newton Dexter, recorded by Reginald Heber Howe, Jr.;[7] bird taken September 7, 1908, at Sakonnet Point by a gunner named Merritt and recorded by Harry S. Hathaway.[8] *Connecticut:* West Haven, adult female taken August 26, 1909, by William Ganung, and preserved in the collection of Dr. L. B. Bishop.[9]

SEASON IN MASSACHUSETTS. — May 20–23; July 17 to September 7.

HAUNTS AND HABITS. There is some reason to believe that the Marbled Godwit, a great, peculiar, handsome shore bird, was not rare in Massachusetts in migration early in the last century. Audubon tells of immense flocks passing along the coast from Florida to Massachusetts. Peabody (1839) said that in August they appeared here in large numbers. DeKay (1844) said that they returned in large flocks in August to the coast of New York. So far as we know it always bred in the interior, though it may have nested casually in New England.[10]

Its principal breeding-grounds are believed to have been always near the center of the continent, but in migration numbers formerly appeared on the coast of southern Alaska, on Vancouver Island, in the Maritime Provinces of Canada and in New England, apparently going almost directly east and west to the two oceans. It has been extirpated from a large part of its former breeding range, and although it still breeds in some numbers in south central Canada, it is now a mere accidental straggler to New England. While here it visits the salt-marshes along the coast, pools of salt and fresh water, mud flats and

---

[1] Journal Maine Ornithological Society, Vol. II, 1900, p. 33.
[2] Auk, Vol. XXIV, 1907, p. 94. See also Journal of Maine Ornithological Society, Vol. VI, 1904, p. 76.
[3] Birds of Essex County, 1905, p. 181.
[4] Hemenway, Lawrence: *in litt.*
[5] Fuller, Arthur B.: Auk, Vol. XXXIX, 1922, p. 425.
[6] Brooks, W. Sprague: *in litt.*
[7] Notes on Rhode Island Ornithology, Vol. I, 1900, p. 22.
[8] Auk, Vol. XXX, 1913, p. 551.
[9] Bishop, Louis B.: Auk, Vol. XXVII, 1910, p. 462.
[10] In Shooting and Fishing, Vol. IX, 1890, p. 12, Mr. Fletcher Osgood records that he was informed that "back in the 40's probably" it bred now and then on the Lynn marsh.

beaches.   Audubon describes its habits as observed by him in the eastern United States and Messrs. Bent [1] and Job [2] give descriptions of its breeding habits in Saskatchewan.

This fine bird is a valuable insect destroyer.   In the interior it feeds largely on insects and is very destructive to grasshoppers and locusts.   Now, however, it has been driven from nearly all its breeding-grounds in the United States and its early extinction may be anticipated, unless it can be strictly protected throughout its range.

ECONOMIC STATUS.   See page 372.

Limosa hæmástica (LINNÆUS).   Hudsonian Godwit.

Other names: SPOT-RUMP; WHITE-RUMP; STRAIGHT-BILLED CURLEW; RING-TAILED MARLIN; BLACK-TAIL; BRANT-BIRD; GODWIT; GOOSE-BIRD.

Plate 29.

DESCRIPTION. — Bill, tail and feet formed much as in Marbled Godwit but bird *smaller, darker* and *tail not barred.   Adults in breeding plumage (sexes alike):* Head and neck pale buff or whitish to cinnamon-buff, but so thickly streaked dusky as to appear very dark on the crown; a nearly unstreaked broad whitish line from base of bill over eye; line through eye streaked darkly; (sometimes chin and upper throat almost unstreaked); back and scapulars sooty-black, irregularly marked cinnamon or pale brownish-buff, mostly on feather-margins, rump dusky-brown; *anterior upper tail-coverts white;* longer (posterior) ones abruptly sooty-black, sometimes with small white tips; tail sooty-black, tipped white, its concealed base also white, except on middle feathers, white increasing in extent from middle to outer feathers; wing-coverts plain grayish-brown with lighter margins; greater and primary coverts broadly tipped white or whitish; middle coverts sometimes spotted dusky; flight-feathers mostly dark or dusky-grayish-brown to blackish; shafts of primaries mainly white, and some inner primaries have some white on basal part of webs; tertials irregularly edged buffy or cinnamon; below mainly russet or "chestnut red" irregularly barred dusky and whitish, bars more distinct on sides and flanks, and broader on longer under tail-coverts; *axillars and under wing-coverts mainly very dark sooty-brown or "sooty gray";* bill light flesh-color on basal half, darkening toward end, tipped blackish; iris dark brown; legs and feet bluish-gray.   *Adults in winter plumage:* Back scapulars and wing-coverts plain brownish-gray or grayish-brown, head and neck paler, sometimes suffused very pale buffy; under plumage pale grayish-buffy to whitish, shaded brownish-gray on neck and breast; otherwise as breeding plumage; "bill olive black, flesh color toward base; iris deep olive brown, legs dark greenish-olive" (Francis Harper).   *Young in first winter plumage:* Similar to adult winter, but recognizable by retained juvenal wing-coverts.   *Young in juvenal plumage:* Very different from adult; crown-feathers with dark brown centers; back of neck a rather sooty brown with "fulvous and dull ashy edgings"; bases of back-feathers dull ashy with sub-terminal margin of blackish, bordered at tip or outer edge by "dull buffy or fulvous"; rump dark ashy or blackish; upper tail-coverts white; tail as adult but duller with markings less defined; under tail-coverts white with some ashy-brown wash, no barring; sides of head "pale fulvous," mottled dull ashy; band of dull fulvous ashy across breast; elsewhere below dull fulvous (E. W. Nelson).

MEASUREMENTS. — Length 14.00 to 16.75 in.; spread 25.00 to 28.00; folded wing 7.50 to 8.60; tail 2.50 to 3.25; bill 2.20 to 3.50; tarsus 2.02 to 2.55.   Weight 9 to 13 oz.   Female averages larger than male.

MOLTS. — Juvenal body-feathers and some of wing and tail are molted August to January.   After the partial prenuptial molt in spring some birds may assume a plumage similar to breeding adult; others may not, but at the postnuptial complete molt probably most or all young birds become as winter adults.

[1] Auk, Vol. XXIV, 1907, pp. 160–167.
[2] Job. H. K.: Nature Lovers Library, Birds of America, Vol. I, pp. 241–242.

Adults have a partial prenuptial molt in spring (completed in May) and complete postnuptial molt in autumn (August to winter); outer edges and tips of many feathers are shed in spring thus completing the spring color-change.

FIELD MARKS. — Larger than Greater Yellow-legs; size of Willet or larger; in fall plumage (seen in New England) resembles gray autumnal Willet (some in changing plumage are mottled with reddish below) but *white upper tail-coverts more conspicuous in flight;* also Willet has much more white in wing showing well in flight; long, slightly upturned bill and white upper tail-coverts distinguish this godwit from curlews; dark axillars and wing linings are conspicuous in flight; in breeding or transition plumage the bird is much darker than Marbled Godwit, males seeming nearly black at a distance.

VOICE. — Mr. T. C. Wilson describes the note as peculiar and easily recognized; a low, double note, frequently emitted as bird comes in to decoys (C. W. Townsend); "their call-note is a soft *chip* . . . and when alarmed they utter a low Sandpiper-like chattering" (C. Harrold).

BREEDING. — Said to breed in or near marshes or tundra and in Barren Grounds. *Nest:* A hollow in ground lined with leaves. *Eggs:* 2 to 4; 2.22 by 1.40 to 2.15 by 1.35 in.; pear-shaped; variable, but probably usually dark greenish-brown, olivaceous-drab, deep olive or hair-brown almost like those of a loon; somewhat obscurely blotched with dark brown or burnt-umber. *Dates:* June 9, Fort Anderson, Mackenzie. *Incubation:* Period, probably about 24 days, but not known; probably by both sexes. Probably one brood yearly.

RANGE. — North and South America. Breeds from Lower Anderson River probably southeast toward Hudson Bay (possibly also on east side of Bay), on Southampton Island in Hudson Bay, north to Cumberland Sound and west to Port Clarence, Alaska; winters in Chile, Argentina, Patagonia and Falkland Islands; in migration occurs principally east of Great Plains, most commonly on Atlantic coast in autumn and in Mississippi valley in spring; casual in Bermuda.

DISTRIBUTION IN NEW ENGLAND. — Rare irregular fall migrant in all the states; mainly coastwise; accidental in spring.

SEASON IN MASSACHUSETTS. — April 29 to May 25; July 15 to November 12.

HAUNTS AND HABITS. Probably the Hudsonian Godwit was once as common in autumn on the coasts of New England in migration as in any part of the United States. It was particularly numerous on Cape Cod at times, but doubtless it was never regularly common even there; for so far as can be determined from what little we know of its migrations, it moves southeast from Hudson Bay to the Atlantic coast in its autumnal migration, and then puts out to sea on its journey to the Lesser Antilles and South America. Therefore, it would not be liable to delay in any great numbers on our coasts unless held back or driven back on its course by high opposing winds. When, during its migrations, great easterly storms occur with high winds, we may expect it here. Thus on August 31, 1903,* a large flight of the species appeared on Long Island and earlier (the 29th) after a wind had blown from the east and northeast for six days numbers appeared on Cape Cod. On August 26, 1908, a flock of about 50 birds was reported from Ipswich.[1] Dr. C. W. Townsend records 70 birds at Ipswich on the same date. Again in August, 1910, flocks of 10 to 50 birds were reported from Cape Cod and a number of single birds were taken. Mr. S. Prescott Fay records the killing of 15 of these birds in August and September of that year, mostly on Cape Cod.[2] Since then comparatively few birds of this species have been reported. Probably, however, easterly storms in

---

[1] Massachusetts State Board of Agriculture: A History of the Game Birds, Wild-fowl and Shore Birds, 1912, p. 298.
[2] Auk, 1911, Vol. 28, pp. 257, 258.   * Date Aug. 13, given in Game Birds, Wild-fowl and Shore Birds, is an error.

August after any favorable breeding season will scatter this species along our coast again. On the northward flight in spring the Hudsonian Godwit probably crosses the Gulf of Mexico, for it is a well-known fact that it goes up the western part of the Mississippi Valley region, east of the Great Plains. While with us it seems to have a preference for sandy shores and sandspits, but it also frequents mud flats, beaches and creeks in the salt-marsh and sometimes goes to the uplands after insects.

The food of the Hudsonian Godwit includes worms, many insects (including horse-flies and mosquitoes), mollusks and crustaceans, and various small forms of marine life.

ECONOMIC STATUS. See page 372.

Philomáchus púgnax (LINNÆUS). Ruff.

Fig. 33.

DESCRIPTION. — Bill about as long as head, tapering, when viewed from side but with edges nearly parallel when viewed from above, tip slightly expanded and a little (but distinctly) downcurved; tail rounded, of 12 feathers, two middle feathers slightly longer than rest; a small web between bases of middle and outer toes. *Adult male in breeding plumage:* Front face more or less naked, with small reddish, yellow or pink, warty excrescences; neck with a large, conspicuous, shield-like, erectile ruff of elongated feathers; back of head with two peculiar elongated tufts; head, neck and breast varying remarkably in color in different specimens; ruff and tufts solid black or brown with purplish gloss or barred or in other cases purple, white or whitish, sandy-buff, brown, chestnut and purplish etc.; black appears in various combinations of barring, streaking or speckling with purple reflections; back and scapulars marked irregularly with black, gray, buffy and whitish, black usually predominating, whitish often in irregular bars; rump grayish-brown with paler margins; middle upper tail-coverts variegated with blackish, pale buffy and pale brownish-gray or whitish, outer upper tail-coverts white; middle tail-feathers brownish-gray, indistinctly barred dusky, each with a large spot of black near tip; other tail-feathers light grayish-brown; wing-coverts mostly grayish-brown, margined a little paler, secondaries similar, but with narrow white edgings; primary coverts and primaries darker, former narrowly a little paler at tips, shafts white or yellowish-white; tertials broadly barred black and grayish-brown, brown intermixed with whitish; below, including abdomen, under tail-coverts, most of under wing-coverts and axillars white. *Adult male in winter plumage:* Front face feathered; no ruffs or tufts; top of head and hind neck light grayish-brown, former narrowly streaked darker more or less; upper surface of body (except outer upper tail-coverts) mainly grayish-brown, with dark feather centers and paler margins; greater wing-coverts tipped white; sides of head and neck, fore neck, upper breast and sides light grayish, brown or pinkish-buff, feathers tipped whitish or brownish-white; chin and throat mostly white; cheeks, ear coverts, lower throat and sides of neck faintly spotted brownish or dusky; otherwise, including white outer upper tail-coverts as in breeding plumage. *Adult female in breeding plumage:* Similar to winter male, but upper plumage much darker; feathers of upper surface of body blackish (often glossed purplish) and margined buff or cinnamon; tertials often barred blackish and rusty; feathers of breast blackish centrally, and tail-feathers partly barred cinnamon or rusty, thrush-like spots on sides of upper breast. *Adult female in winter plumage:* Similar to winter male but much smaller. *Young in first winter plumage:* Similar to winter adult, retaining some juvenal scapulars and inner secondaries, which are brownish-black with buff edges, and some wing-coverts edged buffy. *Young in juvenal plumage:* Resembles adult winter, but much more tawny; feathers of upper surface of body blackish with buffy or whitish margins and tips; upper tail-coverts as adult winter but dark feathers edged warm buff; wing-coverts like back with buffy edgings; top of head dark brown, feathers edged buffy; back of nape ashy-brown with buff edges; sides of head buffy with wavy black bars and streaks; lower throat and breast fawn or buffy; sides washed buff; tail mainly dark brown.

MEASUREMENTS. — *Male:* Length about 12.50 in.; folded wing 6.40 to 7.00; tail 2.60 to 3.00; bill 1.25 to 1.50; tarsus 1.60 to 2.00. *Female:* Much smaller than male; length about 10.00 in.; folded wing 5.95 to 6.25; bill 1.15 to 1.24; tarsus about 1.40.

MOLTS. — The juvenal plumage is partially molted (August to December); a partial prenuptial molt in spring is followed by a plumage nearly indistinguishable from that of adult, and after a complete postnuptial molt in late summer and autumn, adult winter plumage probably is assumed; adults have partial molt in spring and complete molt in autumn; after prenuptial molt when breeding plumage has been attained, feathers of forehead and front face of male are lost and replaced by numerous tubercles.

FIELD MARKS. — Male in summer, with its extravagant ruffs, is unlike any other American bird; female in summer has thrush-like spots on sides of upper breast; in winter plumage "a narrow white wing-bar shows in flight as does an oval white patch on each side of *brown coloured median area in tail*" (Practical Handbook of British Birds). She somewhat resembles the Upland Plover.

VOICE. — Usually silent; a low *tu whit;* a loud whistle when migrating (Practical Handbook of British Birds).

BREEDING. — In meadows. *Nest:* In thick grass, well hidden; a hollow in ground lined with grass. *Eggs:* Usually 4; 1.80 by 1.25 to 1.60 by 1.15 in.; pear-shaped; pale gray or yellowish to pale green or blue, boldly spotted and blotched with dark brown and ashy, clustering most thickly at large end. *Incubation:* Period, probably 17 to 19 days (Naumann), not definitely known; by female. One brood yearly.

RANGE. — Eastern Hemisphere. Breeds from Arctic coast south to Great Britain, Holland, Belgium, northern France, Bavaria, Hungary, southern Russia and Siberia; winters throughout Africa, India, Ceylon and Burmah; rare to casual in Iceland, on Madeira and Canary Islands, in China, Japan and Borneo; has occurred in Greenland, Ontario, Maine, New Hampshire, Massachusetts, Rhode Island, New York, Ohio, Indiana, District of Columbia, Virginia, North Carolina, Barbados, Guadeloupe and Surinam; casual on Bering and Pribilof Islands.

DISTRIBUTION IN NEW ENGLAND. — Casual or accidental from Eastern Hemisphere. Records: *Maine:* Scarborough, female taken April 10, 1870, by Everett Smith;[1] Upton, young female taken September 8, 1874, and recorded by William Brewster;[2] Camden, female taken September 14, 1900, by Sidney Clark, recorded by Hon. John E. Thayer;[3] Scarborough, female taken October 16, 1912, on Nonesuch River by I. W. Pillsbury, recorded by Arthur H. Norton.[4] *New Hampshire:* Seabrook, female taken September 23, 1907, by Charles Fowler, recorded by John H. Hardy, Jr., and also by Hon. John E. Thayer who received it from Mr. Hardy.[5] *Massachusetts:* Newburyport, adult female taken on marshes May 20, 1871, recorded by William Brewster;[6] Chatham, young male taken September 11, 1880, secured by Gordon Plummer[7] and now in the collection of the Brookline High School; Nantucket, female shot in late July, 1901, by Alfred Dabney, in the collection of Hon. John E. Thayer at Lancaster, recorded by T. S. Palmer.[8] *Rhode Island:* Little Compton, Sakonnet, female taken July 30, 1900, by Newton Dexter;[9] Narragansett, immature female taken at Point Judith August 31, 1903, preserved in collection of LeRoy King by whom recorded;[10] immature female taken at same place September 7, 1909, by William T. Bowler, recorded by Harry S. Hathaway.[11]

[1] Smith, Everett: Forest and Stream, Vol. XX, 1883, p. 85.
[2] Bulletin of the Nuttall Ornithological Club, Vol. I, 1876, p. 19.
[3] Auk, Vol. XXII, 1905, p. 409.
[4] *Ibid.*, Vol. XXX, 1913, p. 576.
[5] *Ibid.*, Vol. XXV, 1908, p. 82, and Vol. XXVI, 1909, p. 77.
[6] American Naturalist, Vol. VI, 1872, p. 306.
[7] Forest and Stream, Vol. XV, 1880, p. 186.
[8] Auk, Vol. XXIII, 1906, p. 98.   [9] Hathaway, H. S.: Notes on Rhode Island Ornithology, Vol. I, 1900, p. 20.
[10] Auk, Vol. XXI, 1904, p. 85.   [11] *Ibid.*, Vol. XXX, 1913, p. 552.

FIG. 32. — CURLEW SANDPIPER
From a Specimen in the Museum of the Boston Society
of Natural History.   Page 417

FIG. 33. — RUFF

Female   Male in nuptial plumage
From specimens in the Museum of Comparative Zoölogy

HAUNTS AND HABITS. The Ruff is one of the few shore birds in which the breeding plumage of the female does not resemble that of the male. The two are so unlike that in England the female is called the Reeve. About 30 individuals of this Old World species have been taken and recorded on this side of the Atlantic, but in one case a bird reported in Ontario was later identified as an Upland Plover. This indicates how readily the bird might be overlooked. The male in breeding plumage would be readily recognized, but as the birds taken in this country have been mainly females and young, which have a general resemblance to the Upland Plover, no one knows how many may have been taken by market hunters and sold unrecognized. Collectors should be on the lookout for this species. Its occasional occurrence here and the taking of a number of our own shore birds on the other side of the Atlantic are facts which illustrate the great powers of flight with which these birds are endowed. The Ruff haunts salt-marshes, swamps and margins of lakes. In this country the greater number naturally have been taken near the sea, but the species has appeared inland in Ohio and Indiana. In the mating season the males meet on selected spots of bare ground where they display their plumage and engage in combat much in the manner of game cocks, but less savagely.

The Ruff seems to be silent here, as a rule, walks quite erect, rather deliberately, and probes in the mud for its food, which is chiefly worms, crustaceans and insects, with some seeds and other vegetal matter.

ECONOMIC STATUS. See page 372.

Tryngítes subruficóllis (VIEILLOT). Buff-breasted Sandpiper.

Other name: HILL GRASS-BIRD.

Plate 31.

DESCRIPTION. — Bill short for a sandpiper, shorter than head, feathers extending farther forward on sides of lower mandible than on upper mandible and farther still underneath former; tail little rounded, middle feathers somewhat projecting; legs rather short for a sandpiper but tibia partly bare; toes cleft to base or with slight rudimentary webbing. *Adults in breeding plumage (sexes alike)*: Top of head and back of neck rather light buff, spotted and streaked blackish, heavily on head, lightly on neck; elsewhere above largely brownish-black, feathers broadly margined and tipped light grayish-buff, tawny, pinkish-buff or yellowish-brown; middle tail-feathers greenish or grayish-brown, shading to blackish at ends, edges of tips narrowly whitish, other tail-feathers paler, with white tips preceded by black; middle wing-coverts irregularly marked dark brown in V, Y or semicircular form; primaries and secondaries ashy-brown or olive-brown, darkening toward edges of outer webs and blackening toward tips; edges of extreme tips of these feathers and those of primary coverts white or cream-colored; *most of inner webs of primaries and both webs of secondaries pearly-white, curiously marbled and spotted dark brown or blackish*, most evident on under sides of wings and also on under primary coverts; sides of head and neck, and under plumage light pinkish-cinnamon or deep pinkish-buff, passing into buffy-white on abdomen, flanks and under tail-coverts; feathers of fore neck, breast and sides more or less indistinctly tipped lighter, with some black spots on breast; axillars, wing-linings and basal part of inner webs of primaries mainly white; bill black, growing lighter or brownish toward base; iris dark brown; legs and feet dull greenish, yellowish-green or yellowish. *Adults in winter plumage:* Similar to breeding plumage; under plumage less rufescent, sometimes tawny-whitish, broad tawny or buffy edges of upper plumage replaced by narrow whitish (Coues). *Young in juvenal plumage:* Similar to adult, but with colors less sharply contrasted above, each feather margined whitish; sides of neck finely dotted dusky and with dark brown markings on inner webs of primaries and under primary-coverts finer, closer together and more dot-like; "bill black; feet ochraceous-yellow" (Allan Brooks).

MEASUREMENTS. — Length 7.50 to 8.90 in.; spread 15.75 to 17.40; folded wing 4.95 to 5.43; tail 2.15 to 2.64; bill .67 to .75; tarsus 1.20 to 1.35. Weight 2½ oz. (Audubon). Male larger than female.

MOLTS. — Young birds have at least a partial postjuvenal molt in autumn (then assuming first winter plumage) and a prenuptial molt during late winter and early spring months; apparently they become practically like adults the next summer; adults apparently molt body-feathers (not all scapulars), sometimes some or all tail-feathers and some wing-coverts in spring, and have a complete postnuptial fall molt extending into winter.

FIELD MARKS. — Slightly larger than Spotted Sandpiper; rather tawny like Upland Plover but much smaller and not so slender; its short tail does not reach to the tips of its long, pointed, closed wings while the long tail of the Upland Plover projects beyond the tips of its closed wings; frequents fields, pastures and hillsides near coast.

VOICE. — A very silent bird. "A weak *tweet*" (D. G. Elliot) repeated once or twice.

BREEDING. — On the higher dryer parts of Arctic tundra and on Barren Grounds. *Nest:* A mere hollow in moss or a shallow depression in ground, lined with a little moss or a few leaves and grasses. *Eggs:* Usually 4, rarely 5; 1.40 to 1.51 by 1.02 to 1.10; pear-shaped; ashy-drab or clay color, sometimes with grayish or olive tinge, with profuse, bold markings, splashes and blotches of "deep sepia" or varying shades of rich umber-brown and some washes of pale purplish-slate; markings often tend to cluster about large end. *Dates:* June 18 to July 9, Alaska and Mackenzie. *Incubation:* By female. Probably one brood yearly.

RANGE. — North and South America. Breeds along Arctic coast from northern Alaska to northern Keewatin, probably west to easternmost Arctic Asia and east to Hudson Bay; winters in Argentina and Uruguay; most abundant in migration in Mississippi valley; rare in fall in eastern Alberta and Colorado; and on North Atlantic coast from northern Ungava (northern Quebec) to Long Island; is rare on South Atlantic coast of United States and on Pacific coast north to St. Michael, Alaska; common in northeastern Siberia; casual or accidental in Bermuda, West Indies and western Europe and on Asiatic coast of Pacific to Sea of Okhotsk and northern Japan.

DISTRIBUTION IN NEW ENGLAND. — Rare fall migrant in coastwise states; doubtfully recorded from Vermont.

SEASON IN MASSACHUSETTS. — July 8 to September 24.

HAUNTS AND HABITS. The Buff-breasted Sandpiper resembles the Upland Plover somewhat in appearance and frequents the same localities, sometimes in company with the former or with the Golden Plover or Black-breasted Plover, usually on grassy hills along the sea-coast, sometimes near water, or even on the beach. Formerly it was perhaps not uncommon in New England; now it is one of the rarest sandpipers. Mr. E. A. Doolittle, who watched the feeding habits of a bird of this species, says that the legs were bent, giving the bird a crouching attitude, and that the feet were lifted high at each step, as if "stepping over and through grass." Although the bird was on the beach it straightened up every few feet as if peering over grass; showing a decided resemblance, with its extended neck, to the Upland Plover.[1] This bird is unsuspicious and ordinarily may be closely approached.

Professor W. W. Cooke expressed the belief that the majority of this species in its

---

[1] Auk, Vol. XL, 1923, p. 692.

southward migration takes a zigzag route, going first easterly to Hudson Bay (some continuing to the Atlantic coast), thence southerly to the Gulf of Mexico, thence through Central America to the northwestern coast of South America, thence southeasterly to Argentina. Such a peculiar, erratic course is followed by no other North American shore bird. This may explain why the bird is a *rara avis* on the South Atlantic coast of the United States and in the West Indies. This species, like the Upland Plover, feeds very largely on insects.[1] Its former vast numbers have been greatly reduced by spring shooting in the Mississippi Valley.

ECONOMIC STATUS. A useful, valuable bird but now too rare to be of any appreciable service in New England.

SUBFAMILY **NUMENIINÆ**. TATTLERS AND CURLEWS.

Number of species in North America 16; in Massachusetts 9.

This subfamily includes large *Limicolæ*, with bills, legs and wings usually long; the bill is either practically straight or curved downward, the greatest length of bill being found in the curlew. Tattlers received their name from their loud and clamorous voices; curlews are less vociferous.

Tótanus melanoleúcus (GMELIN). Greater Yellow-legs.

Other names: WINTER YELLOW-LEG; WINTER TURKEY-BACK; CUCU; BIG YELLOW-LEG; HORSE YELLOW-LEG; GREATER TATTLER OR TELL-TALE.

Plate 30.

DESCRIPTION. — Bill long and rather slender, but stout in comparison with that of smaller yellow-legs; straight or a little upturned toward end; neck and legs also long and slender; basal web between outer and middle toes. *Adults in breeding plumage (sexes alike):* Top of head and back of neck streaked white or grayish-white and dusky or blackish; above mainly light gray, spotted black and pale gray or whitish on upper back, scapulars, wing-coverts and tertials, pale gray or whitish predominating on feather-margins; lower back and rump dusky brownish-gray with pale gray feather-tips and subterminal dusky bars; upper tail-coverts white, longer ones barred dusky, shorter ones less marked; two or more middle tail-feathers brownish-gray and whitish, barred dusky along edges, rest of tail-feathers white, barred dusky; primaries and their coverts brownish-black, 3 or 4 innermost paler with whitish edges to their tips; *under surface of flight-feathers more or less marbled;* sides of head, neck, and under plumage white, two former streaked dusky; breast more or less heavily streaked and spotted and with some V-shaped or arrow-head marks; sides, flanks and under tail-coverts more or less barred with same; axillars and under wing-coverts white, former irregularly barred brownish-gray, latter with V-shaped dusky marks; bill blackish, lightening toward base; iris dark brown; legs and feet bright yellow. *Adults in winter plumage:* General colors as in breeding plumage, but lacking blackish markings above; fore neck and upper breast more narrowly streaked; lower breast unmarked or little marked, abdomen unmarked; sides and flanks irregularly and lightly marked grayish. *Young in first winter plumage:* Similar to winter adult, but feathers of upper back and scapulars with buffy end margins and each with subterminal dusky crescent. *Young in juvenal plumage:* Similar to adult breeding plumage, but generally dark brown above with fewer light markings, mostly marginal, and tinged buffy; markings of

[1] United States Department of Agriculture, Biological Survey, Bulletin No. 35, 1910, p. 68.

under plumage dull brown; "feet bright ocher-yellow, dusky on joints of toes; bill grayish-olive black toward tip" (Allan Brooks).

MEASUREMENTS. — Very variable; length 12.15 to 15.00 in.; spread 23.00 to 26.00; folded wing 6.97 to 8.00; tail 2.75 to 3.50; bill 2.00 to 2.30; tarsus 2.19 to 2.75.　Weight 5 to 10 oz., usually 6 to 8.　Female larger than male.

MOLTS. — Postjuvenal molt (September to February) includes body-feathers, a few central tail-feathers, some scapulars, secondaries and wing-coverts; at first prenuptial molt in spring some young birds appear to acquire some breeding plumage and others to assume a winter plumage similar to that of adult; all probably become as winter adult after complete postnuptial molt; adults have complete molt in autumn and partial molt of most body-feathers, tail-feathers and some wing-feathers and coverts (February to May).

FIELD MARKS. — Readily distinguished from all our shore birds except the smaller Yellow-legs by its large size, height, slender appearance, cries, gray plumage, conspicuous white tail-coverts and *long yellow legs* and from the Lesser Yellow-legs by the relatively longer, *larger, stouter bill* and larger size.

VOICE. — A variety of notes.　The principal ones follow: (1) A rather pentrating, insistent, mellow, whistled series all on one pitch, usually in threes or fours, *whèw-whew-whew*, sometimes a single whistle is interpolated; (2) the summons call pleasant, musical, oft repeated, *too-whee, too-whee, too-whee, too-whee, too-whee;* (3) an emphatic hen-like cackle, *kaouw, kaouw, kaouw, kaouw;* a lone bird standing and calling thus bobs the head vigorously with each note (J. T. Nichols); (4) on rare occasions while flying about in spring a scream, *keá rr, keá rr*, much like Common Tern; (5) courtship note *wull yer? wull yer?* (C. W. Townsend).

BREEDING. — Usually in forested regions near a lake or stream, sometimes on an island.　*Nest:* A depression in ground.　*Eggs:* 4; 1.66 to 1.97 by 1.16 to 1.36 in.; pear-shaped; grayish-white, boldly splashed with shades of brown and lilac (C. A. Reed).　*Dates:* May 20 to 31, British Columbia; May 20 to June 13, Newfoundland.　*Incubation:* Probably chiefly by female.　Probably one brood yearly.

RANGE. — North and South America.　Breeds in timbered regions from Mt. Iliamna, Alaska, southern Mackenzie and southern Ungava (central Quebec), south to southern British Columbia, southern Manitoba, Labrador, Newfoundland, Mingan, Anticosti and Magdalen Islands; winters from Washington (casually), southern California, Texas, Louisiana and South Carolina (occasionally North Carolina) south to Patagonia; found every month of the year in West Indies, Bahamas, Florida, Texas and California; occurs in Bermuda; accidental in British Isles.

DISTRIBUTION IN NEW ENGLAND. — Common migrant largely coastwise; less common to rare in Vermont; a few non-breeding birds may summer rarely, as in Massachusetts.

SEASON IN MASSACHUSETTS. — (March 27) April 3 to June 16 (June 28); (July 6) July 20 to November 17 (November 22).

HAUNTS AND HABITS.　Every marshland hunter knows the Greater Yellow-legs as a telltale.　This shy, wild bird seems always on the lookout for danger and its cries of alarm are well understood by every wild denizen of marsh and shore.　In New England it frequents mainly the mud flats, estuaries and pools in the marsh or along the shore where it wades sometimes up to its body in the water.　In August and early September, when interior waters are low, it may be seen in small numbers about their margins.　At all seasons it is rather rare along the outer sea beaches.　The following by Dr. C. W. Townsend is excellently descriptive of the habits of the species:

"This beautiful and interesting bird is rarely to be found on the beach, preferring the sloughs of the marsh or the muddy creeks, where it can catch small fish in the water and probe the soft mud with its long bill.　Persistently sought by the gunner, eagerly

PLATE 30

PLATE 30

SPOTTED SANDPIPER

Page 450

Adult in Breeding Plumage (Spring)

Young Coming into Winter
Plumage (Autumn)

SOLITARY SANDPIPER

Page 440

Adult

GREATER YELLOW-LEGS

Page 435

Adult

YELLOW-LEGS

Page 438

Adult

All one-half natural size.

responding to the easily imitated call, and offering on its approach to the decoys an extremely easy shot, the Greater Yellow-legs still remains common, although its numbers have been greatly reduced in the last twenty years. Like all shore birds, its numbers on the coast vary greatly in different years, owing not so much to the actual number of birds as to the direction of the flight, whether along the coast or farther out to sea. This, in turn, depends largely on the weather conditions. As an illustration of the immense numbers of birds that are sometimes killed, it may be stated that 463 Greater Yellow-legs were sent from Newburyport and vicinity on one day, October 11, 1904, to a single stall in Boston Market.

"In flying, the Greater Yellow-legs is a conspicuous object. Its long yellow legs are extended out behind, its long neck and bill in front, while its white rump flashes out as the bird turns or flies away. The wings, dark and pointed, are curved downward with vigorous strokes, as the bird flies and scales alternately. In alighting, it first sets its wings, sails gracefully downward, drops its long legs, and as soon as it is firmly on the ground it frequently spreads and lifts its wings straight up over its back, then folds them carefully, and after 'tetering,' in which process it moves its whole body up and down on its legs as a fulcrum, it proceeds to go about the business of the day in feeding." [1]

"The courtship song of the Greater Yellow-legs comes up from the marshes of Essex County throughout the month of May, but is heard in greater volume during the two middle weeks. It has a sweet and pleading character and seems to say *wull yer? wull yer?* Although it differs from the Flicker-like call described in the original Memoir, which may be heard at the same time, it too has a decided Flicker-like flavor. It is heard throughout the day, but in the evening until it is nearly dark, the marshes often resound with the plaintive callings.

"In walking in the shallow water of a pond these long-legged birds kick out their legs behind as if to rid them of weeds or grass. They dab at the mud or water like a plover instead of deliberately probing it like a sandpiper with head down. They often pick off insects from the grass or the surface of the water, and I have found small fish in their stomachs." [2]

In its long spring migration from Patagonia or other South American regions to Canada and Alaska the Greater Yellow-legs appears in New England in greatest numbers in May, and on the return flight is most common in late August and September or early October.

The food of this species seems to consist more largely of small fish than that of other shore birds. A small party of these Yellow-legs may be commonly seen in shallow water running rapidly in different directions in pursuit of little fish. Each bird, darting its bill into the water from time to time, now and then succeeds in catching one of the tiny creatures, which is swallowed with little effort. Occasionally, however, a bird catches a fish so large and long that it can be swallowed only with great difficulty. In addition to

---

[1] Birds of Essex County, 1905, pp. 182, 183.
[2] Supplement to Birds of Essex County, 1920, p. 86.

its fish diet the species takes the usual toll of mollusks and crustaceans and in the interior a great many insects.

ECONOMIC STATUS. The Greater Yellow-legs is an important game bird because of its large numbers, size and wide distribution. It is not the equal of Wilson's Snipe or Woodcock in an epicurean sense, particularly when it has fed on small fish, but in autumn it often becomes very fat and toothsome.

Totanus flávipes (GMELIN). Yellow-legs.

Other names: LESSER YELLOW-LEGS; SUMMER YELLOW-LEGS; SMALL CUCU.

Plate 30.

DESCRIPTION. — Essentially like Greater Yellow-legs in all plumages (see page 435), but smaller and somewhat more delicate in form; bill proportionally smaller and more slender and legs relatively longer; *lacks fine marbling on inner surface of flight-feathers* seen in Greater Yellow-legs and is not marked so extensively on under plumage.

MEASUREMENTS. — Length 9.25 to 11.15 in.; spread 19.00 to 21.50; folded wing 5.80 to 6.70; tail 2.36 to 2.50; bill 1.30 to 1.55; tarsus 1.94 to 2.15. Weight 2½ to 3⅓ oz. Female larger than male.

MOLTS. — Similar to those of Greater Yellow-legs; some young birds apparently pass through first summer in winter plumage; young become indistinguishable from adults during second winter.

FIELD MARKS. — Similar to those of Greater Yellow-legs (see page 436) but one-third smaller and bill more slender.

VOICE. — Note in flocks, an abrupt *kip* or *keup*; when single, more often one whistled *wheu* or a double *wheu-wheu*, "the combination *whew hip* is frequent" (J. T. Nichols); also the *too-whee* call often repeated like that of Greater Yellow-legs but apparently not so loud.

BREEDING. — In Barren Grounds, about shores of rivers, lakes and marshes. *Nest:* On dry ground, often among bushes or at foot of a bush or a bunch of grass; a mere hollow lined with a few leaves or grasses. *Eggs:* Usually 4; 1.58 to 1.78 by 1.12 to 1.16; pear-shaped; variable, light to dark drab, clay, buffy or cream with splashed blotches of chocolate, umber-brown, bistre or blackish and ashy-gray, sometimes massed or even confluent at large end, sometimes almost unmarked. *Dates:* June 1 to 20, Yukon and Mackenzie. *Incubation:* Probably chiefly by female. Probably one brood yearly.

RANGE. — North and South America. Breeds from Kotzebue Sound and upper Yukon valley, Alaska, northern Mackenzie, northern Manitoba and southern Ungava (Quebec) south to Lake Marsh, Yukon, southern Saskatchewan and Alberta, and (probably southern Manitoba), central Quebec, (formerly possibly Minnesota, Illinois and New York); winters in Argentina, Chile and Patagonia and casually or occasionally in Mexico, Louisiana, Florida and Bahamas; occurs in migration in Pribilof Islands, Greenland and Bermuda; usually rare in spring on Atlantic coast north of Long Island; accidental in Great Britain.

DISTRIBUTION IN NEW ENGLAND. — Rare spring and common fall migrant; most common coastwise; not common in Vermont even in autumn.

SEASON IN MASSACHUSETTS. — April 29 to June 2 (June 28); July 8 to September 29 (October 7 to 30); (Dec. 12).

HAUNTS AND HABITS. The Yellow-legs is one of the most generally common of our migrant shore birds. Its double whistle may be heard in August or early September about all large bodies of water. The spring flight of this species goes largely up the Mississippi valley. It seems to be uncommon to rare in spring north of South Carolina, from which state it migrates in a northwesterly direction.   Dr. P. L. Hatch gives the following account of its appearance at this season in Minnesota :

"From the first to the tenth of April the Yellow-legs appear about the shallow pools and muddy ponds in small parties.   In these they wade about constantly for hours at a time when unmolested, and when driven to wing, fly very swiftly away in an irregular, snipe-like manner, making a loud, whistling note, illy adapted to concert melody.   Their flight is wonderfully compact, the flock moving as if by one impulse through all the gyrations incident to indecision where next to go, which however often results in their return to the same pool when the gunner has concealed himself effectually.   From the repeated observation of this phenomenon in many species of bird life, I am convinced that in such cases only the individual leading the flock takes the least cognizance of their surroundings, all others maintaining an instinctive attention to the motions of the leader alone.   If by an exceptionally sudden surprise the flock is momentarily deranged, in an instant the former compactness is resumed as if nothing had occurred, which would be impossible upon any other conceivable hypothesis.   The noisy, whistling notes of the species soon become familiar to the gunner, which some of them learn to imitate so well that the deluded flock easily falls into the range of his deadly missile.   Their meat is scarcely less palatable than the best of the Snipe kind.   By the first of May most of them have gone, probably much farther north, to multiply by reproduction and return here again about the first week in September." [1]

This description of the species in the interior in spring may well be supplemented by another by Mr. J. T. Nichols describing its habits in autumn on the Atlantic coast :

"The Lesser Yellow-legs frequents the shallow pools in the salt-marshes, and is seen now and then on the mud flats or on stranded layers of eel-grass along the shores of coves and bays.   It is also very partial to brackish meadows with standing water ; at such a favorable spot, on the inner beach opposite Mastic, 50 to 100 birds kept congregating for days near the end of August, 1913, despite persecution by gunners.

"It is a very gregarious bird, and pairs or small flocks are more frequently observed than solitary individuals.   It often associates with other species, such as the Dowitcher, Robin Snipe, and Greater Yellow-legs.   In comparison with the last-named species, it generally travels in larger bodies, and is much less suspicious, stooling more readily and alighting closer to the blind.   Its flight is similar, though perhaps not quite so strong as that of the larger bird, which at times covers distance with surprising speed.   In all its movements and attitudes — whether wading among the decoys in water up to its thighs, bathing, running about over a mud bar, standing at rest with neck drawn in, scratching its bill with a foot, or curving its slender wings in easy flight — the Lesser Yellow-legs is an exceedingly graceful bird." [2]

We see so few of these birds in New England in spring that their arrival is always a welcome sight.   More than thirty years ago while driving through Somerville, one bright spring morning, I was surprised to see two Yellow-legs in a small puddle beside the street.

[1] Notes on the Birds of Minnesota, 1892, p. 135.   [2] Auk, Vol. XXXIII, 1916, p. 250.

These birds were so unsuspicious that they did not rise as I drove by. Occasionally perhaps some of them are driven out of their course by a spring gale, and land on Cape Cod. This must have happened in the spring of 1921 when a considerable number were reported on the Cape and a very few on other parts of the Massachusetts coast.

In the fall migration Yellow-legs appear in some numbers in August and early September along the margins of lakes and rivers, wherever flats or bars are exposed by low water. They frequent sewer-beds, fresh and salt-marshes, flats exposed at low tide, and sometimes may be seen even on the beach. They are more gregarious than the Greater Yellow-legs, and collect in larger flocks. They are not quite so shy as the larger species, and like that and the godwits, if one is wounded, the others, in their anxiety, are likely to return and flutter overhead, regardless of the gunner, until their ranks are sadly thinned. The Yellow-legs begins its autumnal migration early in July, and large flights usually pass New England before the shooting season opens. This tends to preserve the bird.

ECONOMIC STATUS. This species is important as a game bird. In autumn it grows fat on grasshoppers and other insects and doubtless is valuable in the interior as an insect destroyer. As a table bird its flavor is not equal to that of snipe or woodcock but is rather superior to that of the Greater Yellow-legs as it is not so much addicted to a fish diet.

Trínga solitária solitaria WILSON. Solitary Sandpiper.

Other names: BARNYARD-PLOVER; BLACK SNIPE.

Plate 30.

DESCRIPTION. — Bill somewhat longer than head, very straight and slim; legs not very long, mere rudimentary web between inner and middle toe, moderate one between that toe and outer one; tail rounded. *Adults in breeding plumage (sexes alike)*: Above generally dark grayish-brown with an olive cast; top of head and hind neck narrowly streaked whitish; back, scapulars and wing-coverts rather sparsely speckled same; upper tail-coverts and tail barred white and dark grayish-brown and, except two middle tail-feathers which are dusky grayish-brown, dotted white on outer edges; primary coverts and outer flight-feathers generally blackish, flight-feathers growing lighter toward body, and (in some specimens) gaining white spots; eyelids and under plumage white; sides of head, sides of neck, fore neck and upper breast thickly streaked or spotted dusky grayish-brown, in strong contrast to white of under plumage, more or less spots and bars of same on sides, flanks and under tail-coverts; axillars and under wing-coverts regularly and broadly barred white and blackish, darker color predominating on under primary coverts, lighter on edge of wing; bill greenish horn color at base, blackening at tip; iris dark brown; legs and feet dark, dull olive-greenish; "bill greenish-black; iris brown; feet greenish-gray" (Audubon); base of lower mandible grayish flesh color, legs and feet light yellowish-olive (L. A. Fuertes); bill black-brown, green at base of lower mandible; legs dull green (Practical Handbook of British Birds); bill greenish-brown; legs and feet olive-green (D. G. Elliot); bill and legs dark greenish-brown; iris hazel (Baird); bill and feet very dark olive-green (A. W. Butler).

NOTE. The above descriptions of colors of soft parts are given to show the ordinary variations in such descriptions. There may be similar or greater variations in the specimens. The iris is said to be rarely white. We may infer, however, that the eyes, bill and feet are usually dark, which is the case.

Adults and young in winter plumage: Similar to breeding plumage but upper plumage more grayish, less distinctly speckled white; fore neck, upper breast, sides, etc., very indistinctly streaked or merely washed grayish. *Young in juvenal plumage:* Lighter and more washed olive than adults, above thickly speckled white or buffy-whitish; top of head and hind neck pale brownish-gray; sides of head and neck nearly uniform plain gray, fore neck streaked darker.

MEASUREMENTS. — Length 7.50 to 9.00 in.; spread 15.00 to 17.00; folded wing 4.75 to 5.50; tail 2.12 to 2.25; bill 1.12 to 1.30; tarsus 1.07 to 1.25 (Ridgway). Weight 1¾ oz. (Audubon).

MOLTS. — This species has no autumnal postjuvenal molt and comes to resemble the winter adult merely by wear of feathers; there is a midwinter molt, probably complete, after which the young bird assumes its first nuptial plumage which closely resembles that of adults; after the complete postnuptial molt in autumn of its second year, young bird becomes as winter adult; adults have a complete autumnal or postnuptial molt and an incomplete spring molt (February to May).

FIELD MARKS. — Size a littler larger than Spotted Sandpiper; very dark above, olive legs and dark, slender bill; both upper and under sides of wings appear very dark; tail, spread when about to alight, appears white with contrasting dark middle feathers; flight swift; on alighting, drops quickly like a snipe; in moving only a few yards, has a peculiar jerky flight, with wings partly spread (J. T. Nichols); teeters much like Spotted Sandpiper but does not *exaggerate* so much with its hinder part. Distinguished from young Spotted Sandpiper by darker color above, absence of white bar in wing (which in Spotted Sandpiper shows in flight), sharp contrast between dark streaked breast and white belly, and from adult Spotted Sandpiper in summer by pure white belly with no round spots below.

VOICE. — A *peet, weet* like that of Spotted Sandpiper but a little higher pitched and thinner; a sharp whistle of three or four notes; a weak flight song on its breeding-grounds; other calls *pit-pit* or *chic-tit* and *kikikiki* (J. T. Nichols).

BREEDING. — Usually in woods, near some wooded lake or stream. *Nest:* Old nest of some other bird (abandoned by the owner) in bush or tree, such as those of Robin, Bronzed Grackle, Cedar Waxwing, Canada Jay, Kingbird and Brewer's Blackbird. *Eggs:* 4 or 5; 1.36 by .98 in. (Walter Raine); the average size of 4 eggs taken by A. D. Henderson in Alberta is 1.44 by 1.00, their ground color being "greenish with reddish-brown and umber spots . . . rather sparingly distributed from the small end to past the bulge of the egg when they join into reddish-brown blotches" almost obscuring the ground color; pear-shaped; pale greenish-white, heavily blotched and spotted, chiefly at larger ends, with Vandyke brown, chestnut-brown and purplish-gray. *Date:* June 9, northern Alberta. Probably one brood yearly.

RANGE. — Eastern North and South America. Summers from central Alberta, northern Manitoba, northern Ungava (northern Quebec) and Newfoundland south to northern Nebraska, northern Iowa, Illinois, Indiana, northern Ohio and Pennsylvania; occurs in British Columbia and recorded in New Mexico and California.[1] Probably breeds more or less in all parts of its regular summer range; winters from West Indies to Argentina; casual in Greenland, Bermuda and Great Britain.

DISTRIBUTION IN NEW ENGLAND. — Common migrant and rare summer resident in Maine, New Hampshire and Vermont, probably breeding in northern sections of each; common migrant in Massachusetts, Rhode Island and Connecticut; least common in Rhode Island.

SEASON IN MASSACHUSETTS. — April 30 to May 30 (June); July 4 to October 27 (November 28).

HAUNTS AND HABITS. The Solitary Sandpiper is remarkably graceful and active on foot or on the wing. Its aërial evolutions will equal or exceed those of Wilson's Snipe. It gets insects on the wing as readily as do many of the smaller birds. I have described elsewhere its ingenious method of stirring the silt in the bottom of a ditch by moving one foot so rapidly and gently that though the water was not roiled its insect prey was started from the bottom and seized by its ready bill.[2] I have never known any other bird to perform this feat so skilfully and I know from experiment that I cannot in any way stir

---

[1] Oberholser, H. C.: Auk, Vol. XXXV, 1918, p. 223. Brooks, Allan: Condor, Vol. XXVI, 1924, p. 38.
[2] Massachusetts State Board of Agriculture; Game Birds, Wild-fowl and Shore Birds, 1912, p. 308.

this ooze without clouding the water.   Dr. Elliot Coues [1] described the habits of this bird in his inimitable way:

"They cannot be said with entire propriety to be 'solitary', though this name is well enough to indicate less social propensities than most of the waders possess.   I generally found from two or three to half a dozen together; frequently only one at a time; occasionally, but not often, upwards of a score, that seemed, however, to be drawn together by their common tastes in the matter of feeding-grounds, rather than by any gregarious instinct. They are, moreover, pretty exclusive in their own set; rather declining than encouraging familiarity on the part of other waders; though the Peetweets and others sometimes intrude hoydenish society upon the more sedate and aristocratic members of the long-legged circle.   They should rightly, however, rather embrace, than merely endure such company, for they are of easy-going contemplative natures, and their sharper-eyed associates often do them good service in sounding alarms.

"These Tattlers indulge on all occasions a propensity for nodding, like Lord Burleigh or the Chinese mandarins in front of tea shops; and when they see something they cannot quite make out, seem to reason with themselves, and finally come to a conclusion in this way; impressing themselves heavily with a sense of their own logic.   They go through the bowing exercise with a gravity that may quite upset that of a disinterested spectator, and yet all through the performance, so ludicrous in itself, contrive to preserve something of the passive sedateness that marks all their movements. . . .   The Solitary Tattlers . . . are fond of standing motionless in the water when they have satisfied their hunger, or of wading about, up to their bellies, with slow, measured steps. If startled at such times, they rise easily and lightly on wing, fly rather slowly a little distance with dangling legs and outstretched neck, to soon re-alight and look about with a dazed expression.   Just as their feet touch the ground, the long, pointed wings are lifted till their tips nearly meet above, and are then deliberately folded.   The Esquimaux Curlews and some other birds have the same habit.   The Tattlers are unusually silent birds; but when suddenly alarmed, they utter a low and rather pleasing whistle as they fly off, or even without moving."

This is the only New England sandpiper that habitually frequents wooded highlands.   It may be found on some of the higher wooded mountains of New England as well as in the lowlands, and is rather rarely seen on the sea-shore, although it visits Cape Cod and the islands lying south of the Cape.

It appears in migration in greatest numbers about the middle of May and again in the latter half of August and early September when from six to nine birds may sometimes be found about a small pond.

ECONOMIC STATUS.   The Solitary Sandpiper is of some service as a destroyer of noxious insects, as it eats grasshoppers, locusts and many other insects.   It is too small and too solitary to be of any value as a game bird, and its present protection by law should be continued perpetually.

----

[1] Birds of the Northwest, 1874, pp. 499, 500.

PLATE 31

PLATE 31

WILLET
Page 443

Adult Breeding Plumage (Spring)

WESTERN WILLET
Page 445

Adult Winter Plumage (Autumn)

UPLAND PLOVER
Page 447

BUFF–BREASTED SANDPIPER
Page 433

All one-third natural size.

Catoptróphorus semipalmátus semipalmatus (GMELIN). **Willet.**

Other names: HUMILITY; PIED-WING CURLEW; WHITE-WING.

Plate 31.

DESCRIPTION. — Bill longer than head, straight or a *trifle* upturned, legs rather stout, front toes basally webbed. *Adults in breeding plumage (sexes alike):* Above brownish-gray; top of head and hind neck streaked dusky; back and scapulars irregularly spotted and barred dusky or blackish, this color sometimes the prevailing tint, but in some specimens restricted to irregular central feather marks; upper tail-coverts mostly white, longer ones barred like tail but less heavily; tail light brownish-gray, whitening on outer feathers and more or less distinctly cross-mottled or barred darker gray or blackish; wing-coverts mainly brownish-gray, greater coverts paler (mottled on basal parts, whitening toward tips); secondaries largely white; primary coverts dusky; nearly all basal half of primaries white, rest dusky; below white; fore neck and upper breast irregularly spotted dusky; sides irregularly barred or arrow-headed same; axillars and under wing-coverts mainly dusky or sooty-blackish; bill blackish, becoming bluish-gray or horn colored at base (L. A. Fuertes); iris dark brown; legs and feet grayish or bluish. *Winter plumage:* Above brownish-gray with darker shaft streaks; below dull white, shaded pale gray on fore neck; tail nearly white; wings and coverts as in breeding plumage; "wing, bill and feet about as in summer" (G. Trumbull); bill light blue, dusky toward end; iris brown; feet light blue (Audubon). *Young in juvenal plumage:* Above brownish-gray, feather margins pale yellowish or buffy; sides tinged same, and finely cross-mottled grayish; otherwise resembling winter adults. *Downy young:* Above variegated with dusky and dull whitish or pale brownish-gray (tinged in places pale brown), and dusky; front and sides of forehead whitish; sides of head and under plumage white, a dusky line from bill through eye or before eye.

MEASUREMENTS. — Length 14.00 to 16.00 in.; spread 24.00 to 29.00; folded wing 7.06 to 7.75; tail 2.71 to 3.30; bill 1.90 to 2.31; tarsus 1.95 to 2.42. Weight 7 to 10 oz. (Audubon). Female larger than male.

MOLTS. — Young Willets have a partial postjuvenal molt (August to November) after which they resemble adult in winter plumage; I have not been able to trace the spring or prenuptial molt; after a complete postnuptial molt in the second autumn immature birds probably become as winter adults; adults have a partial prenuptial molt in spring (March to May) and a complete postnuptial molt in autumn, beginning in July.

FIELD MARKS. — Larger than Greater Yellow-legs; in gray winter plumage Willet somewhat resembles Hudsonian Godwit in the same plumage but when it flies or even raises its wings the unmistakable long, wide, white patches up both upper and under surfaces of blackish wing identify it; no other bird like it on our coast except its sister variety, the Western Willet.

VOICE. — A variety of loud calls; full rounded whistles; common call in flight often written down as *"willet willet"* or *"pill-will-willet"* repeated over and over; or *"pilly willet pilly willet"*; or *"pil-willet-it-pil-willet"*; also a loud clicking note (Wilson); when alarmed on ground in breeding season, *yip, yip, yip* repeated with mechanical precision for a quarter of an hour at a stretch (H. K. Job); a loud, high, infrequent *kree-uk;* a series of *kuks;* flight note a far-reaching, gull-like *kiyuk* (J. T. Nichols).

BREEDING. — Mainly along Atlantic coast, among sand dunes or in long grass near bays and sounds; in salt-marsh or in fields. *Nest:* On ground; a slight hollow lined with a little grass. *Eggs:* Usually 4; 1.70 to 2.18 by 1.45 to 1.58; pear-shaped, but less pointedly so than in most shore birds; colors very variable; greenish-white or light bluish-gray to clay color, buffy-olive, dark brownish-olive or dark rufous-drab spotted with various shades of umber-brown or bistre and obscure purplish shell markings. *Dates:* April 22, Georgia; May 25, South Carolina; May 17 to June 5, Virginia.

RANGE. — Eastern North America and northern South America. Breeds on Atlantic coast in Nova Scotia and Prince Edward Island and from New Jersey to Florida; on Gulf coast to Texas, and in Bahamas;

winters from South Carolina and Bahamas to Brazil and Bolivia; accidental in Kansas (one record),[1] Bermuda and Europe.

DISTRIBUTION IN NEW ENGLAND. — Probably formerly a common migrant coastwise in New England (rare in Vermont) and a rare summer resident in Massachusetts and Connecticut; now a rare to accidental migrant; probably most Willets now seen in New England are Western Willets.

SEASON IN MASSACHUSETTS. — May 2 to June 4 (June 17); July 8 to September 30. (Probably some of these dates refer to Western Willets.)

HAUNTS AND HABITS. The Willet, a great, strikingly marked shore bird which once bred in New England, has been gradually reduced in numbers in this region until it has become one of the rarest of shore birds. According to Audubon it once bred near New Bedford. Dr. T. M. Brewer records that he found it breeding on Muskeget, and Samuels (1870) said that it occasionally bred within the limits of New England, usually preferring a sandy island to the main shore; "but," he wrote, "it sometimes selects a locality in a marsh for its nest, and has been known to breed in a rye field twenty miles from the seashore." [2]

This is interesting historically, as the bird has been long since extirpated from New England as a breeder. Samuels asserts that the nest is built about the last week in May, which would extend the breeding season into June.

The Willet was not considered a very edible fowl, but its eggs were highly prized for the table. This consideration and its availability as a target for the shotgun were sufficient to insure its extirpation as a breeding bird in New England. Unless the most stringent measures for its protection are taken it will disappear as a breeder from the entire Atlantic coast.

Like other large shore birds it is very solicitous for the safety of its young. The mother throws herself before the intruder and simulates lameness to entice him away or flutters overhead with wild shrill cries of distress, exposing herself recklessly to the aim of the gunner. Mr. Arthur T. Wayne tells how he watched an anxious pair of Willets with newly-hatched young until he saw one of the parents carry the young, one at a time, across the marsh and over three creeks to an island a quarter of a mile away.[3]

Often like the Snipe and other shore birds in the breeding season the Willet alights on dead trees or even on living ones. Crows, particularly Fish Crows, are very destructive to its eggs and young. While here it visits salt-marshes and beaches. It is an habitual wader, often wading in up to its belly, and it swims readily and well. Wherever it is common it is usually seen in flocks, but now on the coast of New England single birds are more often noted and these rarely. A flock of nearly one thousand of this species has been seen in May floating on the water off the Grand Banks.[4] Probably a few Willets which appear on the coast of New England early in July come here from Nova Scotia where they breed, but most of those taken later in the season are specimens of the Western Willet.

[1] Rinker, G. C.: Auk, Vol. XXXI, 1914, p. 105.
[2] Samuels, E. A.: Birds of New England, 1870, p. 453.
[3] Birds of South Carolina, 1910, p. 54.   [4] Grinnell, George Bird: Auk, Vol. XXXIII, 1916, p. 198.

The food of the Willet consists of insects, mollusks, crustaceans, worms and other marine life on the coast; it also eats fish and small fry, grasses, tender rootlets, seeds, and is said to take some rice in the rice fields of the south Atlantic coast.

ECONOMIC STATUS. The Willet is now too rare to be of any economic importance in New England.

Catoptrophorus semipalmatus inornátus (BREWSTER). Western Willet.
Other names: SAME AS WILLET. (See page 443.)

Plate 31.

DESCRIPTION. — Similar to Willet but decidedly larger; bill longer and more slender; summer adult with upper plumage paler, and not so conspicuously marked dusky or blackish, these markings fewer, finer; in typical specimens there is *no blackish cross-spotting or barring on middle tail feathers;* when present these marks are fainter than in eastern Willet; under plumage also less heavily marked in front and on sides, sometimes suffused pink-salmon; "bill slaty-black, changing to gray at base"; "legs and feet light olive gray" (Grinnell, Bryant and Storer); distinguishable from Willet in winter plumage only by measurements, but sometimes much grayer above.

MEASUREMENTS. — Length 14.90 to 17.00 in.; spread 28.00 to 31.00; folded wing 8.03 to 9.00; tail 3.20 to 3.45; bill 2.23 to 2.75; tarsus 2.52 to 2.85. Weight 8 to 16 oz. Female averages larger than male.

MOLTS. — Similar to those of Willet.

FIELD MARKS. — Indistinguishable from Willet in field (see "Field Marks" of Willet, page 443).

VOICE. — Similar to that of Willet; also a high-pitched *ke-lee-er* (Grinnell, Bryant and Storer).

BREEDING. — Similar to that of Willet but largely in the interior on mountains, marshland or prairie and not always near water. *Nest:* Usually a sparsely lined hollow, but sometimes quite bulky with grasses, etc. and built in a tussock of grass. *Eggs:* 3 or 4; indistinguishable from those of Willet (see page 443). *Dates:* April 30, Texas; May 2 to June 14 in various parts of United States.

RANGE. — Chiefly western North America and middle America. Breeds from central Oregon, Alberta, Saskatchewan and southwestern Manitoba south to northern California, central Utah, central Colorado, southern South Dakota, western Minnesota, and northern Iowa (formerly possibly east to Illinois and even Ohio), and on coasts of Texas and Louisiana; winters from northern California, Texas, Louisiana and Gulf coast of Florida through Mexico and western coast of Central America to western Ecuador, Peru and the Galapagos Islands; in fall migration occurs on Pacific coast from British Columbia southward, and on Atlantic side from New England southward; the spring migration passes through the region extending from Alabama and Mississippi River west to Pacific coast.

DISTRIBUTION IN NEW ENGLAND. — Usually rare, but irregularly a not uncommon fall migrant coastwise in Massachusetts, Rhode Island and Connecticut; distribution in other New England states not definitely known.

SEASON IN MASSACHUSETTS. — Chiefly August and September.

HAUNTS AND HABITS. Probably the Western Willet is virtually the only Willet that will be seen in New England in the future, though there are Willets breeding still in Nova Scotia. Messrs. A. C. Bent in Massachusetts and H. S. Hathaway in Rhode Island find that practically all the birds taken here in recent years and examined by them are referable to this form. Its habits are similar while here to those of the Willet and it haunts the same localities, chiefly along the coast. Like the Willet, it has a habit of raising its wings straight upward when it alights, thus displaying their conspicuous black and white pattern. A very good description of the habits of this bird is given by Grinnell, Bryant and Storer in their excellent work "The Game Birds of California," pp. 419–420, from which the following extract is taken:

"In its chosen haunts the Willet stalks about in search of the aquatic animals which constitute its food, sometimes wading breast deep in the water. Its half-webbed feet allow it to swim easily and this the bird often does when lifted beyond its depth by a wave, or when pursued. . . . These birds are often more suspicious than most other large shore birds. The Willets do not decoy so readily, and even when passing over decoys the least movement will frighten them, after which no amount of skillful whistling will induce them to return.

"A flock of six observed on the Alameda marsh, upon rising flew in the zigzag manner of sandpipers, but with longer straight flights preceding the changes in direction. When the birds alighted on a sand bar they stood very erect, and now and then spasmodically raised the head still higher for an instant in a haughty manner — a backward bow! During high tide the birds retired inland along the sloughs where they stood heel deep, preening, and at short intervals they seemingly rinsed their bills. (Grinnell and Storer, MS.)

"The flight of the Willet when well under way is quite direct, with a flat wing beat. The wings rarely rise above the level of the back, and consequently the upper surface of the body is almost continually in view. The bird sails with set wings only when descending from a higher to a lower level, or when about to alight. A change in the direction of flight is seemingly accomplished by a difference in the intensity of the two wing beats and a rolling of the body. The feet, which extend considerably beyond the tail, probably assist somewhat in steering. During high tide when the feeding grounds of the Willet are covered with water the birds choose some higher situation which will not be inundated, and there they rest, many of the flock tucking their heads under their wings as they sleep. There is, however, one or more constantly on watch, and on the approach of danger a shrill cry of alarm is sounded, the flock at once taking wing and rapidly making off to some safer place."

The bird is already growing rare in some of the states west of the Mississippi where it formerly bred commonly, and unless it can be stringently protected, it will in time disappear from New England.

Many individuals migrate easterly or southeasterly in autumn and so reach the Atlantic coast, from New England at least to the Carolinas. In spring apparently they go west from Florida and then move northward west of the Mississippi.

Probably the food of this bird is similar to that of the Willet. Grinnell, Bryant and Storer quote Mr. Paul J. Fair who found small clams in the stomachs of specimens taken by him.

Economic Status. Not much is known about the economic value of the Western Willet. It is not valued by the epicure as its flesh often has a rank flavor.

Bartrámia longicaúda (Bechstein). **Upland Plover.**

Other names: Bartramian Sandpiper; Highland Plover; Land Plover; Grass Plover; Uplander; Hill-bird; Pasture Plover; Field Plover.

Plate 31.

Description. — Form long and slender; bill rather shorter than head, straight, rather slender, upper mandible slightly downcurved at tip; gape very wide and deep, reaching below eyes; four toes, outer and middle ones webbed together at base; tertials long, longest reaching near tip of longest primary on folded wing; *tail long* for a shore bird and evenly rounded, two middle feathers not projecting abruptly beyond rest. *Adults in breeding plumage (sexes alike):* Top of head dusky-grayish-brown, more or less streaked buffy, and divided by a more or less indistinct or broken middle line of same; forehead streaked dusky and buffy; nape, pale buffy, this becoming grayish on lower back of neck; hind neck streaked blackish; back and scapulars sooty-blackish, with pale buffy and very pale buffy-grayish-brown feather margins, some longer scapulars barred blackish; rump and upper tail-coverts dark brown or sooty-blackish, longer upper tail-coverts marked toward ends with light grayish-brown and pale buffy; two middle tail-feathers grayish-brown (paling slightly on edges); color of rest of tail passes outwardly from pinkish-cinnamon to light pinkish-buff and even to white on bases of outer feathers, entire outer web of outer feather and broad end space on inner web pale or white; four outer feathers on each side broadly tipped white, entire tail sparsely barred black, barring most regular and distinct on two middle feathers; wing-coverts grayish-brown with lighter buffy or even white edges and some blackish markings; tertials similar with very narrow light edgings, both tertials and greater coverts sparsely barred blackish; primary coverts and primaries dark grayish-brown or dusky, with more or less white on some terminal margins of inner primaries; *1st (outer) primary (sometimes others also) with white bars on inner web, tip dark, shaft of 1st white, of others brown;* sides of head and neck, fore neck and upper breast pale buff, narrowly streaked black; broad streak from front of head over eye white or pale buffy; chin, upper throat and under plumage white; part of upper breast, fore neck, sides of lower breast, sides and flanks suffused buffy and marked with blackish marks, showing tendency to V-shape; *axillars white, barred blackish;* wing-linings white, spotted and barred same; entire underside of wing more or less barred dusky and whitish; bill yellow (except black ridge and tip), becoming gradually dusky toward tip; iris dark brown or bluish-black; legs and feet dull greenish-yellow or "light gray, tinged greenish-yellow" (G. Trumbull). *Adults in winter plumage:* Similar to breeding plumage but paler. *Young in first winter plumage:* Like adult but lacks most of dark barring on scapulars and most of middle wing-coverts. *Young in juvenal plumage:* Similar to adult but generally darker on upper back, and buff of head, neck, breast, wings, etc., much deeper; streaks on fore neck and breast much less distinct. *Downy young:* Above a fine mixed pattern of black, white and buff or yellowish-brown; stripe from base of bill over top of head black; sides of head, and chin white; below generally white; a band of buff or yellowish-brown across upper breast.

Measurements. — Length 11.00 to 12.75 in.; spread 21.00 to 23.00; folded wing 6.25 to 7.00; tail 3.00 to 3.50; bill 1.00 to 1.25 (1.50, Wilson); tarsus 1.65 to 2.05. Weight 6 to 7 oz. (Audubon). Sexes similar in size.

Molts. — Beginning in August juvenal bird molts body-feathers, some innermost secondaries and their coverts and some middle and lesser coverts and gradually assumes first winter plumage; in spring there is a prenuptial molt after which young apparently become practically indistinguishable from adults; a complete postnuptial molt begins in August and the next winter the bird is as winter adult; adults have a partial molt in spring, including body-feathers, some secondaries and wing-coverts and a complete postnuptial molt (August to January).

Field Marks. — Larger than a Killdeer; no conspicuous marks but most terrestrial of our shore birds; seen in meadows, fields and hill pastures; axillars and wing-coverts show barring when wing is raised; known by brownish appearance, relatively short, slender bill, long neck and tail and general slenderness and common habit of raising wings straight up when it alights.

VOICE. — The alarm, *quip-ip-ip-ip*, *quip-ip-ip-ip* (Langille); *quitty-quit-it-it* (O. W. Knight); song, a prolonged, weird, mournful but mellow, rolling whistle like that of autumn wind "*wh-e-e-e-e-e-e-e-e-e-e-o-o-o-o-o-o-o-o-o*" (O. W. Knight); female's "weird whistle entirely different from that of the male" (O. Reineke).

BREEDING. — In meadows, sometimes where wet and boggy, in grass fields, hill pastures, on dry prairies of West or in corn fields. *Nest:* On ground, sometimes a mere depression lined with a little grass, often better built, usually well hidden in grass or under tussock or small bush. *Eggs:* Normally 4; 1.65 to 1.97 by 1.22 to 1.44 in.; short, bluntly pear-shaped but more ovoid than most waders' eggs, resembling those of Woodcock but average larger; creamy to olive-buff, cinnamon-buff or "deep pinkish drab" finely spotted with reddish-brown, dark brown or chocolate (usually two shades of brown) with a few large spots or blotches and some violet-gray, lilac-gray or slaty shell marks. *Dates:* About May 20 to June 22, New England. *Incubation:* Period probably about 17 days (Burns) but not positively known; chiefly by female. One brood yearly.

RANGE. — North and South America. Breeds from northwestern Alaska, northern Yukon, southern Mackenzie, northern Manitoba, central Wisconsin, southern Michigan, southern Ontario, southern Quebec and southern Maine south to southern Oregon, northeastern Utah, Colorado, southern Oklahoma, southern Missouri, southern Illinois, southern Indiana, and northern Virginia; rare on Pacific coast of North America; winters on pampas of South America to Chile and Argentina; in migration occurs north to Newfoundland; occasional in Bermuda and casual in western Europe; doubtfully recorded in Australia.

DISTRIBUTION IN NEW ENGLAND. — Formerly common local summer resident and abundant migrant from northern and eastern Maine southward and westward; now rarer summer resident in Maine, New Hampshire and Vermont; very rare summer resident in Massachusetts and Connecticut and not known to breed in Rhode Island. Occasional in migration in all New England states.

SEASON IN MASSACHUSETTS. — April 3 to May 10; (summer); July 16 to October 26.

HAUNTS AND HABITS. The tale of the destruction of this lovely bird is a sad one. Harmless and eminently useful, it nevertheless is one of the most luscious morsels to delight the epicurean palate, and so the greed of man has almost swept it from the earth. The market demanded it and got it. It occupied open and cultivated fields and wide prairies. It was not a bird to hide in sheltering forests or thickets; it lived in the open for all to see and when the market hunters and netters had destroyed the Passenger Pigeon, when they turned to a new supply for the insatiable market demand, they found it in the birds of the open land, the Upland Plover, Eskimo Curlew, Golden Plover and Buff-breasted Sandpiper which then swarmed in spring in the Mississippi valley. In comparatively few years thereafter these birds, destroyed by hundreds of thousands, were nearly extirpated from the land.

I well remember when in my boyhood the Upland Plover nested in the fields behind my father's house in Worcester, when during the warm, clear nights of early May the notes of this gentle bird fell from out the sky in all directions as the flocks migrated to their summer homes. Then it bred in the fields all over New England, but from the 15th of July until the last plover went south they were pursued by gunners everywhere. And now I know of only two places in Massachusetts where one can feel reasonably sure of finding one in the breeding season. They were followed in the same way north, south, east and west as their price in the city markets continued to rise. Here is what Dr. Roberts has to say on their past and present condition in Minnesota:

"To recite the history of the Upland Plover in Minnesota is to tell a sad tale of dreadful slaughter and destruction that has resulted in the almost complete extermination of this valuable and once abundant bird. Fifty years ago it was present all through the summer, everywhere in open country, in countless thousands. Now it is nearing extinction. Here and there an occasional breeding pair may yet be found, but they are lonely occupants of the places where their ancestors dwelt in vast numbers. The fact that they were an excellent table bird, were tame and unsuspicious, raised only a single brood of four each year and were unprotected at the time when most easily killed, constituted conditions, which, taken together, led surely and rapidly to their disappearance. In the early seventies they were one of the most common and noticeable birds on the prairies about Minneapolis. In those days a small sandy prairie bordering a little lake known as Sandy Lake and lying just north of the city (long since thickly settled and included as an outlying suburb under the name of Shoreham) was a favorite congregating place of these birds in July and August and the writer has figures to show that 152, probably many more, Upland Plover were shot on this limited area between July 27 and August 13, 1874. No one thought seriously of such practices in those days, just as a hunter at that time did not feel guilty after killing fifty or sixty Wild Pigeons in a morning. The controlling conscience of the true sportsman had not been generally aroused, nor had a realization come to many of what must be the inevitable result.

"In May, 1893, the writer visited Jackson and Pipestone counties and Upland Plovers were present everywhere on the prairie. A return visit was made in 1899 and they were gone — the incessant and musical 'qua-a-a-ily, qua-a-a-ily' of the hovering birds was a voice of the past. Stories were rife, whether true or not is not positively known, that market hunters from eastern cities had come into those parts and had killed the Plover in great numbers in the nesting season and shipped them back to wholesale dealers, by whom they were in great demand for home and foreign sale." [1]

A similar decrease is noted in every state where the bird was formerly abundant. The gunner is not to be blamed for all this. Civilization brings many adverse influences. Millions of unrestrained dogs and cats destroy young birds or catch the mother at night on her nest; mowing and reaping machines and late plowing take their toll. Now, although this bird is protected at all times by statute, the law cannot be fully enforced, and there is no protection for it on the pampas of South America where it passes the winter. Our children's children may never see an Upland Plover in the sky or hear its rich notes on the summer air. Its cries are among the most pleasing and remarkable sounds of rural life. They rank with the mating music of the Woodcock and the Wilson's Snipe. That long-drawn, rolling, mellow whistle as the bird mounts high in air has the sad quality of the November wind. Except the wail of the wind there is nothing else

---

[1] Roberts, Thomas S.: Water Birds of Minnesota; Past and Present, from Biennial Report of the State Game and Fish Commission of Minnesota, for the Biennial Period ending July 31, 1918–1919, p. 83.

like it in nature. It is an ethereal sound which might well pass for the utterance of the fabled "wind spirit" and its *quitty quit,* as it rises startled from the grass, is a distinctive, unique and pleasing call unlike that heard from any other bird. Its long legs seem made for wading in pond or marsh, yet I have never seen it in the water. It wades in the grass of field or prairie and approaches its nest from a distance by walking cautiously through the grass, head held low and squatting lower and lower, and leaves it with like caution. It subsists on insects, and is particularly destructive to grass pests such as grasshoppers, locusts, cutworms, etc. Among the important first class pests that it destroys are weevils, crane-flies, fever ticks, white grubs, cotton worms, cotton cutworms, and crayfishes (W. L. McAtee). It pursues flying insects with swiftness and skill, running rapidly and even leaping into the air in their pursuit. It feeds also on the seeds of weeds and grasses and on waste small grains, particularly wheat, which it gathers from the ground.

ECONOMIC STATUS. The Upland Plover is one of the most important of all game birds and an insect destroyer of great value, but now (1924) so rare as to be of little service in New England.

Actítis maculária (LINNÆUS). Spotted Sandpiper.

Other names: TIP-UP; TIP-TAIL; SAND-BIRD; TEETER; TEETER-BOB; TEETER-TAIL; TEETER-PEEP; TWITCHET; PEET-WEET; PERR-WIPE; PEE-WEET.

Plate 30.

DESCRIPTION. — Bill straight or nearly so, moderately stout, about as long as head; tail rounded, fully half as long as wing; legs not long for a sandpiper; outer and middle toes connected by basal web as far as first joints. *Adults in breeding plumage (sexes practically alike)*: Above "greenish or bronzy grayish-brown" (as in our cuckoos) with slight metallic luster; back, scapulars, wing-coverts and upper tail-coverts irregularly marked with cross lines or arrow-heads of blackish; six middle feathers of tail bronzy grayish-brown; other (outer) feathers barred white, all tipped white except middle pair; primaries dusky; secondaries same, but more than basal half white and with broad white tips; this makes the familiar white wing-bar; inner webs of flight-feathers (except 1st primary and in some cases the 2d) with a lengthwise field of white increasing in width to the innermost where white extends to shaft; dark line through eye, stripe over eye, and under plumage white, marked everywhere, except chin (of some) with roundish spots of black or dusky, these smallest toward head and tail; axillars and wing-linings white, latter with oblique dusky bar; upper mandible mainly black and dusky, yellowing on edges, flesh colored toward base, lower mandible chiefly yellow or orange; iris dark brown; legs pale yellowish-clay or greenish-yellow, in some individuals light flesh color. *Adults and young in winter plumage:* "Above plain grayish olive, or bronzy olive" with more or less distinct dusky shaft-streaks, and some very slight subterminal barring on upper plumage which disappears by fading or wear; without other markings, except on wing-coverts, which are more or less barred dusky; below unspotted white with a grayish shade across upper breast; otherwise as breeding plumage. *Young in juvenal plumage:* Similar to winter plumage, but feathers of upper back and scapulars with faint subterminal dusky edgings and buff tips; wing-coverts and upper tail-coverts similarly marked or barred, wing-coverts having a second indistinct bar; two buffy bars on each feather where adults have but one; "base of bill dull purplish or livid flesh color" (Ridgway). *Downy young:* Above mottled brownish-gray; top of head, and nape with a middle black streak, another, wider, down middle of lower back and rump and a narrow one through eye extending to nape; sides of neck, chin and throat whitish, passing into pure white on lower neck and under body.

MEASUREMENTS. — Length 6.74 to 8.00 in.; spread 13.00 to 14.00; folded wing 3.66 to 4.60; tail 1.60 to 2.10; bill .79 to 1.05; tarsus .86 to 1.05. Weight about 1½ to 2 oz. Female larger than male.

MOLTS. — The young bird after donning juvenal plumage apparently has no autumnal postjuvenal molt. Its winter plumage is merely the worn juvenal, with light feather tips worn off (often even the subterminal bars are lost) and feathers generally faded, leaving upper plumage uniformly olive except a few dusky spots on wing-coverts. There is a prenuptial molt (January to April) after which first nuptial plumage is perfected, which closely resembles adults; after a complete postnuptial molt in autumn the young bird assumes adult winter plumage. Adults have the usual partial molt in spring and complete molt in autumn.

DOWNY YOUNG SPOTTED SAND-PIPER

About ½ natural size.

FIELD MARKS. — In spring plumage the white, black-spotted breast is distinctive; in any plumage broad white bar across wing is noticeable in flight; young birds and winter adults are white below with an ashy tint on upper breast; distinguished in this plumage from Solitary Sandpiper by lighter color above, unstreaked breast, and, in flight, by white in wing; extreme lifting and bobbing of head and tail is characteristic.

VOICE. — Ordinary cry *peet-weet* or *teeter teet*, with many repetitions of either or both syllables; sometimes a "long tremulous *w-e-e-e-t*" (Walter H. Rich), also *pip! pip! pip!* (J. T. Nichols).

BREEDING. — In single pairs or in small colonies, along sandy or rocky sea-shores, on banks of rivers and lakes or on uplands, in grass fields, corn fields, potato fields, strawberry beds, etc. at some distance from water or quite near it. *Nest:* On ground, rocky, stony, sandy, grassy, or cultivated; sometimes in cavity under large rock; a depression, usually slightly lined with grasses, weed-stalks or mosses, but often more grass is utilized; sometimes in seaweed on beach; sometimes an egg may be laid on black mud without any sign of nest, which, by the time full set is deposited, will be replaced by a structure of broken bits of sedge, etc.[1] *Eggs:* 3 to 5; usually 4; 1.17 to 1.40 by .87 to 1.00 in., pear-shaped; from pale clay color or light drab to dark cream, spotted and blotched with dark chocolate-brown or blackish, and ashy-gray. *Dates:* May 14 to July 1, New England. *Incubation:* Period about 15 days (O. W. Knight); 15 to 16 days (Burns); chiefly by female. One brood yearly.

RANGE. — North and South America. Breeds from tree limit in northern and northwestern Alaska, northern Mackenzie, northern Manitoba, northern Ungava (northern Quebec) and Newfoundland, south to southern California, central Arizona, southern New Mexico, southern Texas, southern Louisiana, central Alabama and northern South Carolina; winters from California, Louisiana and South Carolina south to southern Brazil, central Peru and central Bolivia; casual in Great Britain, Heligoland, western Germany and Belgium.

DISTRIBUTION IN NEW ENGLAND. — Common migrant and summer resident, distributed abundantly along sea-coast and common near streams and about ponds, lakes and pools in interior.

SEASON IN MASSACHUSETTS. — (March 31) April 19 to November 6 (November 17).

HAUNTS AND HABITS. The cheery little Spotted Sandpiper is the best known and most widely and commonly distributed shore bird that inhabits North America. In these respects it rivals even the Killdeer for, although its breeding range does not extend so far south, it is much more common in the northern part of its range. Its characteristic attitudes and motions are thus graphically described by Dr. Elliott Coues:

"This bobbing of the head and foreparts (of the Solitary Sandpiper) is the correspondent and counterpart of the still more curious actions of the Spotted Tattlers, or 'Tip-ups'

---

[1] A similar habit has been observed in the Mountain Plover.

as they are aptly called, from this circumstance; a queer balancing of the body upon the legs, constituting an amusement of which these last named birds are extremely fond. As often as the Tip-up, or 'Teeter-tail,' as it is also called, stops in its pursuit of insects, the fore part of the body is lowered a little, the head drawn in, the legs slightly bent, whilst the hinder parts and tail are alternately hoisted with a peculiar jerk, and drawn down again, with the regularity of clockwork. The movement is more conspicuous in the upward than in the downward part of the performance; as if the tail were spring-hinged, in constant danger of flying up, and needing constant presence of mind to keep it down. It is amusing to see an old male in the breeding season busy with this operation. Upon some rock jutting out of the water he stands, swelling with amorous pride and self-sufficiency, puffing out his plumage till he looks twice as big as natural, facing about on his narrow pedestal, and bowing with his hinder parts to all points of the compass. A sensitive and fastidious person might see something derisive, if not actually insulting, in this, and feel as Crusoe may be presumed to have felt when the savages who attacked his ship in canoes showed the signs of contumaceous scorn that DeFoe records. But it would not be worth while to feel offended, since this is only the entirely original and peculiar way the Tip-up has of conducting his courtships. Ornithologists are not agreed upon the useful purpose subserved in this way, and have as yet failed to account for the extraordinary performance." [1]

Soon after the middle of May the mated birds decide upon a nesting-place where they scratch and scuffle out a hollow, which, by the joint endeavor of both, is soon ready for the eggs. The female often begins to incubate as soon as the first egg is laid, and for this reason some eggs may hatch before the others, but usually the young emerge within the space of two days subsequent to the hatching of the first egg. As with various other birds the devoted male often feeds his sitting mate. The comical motions of the adults become even more ridiculous when indulged in by the tiny young which are no sooner out of the parental nest than they discover the "same uncontrollable ambition" in their posterior ends and "say 'how do you do' backward, with imperturbable gravity." After they have been hatched, if undisturbed, they remain for a day or two in the nest, but if frightened, they can run and hide almost immediately.

The Spotted Sandpiper swims and dives readily. It can dive from the surface of the water or from full flight, at need. Under water it progresses by using its wings which it spreads quite widely, and in shallow water it can go to the bottom and run a short distance with head held low and tail raised like an Ouzel or Dipper. When the adults are disturbed on the borders of lake or river, they usually start up with many *peet-weets* and fly out low over the water, often scaling with quivering down-bent wings, rocking from one side to the other, soon to swing in and return to shore farther on. Sometimes they alight in trees, and often they perch on fence posts, rails, stone walls and moored boats.

In the North they seldom flock at all but in the south in winter they sometimes assemble in large companies.

---

[1] Birds of the Northwest, 1874, p. 500.

A Spotted Sandpiper has been seen to catch crickets and immerse them in water before eating them.[1] In the Condor for July, 1913 (p. 173), Mr. L. E. Wyman notes that he once found a Spotted Sandpiper with a mussel (the ordinary edible kind) clinched to its foot. "The bird could hardly fly," he says, "and tried to escape me by crawling into the beach grass where I caught it. The middle toe was almost severed and hanging by a thread, so I cut it off and let the bird go, minus a toe, but evidently happy to be rid of the burden that must have given it great pain." Grinnell, Bryant and Storer in "The Game Birds of California," tell of three birds of this species that had lost parts of their legs or feet in some such way.

Economic Status. Spotted Sandpipers often frequent cultivated fields at some distance from water, and as they feed largely on locusts, grasshoppers and caterpillars, such as cutworms, cabbage worms and army worms, also beetles, grubs and other pests of cultivated lands, the birds should be preserved for the good work that they do among the crops.

Numénius americánus Bechstein. Long-billed Curlew.

Other names: SICKLE-BILL; OLD HEN CURLEW; BIG CURLEW.

Plate 29.

DESCRIPTION. — Bill exceedingly long, slender, and downcurved; tarsus long; front toes webbed toward base, web between outer and middle toes larger than that between middle and inner. *Adults in breeding plumage (sexes alike)*: Similar to that of Marbled Godwit (see page 427); reddish or cinnamon in tone, varying in intensity in different individuals; top of head quite dark, with no distinct light

AXILLARS AND FIRST PRIMARY OF LONG-BILLED CURLEW. (After Cory.)

middle line, such as is found in Hudsonian Curlew; general color light pinkish-cinnamon (much paler on chin and throat), curiously marked above with streaks, spots and bars of dusky grayish-brown or blackish-brown; secondaries, tertials, inner webs of primaries, greater wing-coverts, upper tail-coverts and tail thus barred; primary coverts and outer webs of primaries dusky grayish-brown; shaft of outermost primary white, rest darker or brown; fore neck finely streaked dark grayish-brown; sides and flanks rather narrowly and sparsely barred same; axillars and wing-linings deeper pinkish-cinnamon than other under plumage, *usually not much marked*, sometimes sparsely and narrowly barred or streaked dark grayish-brown; bill dusky, paling to flesh color toward base; iris dark brown; legs and feet bluish-gray. *Adults in winter plumage:* Similar to breeding plumage but general color deeper pink-cinnamon, especially below. *Young in juvenal plumage:* Similar to that of adult; distinguishable only by soft juvenal character of plumage. *Downy young:* "Pale ochre yellow" or buff above, deepening somewhat below or turning to pale orange-yellow, palest on chin and sides of neck; upper surface of head and body coarsely mottled and streaked black; bill straight, no longer than head.

[1] Jewell, H. W.: Journal Maine Ornithological Society, Vol. XI, 1909, p. 123.

MEASUREMENTS. — Length 20.00 to 26.00 in.; spread 36.00 to 40.00; folded wing 9.85 to 12.00; tail 3.50 to 4.10; bill from 2.30 in some young male birds to 9.00 in some old females; tarsus 2.75 to 3.63. Weight about 1 lb. 12 oz. to 2 lbs. Female larger than male.

MOLTS. — Molts of curlews seem to be similar to those of snipes and sandpipers, for curlews are merely large, specialized snipes; apparently in their case there is a postjuvenal molt and a succeeding first winter plumage, when young bird appears much like winter adult, but probably does not become fully developed until after first postnuptial molt or perhaps not until after second prenuptial molt when bird assumes adult breeding plumage and is then nearly two years old.

FIELD MARKS. — Length of bill cannot be relied upon always to distinguish this bird from Hudsonian Curlew, as bill varies much with age and sex in both species; an old female Hudsonian may have a longer bill than a young male Long-bill; Long-bill may be known, however, by great size (largest of our shore birds) and absence of a distinct dark line from bill through eye, and from Marbled Godwit by its downcurved bill.

VOICE. — A startling, shrill *curlew curlew curlew*, rather harsh and loud.

BREEDING. — In wet meadows or on dry prairies. *Nest:* On ground, a slight hollow, lined with grasses and weeds. *Eggs:* Usually 4; 2.40 to 2.90 by 1.78 to 2.00 in.; pear-shaped; varying from ashy-yellow to light greenish-olive, spotted and blotched with rounded marks of reddish-brown or dark umber, chocolate, blackish and varying shades of lilac. *Dates:* April 30, Oregon, to May 21, Idaho. *Incubation:* Period not definitely known but probably about 30 days.

RANGE. — Chiefly temperate North America and Middle America. Breeds (or formerly bred) from central British Columbia, southern Alberta, southern Saskatchewan and southern Manitoba (formerly southern Wisconsin, Iowa, northern Illinois, eastern Nebraska, and at least eastern Kansas) south to southern Louisiana (rarely), Oklahoma, southern Texas, central New Mexico, southern Arizona and northeastern California; winters from central California, southern Arizona, southern Texas, southern Louisiana, Florida and South Carolina south to Guatemala; occasional in some of West Indies in winter; formerly ranged most of North America north to Newfoundland and Labrador; now confined practically to region west of Mississippi River, and rare or wanting in many localities there where once common. A few may still be seen in summer on the North Carolina coast.[1]

NOTE. A smaller race, occupying the northern part of this range has been described, but this has not been accepted (1924) by the A. O. U.

DISTRIBUTION IN NEW ENGLAND. — Formerly an irregularly common to uncommon or rare migrant, chiefly in fall; now practically extirpated. On Plum Island a bird was shot Sept. 2, 1895, by George B. Short of the Plum Island Life Saving Station which is now in the collection of J. H. Wheeler.[2]

SEASON IN MASSACHUSETTS. — July 20 to October 18.

HAUNTS AND HABITS. The Long-billed Curlew, largest of all American shore birds, must have been once irregularly common in New England. Old gunners have assured me that it was frequently seen on the coast of Massachusetts as late as the 60's of the nineteenth century. Dr. Brewer told Peabody that he had seen large flocks at Nahant.[3] This must have been about the time when Audubon was preparing his drawings for the Birds of America. When I first went to Florida in 1877 there were many then on the wilder parts of the east coast but the bird soon practically disappeared from the entire East. It is now rare or wanting in a large part of the West, where it once bred, and only the strictest protection can save it from early extinction. In New England it re-

---

[1] Coles, Russell J.: Auk, Vol. XLI, 1924, p. 153.   [2] Wheeler, J. H.: *in litt.*

[3] Peabody, W. B. P. O.: A Report on the Ornithology of Massachusetts. Reports on the Fishes, Reptiles and Birds of Massachusetts (Storer and Peabody), 1839, p. 366.

sorted chiefly to the sea-coast.   Mr. C. J. Maynard says that he used to see it at Ipswich quite often in his early days.   Occasionally some one reports the bird as "seen" along the New England coast, but sight records should not be accepted, as some female Hudsonian Curlews have very long bills, considerably longer than that of a young male Long-billed Curlew, and mistakes in identification are common.

This bird is naturally shy, except in defense of its young or when one of its companions is wounded.   When one or more have been shot down its companions often return and with piercing cries flutter over the wounded ones until in some cases nearly all fall victims.

The great Curlew frequents mud flats, beaches, creeks in the salt-marsh on the sea-coast, and meadows and prairies in the interior.

It probes with its long bill into the holes of crabs and crawfish.   In addition to the usual food of shore birds it eats many berries and a few seeds.

ECONOMIC STATUS.   Professor Aughey found in the stomachs of eight Long-billed Curlews 483 locusts and 158 other insects, which indicates that these birds are valuable as insect eaters.   Their value as game birds is considerable.

Numenius hudsónicus.   LATHAM.   Hudsonian Curlew.

Other names: JACK CURLEW; JACK; FOOLISH CURLEW; BLUE-LEGS.

Plate 29.

DESCRIPTION. — Quite different from Long-billed Curlew, smaller, bill (usually) shorter, upper plumage of a grayer shade, and striped on top and sides of head. *Adults in breeding plumage (sexes alike)*: Variable; top of head mainly very dark grayish-brown with a central whitish or very pale buffy streak; dusky streak through eye; a broad pale streak above it; rest of upper plumage mainly varied with very dark to pale grayish-brown and pale grayish-buffy to whitish; tail grayish-brown or grayish-drab, barred dusky, outer feathers tinged cinnamon; primary coverts and primaries dark grayish-brown; inner webs of primaries barred light pinkish-buff or pinkish-cinnamon, shaft of outermost white, that

AXILLARS AND FIRST PRIMARY OF HUDSONIAN CURLEW.   (After Cory.)

of next whitish, rest brownish; tips of primary coverts white; tips of inner primaries white, the white gradually increasing on innermost; chin and more or less of throat white; sides of head, neck and under plumage pale buffy, grayish-buffy or whitish and streaked dark grayish-brown; sides and breast streaked grayish-brown, flanks more or less tinged cinnamon and barred or cross-spotted grayish-brown; under tail-coverts more or less similarly but less heavily marked; *axillars pinkish-buff, obliquely barred grayish-brown;* linings of wings similar, spotted or barred with same; whole surface of wing similarly barred; bill blackish, base pale purplish-flesh color; iris dark brown; legs and feet bluish-gray. *Young in juvenal plumage:* Like that of adults but whole upper plumage appears lighter; light spots on upper surface larger, these spots and whole lower surface more pervaded with pinkish-buff.

MEASUREMENTS. — Length 15.00 to 18.75 in.; spread 31.00 to 33.00; folded wing 9.00 to 10.30; tail 3.50 to 4.00; bill 2.75 to 4.00; tarsus 2.18 to 2.70.   Female larger than male.

MOLTS. — Similar to those of Long-billed Curlew (see page 454). Adults molt completely August to winter and probably have an incomplete molt in spring; not sufficient material available to trace the progress of young birds to maturity.

FIELD MARKS. — Practically the only Curlew now on New England coast; distinguished from other shore birds by large size and downcurved bill and from Long-billed Curlew by smaller size, grayer coloration and (usually) shorter bill; very shy, but young much less so and also lighter colored.

VOICE. — Call, a series of clear, penetrating, staccato whistles; also a rolling note lasting as long as it would take to count 6 or 7 (George H. Mackay); a soft, musical whistled two-note *kur-lew;* call "resembles that of Greater Yellow-legs" but "less modulated and usually lower pitched . . . commonly four short whistles" but "frequently prolonged even into a trill" (J. T. Nichols).

BREEDING. — On Barren Grounds and on open Arctic tundra, often near lakes or timber. *Nest:* Usually a depression on tussock or dry moss in wet spots. *Eggs:* Usually 4; 2.20 to 2.54 by 1.50 to 1.70 in.; pear-shaped; variable; probably indistinguishable from eggs of other curlews except by size (see page 454). *Dates:* Mid-June to early July, northern Mackenzie and Alaska. *Incubation:* Period probably not over 25 days; probably by both sexes. One brood yearly.

RANGE. — North and South America. Breeds on coast of Alaska from Yukon mouth to coastal region of northern Mackenzie; winters chiefly on Pacific coast from lower California to southern Honduras and Guatemala, on Galapagos Islands and from Ecuador to southern Chile; occurs in migration from British Guiana to mouth of Amazon; one winter record for South Carolina, December 11, 1917;[1] migrates mainly on sea-coasts; rare in interior (recorded in Saskatchewan); casual in Pribilof Islands and in southern Greenland and Bermuda. Accidental in Iceland and Spain.

DISTRIBUTION IN NEW ENGLAND. — Uncommon or rare migrant, mainly coastwise; most common at outer points and on extreme outer coasts and islands; not recorded from Vermont.

SEASON IN MASSACHUSETTS. — April 10 to May 30; (June 23) July 5 to October 26.

HAUNTS AND HABITS. The Hudsonian Curlew is now practically the only Curlew to be seen on the New England coast. It is considered rare in spring, when a few may be seen between May 20 and 30, but many small companies pass along the coast from the latter part of July until well into September. They alight mostly on outlying points where few people see them. They are more often seen flying along the sea-coast, from just outside the beach to ten or twelve miles off shore. In feeding they usually frequent tide flats at low water, retiring sometimes to wide salt-marshes to rest and feed at high tide, and they sometimes frequent beach-grass near sandy shores. In flight the flocks are often formed like those of geese or ducks.

Mr. George H. Mackay has written an excellent account of the habits of this bird in the Auk for October, 1892, in which he says that it feeds on fiddler crabs, grasshoppers and large, gray, sand spiders; also on beetles and "huckleberries." It probes the sand or mud deeply with its bill in search of crustaceans and other forms of aquatic life. Mr. J. H. Wheeler writes from Tabucintac, New Brunswick, that this species feeds on cloudberries and blueberries. Mr. L. L. Jewel, writing in the Auk (Vol. XXX, 1913, p. 426) of Panama birds, says: "One of the bird surprises of my life was to see a Hudsonian Curlew tip-toe and catch butterflies within 20 feet of my front door at Gatun. The clearings in and around town seemed very attractive to these birds and they were fairly tame. Marching or advancing by rushes, always with graceful dignity, sometimes

---

[1] Wayne, Arthur T.: Auk, Vol. XXXV, 1918, p. 438.

singly but more often in groups of four or five, they foraged through the shorter grass, picking up or catching on the wing their insect food."

ECONOMIC STATUS. The Hudsonian is not so useful as is the Long-billed Curlew, as it does not frequent agricultural regions in the United States nor feed so much on upland insects. As game it is inferior in flavor to other curlews.

Numenius boreális (J. R. FORSTER). Eskimo Curlew.

Other names: DOE-BIRD, SOMETIMES SPELLED DOUGH-BIRD.

Plate 29.

DESCRIPTION. — Unmistakable; smallest of curlews; bill short, slender, little curved, axillars barred but *rounded at tips,* not pointed as in Hudsonian Curlew; *primaries not barred as in other curlews but unmarked.* *Adults (sexes alike)*: General color warm buff or pale cinnamon-brown, so much streaked and obscured with dusky or brownish-black above that in some specimens the back appears blackish; tail barred brownish-black as in Hudsonian Curlew; top of head dark, in some specimens showing a lighter stripe in the middle of crown; a very light stripe over eye and a dark line through it; sides of head and neck and all under plumage much less marked and appearing much lighter than upper plumage; very variable, sometimes quite pale, but always more or less marked as in other curlews with dusky streaks

AXILLARS AND FIRST PRIMARY OF ESKIMO CURLEW. (After Cory.)

and arrow-heads and many bars, chiefly on breast, sides and flanks, but sometimes covering whole lower surface, excepting only chin and middle of belly; axillars and linings of wings reddish-brown, barred dark brown; bill black, base of lower mandible lighter or yellowish; iris dark brown; legs grayish-blue. *Young:* Very similar to adults.

MEASUREMENTS. — Length 12.00 to 15.00 in.; spread about 26.00 to 30.00; folded wing 8.00 to 8.75; tail 2.80 to 3.10; bill 2.00 to 2.58; tarsus 1.65 to 1.95.

MOLTS. — Not enough material examined to determine molts, which however are probably similar to those of the Hudsonian Curlew.

FIELD MARKS. — None that can be depended upon to distinguish the bird from the Hudsonian Curlew, unless the unbarred primaries can be seen distinctly when spread.

VOICE. — A soft melodious whistle, *bee, bee;* a squeak like that of Wilson's Tern but finer (Geo. H. Mackay); a note when in extensive flocks that may be compared to the chatter of many blackbirds; when pursued or captured "a harsh hen-like scream" (Coues).

BREEDING. — On open plains in the Barren Grounds. *Nest:* a depression in soil, lined with grasses or leaves. *Eggs:* usually 4; 2.12 by 1.33 to 1.90 by 1.40 in.; more ovate than pear-shaped; pale olive-greenish or olive-brownish, distinctly spotted, chiefly on larger end, with deep or dark brown; very variable in color.

RANGE. — Eastern North America and South America. Breeds (or formerly bred) on barren grounds of Canadian Northwest, chiefly in northern Mackenzie and northwest to Norton Sound, Alaska. Winters (or formerly wintered) on the plains of southern South America, chiefly in Argentina and Patagonia. Accidental or casual in northeastern Siberia, Pribilof Islands, California, Greenland, Bermuda, Falkland Islands, Iceland and the British Isles.

DISTRIBUTION IN NEW ENGLAND. — Formerly periodically abundant fall migrant coastwise, never recorded from Vermont; now nearly or quite extinct.

SEASON IN MASSACHUSETTS. — July 15 to October 2; accidental in spring.

HAUNTS AND HABITS. The Eskimo Curlew formerly was one of the extremely abundant birds of America. It was said to have visited Newfoundland in autumn in millions that darkened the sky. Audubon, Dr. Elliott Coues and Dr. A. S. Packard tell of immense flights. In the prairie states the numbers so resembled the tremendous flights of Passenger Pigeons that they were called "Prairie Pigeons." A single flock on alighting in Nebraska was said to have covered 40 or 50 acres of ground.[1] Breeding in the Barren Grounds of Canada, they migrated in August southeast to Labrador and Newfoundland, fed there to repletion on curlew berries (*Empetrum nigrum*) and snails, and waxing fat started out across the sea for South America. An easterly storm, like the West Indian hurricanes that sometimes occur in August and September, occasionally drove them on the New England coast. A high westerly gale might send some of them even to European shores, where the species has been taken occasionally. Traveling south, they were driven at times by westerly winds to Bermuda. They often touched on the Lesser Antilles and then passed across the sea to the coast of Brazil and so on to Argentina and Patagonia. The spring route through South America is unknown, but this Curlew probably crossed the Gulf of Mexico, arriving in March in southern Texas, and passed up the western Mississippi valley region to South Dakota and thence on north to the breeding-grounds. The destruction of the Eskimo Curlew followed that of the Passenger Pigeon, whose place it took in the markets of the country. In the spring migration in the West it was slaughtered at times by wagon-loads. Market hunters made it their business to follow the birds from state to state during the migration. On the Atlantic coast in autumn the curlews met with a similar reception, while the South Americans hunted them in winter. From 1870 to 1880 they began to decrease. Between 1886 and 1892 they diminished very rapidly and after that were never seen in numbers on the Labrador coast. Since that time the records show comparatively few birds killed in any part of their range. The last specimen known in New England was a lone bird shot September 5, 1913, at East Orleans, Massachusetts.[2] The last taken in the West of which we have record was a bird killed April 17, 1915, ten miles south of Norfolk, Nebraska. This came into the possession of Mr. Paul I. Hoagland, of Omaha, who had it mounted.[3] On the same day five others were reported near the same place.

The species might now be listed as extinct were it not for the following extract from a letter from Dr. Roberto Dabbene of the Museo Nacional de Historia Natural at Buenos Aires. Dr. Dabbene writes:

"Several specimens (5 or 6) of *Mesoscolopax borealis* have been seen in a flock of Golden Plovers, at Rosas, F. C. S. Province Buenos Aires, on February 7, 1924. One

[1] Swenk, Myron H.: The Eskimo Curlew and its Disappearance. Annual Report Smithsonian Institution, 1915, p. 334.
[2] Lamb, Charles R.: Auk, Vol. XXX, 1913, p. 581.
[3] Swenk, Myron H.: Annual Report Smithsonian Institution for 1915, 1916, p. 338.

PLATE 32

PLATE 32

OYSTERCATCHER

Page 479

Adult in Breeding Plumage

KILLDEER

Page 465

Adult in Breeding Plumage

AMERICAN BLACK-BELLIED PLOVER

Page 459

Young in First Winter
Plumage

Adult in Breeding Plumage

GOLDEN PLOVER

Page 462

Young in First Winter
Plumage

Adult in Breeding
Plumage

All one-third natural size.

of them has been captured by Señor Juan B. Daguerre and sent to the Museo Nacional de Historia Natural, Buenos Aires. (See El Hornero, III, No. 3, 1924, p. 284.)

"Another solitary specimen of Esquimo Curlew has been captured on the bank of a small river at the same locality (Rosas, F. C. S.) on January 11, 1925, by J. B. Daguerre. Sent also to the Nat. Mus. Buenos Aires."

The Eskimo Curlew was considered a great table delicacy, and although a very useful bird in the prairie states where it fed on such destructive insect pests as the Rocky Mountain locust, it was rapidly and completely destroyed like the Passenger Pigeon for the price that it brought in the market.

FAMILY **CHARADRIIDÆ**. PLOVERS.

Number of species in North America 14; in Massachusetts **7**.

Plovers form a large family of so-called shore birds, mainly of small or medium size, many of which are not confined to the sea-coast. The bill is usually short, never longer than head, and shaped much like that of a pigeon; body plump and well rounded; legs of medium length, feet partly webbed, and hind toe usually either wanting or rudimentary.

Squatárola squatarola cynosúræ THAYER AND BANGS. **American Black-bellied Plover.**

Other names: BLACK-BREAST; BLACK-HEART; BULL-HEAD; BEETLE-HEAD; CHUCKLE-HEAD; BOTTLE-HEAD; GUMP; GRAY PLOVER.

Plate 32.

DESCRIPTION. — Bill large, stout, shorter than head, deep at base; head and eye large; front toes webbed at base, web between outer and middle toes much larger than that between middle and inner toes; hind toe very small, higher than others, sometimes wanting; *axillars black or blackish in all stages.* *Adults in breeding plumage (sexes alike or similar):* Above mainly pale gray or grayish-white; forehead, sides of head above eye and sides of neck and upper breast white; top of head, back of neck, back and scapulars marked more or less brownish-black, mostly on feather centers; greater wing-coverts spotted and tertials barred same; primaries dusky, *edged and marked white* (chiefly on inner webs); primary coverts tipped white; greater wing-coverts and secondaries edged and tipped same; upper tail-coverts and base of tail mainly white; rest of tail white, barred blackish; lower face back to ears, fore neck and all under plumage back to thighs black, with a faint, coppery gloss; rest of under plumage mainly white, except axillars, which are blackish, and some blackish markings on outer under tail-coverts; bill black; iris dark brown to bluish-black; legs and feet dark bluish-gray to black; *some breeding females* have white on head and back, not so clear and bright as male, and black of under plumage duller, interspersed with white feathers. *Adults in winter plumage:* Sides of head, and under plumage mainly white, former more or less streaked finely with dusky; chin white; fore neck and upper breast tinged brownish-gray, slightly streaked dusky; upper plumage mottled brownish-gray and white or whitish; feathers with dark grayish subterminal markings otherwise as breeding plumage but barring on tail not so dark. *Young in first winter plumage:* Similar to juvenal plumage but some are spotted with white or whitish above and middle wing-coverts and feathers of rump creamy at tips (fading to white or whitish later in season) and one or more worn juvenal innermost secondaries retained. *Young in juvenal plumage:* Similar to winter adults, but upper plumage (especially top of head and back) speckled with pale buffy or yellowish-white; parts of tail slightly tinged buffy; legs and feet lead-colored. *Downy young:* Above mainly olive-yellow, spotted black; below, and hind neck white; black lines on sides of crown, from bill to eye, and below eye.

MEASUREMENTS. — Length 10.50 to 13.65 in.; spread 22.00 to 25.00; folded wing 7.00 to 8.00; tail 2.50 to 3.00; bill 1.00 to 1.26; tarsus 1.50 to 2.04. Weight, 6 to 10½ oz. Female averages larger than male.

MOLTS. — A postjuvenal molt (August or September to January) precedes first winter plumage; a partial prenuptial molt (February to May) includes many body-feathers, some inner secondaries and some wing-coverts and sometimes some or all tail-feathers; in succeeding first nuptial plumage bird resembles adult except for some retained winter feathers; some birds still retain winter plumage until June 1 and may pass summer in this plumage; a complete postnuptial molt (July to December) produces a winter plumage as adult; adults have a partial prenuptial molt (February to May) and a complete postnuptial molt beginning in July.

FIELD MARKS. — Largest of New England plovers; in spring plumage unmistakable at a long distance; black fore parts are first seen when rest of bird is practically invisible; large head, high white forehead and stout bill distinguish it from Golden Plover; adults are much grayer on back than latter; young may be confused with young of Golden Plover which, however, are generally more yellowish above and on sides of neck and fore neck; in flight Black-bellied Plovers of all ages or sexes show *white in wing*, and *black axillars* are shown on sides of body under wing when it is raised; white upper tail-coverts and white black-barred tail also show in flight.

VOICE. — A loud, ringing *wher-rell* of a distinctly mellow quality (J. Grinnell); call most often heard consists of three syllables not unlike the *toor-a-wee* of Bluebird, but "lower in pitch, more prolonged and mournful" (R. Hoffmann); flight note a clear ringing *pe-oo-ee*, shortened and varied at times, another flocking note, a soft, mellow, *quu-hu*, from a bird on the ground *cuck, cuck, cuck, cuck, cuck, cuck, cuck, cuck, cuck* (J. T. Nichols).

BREEDING. — On Arctic tundra or some slight eminence near it. *Nest:* A hollow in ground, sometimes in grass or moss, lined with grass, leaves or bits of mosses or lichens, etc. *Eggs:* Normally 4; 1.84 to 2.30 by 1.25 to 1.47 in.; pear-shaped; light, buffy-olive to deep olive-buff, heavily and thickly spotted, chiefly on large end, with brownish-black and black, but variable, some "light greenish drab or rufous drab, with quite uniformly colored spots of dark amber or bister and marks of lighter color." *Dates:* Latter half of June and early July in both Arctic Mackenzie and Arctic Russia. *Incubation:* By both sexes. One brood yearly.

RANGE. — Nearly cosmopolitan. Breeds on Arctic coast of North America from Point Barrow to Melville Peninsula, in Greenland and on Arctic coast of Eurasia; winters from Washington (probably), California, Louisiana and North Carolina south to Brazil and Peru and from Mediterranean to Madagascar and South Africa; occurs in migration in most intervening areas but most abundant on sea-coasts. (A closely allied form breeds in northeastern Siberia and winters south to Malayan Archipelago and from India to Australia.)

DISTRIBUTION IN NEW ENGLAND. — Common migrant coastwise; rather rare migrant in Vermont and elsewhere in interior. Now increasing in spring in Connecticut (A. A. Saunders).

SEASON IN MASSACHUSETTS. — April 15 to June 13; (summer); July 5 to November 20; (December).

HAUNTS AND HABITS. The Black-bellied Plover is misnamed, as the black extends below only to the thighs. The Golden Plover is the real black-bellied bird.

With the ebbing tide thousands of acres of Cape Cod Bay marshes and flats, from West Barnstable to Yarmouth, are laid bare. In late May these flats are the haunts of thousands of shore birds and marsh birds. Between Yarmouth shore and the tip of Sandy Neck, Barnstable, and outside of the Neck stretching far out into the bay, and also back up Barnstable Harbor to the great marshes lie the sand flats. All along the inner shores and up toward West Barnstable stretch the marshes. At high water the shore birds scatter over the higher parts of the marsh or the upper beaches, but when the tide is out their table is spread, and then they gather on the flats, scattering here and there, and following the receding brine to pick up what the retiring sea has left. Then their flocks spread over the flats for miles and miles. In the latter half of May the predominant birds are the Black-breasted Plovers, giants among the smaller shore birds. They may be found anywhere along the edges of the sand-flats or where the streams from the marshes pour their shallow floods far over the sands. At the first of the ebb they station themselves on the higher sand bars near shore; as the tide recedes they follow, until some have reached the outermost spits a mile or more from the shore. For hours they patrol the sandy strand, and then there is a change. The army is on the retreat. The tide is coming in. Preceded by a line of foam or froth, the wavelets wash fast along the sands to reclaim their own. As the sea advances over the wide land-wash the shore birds are the first to go, but gulls and terns stay on until the whirling wavelets wash all round them and they seem to be sitting on the surface of the sea. The shore birds are forced back at last to the beach and finally, driven from their last sandy feeding-ground, they wing their way far up into the marsh. The incoming waves bring fishes, crabs, algæ and various other forms of sea life to feed the birds again when later the tide has retreated. During the ebb and flow a person seated in a stranded boat with a telescope at hand may observe at his leisure the habits of the Black-breasted Plover. While the tide is out they run about with heads up, apparently without aim or purpose, but now and then one thrusts its open bill down into sand or water and pulls up a long marine worm. These seem to be a favorite food, and the birds apparently like to wash the sand from them if there is water near by. A Plover sees a Turnstone taking something from the sand, steps up quickly and strikes at the smaller bird to drive it away. Another wades into the incoming wash until its breast is partly submerged and then ducks and splashes, throwing water over itself like a timid girl bather. Two beautifully plumaged adult birds apparently run a race for several rods, trotting, and stepping high, with heads in the air. First, one is ahead, then the other; then they turn and run toward us side by side a yard apart. The race continues for about three minutes, during which there is no stop for eating, though twice one snatches up something. Then one flies away, with the other in full pursuit. This looks like courtship and as one was a little brighter in plumage than the other, the birds probably were a pair, and one at least had "intentions." About one in five of the birds in the various groups is a full plumaged male and perhaps one in a hundred seems to be still in full winter plumage, while between the two extremes are all sorts of "speckle-bellies." Two small birds in winter plumage appear to be fed by two larger ones in full plumage, but we can see no food pass, and probably the exercise is mere billing, a form of greeting like that of kissing among human kind. The Black-bellied Plover is a glorious bird and well worth watching. It is usually shy, however, and keeps well beyond ordinary gunshot range.

In the spring migration it is rare in April but usually appears on Cape Cod in considerable numbers by the middle of May and is often abundant until about June 1. Now and then stragglers are seen during June even as far south as Florida. By the first week in July a few adult birds, stragglers from the north, appear on Cape Cod, but the great southward flight comes in August, the young birds coming later than the adults. In flock formation the plovers fly in lines, V's or in massed flocks, like those of many ducks.

The food of the Black-bellied Plover consists of mollusks, crustaceans, marine worms, earthworms, spiders, cutworms, locusts, grasshoppers, grubs and other forms of marine and insect life.

ECONOMIC STATUS. As an object of sport this bird is today one of the most important of shore birds and no doubt is of some service as an insect eater.

Pluviális domínica dominica (MÜLLER). Golden Plover.

Other names: BLACK-BREAST; FIELD-BIRD; GOLDEN-BACK; GREEN-BACK; GREEN PLOVER; GREEN-HEAD; PALE-BREAST; PASTURE-BIRD; SQUEALER; TOAD-HEAD; TROUT-BIRD; BRASS-BACK; FROST-BIRD; MUDDY-BREAST; PALE-BELLY; THREETOES; BULLHEAD.

Plate 32.

DESCRIPTION. — Similar in form to Black-bellied Plover but less stout and smaller; *bill much smaller, more slender*, much shorter than head and *hind toe wanting*; basal webs as in previous species but smaller. *Adults in breeding plumage (sexes alike):* Above dusky or blackish, speckled with ochre-yellow or golden-yellow, with some whitish spots; hind neck less strongly marked than top of head where darker markings prevail; tail grayish-brown and pale gray, shading into whitish on outer feathers, and barred with darker; fore and middle wing-coverts dark brownish-gray, lighter grayish-yellow, black and white (or whitish); lower wing, including primaries and their coverts blackish; tips of primaries faintly and very narrowly outlined whitish, the coverts more distinctly white-tipped; forehead, broad stripe over eye extending over ear and down sides of neck and upper breast, lower face, cheeks, ear-coverts, chin, throat, fore neck, breast and belly black (in female often intermixed with some white); under tail-coverts white, mainly black on anterior feathers, rest white, marked black; axillars and under wing-coverts sooty-gray with some grayish-brown spots near edge of wing; bill black; iris dark brown to bluish-black; legs and feet grayish-black or "dark bluish-gray" (G. Trumbull). *Adults and young in winter plumage:* Less conspicuously marked above with blackish and yellow than in summer; no black on sides of head or under plumage and no white streak on sides of head and neck; forehead creamy or whitish, feathers with dusky centers; stripe over eye, and sides of head whitish, streaked dusky, ear-coverts quite dusky; fore neck, breast, sides and flanks tinged pale grayish-brown, streaked darker; wings and tail much as in breeding plumage. *Young in juvenal plumage:* Somewhat like winter plumage but dark markings above more brownish and more conspicuously speckled yellow; below more brownish and yellowish; eye stripe, ear-coverts, cheeks and sides of neck streaked always dusky; flanks pale grayish-brown or whitish, tipped and barred darker, and barred white or buffy; belly washed pale grayish-brown, sometimes barred darker. *Downy young:* Above dull, buffy-yellow, marbled black; forehead and streak over eye "dull to pale yellowish buff," former with central streak or series of spots, and latter with irregular markings, black or blackish; a streak of spots of same before eye; lower face and under plumage dull white, former sparsely marked black.

MEASUREMENTS. — Length 9.75 to 11.00 in.; spread 20.50 to 23.00; folded wing 6.58 to 7.50; tail 2.40 to 3.00; bill .80 to 1.00; tarsus 1.50 to 1.95. Weight 4 to 9 oz. Sexes about same size.

Molts. — The postjuvenal molt (September to December) is partial, including most body-feathers, some inner secondaries and some wing-coverts; first winter plumage which follows is like that of winter adult; some backward young birds may retain this plumage through ensuing summer but apparently most birds become similar to breeding adults by a practically complete prenuptial molt (February to June); probably young birds do not reach their full development until second winter when after a complete molt, adult winter plumage is assumed; adults have partial prenuptial molt (March to June), including most body-feathers, innermost secondaries and some wing-coverts (some may lose more or less tail-feathers), and a complete postnuptial molt (August to February).

Field Marks. — Slightly smaller and more slender than Black-bellied Plover, with shorter, smaller bill, wings relatively longer, flight swifter, and more buoyant; *no black axillars* but under surface of wings gray; generally more yellowish above and below than Black-belly in autumn; shows no conspicuous white in wings or on upper tail-coverts as does the Black-bellied Plover; when on ground they bob frequently (C. W. Townsend); apparently Black-bellied Plover seldom bobs its head.

Voice. — Flight note a far-reaching *quee-i-i-a* with a quaver in the middle, falling at end; less mellow and whistled than that of Black-bellied Plover, suggesting that call reversed, with thrilling plover quality (J. T. Nichols); a plaintive *too-lee-e* (E. W. Nelson); call note a *chuckle* or *queedle* (C. W. Townsend); when coming in to decoys every bird whistling *coodle* (George H. Mackay); a harsh *queedle* (Ludlow Griscom).

Breeding. — On Arctic tundra and in Barren Grounds. *Nest:* A depression in earth, lined with a few leaves, etc. *Eggs:* Normally 4, rarely 5; 1.80 to 2.10 by 1.25 to 1.45 in.; pear-shaped; indistinguishable in color and markings from those of Black-bellied Plover (see page 460) but smaller and averaging slightly narrower in proportion to their length. *Dates:* June 16 to early July. *Incubation:* Period probably close to that of European Golden Plover, 27 days in incubator (Evans); by both sexes. One brood yearly.

Range. — North and South America. Breeds from Kotzebue Sound, Alaska, in Arctic coastal region, and on Arctic islands north to about latitude 77° on Melville Island and southeast to northwestern coast of Hudson Bay; winters on pampas of Brazil and Argentina and in Paraguay, Uruguay and Bolivia; migrates from Nova Scotia and New Brunswick south over the Atlantic; a few pass south in autumn along Atlantic coast, and some through Mississippi valley and practically all go north in spring by latter route; in migration occurs in California, Washington, British Columbia, Greenland, West Indies and Bermuda; accidental in Great Britain and Heligoland.

Distribution in New England. — Formerly irregularly common to abundant locally in fall migration both on coast and in interior; very rare spring migrant; now rare fall migrant coastwise. A recent spring record is that of James L. Peters who took a male April 8, 1911, at Plum Island.[1]

Season in Massachusetts. — April 8 to May 18 (June 5, 1921); August 12 to November 19 (November 25).

Haunts and Habits. As the Golden Plover does not normally visit New England in spring and as its usual route to South America in fall takes it out to sea from Nova Scotia to South America, it never was abundant in New England except in autumn, and then only when driven off its usual route by high adverse winds. At such times it appeared here in enormous numbers not only along the coasts but on the hills of the interior. In spring it passed up the Mississippi Valley in countless hordes and this great migration continued annually until about the time that the hosts of the Passenger Pigeon began to disappear. Then the Golden Plover commenced to come into the chief game markets of the United States in barrels to take the place of the pigeons. After that the decrease

[1] Auk, Vol. XXVIII, 1911, p. 368.

of the species was rapid and it narrowly escaped extinction, pursued as it was by gunners, not only throughout its spring passage up the Mississippi Valley but also in its fall flights wherever it landed either on our coasts or the Bermudas, the Antilles or in South America. All along its route in the settled and civilized parts of both continents it was unremittingly slaughtered except when at sea, and there its ranks probably were decimated by storms. Protection in spring in the Mississippi Valley and in Canada and prohibition of sale may save the species from extinction.

An easterly gale with heavy rain during the fall migrations in the latter part of August or the first part of September is very likely now to bring a number of Golden Plovers to outlying points of the New England coast such as Plum Island, Ipswich, Cape Cod, Nantucket and Marthas Vineyard. Some adults still retain most of the breeding plumage at that time.

Of late a slight increase in the numbers of this species has been noted.[1]

I have never had a good opportunity to watch the habits of this bird and therefore quote an excellent account written by my friend, Mr. George H. Mackay of Nantucket:

"Various authorities state that along the Atlantic coast the food of the Golden Plover consists principally of grasshoppers, on which they become very fat. I can only say, in answer to this statement, that in my experience I have never seen them eat any, and I have watched them when on the ground quite near, as well as through a strong field glass. I have also examined the stomachs of a good many which I have shot on Nantucket, and have never found any grasshoppers in them, nor in fact anything but crickets (which seem their principal food there), grass seeds, a little vegetable matter, like seaweed, coarse sand, and small stones. I have also frequently shot them with the vent stained purple, probably from the berries of the *Empetrum nigrum*. I have rarely seen a poor or lean bird that landed while making the southern migration. While they are not all in the same condition they are, as a rule, quite fat. The eye is dark hazel, very lustrous, and appealing, and is their most beautiful feature to my mind. Those birds killed soon after landing have the bottoms of their feet quite black; after living on the Island awhile, they turn whitish. I have no reason to offer for this change. . . . When scattered over considerable ground, as is usual after they have been any length of time on their feeding ground, every bird apparently on its own hook, if alarmed, a note is sounded; they then rise so as to meet as soon as possible at a common centre, which gained, away they go in a compact body. When high up in the air, flying on their migration, I have often noticed the flocks assume shapes that reminded me of the flight of Geese; they also fly in the form of a cluster, with one or more single lines out behind; also broadside in long straight lines, with an apparent velocity of about one and a half miles a minute, measured by the eye as they pass along the headlands. When flying near the ground they course over it at a high rate of speed, in every variety of form, the shape of the flock constantly changing, and frequently following every undulation of the surface, stopping suddenly and alighting when a favorable spot is noticed. They are extremely gregarious, and I

---

[1] Nichols, J. T.: Bird-Lore, Vol. XXVI, 1924, p. 413.

have had the same flock return to my decoys as many as four times, after some of their number had been shot each time. When approaching the decoys every bird seems to be whistling, or, as I have often expressed it, uttering a note like *coodle, coodle, coodle*. During the middle of the day they are fond of seeking the margins of ponds, where they sit quietly for a long time, if undisturbed. When disturbed they are almost certain to return, in a short time, to the same spot from which they have been started, that is, if they have been resting or feeding there any length of time. When suspicious, it is very difficult to approach, decoy, or call them; if not harassed, they are as a rule quite tame and gentle, and can be easily driven up to with horse and wagon." [1]

In the fall migration on our coast the adults usually appear first. They have a habit when on the ground (particularly when first alighting) of raising the wings high over the back and slowly folding them down. Hudson tells us that sometimes when a few birds flying high over the pampas see others on the ground they drop rapidly and almost vertically, with fixed wings, to the earth, producing a loud sound resembling the blowing of a horn.

The food of the Golden Plover, especially in the interior, consists largely of insects. It feeds ravenously on several destructive insect pests, such as grasshoppers, locusts, crickets, white grubs, cutworms and wireworms. Stomachs of the Golden Plover are often found packed and crowded with worms and insects. They also eat berries and a small quantity of other vegetal food.

ECONOMIC STATUS. Here is one of the useful American birds, recently in danger of extinction because of the mouthful of flesh that it furnishes. Its importance as a game bird has been allowed to outweigh its service to agriculture. Alive they do their appointed useful work on prairie, field, farm and shore, but, as Mrs. Mabel Osgood Wright well says of small marsh birds, when dead they merely serve "to lengthen some weary dinner where a collection of animal and vegetable bric-a-brac takes the place of satisfactory nourishment."

Oxyéchus vocíferus (LINNÆUS). **Killdeer.**

Other names: KILLDEER PLOVER; KILDEE.

Plate 32 and Fig. 35.

DESCRIPTION. — Bill much shorter than head, rather slender; tail long for a plover, extending considerably beyond tips of closed wings and well rounded; toes not webbed at base; little seasonal difference in plumage. *Adults (sexes alike):* Above, including ear-region, grayish-brown, *lower back rump and upper tail-coverts bright colored* "varying from tawny or orange-brown to cinnamon-brown or chestnut, paling on upper tail-coverts; forehead, broad stripe from above eye over ear, chin, throat, collar around neck, and under plumage generally white, interrupted by a *broad black collar around lower neck* and *another across junction of neck and breast;* lower under tail-coverts sometimes tinged tawny and marked brown; stripe over forehead from eye to eye and one from base of bill extending back under eye black, latter broadening and fading into brownish-gray of ear coverts; primaries blackish, some with white on

---

[1] Auk, Vol. VIII, 1891, pp. 18–20.

outer webs, all with white spaces on inner webs; greater wing-coverts broadly tipped white, primary coverts narrowly so tipped; secondaries dusky with white bases and tips; middle tail-feathers grayish-brown, darker toward tips, which are broadly colored like rump; rest of tail like rump but with black subterminal band, outer tail-feathers chiefly black and white; bill black, iris dark brown; naked eye-ring "orange red or scarlet"; legs and feet variable, pale pinkish-gray to pale grayish-yellow, flesh color or "pale light clay color." *Young in first winter plumage:* Similar to adult breeding plumage. *Young in juvenal plumage:* Like adults, but feathers of upper plumage more or less distinctly margined rusty or buffy, and black bands narrower, black more or less replaced by gray or brownish feathers; white of neck-band often tinted brown in front. *Downy young:* Above brownish-gray minutely and indistinctly mottled darker; head with blackish line from eye to eye over forehead continued round back of head, another behind eye similar to those of adults; lower back and rump with middle stripe and two side stripes of black; sides occasionally pinkish-cinnamon; fore wing striped black, hind wing white; forehead and under down white, a white collar and a black one encircle neck in order named.

DOWNY YOUNG KILLDEER

About ½ natural size.

MEASUREMENTS. — Length 9.00 to 11.25 in.; spread 19.00 to 21.00; folded wing 5.97 to 7.20; tail 3.50 to 4.50; bill .60 to .90; tarsus 1.30 to 1.65. Weight about 3 to 3¼ oz. Sexes about same size.

MOLTS. — Juvenal body-plumage (not including back, rump or all scapulars) some or all of tail, some innermost secondaries and wing-coverts are molted August to October; next, or prenuptial, molt in spring is like that of adults and bird then becomes as adult; adults have an incomplete prenuptial molt (February to June), including mainly body-feathers (but not all of back, rump or scapulars), some inner secondaries and wing-coverts, and a complete molt (July to November).

FIELD MARKS. — Size larger than any of smaller sandpipers or plovers; may be known at once by white collar and *two black bands* across lower neck and upper breast; its brightly marked rump and long tail, large amount of white in wings, shown in flight, and by noisy cries; bobs head and neck frequently when on ground; flight swift.

VOICE. — Sharp, ringing cries *kee-he* or *kildee* (J. T. Nichols); a loud, high-pitched *kill-deer* or *kill-dee* rapidly enunciated; when bird is flushed it becomes (excitedly) *kill-dee, dee, dee, dee-ey* or *til-dé-o, til-dé-dé-oo;* when running along ahead of observer, a softer *dee-e-e-e-et* is sometimes uttered (Grinnell, Bryant and Storer).

BREEDING. — In marshlands, pastures, dry beds of creeks, meadows, plowed lands, cultivated fields and gardens. *Nest:* A hollow in ground, sometimes lined with a few pebbles and some grasses or dry refuse from cultivated crops; sometimes on bare rock with no lining. *Eggs:* Normally 4; 1.35 to 1.60 by 1.00 to 1.10 in.; somewhat pear-shaped; from drab to light clay color or dull creamy-buff, thickly speckled, streaked and blotched with dark brown, black or blackish and dull lavender, spots often most numerous at large end. *Dates:* April 14 to May 30, various northern states. *Incubation:* Period, variously reported, from 26 to 28 days; by both sexes. Sometimes raises two broods in a year.

RANGE. — North and South America. Breeds from central British Columbia, southern Mackenzie, northern Manitoba, northern Ontario and southeastern Quebec (Point des Monts) south to Bahamas, Gulf coast, central Mexico and southern Lower California; winters from Chilliwack District, British Columbia, Puget Sound, Arizona, Colorado, Texas, Missouri, southern Illinois, southern Indiana, western New York, New Jersey (casually New Hampshire, southern New England and Bermuda) south to northern Venezuela and northwestern Peru; casual in Newfoundland, Paraguay and Chile; accidental in Great Britain; said to have occurred in Madeira.

FIG. 34. — EGGS OF PIPING PLOVER IN SITUATION
Cape Cod
Page 471

FIG. 35. — NEST AND EGGS OF KILLDEER
Ithaca, New York

DISTRIBUTION IN NEW ENGLAND. — *Maine:* Rare migrant chiefly in autumn. *New Hampshire:* Rare migrant chiefly coastwise and rare summer resident in southern part; accidental winter resident. *Vermont:* Rare migrant (breeds). *Massachusetts, Rhode Island* and *Connecticut:* Common to rare local migrant, and "not uncommon" to rare and local summer resident; accidental in winter (1888–89 and in Connecticut 1922–23).

SEASON IN MASSACHUSETTS. — (February 26) March 1 to December 15 (winter).

HAUNTS AND HABITS.   The handsome, noisy Killdeer was once a common breeding bird in New England.   Early in the present century it became so reduced in numbers that it was believed to have been practically extirpated as a breeding species.   It was known to have bred once in Rhode Island as late as 1895 [1] and it nested a little later in the Connecticut valley and in southeastern Massachusetts.   Legislation protecting it perpetually has resulted in a gradual increase of the species, which is now nesting locally but not uncommonly in the coastal region and river valleys of southern New England.*   There are no records of the species wintering in Massachusetts since the great November storm of 1888 which distributed them all along the New England coast, but throughout the winter of 1922–23 they were reported nearly every week in southern Connecticut and occasionally a casual winter record has been made in eastern Massachusetts or Rhode Island.

The Killdeer is a friend of mankind.   Although it sometimes nests about the edges of the salt-marsh, it seems generally to prefer to rear its young about cultivated land and gardens (but not in fields where grass or grain grows thickly), probably because it finds that the insects on which it feeds are abundant in such situations.   When a nest is approached the female, usually watchful, sneaks away while the intruder is a long distance off, but if she is surprised on the nest or if the interloper closely approaches eggs or young, she uses every artifice to lead him away, floundering along the ground, shrieking and beating the earth with her wings as if in terrible agony.   Thus she may induce the novice in Killdeer wiles to follow her.   If so, when she has led him far enough astray, she miraculously recovers; her mate meantime wings his way near by with clamorous cries.   As in the great shore bird group in general the eggs are four in number, placed with their smaller ends together at the center of the nest.   If this arrangement is disturbed the Killdeer will soon restore it.

The funny little downy young are recognizable as Killdeers as soon as their natal down has dried, for their markings resemble those of the parents.   From the first they are able to pick up their own living, as they are hatched in a time of plenty.   Killdeers are fond of newly plowed land.   They follow the plow and the cultivator in search of grubs and worms.   Corn, potato, turnip, clover, alfalfa and other fields and gardens furnish them an abundance of insect food.   The Killdeer is an exceedingly swift and graceful bird on the ground or in the air.   To "run like a Killdeer" is a common saying in the South.   On the wing it performs wonderful evolutions, particularly in the mating

---

[1] Remington, C. H.: A Check List of Rhode Island Nesting Birds, 1908, p. 2.

* "Has increased remarkably and is now a fairly common summer resident in this region and often occurs in winter." Aretas A. Saunders, Fairfield, Connecticut, *in litt.*

season, showing off the bright markings of its wings, rump and tail to excellent advantage. It flies and cries in the dusk of evening, on moonlit nights, and before daylight in the early morning. Gunners detest the bird because of its extreme watchfulness and its wild piercing cries which communicate its alarm to every bird within hearing. It is often shot for that reason.

In New England, the Killdeer migrates chiefly along the coast and down the large river valleys. In the North, it is rarely seen in flocks, although as many as fifty have been observed together in recent years. In the South, however, flocks are not uncommon during migrations.

The food of the Killdeer consists very largely of insects and earthworms. When feeding about the water it secures crustaceans and other aquatic forms of life. It is very destructive to many farm pests such as mosquitoes, flies, grasshoppers, hop flea-beetles, locusts, ticks, crane-flies, army worms, and other caterpillars, such as cutworms, curculios or weevils, wireworms, etc.

ECONOMIC STATUS. The Killdeer is one of the most beneficial birds of the farm. As a game bird it is of little value, as its flesh is rather inferior. It should be protected by law at all times and forever.

Charádrius semipalmátus BONAPARTE. Semipalmated Plover.

Other names: RING-NECK; LITTLE RING-NECK.

Plate 33.

DESCRIPTION. — Bill very short; tail short, not extending beyond tips of closed wings; hind toe wanting and *front toes partly webbed*, web between outer and middle toe reaching second joint of latter, smaller web between middle and inner toe. *Adult male in breeding plumage (sexes alike or similar)*: Head marked and colored much as in Killdeer but with smaller light and dark areas (usually some white) behind eye; forehead, chin, throat and collar (extending from throat around neck) white; a black collar below the white; above mainly grayish-brown; tail lighter grayish-brown, blackish near end, and white at tip; outermost tail-feathers mostly white; the next with white outer webs; greater wing-coverts tipped white; primaries dusky or blackish, shafts and basal parts of outer webs white in some specimens; below, white from black collar to tail, including axillars and under wing-coverts, except under-primary-coverts which are pale grayish-brown; bill black at tip, yellow or orange-yellow at base; legs and feet orange-yellow, pale yellowish or flesh color. *Adult female in breeding plumage:* Sometimes as male but usually black markings duller; black collar showing some grayish-brown on each side. *Adults and young in winter plumage:* Black markings replaced by grayish-brown; otherwise as in breeding plumage. *Young in juvenal plumage:* Similar to winter plumage but black collar narrowed in front; feather ends of upper plumage margined light buff; tail broadly tipped buffy. *Downy young:* Above, mainly pale grayish-brown or buffy, mottled black; forehead, streak over eye and spot below it pale grayish-buffy; broad collar, a narrow black band passing around back of head, and under surface white.

MEASUREMENTS. — Length 6.50 to 8.05 in.; spread 14.00 to 16.00; folded wing 4.51 to 5.70; tail 2.00 to 2.30; bill .43 to .60; tarsus .80 to 1.05. Weight $1\frac{1}{16}$ to $1\frac{10}{16}$ oz. Sexes similar in size.

MOLTS. — Similar to those of Killdeer (see page 466).

FIELD MARKS. — Size larger than Semipalmated Sandpiper but much smaller than Killdeer from which distinguished also by short tail and *one* black collar; resembles Piping Plover but much darker above; color of wet sand while Piping Plover is that of dry sand; more completely collared with black

PLATE 33

PLATE 33

RUDDY TURNSTONE
Page 478

Young in Juvenal Plumage

Adult in Breeding Plumage

WILSON'S PLOVER
Page 473

Adult in Breeding Plumage

PIPING PLOVER
Page 470

Adult in Breeding Plumage

SEMIPALMATED PLOVER
Page 468

Adult in Breeding Plumage

All one-half natural size.

than Piping Plover; distinguished from Wilson's Plover by smaller size, much shorter bill, with yellow or orange-yellow base where other is black (see also Field Marks, of Wilson's Plover, page 473).

VOICE. — A simple, sweet, plaintive call, *chee-wee* (R. Hoffmann); when on wing calls *tyoo-eep* a short, mellow, far-reaching whistle; another rougher note is usually uttered singly, but sometimes a standing bird gives "a rapid *descendo* series of these questioning notes, *keup-keup-keup-keup*, etc., the last few almost running together" (J. T. Nichols); flight song of male a harsh, resonant *tschup* repeated many times in succession (J. Dwight).

BREEDING. — Usually about sandy or gravelly low-lying sea-shores, sometimes on higher lands, on the shores of estuaries or inland lakes near coast and on islands in rivers. *Nest:* A depression in sand or gravel or in short grass with or without sparse lining of grasses or leaves. *Eggs:* Normally 4; 1.20 to 1.40 by .90 to 1.00 in.; pear-shaped; whitish, "greenish buff," "buffy white," creamy, drab or "yellowish ash"; spotted irregularly with blackish-brown, umber or varying shades of brown; like those of Killdeer but smaller and known by absence of lines. *Dates:* Latter half of June and early July, northern Canada. *Incubation:* Period probably between 23 and 25 days; probably by both sexes.

RANGE. — North and South America. Breeds from Melville Island, Wellington Channel, Cumberland Sound and Davis Inlet south to Yukon mouth, valley of Upper Yukon, southern Yukon, east central Manitoba, southern James Bay, Gulf of St. Lawrence, New Brunswick and Nova Scotia; winters from southern California, Louisiana and South Carolina to Galapagos Islands, Chile and Patagonia; casual in eastern Siberia, Greenland and Bermuda; accidental in England.

DISTRIBUTION IN NEW ENGLAND. — Common migrant, mainly coastwise; rare migrant in Vermont.

SEASON IN MASSACHUSETTS. — (April 1) late April to June 14, July 7 to October 28 (November 10 to 15); scattered dates all through June indicate that a few non-breeding birds may summer.

HAUNTS AND HABITS. Dr. C. W. Townsend in the Birds of Essex County gives an excellent account of the Semipalmated Plover as follows:

"The Semipalmated Plover or Ring-neck as it is universally called, is one of the abundant birds of the beach in flocks of from two or three up to forty or fifty. They are found alone or associated with Peep or other shore birds. They also visit the sloughs of the salt-marshes, and are occasionally seen still farther inland. Thus Dr. Phillips records one at Wenham Lake on September 12th, 1904.

"The flocks on the wing, although sometimes compact, are apt to fly in loose order. On the sand, the birds at once spread out, not keeping together like Sandpipers, so that the pot-hunter spends many anxious moments waiting for a good combination, and often to his chagrin misses them all as the frightened birds take wing. Unlike the Sandpipers also, but in true plover fashion, instead of moving along close to the wave line with heads down, diligently probing the sand, they run rapidly about in different directions with heads up, often pausing and standing still as if in thought, occasionally jerking or bobbing their heads and necks nervously, and ever and anon dabbing quickly at some morsel of food.

"Like all shore birds, the Ring-neck often snatches moments of sleep in the day, especially during high tide when their best feeding places are covered. At these times it is not uncommon to see whole flocks huddled together fast asleep on the upper part of the beach, their heads turned to one side and thrust into the feathers of the back. There are always a few birds awake and on the lookout, and by close watching one may see even those apparently asleep, open their eyes occasionally. Ring-necks also sleep with heads sunk down between the shoulders. Their sleepiness in the day is accounted for by the fact that they feed and migrate by night as well as by day. . . .

"Like all shore birds also, the Ring-neck is often exceedingly fat in the autumn and I have known the fat of the breast to split open when the bird struck the ground after being shot when flying at a height. The fat is not only everywhere under the skin but it envelops all the viscera, and the liver is often pale from fatty infiltration. How birds under these circumstances are able to fly so vigorously on their long migrations, or even to fly at all is certainly a mystery." [1]

The following paragraph shows that the species is of some value to mankind as a destroyer of insects:

"Its food on the coast consists largely of small crustaceans, mollusks, eggs of marine animals, and insects, which it sometimes gleans from ploughed fields. In the interior it feeds on locusts, other *Orthoptera* and many other terrestrial insects. Professor Aughey examined the stomach contents of eleven Ring-necks taken in four counties of Nebraska between April, 1865, and July, 1875, and found all of them filled with insects. Eight stomachs contained from forty to sixty Rocky Mountain locusts each, and in all but one of the eleven there were other insects." [2]

ECONOMIC STATUS. This Plover is so small as to be of little value as game but as it is of some service as a destroyer of noxious insects it should be perpetually protected as a part of the interesting life of our summer beaches.

Charádrius melódus ORD. Piping Plover.

Other names: BEACH-BIRD; BEACH PLOVER; BUTTER-BIRD; CLAM-BIRD; MOURNING-BIRD; PALE RING-NECK; RING-NECK; PEEP-LO; TEE-O; FEEBLE.

Plate 33 and Fig. 34.

DESCRIPTION. — Bill very short, rather stout; tail rounded, short, web between middle and outer toes not reaching first joint of latter; lightest in color above of New England plovers. *Adults in breeding plumage (sexes alike or similar):* Above mainly pale grayish-brown or pale ashy-brown, paling on rump and upper tail-coverts and fading into white on outer tail-feathers, all except outer pair with a blackish area near tips; anterior lesser wing-coverts darker than back; primaries blackish; patch crossing above forehead from eye to eye and more or less (usually less) complete ring round base of neck black (in some a short black line extending backward from upper mandible); indistinct dusky streak behind eye; forehead, stripe behind eye over ear-coverts, cheeks, collar round back of neck, all under plumage (except where neck is ringed), outer upper tail-coverts, sides of rump, greater wing-coverts and secondaries, mostly white; *female* often but not always distinguishable by more restricted and duller black markings on head and at base of neck; bill black at tip, orange or orange-yellow at base; iris dark brown or blackish; naked edges of lids yellow or orange; legs and feet orange or orange-yellow. *Adults and young in winter plumage:* Like breeding plumage, but without black on top of head, and dark at base of neck not black but dusky brownish and much restricted. *Young in juvenal plumage:* Similar to winter but feathers of upper plumage largely margined pale buff or whitish; little, if any, trace of dark ring at base of neck. *Downy young:* Above pale grayish-buffy with irregular markings of dusky-brown; sides

---

[1] Birds of Essex County; 1905, pp. 196–197.
[2] Game Birds, Wild-Fowl and Shore Birds, Massachusetts State Board of Agriculture, 1916, p. 353.

of rump with an ill-defined patch or stripe of dark brown; forehead, sides of head, end of wing, neck all round and under plumage white.

MEASUREMENTS. — Length 6.00 to 7.80 in.; spread 14.00 to 16.00; folded wing 4.50 to 5.03; tail 1.90 to 2.65; bill .45 to .52; tarsus .85 to 1.00. Weight 3 oz. (Audubon). Sexes nearly alike in size; male usually largest.

MOLTS. — Similar to those of Killdeer (see page 466); black neck markings of male probably are perfected with age, complete ring about neck signifying a fully mature bird.

FIELD MARKS. — Size of Semipalmated Plover or Ring-neck; the only *pale* ring-neck on beach; color of dry sand above; black band above white forehead and partial or entire black ring round neck; in flight shows much white in wings.

VOICE. — A plaintive, piping whistle, *queep, queep, queepo* (J. H. Langille); common note *queep;* some of its local names are derived from its notes as *Peep-lo, Tee-o* and *Feeble.*

BREEDING. — On wide, bare sand beaches or among sparse beach grass; sometimes at base of a low sand dune. *Nest:* A slight hollow in sand, lined (or not) with pebbles, bits of shell, etc. *Eggs:* Normally 4; 1.20 to 1.30 by .95 to 1.00 in.; approaching pear-shape; size of eggs of Semipalmated Plover but usually rather paler and a little less elongated and pointed; clay color, very pale creamy-brown or creamy-white, finely dotted or speckled with chocolate or blackish-brown; practically no lines but a "few obscure shell marks of lilac or lavender." *Dates:* May 10 to June 14 (July 20) Massachusetts. *Incubation:* Probably by female alone. One brood yearly.

DOWNY YOUNG PIPING
PLOVER

About ½ natural size.

RANGE. — Eastern North America. Breeds locally from southern Saskatchewan, southern Manitoba, southern Ontario, southern Quebec, Magdalen and Amherst Islands, Newfoundland, Prince Edward Island and Nova Scotia south to central Nebraska, Kansas, northeastern Illinois, northwestern Indiana, northern Ohio, northwestern Pennsylvania and North Carolina; winters on coast of United States from Georgia to Texas and in northern Mexico; casual in migration to Newfoundland, Bermuda, Bahamas and Greater Antilles.

DISTRIBUTION IN NEW ENGLAND. — Now increasing and fast becoming again a common local summer resident coastwise; recorded from Vermont — Dr. L. H. Ross, October 2, 1908, Bennington.

SEASON IN MASSACHUSETTS. — (March 18); March 25 to October 28.

HAUNTS AND HABITS. In the latter part of the nineteenth century the dove-like little Piping Plover came very near extirpation on the New England coast. Destroyed by spring and summer shooting, it had become rare where once it was abundant and was rapidly disappearing, when the Massachusetts Legislature enacted a law giving it protection at all times. Now, protected similarly by Federal law, it is increasing in numbers and reoccupying its former breeding-grounds, wherever the summer population is not too numerous for its comparative safety. Its gentle notes are now heard throughout the summer on all the more lonely sand beaches of New England. It is a bird of the sandy shore. Wide beaches, backed by dunes are its favorite breeding-places, where it runs along the sand at such speed and so gracefully and smoothly that it seems to be gliding swiftly over the beach.

The following from one of my note books gives some idea of the means by which this bird and its young avoid their enemies:

"I was watching a pair of adults trying to lead me away from their young. They threw themselves on the ground breast downward and drooping the flight-feathers or primaries, raised and agitated the secondaries until the motion resembled the fluttering pinions of young birds; meantime pushing themselves along with their feet. As the wings were not spread, the primaries were not noticeable and so the imitation of the struggles of the helpless young was complete. Immediately we began a careful search for

PIPING PLOVER THE DAY OF THE
HATCH
Three young and one egg pipped.

the nest, looking in all the usual hiding places in or under the tufts of beach-grass, but no nest could we find. As the old birds continued their plaintive cries and circled about we extended our search, expecting to find some half-grown young flattened out somewhere on the beach. Finally by searching over the sand we found a nest exactly like that of the Least Tern on the open beach. A few little pebbles had been grouped in a slight hollow, and there, partly beside the pebbles and partly on them lay three lovely little downy chicks and one egg. I attempted to photograph the parents but they would not come to the young and as the little ones had already begun to run about we sunk an old barrel in the beach and put them and the egg in it, that we might know where to find them on the morrow. The day was foggy and cold and during the night a thunderstorm drenched everything, but the next morning the egg had disappeared and four lively youngsters were running around in our barrel. They were now so strong and swift that if one were liberated it was rather difficult to catch it. If hidden it was almost impossible to find it.

"One of my early experiences will serve as an illustration of the difficulty of finding young beach-birds. One day I saw in the distance a downy young Piping Plover running on the beach. Watching it with a powerful glass until it squatted, I marked the spot carefully, walked over and picked it up. I then took it to an open flat part of the beach and released it. It ran a little way, and I have never seen it since. The most careful search failed to solve this puzzle.

"To go back to our little plovers in the barrel. We kept them there two days until we made sure that the parents never feed the young. They brooded

THREE LITTLE ONES SET OUT TO SEE
THE WORLD

them quite constantly but brought no food whatever and we made certain that the young were able and willing to find their own food within twenty-four hours after they were out of the shell. It was seen that unless they were liberated from the tub they would soon starve to death. On the third day they had become so active and vigorous as to lead one quite a chase."

Although some Piping Plovers may be seen on our beaches from late March to late October the great majority of the breeding birds come here in April and early May and depart in August. The late birds probably are hardy migrants from the Provinces.

The food of the Piping Plover consists of insects, crustaceans, mollusks and other small marine animals and their eggs.

ECONOMIC STATUS. This species is harmless and useful. It is too small for a game bird and should be perpetually protected by law.

Pagólla wilsónia wilsonia (ORD). Wilson's Plover.

Other names: RING-NECK; STUTTERING PLOVER.

Plate 33.

DESCRIPTION. — *Bill large, long,* rather stout; no bright colored eye-ring; tail nearly even, rather short, not extending beyond tips of closed wings; *outer toe* and middle toe half webbed, no web between middle and inner. *Adult male in breeding plumage:* Above mostly grayish-brown (somewhat lighter than Semipalmated Plover, much darker than Piping Plover); tail grayish-brown, becoming darker toward end (in some specimens lighter at tip), paling gradually from inner to outer feathers which are white; band above forehead crossing top of head but not reaching either eye, stripe from bill to eye and crescentic band across base of fore neck, black; region about ear, and nape sometimes tinged rusty; forehead, stripe over eye (prolonged from forehead), lower part of cheeks, collar around back of neck, all under plumage (except black bar on upper breast) and tips of greater wing-coverts (narrowly), white; white stripe over eye becomes duller behind eye where it extends about .50 in.; primaries blackish, whitening on inner webs, inner ones also white basally on outer webs; tips of primary coverts white; secondaries mostly white on inner webs and narrowly tipped white; bill black; iris dark brown; legs and feet flesh colored. *Adult female in breeding plumage:* Similar to male but neck-band and stripe before eye not black but dark grayish-brown, both sometimes mixed with rusty; band above forehead a mere trace and duller than in male. *Adults and young in winter plumage:* Similar to adult female. *Young in juvenal plumage:* Like adult female with no black on fore crown; band of grayish-brown across fore neck, and feathers of upper plumage margined grayish. *Downy young:* Buff above, mottled and clouded black; a black stripe behind eye; collar around hind neck, front and sides of head, and under plumage, white.

MEASUREMENTS. — Length 7.00 to 8.15 in.; spread 14.00 to 16.00; folded wing 4.50 to 5.90; tail 1.45 to 2.00; bill .70 to 1.05; tarsus 1.05 to 1.28.

MOLTS. — Similar to those of Killdeer. (See page 466.) Adults have a head and body (partial) molt February to June.

FIELD MARKS. — Size larger than that of Semipalmated or Piping Plovers; color between the two though much nearer Semipalmated; *long, heavy black bill* and black half-ring on fore neck not completed round back of neck distinguish bird from Semipalmated Plover; darker color and large bill differentiate it from Piping Plover.

VOICE. — Male, a stuttering note (C. J. Maynard); a plaintive whistle (A. T. Wayne); an agreeable piping note (Wilson); flute-like notes (H. K. Job); quite different from those of other plovers; half a whistle and half a chirp (Coues); "a tern-like *quip*," or "*quip-ip*," " a surprisingly human whistled '*whip*' " (J. T. Nichols).

BREEDING. — Usually about the mouth of an inlet on the sea-coast where there are both sand and mud. *Nest:* A slight depression in sandy beach just above high water mark, in many cases encircled with broken bits of shells. *Eggs:* 2 to 4, normally 3; 1.22 to 1.45 by 1.00 to 1.05 in.; quite ovate; greenish-gray, pale olive, drab or clay colored; blotched, spotted and lined blackish-brown and light lavender; many lines, marks seldom numerous enough to obscure ground color. *Dates:* May 12 to June 10, Virginia. *Incubation:* Period 24 to 25 days (T. M. Brewer); by female. One brood yearly.

RANGE. — Southern North America and Middle America (Atlantic and Gulf coasts mainly). Breeds from southeastern Virginia (formerly New Jersey) south to northern Bahamas and along Gulf coast to Texas; winters from southern Lower California, Texas and Florida south to Bahamas, southern Guatemala, Honduras and West Indies; casual northward in migration along Atlantic coast to Nova Scotia, and on Pacific coast to California; casual in the interior. (A West Indian form has been separated.)

DISTRIBUTION IN NEW ENGLAND. — *Vermont* and *New Hampshire:* Doubtfully recorded. *Massachusetts:* Accidental visitor. Plymouth, one taken at the Gurnet August 22, 1887, by Arthur S. Fiske;[1] Ipswich, bird found in a gunner's bag, May 8, 1904, by Dr. C. W. Townsend;[2] Dennis, about 25 birds seen Sept. 4, 1920, by the Misses J. Olivia and Sarah B. Crowell.[3] *Rhode Island:* Doubtfully included. *Connecticut:* Stratford, a specimen taken by Rev. James H. Linsey;[4] Bridgeport, bird seen July 28, 1888, by C. K. Averill.[5]

HAUNTS AND HABITS. Wilson's Plover is a slightly faded larger copy of the Semipalmated Plover with somewhat different markings about the head and a bill which, when compared with those of other small plovers, appears about two sizes too large for the bird. When it bred on the New Jersey coast it may have occurred more often in New England than it does today and, if under protection its numbers increase, we may see more of it than in the past. As it is a beach-bird, and migrates across the sea to many islands, it is likely to be blown to our coast by storms in spring or autumn. It frequents the beach, following in and out the wash of the foaming breakers; but though usually seen along the outer shore line, it visits the margins of inlets, and runs over mud flats as the tide recedes. Wayne says that this is a very gentle species, especially in the breeding season and that after the eggs have been deposited or the young hatched it can be approached to within a few feet. It uses the same artifices as the Piping Plover to entice the intruder away from eggs or young.

Its food is similar to that of other beach-birds.

ECONOMIC STATUS. See page 372.

Podasócys montánus (J. K. TOWNSEND). Mountain Plover.
Other name: UPLAND PLOVER.

DESCRIPTION. — Bill shorter than head, rather slim; tail short, not extending beyond tips of closed wings and nearly even; legs long, toes very short, a small basal web between outer and middle toe, none between middle and inner toe. *Adults in breeding plumage (sexes alike):* A conspicuous black band extending over fore part of crown, often wide and sometimes covering a considerable part of crown; a black stripe from base of upper mandible to eye; elsewhere above, mainly grayish-brown, feathers often more or less distinctly margined buffy or rusty; tail usually tipped whitish, subterminally dusky or dark grayish-brown, outer webs of outermost tail-feathers and outermost tail-coverts lighter or white; flight-feathers mainly blackish; some inner primaries with white on basal part of outer webs, shaft of first

[1] Coues, Elliott: Bulletin Nuttall Ornithological Club, 1882, p. 59.
[2] Birds of Essex County, 1905, p. 199.
[3] Crowell, Miss J. O.: *in litt.*
[4] Merriam, C. Hart: Birds of Connecticut, 1877, p. 102.
[5] List of Birds in the Vicinity of Bridgeport, Conn., 1892, p. 9.

white, of others partly white; primary coverts and greater coverts tipped white; space below eye whitish; forehead, connecting stripe over eye and all under plumage, including linings of wings, and axillars white, shaded more or less on breast with pale grayish or pale brownish; bill black; iris dark brown; legs "pale brown" or "dull light brownish-yellow"; toes black. *Adults and young in winter plumage:* Similar to adult breeding plumage, but no black markings on head; feathers of upper plumage more distinctly tipped light rusty "or deep creamy buff"; sides of head, upper breast and sides of body, tinged same. *Young in juvenal plumage:* Similar to winter plumage but light feather-edgings broader and brighter and under plumage more extensively tinged "tawny brown" or "deep creamy buff." *Downy young:* Above velvety and more or less tufted; pale brownish-buff, mottled black, except on forehead and cheeks; in some individuals two black spots on cheek and a very narrow black streak behind eye, terminating in a blotch; below "pale buff" or dull yellowish-white.

HEAD OF MOUNTAIN PLOVER

About ½ natural size.

MEASUREMENTS. — Length 8.00 to 9.50 in.; spread 17.80 to 19.50; folded wing 5.44 to 6.75; tail 2.50 to 3.00; bill .78 to .90; tarsus 1.45 to 1.81. Sexes about equal in size; female may average larger.

MOLTS. — Adults apparently have a complete postnuptial molt beginning in July or August and a partial prenuptial molt in spring (January to May).

FIELD MARKS. — Size of Killdeer and somewhat similar in color but not so slender and no ring around neck; in winter plumage no black marks; linings of wings and axillars show silvery white in flight when the birds alternately flap and sail with down-curved wings.

VOICE. — Soft, low, peculiar notes, vary much; a low, pleasing whistle, somewhat drawling or rather lisping in tone, changing to a somewhat louder and higher one, sometimes sounding harshly (Coues).

BREEDING. — On high dry plains and in desert regions. *Nest:* A hollow in earth, sometimes lined with a few grass blades. *Eggs:* 3 or 4; 1.40 to 1.60 by 1.05 to 1.15 in.; bluntly pear-shaped to nearly ovate, much less pointed than is usual with plovers' eggs; brownish-drab or olive-drab, shaded brown with small rounded spots of blackish-brown. *Dates:* June 9 to July 8, Colorado and Nebraska.

RANGE. — Western North America. Breeds from northern Montana and western Nebraska south to northern New Mexico, northwestern Texas and western Kansas; winters from northern California, southern Arizona and south central Texas to southern Lower California and central Mexico; accidental in Florida and Massachusetts.

DISTRIBUTION IN NEW ENGLAND — Accidental visitor from West. One record in *Massachusetts*, Chatham, an immature male taken at North Beach by A. E. Crowell and recorded by W. Sprague Brooks,[1] now in collection of Boston Society of Natural History.

HAUNTS AND HABITS. The Mountain Plover is not a mountain bird but breeds on the high plains in the Rocky Mountain region. It is one of the few shore birds that lives mainly away from water on dry land and one of the few that in winter migrates westward from its breeding-grounds on its way to the South. Therefore, it is only by the merest accident that we have a single record for it in New England. It is at home on the desert lands of the West and on the shores of the Pacific. It frequents cultivated fields as well as barren plains, prairies and desert lands.

ECONOMIC STATUS. As this bird is believed to feed almost entirely on insects, it may be useful in agricultural regions. As a game bird it is not highly valued as its flesh has a peculiar flavor.

---

[1] Auk, Vol. XXXIV, 1917, p. 86.

Professor Samuel Aughey, who examined the stomach contents of sixteen Mountain Plovers, during the Rocky Mountain locust invasions, prior to 1877, found in their stomachs 749 locusts and 211 other insects. This indicates that the bird is useful in the West and apparently it is not in any way injurious. On its normal range, where it is generally known as the "Upland Plover," it is regarded as a valuable game bird. However, it is now (1924) protected by law at all times.

FAMILY **APHRIZIDÆ**. SURF-BIRDS AND TURNSTONES.

Number of species in North America 3; in Massachusetts 1.

SUBFAMILY **ARENARIINÆ**. TURNSTONES.

Number of species in North America 2; in Massachusetts 1.

Turnstones (a small subfamily) are closely related to plovers but are peculiar in coloration and in the shape and extreme hardness of the bill; also they have four toes and the front toes are cleft to their base. Their habit of overturning objects in search of small animals concealed beneath them differentiates them from other shore birds.

Arenária intérpres interpres (LINNÆUS). **Turnstone.**

DESCRIPTION. — Bill hard, straight, pointed and often slightly upturned, seemingly more like that of a woodpecker than that of a plover; tail short, slightly rounded; legs short and stout. *Adult male in breeding plumage: Variable;* forehead white, feathers at base of ridge of upper mandible and a band, sometimes incomplete, from eye to eye, black; crown streaked dark or blackish, feathers edged white or buffy; nape white, feather-tips sometimes dusky and washed russet; upper back and scapulars (varying) black, glossed green, and russet with many white markings (edgings or faint tippings); lower back and rump white, latter with more or less black bordering upper tail-coverts; anterior, central, upper tail-coverts form a black patch, surrounded by white of rump and other upper tail-coverts (some feathers in this patch sometimes margined yellowish-tawny, sometimes more or less tipped white); some white between eye and base of bill; a black patch below eye connects with black band running from base of lower mandible to breast; a black band extends from this up sides of neck toward or to nape; below the black a broad white band extends on to sides of breast; ear-coverts, eye stripe, chin and upper throat white; lower throat and breast black, some feathers faintly margined white; rest of under plumage white; primaries blackish-brown, inner webs with much white, increasing basally; inner primaries with faint white tips; outer secondaries blackish-brown, white basally, at tips, and on much of inner webs; inner secondaries nearly all white; innermost tertials glossed olive, "notched, margined and varied with russet," sometimes largely colored with same; median and lesser wing-coverts largely russet, some irregularly marked black and russet; tail white at base, black toward end, tipped more or less broadly white; outer tail-feathers largely white; bill black or blackish; iris brown; *legs and feet vermilion to blackish. Adult female in breeding plumage:* Similar to male in color pattern but with less bright rusty or cinnamon, and top of head streaked brownish-gray rather than white. *Adults in winter plumage:* Largely brownish-gray above with little black or rusty; no well-defined black and white areas on head; black of fore neck and upper breast largely replaced by dusky, broken by whitish tips; top of head brownish-gray, streaked dusky; back and scapulars with dusky feather centers and brownish-gray margins. *Young in first winter plumage:* As adult winter plumage, distinguished only by buff or whitish edges of some scapulars, innermost secondaries or tertials and middle coverts left over from juvenal plumage. *Young in juvenal plumage:* Like winter plumage, but scapulars, upper back and tertials abruptly and rather narrowly margined buff or whitish and tail tipped buffy or cinnamon. *Downy young:* Above blackish-gray, washed buffy; nape grayish-white, irregularly marked black or blackish; forehead and stripe over eye buffy-white; black line from bill to eye; below from chin to tail (except for a dusky or blackish area on breast) white or whitish.

MEASUREMENTS. — Length male about 9 in. (Dresser); spread 17.00 to 19.80; folded wing 5.70 to 6.35 (*usually 6.00 or more*); tail 2.30 to 2.50; bill .81 to .91 (male 1 inch, Dresser); tarsus .95 to 1.06. Weight 3 to 4 oz. (Latham). Female larger than male.

MOLTS. — Juvenal body plumage (except some scapulars), some tail-feathers, inner secondaries or tertials and wing-coverts are molted (August to November) and first winter plumage is assumed; a prenuptial body molt (February to June) including some wing-coverts and tail-feathers is followed by first nuptial plumage practically as adult; adults have a partial prenuptial molt (February to June) and a complete postnuptial molt (July to October).

FIELD MARKS. — Size larger than Sanderling; short red legs; straight pointed bill and variable calico pattern of plumage; appearance in flight "boldly pied"; impossible to distinguish in field from Ruddy Turnstone.

VOICE. — In flight a thin, crackling chatter; alarm note *tche, tche* (Practical Handbook of British Birds).

BREEDING. — Mainly on islands near coast. *Nest:* A hollow in ground, sometimes under shelter of plants. *Eggs:* Sometimes 3; usually 4; 1.52 to 1.70 by 1.10 to 1.20 in.; somewhat pear-shaped; grayish to greenish or brownish, spotted dark brown and ashy-purple. *Dates:* Early June to July 30. *Incubation:* By both sexes. One brood yearly.

RANGE. — Mainly Eastern Hemisphere, extending in Western Hemisphere to Greenland and Alaska. Breeds from western Greenland and Iceland, in Arctic and northern Europe, Siberia, Asian Arctic islands and Japan and in Alaska from Yukon delta to Point Barrow (probably Hall Island in Bering Sea); winters on coasts of Europe and Asia to South Africa, Australia, New Zealand, New Caledonia, New Hebrides, etc.; in migration southward over practically all Old World, on Pacific coasts of North and South America to Chile, and casually on Atlantic seaboard; also to Galapagos and many islands in South Pacific.

DISTRIBUTION IN NEW ENGLAND. — Records. *Massachusetts:* Chatham, adult female taken September 8, 1892, by Dr. Louis B. Bishop at Monomoy and recorded by him.

HAUNTS AND HABITS. The Turnstone frequents localities similar to those haunted by the American race, the Ruddy Turnstone (see page 478). The present race has overflowed apparently from its Old World habitat and breeds in Greenland and Alaska. Therefore it is not very remarkable that it should appear casually or accidentally on the Atlantic coast of North America and it may be expected to occur again in New England.

Turnstones wander over the oceans of the world, reaching far islands in the Atlantic and Pacific more than 800 miles from any continent. Mr. H. W. Elliott says that he has met with the Turnstone at sea 700 miles from the nearest land flying northwest toward the Aleutian Islands, his ship being then 800 miles west of the Straits of Fuca (the entrance of Puget Sound). Mr. William Palmer asserts that in their southward migration from St. Paul toward the Aleutian Islands they leave at evening, plunging into thick fog as they go. Capt. Donald B. MacMillan records that he was interested in seeing a large flock alight upon the water in Kennedy Channel.[1] This indicates how they may rest in their long flights over the sea.

---

[1] Four Years in the White North, 1918, p. 409.

Arenaria interpres morinélla (LINNÆUS). Ruddy Turnstone.

Other names: CHICKEN-BIRD; CHICKEN-PLOVER; CHICKEN; ROCK-BIRD; ROCK-PLOVER; BISHOP-PLOVER; CALICO-BACK; CALICO-BIRD; CHICARIC; CREDDOCK; RED-LEGGED PLOVER; STREAKED-BACK; SPARKED-BACK; BRANT-BIRD; HORSE-FOOT SNIPE; SEA-QUAIL.

Plate 33.

DESCRIPTION. — An American race of the Turnstone, similar to it in all stages (see page 476) but averaging smaller, and lighter in color; legs and feet more orange than red. *Adult male in breeding plumage:* Differs from Turnstone in having relatively more extensive cinnamon rufous, rusty or chestnut areas above and black areas correspondingly more restricted; black streaks on top of head narrower and edged whiter. *Adult female in breeding plumage:* Rusty or chestnut replaces some of grayish-brown and black seen in female Turnstone on upper plumage; wings and tail average decidedly shorter. *Young:* Similar to young of Turnstone but averaging smaller; "eyes dark brown; bill less black (than in adult); legs and feet pale orange." *Downy young:* Above light drab or light buff to light gray, marked and finely marbled black; distinct black streak from bill to eye; forehead with central blackish streak; below dull white with a brownish-gray or dusky band across upper breast.

MEASUREMENTS. — Length 7.75 to 9.90 in.; spread 16.00 to 19.50; folded wing 5.45 to 6.08 (*usually less than 6.00*); tail 2.30 to 2.75; bill .80 to 1.00; tarsus .89 to 1.05. Weight 3¼ to 5½ oz. Female larger than male.

MOLTS. — Similar to those of Turnstone (see page 477). Probably some non-breeding birds, remaining south of breeding range, retain winter plumage through summer.

FIELD MARKS. — Size between Sanderling and Knot; about that of Killdeer but more robust and tail shorter; pied black, white and chestnut plumage; short, straight or slightly upturned bill and short, orange colored legs aid in identification; in flight it displays black and white in wings and tail, and three white streaks down back, middle one interrupted by patch of black near base of tail.

VOICE. — A rapidly repeated short *kuk, kuk, kuk;* a loud, twittering note or a chuckling whistle; in flight a clear, deep, melodious *quittock, quittock* from which the name "Creddock" given the bird by Nantucket gunners probably was derived; "a much rarer, loud Plover-like Kik-kyu," also given in flight (J. T. Nichols).

BREEDING. — About sandy or stony shores. *Nest:* A depression in ground, sometimes lined with leaves. *Eggs:* Usually 4; 1.60 to 1.72 by 1.13 to 1.23 in.; variable in shape and size but commonly pear-shaped; light olive-brown, cream color, light drab or deep clay color, spotted and splashed with light brown and lilac; spots most numerous about large end.

RANGE. — North and South America. Breeds on Arctic coasts from mouth of Mackenzie east to Melville Peninsula, north probably to Melville Island, west on Alaskan coast; winters from central California, Texas, Louisiana, Mississippi and South Carolina to southern Brazil, and central Chile; uncommon in migration on Pacific coast of North America.

DISTRIBUTION IN NEW ENGLAND. — Common migrant coastwise; rare in interior; rare migrant in Vermont (Lake Champlain).

SEASON IN MASSACHUSETTS. — May 1 to June 8 (June 24); (July 4) July 24 to October 16.

HAUNTS AND HABITS. The handsome, busy Ruddy Turnstone has increased under the protection of the Federal law until it is becoming quite a common bird in migration along much of the New England coast. It is so striking and its habits are so peculiar that it well repays the watcher who is able to observe it at close range or with a glass. It likes to delve about the foot of a rocky cliff or on a stony beach where great rocks project above the sea and where rockweed and kelp abound. In such surroundings its colors seem to blend with its environment and there it is perfectly at home. As its name implies, it digs and pushes with its beak under stones and overturns them. It roots over heaps of mosses and overthrows clods, but is not by any means always thus occupied, for often it runs along the sand like any sandpiper and follows the retreating waves. At half tide I have often found it far from its rocky shores on wide sand flats where it runs about in shallow pools, seeking its prey, and occasionally prying up and overturning a large shell of sea-clam or quahog in anticipation of finding some lurking prey beneath. It swims well at need and seems to enjoy wading and bathing. On May 24, 1923, a warm, sunny day, I watched Semipalmated Sandpipers, Semipalmated Plovers and Turnstones bathing on the Yarmouth flats. Thirteen lovely Turnstones in elegant nuptial plumage were bathing where the waters of a little creek spreading out over the sand flats met the incoming tide. The tide was advancing so fast that the birds did not need to wade in, but on the shallows where the wavelets flowed in swiftly but softly, they dipped and fluttered in an inch of water which rapidly grew deeper. Here they splashed about, throwing the sparkling drops over their bright and strikingly marked plumage, from which all water seemed to roll off as if from a duck's back. Some, however, must have soaked in, for as each pretty bather finished its ablutions, it fluttered up into the air a foot or two and flying along for three or four feet alighted on a little sand-bar that still showed above the tide, and so shaking its plumage threw off the remaining drops, meantime displaying all its beauties — its white, black-banded tail fully spread and its pied head, chestnut back and black and white wings glistening in the sunlight.

The Turnstone feeds on crustaceans, small mussels and other marine objects and on the eggs of the great crab commonly called Horsefoot or Horse-shoe. In the autumn it often becomes very fat and in excellent condition for the table.

ECONOMIC STATUS. See page 372.

FAMILY **HÆMATOPODIDÆ.** OYSTER-CATCHERS.

Number of species in North America 4; in Massachusetts 1.

This is a small family of but one genus and about a dozen species of large shore birds distributed along the sea-coasts of the world. They are distinguished by their peculiar, dense specialized bills, shaped somewhat like a screw-driver, and used for opening the shells of bivalve mollusks and cutting the attachments of limpets and barnacles.

Hæmátopus palliátus TEMMINCK. **Oyster-catcher.**

Plate 32.

DESCRIPTION. — Bill twice as long as head, hard, shaped somewhat like that of a woodpecker and flattened laterally much like a knife blade; tail short, even at end; legs and feet stout, coarse, rough; no hind toe; front toes basally webbed. *Adults at all seasons (sexes alike)*: Head, neck and upper breast black, with slight bluish-green gloss; small white streak below lower eyelid; back, scapulars, rump, some middle upper tail-coverts and most of wings dark grayish-brown or brownish-gray; outer and terminal upper tail-coverts white, latter sometimes spotted dusky; tail dark brownish-gray, darkening sometimes to blackish at end; tips of some middle wing-coverts, all exposed parts of greater coverts, and most of inner secondaries white; outer secondaries dark brownish-gray, with much of inner webs and basal part of outer webs white, outer webs edged white toward ends; primaries and their coverts dusky or blackish; some inner primaries show some white; under plumage, breast to tail, including axillars and under wing-coverts white, with often some dusky markings near edge of wing; bill vermilion red, deeper in middle, base more orange-red; iris yellow, red or orange, naked edges of eyelids same; legs and feet very pale flesh color. *Young in juvenal plumage:* Head and neck dull, dusky, brownish or blackish mixed with brownish; some white feathers round base of bill; elsewhere above grayish-brown with feather-edgings of buffy or brownish; upper tail-coverts tipped buff; otherwise similar to adults; bill dull brownish; iris brown; feet pale, dull livid-grayish. *Downy young:* Above light tawny or buffy-gray, with dark mottling; two narrow black stripes from upper back to rump, a small dark stripe behind eye and a broad dark stripe bordering back and other upper parts; below white.

Measurements. — Length 17.00 to 21.00 in.; spread 30.00 to 36.00; folded wing 9.60 to 11.00; tail 3.75 to 4.10; bill 2.85 to 4.10; tarsus 2.05 to 2.55. Female, weight 1 lb. 10 oz.; larger than male.

Molts. — The postjuvenal molt in autumn includes most of body-feathers, some wing-coverts and innermost secondaries, and, by midwinter, young are scarcely distinguishable from adults; first prenuptial molt in spring is not complete and young can still be distinguished from breeding adult by browner small wing-coverts; after first postnuptial molt young bird in second winter plumage becomes as adult; adults have partial prenuptial molt, mainly body-feathers, and complete postnuptial molt.

Field Marks. — As large as a Crow; a conspicuous, unmistakable bird; long, red bill; pied plumage which seems black and white and flashes in a startling manner when bird flies.

Voice. — Loud and shrill; *wheep-wheep-wheo* (Wilson). Notes of two Oyster-catchers forced to take wing: *crik-crik-crik*, etc., once a longer *cle-ar* interpolated, which suggested flight calls of Willet and Black-breasted Plover (J. T. Nichols).

Breeding. — On sandy beaches or among sand dunes. *Nest:* A slight hollow in sand, sometimes decorated with pieces of shells. *Eggs:* 2 or 3, very rarely 4; 2.12 to 2.30 by 1.50 to 1.62 in.; ovate, "creamy buff," blotched and spotted with dark brown and lined faintly with lavender. *Dates:* April 10 to May 6, Florida; May 3 to July 12, Virginia. *Incubation:* Period, probably 24 or 25 days; probably by both sexes, chiefly female. One brood yearly.

Range. — Coasts of North and South America, from Virginia (formerly Canadian Labrador, Audubon) to Texas, on both coasts of Mexico and West Indies south to Argentina * and central Chile. Probably breeds throughout its range; casual north to New Brunswick and Nova Scotia.

Distribution in New England. — Accidental visitor from South. Records: *Maine:* Audubon asserted that it occurred in his day from Portland, Maine, to Labrador † and that it bred on the coast of Labrador and in the Bay of Fundy.[1] *Massachusetts:* Boston, a specimen killed in harbor prior to 1814 sent to Alexander Wilson;[2] Marshfield, pair taken in 1837 by Daniel Webster, still in collection of Boston Society of Natural History;[3] Chatham, bird taken in April, 1885, at Monomoy;[4] adult male and a female, probably its mate, taken August [20] 1899;[5] Eastham, 2 birds seen September 10, 1924, on Nauset Marsh by Dr. E. P. and Wyman Richardson.[6] *Connecticut:* Linsley said (1843): "The Oystercatcher is now rare here but fifteen years since they were not very uncommon in autumn."[7]

---

* It is not certain whether the South American birds and those of western Mexico should be referred to this race.

† This, like all of Audubon's references to his own observations in Labrador, refers to Canadian Labrador — the northern shore of the Gulf of St. Lawrence.

[1] Ornithological Biography, Vol. III, 1835, p. 182.

[2] American Ornithology, Vol. VIII, 1814, p. 17.

[3] Baird, Brewer and Ridgway: Water Birds, Vol. I, 1874, p. 113.

[4] Brewster, Wm.: Auk, Vol. II, 1885, p. 384.   [5] Brewster, Wm.: Auk, Vol. XVIII, 1901, p. 136.

[6] Richardson, Wyman: *in litt.* In this connection it is worthy of note that an Oyster-catcher was shot August 28 at Mastic, L. I. (J. T. Nichols in Bird-Lore, Vol. XXVI, 1924, p. 415.)

[7] Linsley, J. H.: A Catalogue of the Birds of Connecticut; American Journal of Science and Arts, Vol. XLIV, 1843, p. 265.

HAUNTS AND HABITS. If we can believe the statements of Audubon, the Oyster-catcher once nested north as far as the (Canadian) Labrador coast. As the Black Oyster-catcher ranges north to Alaska and the European Oyster-catcher to Greenland, our bird may well have bred on the Labrador coast in the old days. If so, it is not the only bird that has disappeared from that region since the settlement of the country. Unfortunately no one corroborates Audubon's statement. Boardman informed Dr. Brewer that the Oyster-catcher occurred occasionally but rarely near Calais, Maine, and that one was taken on Grand Manan. Wilson writes of a bird, shot from a flock near the entrance of Boston Harbor prior to 1814, and Dr. Brewer says that about 1837 it was no uncommon thing to see specimens on sale in the Boston market. With the pair taken by Daniel Webster at Marshfield about that time the history of this species in Massachusetts closed until 1885. The bird may appear again in New England, as Mr. W. H. Osgood saw a flock of about 20 on July 20, 1907, at Digby, Nova Scotia, according to Professor W. W. Cooke.[1] It formerly nested in New Jersey and possibly even on Long Island, but now the remnant of its race is disappearing from Virginia, and one must go to North Carolina to be sure of finding nesting birds.

Many years ago in Florida I watched these birds feeding on the oyster-bars, disabling the small "coon" oysters with a clip of the powerful bill. These oysters are exposed at low tide, and the birds know how to open them as well as any professional oyster-opener. They feast on them until their flesh has the flavor of an oyster. These conspicuous great birds were common then, wading about on bars which were exposed at low tide and going to fresh-water ponds back of the beach to drink and bathe. Their color patterns in flight are so conspicuous that the dullest eye cannot fail to find them. Apparently, they know their danger and constantly keep far out of gunshot. I never saw one far from the coast or from some lagoon near the sea. They frequent wide open beaches and flats and avoid cover of any kind. They pay no attention to decoys and would have an excellent chance to survive were it not for the fact that they deposit usually but two or three eggs, deposited on open beaches or stretches of sand which in the North have become too populous for their safety. Notwithstanding their comparatively short legs, they are swift runners. They are excellent swimmers, dive well at need and fly swiftly.

The food of the Oyster-catcher consists largely of mussels, limpets, oysters, shrimps, small crabs, small clams, razor-clams, sea-worms and other forms of marine life, and many insects. It probes deeply in the sand for small shellfish and knocks others off the rocks.

ECONOMIC STATUS. As a game bird the Oyster-catcher is not a great success. It will not come to man's decoys nor will it await the approach of the gunner. It may be of little service in the destruction of insects, but at any rate, as I have said elsewhere, it is a handsome creature whose alert presence and harmonious cries once lent to our beaches a charm, now gone forever. "Its extirpation in New England has served no good purpose, but merely adds another item to the accounting that shall put 'our race and time to shame in the age to come.'"

---
[1] Bulletin No. 35, U. S. Department of Agriculture, Biological Survey, 1910, p. 99.